EURO-CERAMICS

Volume 3: Engineering Ceramics

The Proceedings of the First European Ceramic Society Conference (ECerS '89) held on 18–23 June 1989 at the Maastricht Exhibition & Congress Centre, The Netherlands.

Volume 1: Processing of Ceramics

Synthesis
Forming
Densification
Phases and Reactions

Volume 2: Properties of Ceramics

Characterisation
Electronic Ceramics
Superconducting Ceramics
Traditional Ceramics

Volume 3: Engineering Ceramics

Bioceramics
Standardisation
Fracture
Deformation and Reinforcement
Composites
Surface-Related Phenomena
Applications

EURO-CERAMICS

Volume 3

Engineering Ceramics

including Bioceramics

Edited by

G. de WITH

Philips Research Laboratories, Eindhoven, The Netherlands

R. A. TERPSTRA

Netherlands Energy Research Foundation, ECN,
Petten, The Netherlands

and

R. METSELAAR

Centre for Technical Ceramics,
Eindhoven University of Technology, The Netherlands

ELSEVIER APPLIED SCIENCE
LONDON and NEW YORK

ELSEVIER SCIENCE PUBLISHERS LTD
Crown House, Linton Road, Barking, Essex IG11 8JU, England

Sole Distributor in the USA and Canada
ELSEVIER SCIENCE PUBLISHING CO., INC.
655 Avenue of the Americas, New York, NY 10010, USA

WITH 95 TABLES AND 411 ILLUSTRATIONS

British Library Cataloguing in Publication Data

Euro-Ceramics.
1. Ceramics
I. With, G. de II. Terpstra, R. A. III. Metselaar, R.
666

ISBN 1-85166-426-2 (set)
ISBN 1-85166-430-0 (Vol. 1)
ISBN 1-85166-431-9 (Vol. 2)
ISBN 1-85166-432-7 (Vol. 3)

Library of Congress CIP data applied for

Printed in Northern Ireland by The Universities Press (Belfast) Ltd.

FOREWORD

In September 1987, during the 14th 'Science of Ceramics' conference, the European Ceramic Society was founded. The primary goal of this new society is to improve and facilitate communications both between European countries and between Europe and the rest of the world. Eleven countries have now joined the new society: Belgium, Federal Republic of Germany, France, Italy, The Netherlands, Norway, Portugal, Spain, Sweden, the United Kingdom and Yugoslavia.

To achieve its goal, the Society has decided to organize a set of conferences. This proceedings volume is a record of the first, ECerS '89, which took place in Maastricht, The Netherlands, in June 1989. The aim was to bring together engineers, scientists, technicians and all others with an interest in ceramics. The meeting covered the whole field of ceramics, from traditional clay-based materials to advanced materials with applications in the fields of engineering, electronics, magnetism and medicine. The 30 years tradition of the 'Science of Ceramics' meetings has been incorporated into the ECerS conferences under the heading of Basic Science. In 1991 the next conference of the European Ceramic Society, ECerS '91, will be held in the Federal Republic of Germany, probably near Munich. Directly after this conference the exhibition 'Ceramitec' will be organized. This will further enlarge the scope of the meeting, hopefully in a way that is appreciated by the European ceramic community.

It has been decided to present at each ECerS conference the A. L. Stuijts Memorial Award. As a research scientist at Philips Research Laboratories, Professor Stuijts contributed considerably to the development of magneto- and electro-ceramics, in particular to a better understanding of the relationship between the science and technology of these materials. To commemorate his contributions to the scientific community, an award with his name will be presented to a ceramist noted for his or her outstanding contributions to ceramic science or technology. The awardee will present a memorial lecture. During ECerS '89 the first Stuijts Memorial Award was presented to Professor R. J. Brook, who gave his Memorial Lecture entitled 'The Mastery of Microstructure'. Hopefully with this first memorial lecture a tradition has been started that will last for many years.

As mentioned by the editors, the space available to the authors in these proceedings is limited. I am pleased to announce that the ECerS now has its own *Journal of the European Ceramic Society*. This journal offers the possibility of publishing full-length papers of high scientific quality.

Organizing a conference is an elaborate task which is impossible without the help of many persons. This was true for ECerS '89 as well. It is impossible to mention all who contributed. An exception must be made for all collaborators of the Maastricht Exhibition & Congress Centre, MECC. Their enthusiastic cooperation has contributed considerably to the success of the conference.

I hope that the new series of conferences will be as successful as its predecessor, 'Science of Ceramics', and will fulfil all the needs of ceramists in Europe and the rest of the world.

R. Metselaar
President of the European Ceramic Society, 1987–1989,
Centre for Technical Ceramics, Eindhoven, The Netherlands.

PREFACE

This proceedings volume contains, besides the text of six key-note lectures and an extended abstract text of the first Stuijts Memorial Lecture, a representative selection of the more than 450 papers presented during ECerS '89.

The division between the various topics was approximately as follows: basic science 40%, engineering ceramics including bioceramics 30%, electronic ceramics including high T_c superconductors 20%, and traditional ceramics 10%. As was to be expected, the division is almost the same as in the American Ceramic Society Annual Meetings during the last few years. The fact that proper processing is the key to good properties is reflected here by the large number of contributions dealing with this topic. Moreover, there was a considerable number of papers discussing the processing and properties of composite materials.

Because of the large number of contributions, the number of pages for each manuscript had to be limited. This may seem a handicap to authors. The usefulness of proceedings is, in our opinion, mainly found in an overview of activities going on, rapidly published after the conference. Detailed theories or extensive descriptions of experimental work are out of place in such proceedings. Therefore, apart from practical reasons, in our view a limited number of pages is sufficient. For reasons of speed only limited reviewing was carried out. This procedure limited itself mainly to format and obvious errors. Opinions expressed remain, however, entirely the responsibility of the authors.

The editing of the proceedings would not have been possible without the help of many individuals. Without mentioning them all personally, this is the proper place to thank all those who contributed. One exception, however, must be made: Miss E. Ramaekers performed many secretarial duties, and without her help the editing of these proceedings could not have been completed in so timely a manner.

G. de With
Philips Research Laboratories and Centre for Technical Ceramics,
Eindhoven, The Netherlands

R. A. Terpstra
Netherlands Energy Research Foundation, ECN,
Petten, The Netherlands

R. Metselaar
Centre for Technical Ceramics, Eindhoven, The Netherlands

Honorary Committee ECerS '89

J. Kremers	Queen's Commissioner of Limburg
Ph. J. I. M. Houben	Mayor of Maastricht
R. W. de Korte	Minister of Economic Affairs
W. J. Deetman	Minister of Education and Science
R. E. Selman	Board of Management DSM
S. van Houten	Board of Management Nederlandse Philips Bedrijven BV
M. C. van Veen	Board of Management Hoogovens Groep BV
G. Kaptein	Board of Management NV Koninklijke Sphinx
G. J. M. Teeuwen	Board of Management Redland Bouwprodukten BV

Advisory Committee ECerS '89

A. McDonald (*Australia*)
F. Cambier (*Belgium*)
P. H. Duvigneaud (*Belgium*)
D. Yen (*China*)
F. Aiazzi (*Italy*)
D. T. Beruto (*Italy*)
G. Ziegler (*FRG*)
G. König (*FRG*)
P. Boch (*France*)
W. Simonet (*France*)
S. Saito (*Japan*)
A. J. Burggraaf (*The Netherlands*)
R. Pampuch (*Poland*)
J. L. Baptista (*Portugal*)
A. E. Benloch (*Spain*)
S. de Aza Pendas (*Spain*)
R. Pompe (*Sweden*)
G. J. Gittens (*UK*)
D. P. Thompson (*UK*)
D. E. Niesz (*USA*)
D. Kolar (*Yugoslavia*)

Scientific Programme Committee ECerS '89

G. de With (*Chairman*)
R. A. Terpstra (*Secretary*)
R. Metselaar
R. Wernicke
R. Nelissen
K. de Groot
K. Keizer
H. J. Timmers

Council of the European Ceramic Society

Belgium:	P. Fierens F. J. Cambier
FRG:	H. Hausner (*President Elect*) M. Blumenberg
France:	R. Cauville D. Broussaud
Italy:	G. N. Babini C. Palmonari
The Netherlands:	J. T. van Konijnenburg R. Metselaar (*President*)
Norway:	Th. Møller J. F. Haslund
Portugal:	A. F. Faria Frasco J. L. Baptista
Spain:	A. G. Verduch M. A. Delgado Méndez
Sweden:	R. Carlsson R. Ahlgren
United Kingdom:	G. J. Gittens D. Taylor
Yugoslavia:	D. Kolar

Sponsors of ECerS '89

City of Maastricht
Commission of the European Communities
Dutch Ministry of Economic Affairs
Elsevier Science Publishers Ltd
NV Gouda Vuurvast
KLM Royal Dutch Airlines
Koninklijke Mosa BV
NV Koninklijke Porceleyne Fles Ao 1653
NV Koninklijke Sphinx
Netherlands Energy Research Foundation (ECN)
D. van Oord & Co. Clay Tiles BV
Philips International BV
Philips Research Laboratories
Redland Bouwprodukten
Strategic Analysis Inc. SAI (Brussels)
Teewen BV
Tichelaar's Koninklijke Makkumer Aardwerk en Tegelfabriek BV
TNO Institute for Applied Physics

CONTENTS

Volume III: ENGINEERING CERAMICS including Bioceramics

III.5 COMPOSITES

THE STUIJTS AWARD

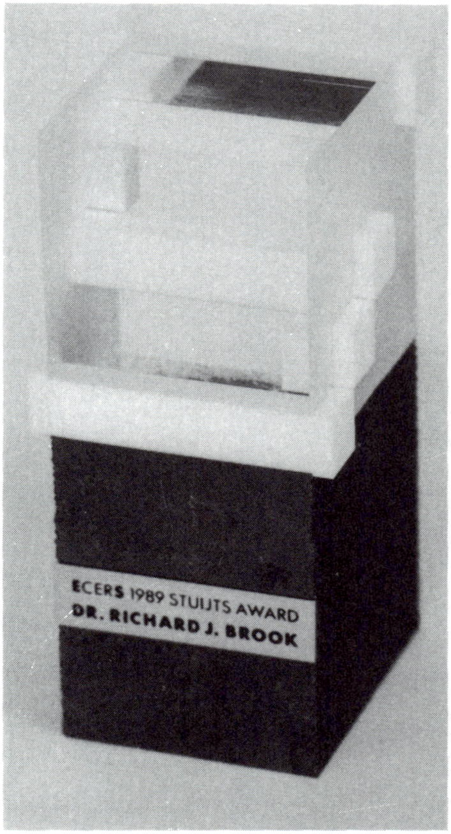

At the founding of the European Ceramic Society it was decided to present at each ECerS conference the A. L. Stuijts Memorial Award. As a research scientist at Philips Research Laboratories, Eindhoven, The Netherlands, Professor A. L. Stuijts (1922–1982) contributed considerably to the development of magneto- and electro-ceramic materials, in particular to a better understanding of the relationship between the microstructure and processing of these materials. He was also a Professor Extraordinary at the Eindhoven University of Technology. In 1976 he was elected Fellow of the American Ceramic Society and in 1977 he delivered the Sosman Memorial Lecture for this society. To commemorate his contributions to the ceramic community, during each conference of the European Ceramic Society an award bearing his name will be presented to a ceramist noted for outstanding contributions to ceramic science or technology. Professor R. J. Brook was the first to receive this award during ECerS '89 in Maastricht, The Netherlands.

Richard J. Brook (1938–) was born in Leeds, UK, and started his career in ceramics at the Massachusetts Institute of Technology, Boston, USA, where he obtained his PhD for research on ferrite thin films in 1966. From 1966 to 1970 he was Assistant Professor of Materials Science at the University of Southern Carolina where he did research on the development of microstructures in ceramics and on electrical properties. After 4 years at the AERE, Harwell, UK, as principal scientist and leader of the Electronic Ceramics Group, where he mainly researched electronic ceramics, Richard Brook joined the University of Leeds as Professor and Head of the Department of Ceramics. Apart from researching ceramic fabrication, solid electrolytes and ceramics processing, he has taken part in many university and external committees. Since 1988 Professor Brook has been one of the directors at the Max Planck Institute for Metals Research, Stuttgart, FRG.

The Stuijts award was presented by Dr F. M. A. Carpay, Executive Director, Philips Research Laboratories, after which Professor Brook delivered the Memorial Lecture entitled 'The Mastery of Microstructure'.

Stuijts Memorial Lecture 1989
"The Mastery of Microstructure"

R.J. Brook
Max Planck Institute for Metals Research
Stuttgart, FRG

In the light of his experience in the successful development of ceramic microstructures to match specific electromagnetic applications, Professor Stuijts proposed a number of themes in 1972 as being ripe for progress in the general task of exploiting ceramics for advanced engineering use. Three of these topics are reviewed with emphasis on the work that has been done and on current attitudes. The three themes are powder preparation, the importance of technological factors, and the need for valid generalised pictures of complex processes.

In powder preparation, the dramatic influence of chemical preparation methods on the quality of powders available for ceramic fabrication is one of the clearest developments of recent years. Major advances in processing convenience and in product reliability have resulted. In respect to technological factors, considerations of cost and of the need for reproducilbility are now seen as critical in determining the rate of adoption of ceramics into new applications; introduction of ceramic components into heat engines which has long been seen as a target in respect to the full and active use of ceramics on the large volume scale is largely determined by such aspects. The very great complexity of ceramics processing science and the resulting risk that detailed explanations of phenomena cannot then be extended for more general use has made the search for precise atomistic interpretation of microstructural change less persuasive than it once was.

Three sectors that have proved fruitful in the intervening years in tackling the issues that were identified as being of concern are the use of mapping techniques, the use of computer modelling and the use of detailed microstructural characterisation notably in the form of electron microscopy.

These methods have allowed the development of a systematic approach to ceramic processing along the lines that Professor Stuijts was seeking. The approach has shown striking success in the development of the set of high strength and toughness ceramics based on the transformation toughening mechanism; it has also proved effective in the work on high temperature materials based on silicon nitride and the sialons.

The path to the mastery of microstructure that was advocated by Professor Stuijts has been found to be a productive one. The early view that detailed knowledge of precise atomistic mechanisms might one day underlie our approach to ceramic processing has if anything been seen as excessively and unnecessarily ambitious; in its place, a pragmatic pattern of development based on good understanding of the possible contributions of generalised mechanisms has developed.

A framework for the successful processing of ceramics is now in place; the need, however, for imagination in the exploitation of this framework remains as true today as at the time of its recognition by Professor Stuijts.

RECENT DEVELOPMENTS IN BIOCERAMICS

GÜNTHER HEIMKE
Dept. of Bioengineering, Clemson University,
301 Rhodes Eng. Res. Center, Clemson, SC 29634 USA
and FRIEDRICHSFELD GmbH, D-6800 Mannheim 71, Germany

ABSTRACT

From the large number of ceramic materials, a few oxide and calciumphosphate ceramics as well as Ca-phosphate containing glasses and glass-ceramics only have either already stood the test of clinical applications or have a property combination worth to be considered for medical applications. From the point of view of the reactions they stimulate in the adjacent tissue, these materials can be grouped into bioinert or bioactive ceramics.- Whilst the range of application of the bioinert ceramics can be regarded as well established already, most of the uses of the bioactive, Ca-phosphate based materials must be regarded as experimental still. Their fascinating ability to stimulate the formation of a mechanically strong bond to living bony tissue inherently implies some kind of surface reactivity which increases their fatigue sensitivity. As their initial strength is relatively low already, their applications have been confined to essentially load free situations. At present, considerable efforts are aiming at using the bonding ability of these bioactive materials for the fixation of load bearing implants by coating them onto high strength substrates or combining them with other materials like organic or ceramic cements.

INTRODUCTION

The large scale application of ceramics in reconstructive surgery is based on two particular kinds of compatibility with bony tissue observed nearly simultanously by Hulbert et al. [1] and L.L. Hench et al.[2] in the late 1960's. They were some kind of extremes: the one had tested the reactions around some Al_2O_3/MgO-ceramics and found very little influence of the material on the remodelling of the surrounding tissue, the other studied some Ca-phosphate containing glasses and glass-ceramics and discovered the fascinating ability of a mechanically strong bond formation to bony tissue. A similarly favourable reaction had already been observed for some Ca-phosphate powders in 1920 [3], but the exploitation of this phenomenon did not commence until the late 1960's when ceramics of this material had become available [4].

At about the same time, the first wave of large scale hip joint replacements, made possible by Charnley's introduction of the polymethylmethacrylate (PMMA) bone cement in 1960 [5], had demonstrated the enormous possibilities of this kind of treatment, but also led to increasing numbers of reoperations demonstrating the necessity for further improvements. Also at that time, a similar situation existed with dental implants. In both cases, the soft tissue layer along most of the implant to bone interfaces was identified as the major reason for the failures [6,7] which was felt to be mainly due to the limited compatibility of the PMMA and the metals mostly used at that time, the stainless steels and the Co-based alloys.

Therefore, the favourable compatibilities of the ceramic materials raised much hope to deal with the shortcomings of the first generation of large scale total joint replacements and dental implants. Now, after about two decades of experiments and clinical experiences, a more detailed but still not final picture can be presented. A more extended report is available in a recent monograph [8].

THE INERT CERAMICS

Nearly immediately following the early publications on the favourable reactions of bony tissue around alumina ceramic implants, several groups extended and detailed the studies in different directions: whilst Boutin [9] immidiately commenced clinical trials others began detailed biocompatibility studies in load free situations and with fully functionally loaded hip joint components [10].

These early experiments established the highly pure, dense alumina ceramic as some kind of a prototype of a bioinert material in the sense summerized in Table 1. The tissue reactions to alumina wear particles and the cancerogenity of this material was also studied at that time [10]. The reorganization of the bony tissue adjacent to such implants was found to nearly exactly follow the pattern of fracture healing. This result opened the possibility for an implant fixation without the soft tissue interface, if the conditions of fracture healing could be realized and maintained along all those interfaces necessary for a reliable implant fixation.

TABLE 1

The definition of a bioinert material

Requirement	Effect
"nothing goes into solution": any matter leaking from the implant into the tissue must not influence cells or cause systemic effects.	No biochemical influence on cell differentiation and proliferation. No biochemical-information to cells on presence of the implant.
Fast and strong absorption of body molecules to the surface of the implant which is, thus, covered, even coated, by the body's own matter.	No enzyme controlled immune reactions. The implant is "camouflaged" against the host's immune system. No foreign body reactions.

The most important requirement is motionlessness along the fracture site. As all other influences from the implant onto the surrounding tissue can be excluded for a bioinert material, it is the stress and strain field created by the insertion of the implant in its environment that controlls the remodelling process [11]. If the shape of the implant can be choosen as to allow for sufficiently large and correctly oriented interfaces, a close bone contact (osseo-integration) and reliable load transmission can be achieved [12].

Load Bearing Implants

Implants designed according to the considerations mentioned above are shown in Fig. 1 and 2. Their clincal results have been documented in several medium and long term follow-up studies. Their details and the high success rates observed can be considered as a confirmation of the validity of the design criteria on which they were based.

Other medium and long term follow-up studies on ceramic hip components which had not been designed according to the rules given above but with articualting interfaces of ceramic against ceramic were given by Boutin [13] and Mittelmeier [14] and confirmed the nearly complete absence of wear in all normal cases.

However, the conically shaped sockets of the latter system were reported recently to cause so many failures that its further application was no longer recommended [15].

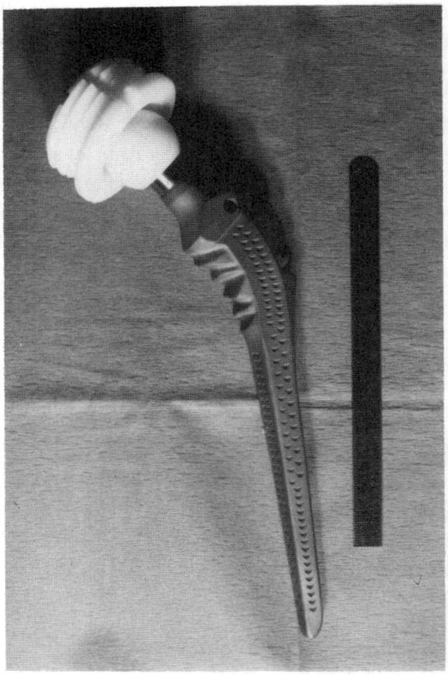

Fig. 1. The FRIALIT hip system with an alumina socket, a ball of the same material, and the BMO (biomechanically optimized) Stepped Stem made of an TiAlFe alloy.

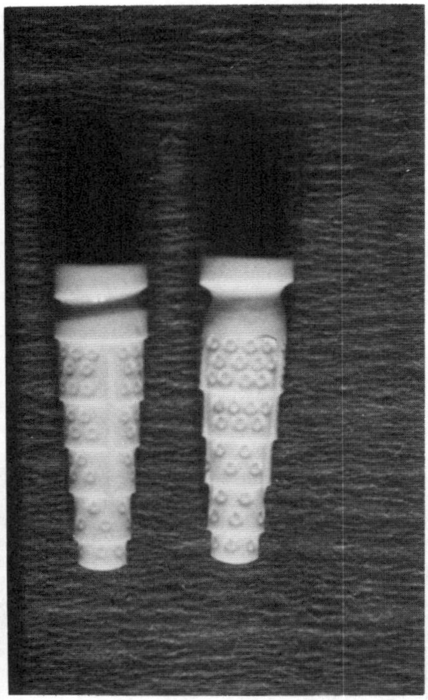

Fig. 2 FRIALIT detal implants, type Tübingen and type München.

Besides the implant systems shown in Fig. 2 only the alumina ceramic dental implant shown in Fig. 3 approximately accounted for the design requirements based on the stress controlled remodelling of the adjacent bone [16]. Their untolerably high failure rate can be attributed to an unsufficient motionlessness during the healing period. The shape of none of the other dental implants made of alumina ceramic (Fig 4) [17,18] or single crystals [19] accounted for these design rules but rather dublicated shapes of previous metal implants. Thus, most of them were not osseo-integrated but rather soft tissue encapsulated [20]. No long term follow-up study of any of these implant system has become available.

Shortly after the mid seventies a considerable reduction of polyethylene wear debris was reported when sockets of this material were articulating against alumina ceramic instead of metal balls [21]. After some exaggerated initial hopes it is now well established that this combination results in a reduction of the wear debris by a factor of about 2. As these polyethylene wear particles have been known for their considerable contribution to implant loosening [22, 23], this material combination has now become widely accepted and constitutes the largest application of ceramics in medicine.

The temptation to enter into this field with implants or procedures of unsufficient safety margin is, obviously, high as must be realized from recent reports of ceramic ball fractures in newpapers and magazins [24]. This is the more surprising as the stress distribution in the ceramic ball is much less critical in the polyethylene than in the ceramic to ceramic combination. The experience of the last ten years have shown that the systems with ceramic to ceramic articulating interfaces and their much more pronounced stress concentrations can be supplied with adequate safety margins [13,14,25,26,27]. Only those systems should be used which meet these high requirements.

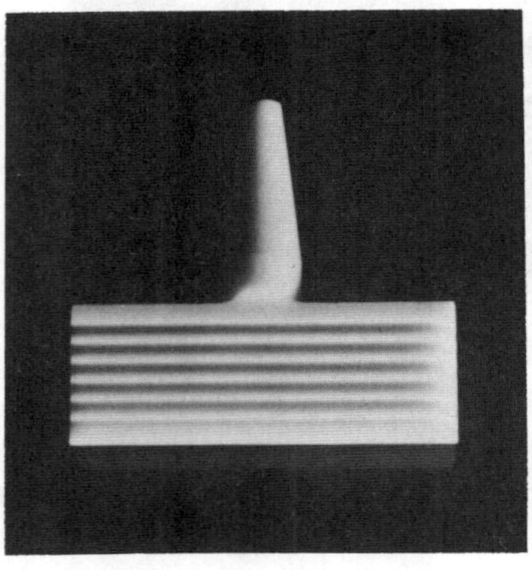

Fig. 3. Ceramic dental implant with asymmetrical grooves [16].

Fig. 4. Blade vent implant of Al_2O_3-ceramic [18]

An attempt to apply the ceramic polyethylene combination to knee joint replacements [28] confirmed their favorable wear properties, but was abandoned because of a too high incident of loosening of the tibial component [29]. Ankle joints of this kind have stood the test of many years of clinical application [30].

Essentially Unloaded Implants

The bioinertness of the highly dense and pure alumina ceramic has also led to some applications in which mechanical requirements are not critical. Fig. 5 shows middle ear implants to replace the ossicular chain partially or totally [31], Fig. 6 is a photograph of a trachea supporting ring [32] to be used in tumor surgery. Other essentially unloaded alumina ceramic implants are keratoprostheses [33], orbital plates [34], and septum supports [35]. Some of these implants are essentially services to general health care rather than commercially justified because their demand is so small that their sales can not even support the necessary insurances!

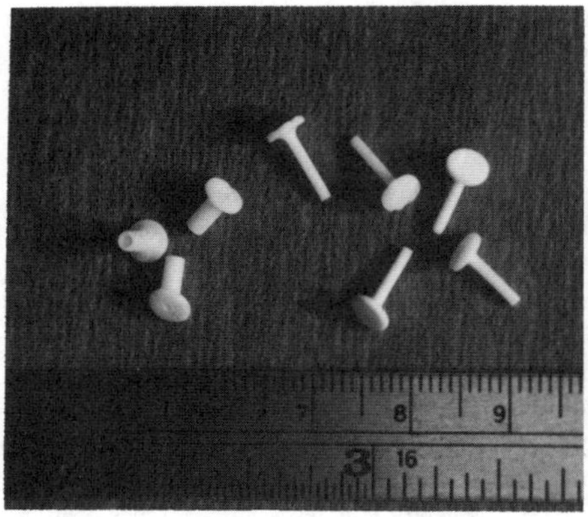

Fig. 5. FRIALIT middle ear implants.

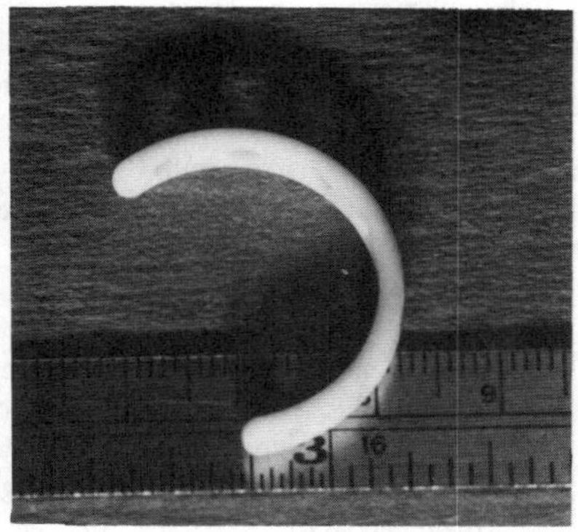

Fig. 6. FRIALIT trachea supporting ring.

THE BIOACTIVE CERAMICS

Whilst the fixation of the implants made of the inert ceramics has to rely on their correct shape accounting for the remodelling ability of the adjacent bony tissue under the influence of the stress and strain field created by the insertion of such implants, the discovery of the bonding ability of some ceramics to bony tissue raised the hope for the reliable anchorage of geometrically much simpler implants. All these Ca-phosphate containing glasses, glass ceramics, and ceramics have some surface reactivities which "activly" contribute to the bond formation. These materials are, therefore, called "bioactive ceramics". For this same reason, none of these ceramics is really stable in body enviroment. Some of them can even be graded as resorbable materials which, of course, can be used as temporary implants only, however, allowing to avoid a second intervention. The more stable ones are even considered for permanent implants.

Load Bearing Bioactive Implants

In spite of about 20 years of considerable efforts no large scale clinical application of this bonding phenomenon for the fixation of load bearing implants could be realized. The reasons for these difficulties are inherently related to the bonding processes. The reactions allowing for the bond formation cause changes of the surfaces which result in a reduction of the mechanical strengths of these materials. Because the initial bend strengths of most of them are, at the best, about half of that of the medical grade alumina ceramics, their remaining strength is much two low for nearly all load bearing applications.

In order to use the bonding ability for the fixation of load transmitting implants coatings of these bioactive materials onto high strength substrates have been considered. Because of their relatively high soluability and the large mismatches of their thermal expansion and elastic behaviour as compared to the possible substrate materials, all attempts to apply enameling or glazing techniques failed. To overcome these problems essentially two paths have been followed: embedding particles of these bioactive materials into matrix materials of sufficient strength and biocompatibility or flame or plasma spraying the bioactive ceramics onto high strength substrates.

In the first of these approaches, the active particles in the surface were expected to form a bond with the adjacent tissue, thus resulting in a fixation like in point welding. In most cases the matrix materials considered were hihgly corrosion resistant enamels [36] or PMMA bone cements [37]. None of these attempts has led to any large scale application, because, obviously, there is no raeson why the fatigue processes effecting the surfaces of the bulk materials should not also desintegrate the embedded particles.

The second approach has been followed more extensively. After the early attempts to use the original bioactive glasses and glass ceramics as enamels or glazes had failed, some more corrosion resistant apatite-wollastonite glass ceramics [38] are presently evaluated. One of their promising properties is an, at least temporary, strength increase found after immersion into simulated body fluid, most probably resulting from the well known surface compression effect of some ion exchanges. If all the other problems, like mechanical and thermal mismatches with the high strength substrate materials, can be solved, remains to be seen.

During the eighties, most efforts have been concentrated on hydroxylapatite (HA) coatings applied by flame or plasma spraying. But these coatings are, of coures, also subject to the interactions with the surrounding tissue and the fatigue processes resulting from them. Most experts, therefore, recently agreed that such HA coatings, whilst they might facilitate the initial healing process because of their bioactivity, might have become desintegrated after about four to six years of actual service [39]. Thus, for long term implants, such coatings would not allow to abandon other means of implant anchorage like the biomechanically optimized surface undulations described above and shown in Fig. 1.

Essentially Unloaded Bioactive Implants

The applications of non loaded bioactive ceramic implants can be subdivided into two groups: permanent and temporary implants.

Permanent implants of hydroxylapatite ceramics have widely been tested in orthognatic surgery for corrections of deformaties of facial bones [40], and have found some large scale applications in oral surgery as filling material of periosteal defects, and alveolar ridge augmentation [41]. In middle ear surgery hydroxylapatite ceramics [42] as well as the bioactive glasses [43] have stood the test of many years of clinical applications.

The resorbable versions of Ca-phosphate ceramics, mainly the tricalciumphosphates, have also been tested extensively [44] but have not yet led to well established large scale applications.

Recently, a porous hydroxylapatite derived from calcium incrusting algae has been found to allow for a particularly through and intimate ingrowth of boney tissue in spite of having a pore size of 10 micrometer only and a specific surface are of 50qm/g [45].

SUMMARY AND CONCLUSIONS

The experiences of the first two decades of experimental studies and clinical applications of ceramics in medicine have established some narrow fields in a few branches of medicine in which a few ceramic materials do offer some advantages. Many attempts, however, could never surpass the experimental stage, others had to be abandoned after early clinical failures. But also those which failed contributed to the present day knowledge and the judgement derived from its understanding.

The possibilities and limits of the medical uses of the essentially bioinert oxide ceramics appear to be relatively well established. Only uncomplete application of the available informations may impair the improvements achieved in their particular fields of health care.

All attempts to elicite the still fascinating bonding ability of the bioactive ceramics for the improvement of the fixation of bone, joint, and dental implants have not yet led to a major break through because of the lack of stability of these materials. Increasingly sophisticated arrangements are presently designed and studied. However, the more complicated the system become, the higher the risk of failure and the greater the effort necessary to well document its safety.

In addition, the traditional implant systems have also been improved considerably during these two decades [46]. This puts the limits any new system must surpass higher and higher. But the final judgement on the improvements achieved can not be reached until at least five, in many cases ten years of clinical experience.

REFERENCES

1. Hulbert, S.F., Klawitter, J.J., Talbert, C.D., and Fitts, C.T., Materials in construction for artificial bone segments. In Res. in Dental and Medical Materials, ed. E. Korostoff, Plenum, New York, 1969

2. Hench, L.L., Splinter, R.J., Allen, W.C. and Greenlee, K., Bonding mechanisms at the interface of ceramic prosthetic materials. J. Biomed. Mater. Res. Symp. 971, 2,117-41.

3. Albee, F.H., Studies in bonegrowth: triple calcium phosphate as a stimulus to osteogenesis. Ann. Surg. 1920, 71, 1920

4. Levitt, S.R., Crayton, P.H., Monroe, E.A., and Condrate, R.A., Forming methods for apatite prosthesis. J. Biomed. Mater. Res. 1969, 3, 1969.

5. Charnley, J., Arthroplasty of the hip: A new operation. Lancet 1961, 1129-32.

6. Willert, H.G. and Puls, G., The reaction of bone to bone cement in hip replacements. Arch. Orthop. Unfall-Chir. 1972, 72, 33-71.

7. Spiekermann, H., Clinical and animal experiences with enosseous implants. In Dental Implants, ed. G. Heimke, Hanser Verlag, München, Wien, 1980, 49-54.

8. Heimke, G. (ed.), Osseo-integrated Implants, Vol.I and II, CRC-Press, Boca Raton, 1989

9. Boutin, P., Total hip replacement with a prosthesis of sintered alumina. Revue de chirurgie othopédique et réparatrice de l'appareil moteur (Paris) 1972, 58, 229-46.

10. Griss, P., Heimke, G., v. Andrian-Werburg, H., Krempien, B., Reipa, S., Lauterbach, H.J., and Hartung, H.J., Mor phological and biomechanical aspects of Al_2O_3 ceramic joint replacements. Experimental results and design considerations for human endoprostheses. J. Biomed. Mater. Res. Symp. 1975, 6, 177-88.

11. Heimke, G., Griss, P. und Jentschura, G., Prinzipien der zementfreien Verankerung keramische Endoprothesen. In Biomaterialien, chirurgische Implantate and künstliche Organe, eds. F. Unger und J. Hager, Medizin Verlag EBM, München, 1981, 215-16.

12. Heimke, G., Schulte, W., D'Hoedt, B., Griss, P., Büsing, C.M., and Stock, D., The influence of fine surface structures on the osseo-integration of implants. J. Artificial Organs 1982, 5, 207-12.

13. Boutin, P.M., T.H.T. using alumina-alumina sliding and a metallic stem: 1330 cases and an 11 years follow-up.Proc. Japan. Soc. Orthop. Ceramic Implants, 1981, vol.1, 11-18.

14. Mittelmeier, H., 4 Jahre Erfahrung mit Autophor-Keramik Hüftprothesen. Med. Orthop. Tech., 1980, 100, 19.

15. Fisher, D.A. and Mallory, Th.H., An experience with non- cemented acetabular cups. AAOS 56th Annual Meeting, Las Vegas, Nevada, USA, 1989, paper no. 9, 45.

16 . Driskell, T.D. and Heller, A.L., Clinical use of aluminum oxide endesseous implants. Oral Implantol. 1977, 7, 1-14.

17. Sandhaus, S., Bone implants and drills and taps for bone surgery. British Patent, 1967, 1083769.

18. Mutschelknaus, E. and Dörre, E., Extensionsimplantate aus Aluminiumoxidkeramik. Quintessenz 1977, 28, 1-10.

19. Kawahara, H. Hirabayashi, M. and Shikita, T., Single crystal alumina for dental implants and bone screws. J. Biomed. Mater. Res. 1980, 14, 597-605.

20. Ehrl, P.A., and Frenkel, G., Experimental and clinical experiences with blade vent abutments of Al2O3-ceramic in the shortened dental row situation of the mandible. In Dental Implants, ed. G. Heimke, Hanser Verlag, München, Wien, 1980, 63-67.

21. Semlitsch, M., Lehmann, M., Weber, H., Dörre, E., and Willert, H.-G., New prospects for a prolonged functional life span of artificial hip joints by using the material combination polyethylen/aluminum oxide ceramic/metal. J. Biomed. Mater. Res., 1977, 11, 537.

22. Willert, H.-G. and Semlitsch, M., Reactions of the articular capsule to artificial joint prostheses. In Biocompatibilty of Implant Materials, ed. D. Williams, Sectore Publishing Ltd., London, 1976, 40-8.

23. Griss, P., Heimke, G., Werner, E., Bleicher, J., and Jentschura, G., Was bedeutet die Resorption des Calcar femoris nach der Totalendoprothesenoperation der Hüfte? Arch. Orthop. Traumat. Surg. 1978, 72, 225-232.

24. Stephan, W. Ich dachte, mir fliegt das Bein weg. Stern, Feb. 1989, 216-218.

25.Dörre, E. and Dawihl, W., Ceramic hip endoprostheses. In Mechanical Properties of Biomaterials, eds. G.W. Hastings and D.F. Williams, John Wiley & Sons, Chichester, New York, Brisbane, Toronto, 1980, 113-27.

26. Heimke, G., Griss, P., Jentschura, G., and Werner, E., Mechanical testing of ceramic materials and components for bone and joint replacement. ibid, 129-45.

27. Soltesz, U. and Heimke, G., Stress analysis in ceramic hip-joints of various shape and fitting. In Biomechanics: Principles and Applications, eds. R. Huiskes, D. van Cam-

pen, and J. de Wijn, Martinus Nijhoff Publishers, The Hague, Boston, London, 1982, 283-90.

28. Oonishi, H., Okabe, N., Hamaguchi, T., and Nabeshima, T., Cementless Alumina Ceramic Total Knee Prosthesis. Proc. of the Japanese Society of Ceramic Orthopedic Implants, 1981, Vol 157-160.

29. Oonishi, H. privat communication 1984.

30. Oonishi, H., Hamaguchi, T., Okabe, N., Nabeshima, T., Hasegawa, T., and Kitamura, Y.,Cementless alumina ceramic artificial ankle joint. In Biomaterials and Biomechanics, eds. P. Ducheyne, G. van der Perre, and A.E. Aubert, Elsevier, Amsterdam, Oxford, New York, Tokyo, 1984, 85-90.

31. Jahnke, K., Otologic surgery with aluminumoxide ceramic implants. In Biomaterials in Otology, ed. J.J. Grote, Martinus Nijhoff, The Hague, 1984, 205-9.

32. Zöllner, Ch., Weerda, H., and Strutz, J., Alumina ceramic supporting frame in tracheal surgery. Arch. Oto. Rhino- Laryngology, Supplement 1983/II, 214-16.

33. Polack, F.M. and Heimke, G., Ceramic keratoprostheses. Ophthalmology, 1980, 87, 693-8.

34. Frenkel, R., Reuther, J., and Dörre, E., The reconstruction of defects of the orbital plate with plates of dense alumina ceramic. Dtsch. Z. Mund-Kiefer- Gesichts-Chir., 1980, 4, 253-5.

35. Godbersen, G.S., Septum support of aluminumoxide ceramic. Laryng. Rhinol. Otol. 1985, 64, 290-1.

36. Brömer, H., Deutscher, K., Blencke, B., Pfeil, E., and Strunz, V, Properties of the bioactive material Ceravital. In Science of Ceramics 9, ed. K.J. de Vries, The Nederlandse Keramische Vereniging 1977, 219-35.

37. Guida,G., Riccio, V., Gatto, S., Migliaresi, C., Nicodemo, L., Nicolais, L., and Palomba, C., A glass bead composite acrylic bone cement. In Biomaterials and Biomechanics1983, eds. P. Ducheyne, G. van der Perre, and A.E. Aubert, Elsevier, Amsterdam, Oxford, New York, Tokyo, 1984 ,19-24.

38. Kokubo, T. Shigematsu, M., Nagashima, Y., Tashiro, M., Nakamura, T., Yamamuro, T, and Higashi, S, Apatite and wollastonite containing glass-ceramics for prosthetic application. Bull. Inst. Chem. Res. Kyoto Univ. 1982, 60, 260-8.

39. Oonishi, H., Acki, H., and Sawaki, K., Bioceramics, Procedings of the 1st International Bioceramic Symposium, Ishiyaku Euro America, Inc. Tokyo, St. Louis, 1989.

40. Swart, J.G.N. and de Groot, K., Clinical experiences with sintered calciumphosphate as oral implant material. In Dental Implants, ed. G. Heimke, Hanser Verlag, München, Wien, 1980, 97-103.

41. Kent, J.N., Quinn, J.H., Zide, M.F., Finger, I.M., Jarcho, M., and Rothstein, S.S., Correction of alveolar ridge deficiencies with nonresorbable hydroxylapatite. J. Am. Dent. Ass., 19882, 105, 993

42. Grote, J.J., Tympanoplasty with calciumphosphate. In Biomaterials in Otology, ed. J.J. Grote, Martinus Nijhoff, The Hague, 1984, 274-80.

43. Reck, R., Tissue reactions to glass ceramics in the middle ear. Clin. Otolaryngol. 1981, 6, 63-5.

44. Zöllner, Ch., Beck, Ch., and Heimke, G., Resorbierbare, posöse Trikalziumphosphat-Keramik in der Mittelohrchirurgie. Erste klinische Ergebnisse. Laryng. Rhinol. Otol. 1983, 62, 269-75.

45. Kasperk, C., Eweas, R., Simons, B., and Kasperk, R, Knochenersatzmaterial Aus Aegen. Dish Zahnarztl. Z. 1988, 43,116-9.

46. Griss, P., Hackenbroch, M.H., Jäger, M., Preussner, B., Schäfer, Th., Seebauer, R., van Eimeren, W., and Winkler, W., Ten year results of total hip replacements. A retrospect multicenter study based on a 10% random sample of 39,000 total hip replacements after ten years of observation. Aktuelle Probleme in Chirurgie und Orthopädie 21, H. Huber Verlag, Bern, 1982,

INTRAPERITONEAL INJECTION OF FIVE CALCIUM PHOSPHATE CERAMICS

CA VAN BLITTERSWIJK, HK KOERTEN*,SC HESSELING, J VOGELAAR, G BECKERS**, M GORIS**, R TERPSTRA**, K DE GROOT***
Ear Nose & Throat Dept., *Laboratory for Electron Microscopy, ***Biomaterials Dept., University of Leiden, **ECN, Petten, The Netherlands

ABSTRACT

In this study granulates of five calcium phosphate ceramics, hydroxyapatite, tricalcium phosphate, tetracalcium phosphate, fluoroapatite, and magnesium whitlockite, were injected into the peritoneal cavity of the mouse. The interactions between the granulates and the peritoneal cells were investigated by light microscopy, scanning electron microscopy and transmission electron microscopy.

In general, the granulates did not show a divergence in total peritoneal cell number as compared to the control experiment (PBS). However, tetracalcium phosphate and fluoroapatite showed a higher cell count after 16 hrs and 24 hrs. Differential cell count, discriminating between neutrophils, lymphocytes and macrophages, revealed a similar inflammatory response to all suspensions including PBS.

All granulates gave rise to the formation of granuloma-like aggregates in which ceramic granules were accumulated. The evaluation of these structures offers the possibility to study biomaterial/host interactions without a predominating wound reaction.

INTRODUCTION

Calcium phosphate ceramics are interesting materials for clinical application, especially in bone replacement surgery. Hydroxyapatite and tricalcium phosphate are already in wide clinical use and many studies have been performed on the behavior of these materials in vitro and in vivo[1]. As regards the biocompatibility of other calcium phosphate ceramics data are more scarce. However, the study of other calcium phosphates might be worthwhile since a variation in calcium phosphate ratio in combination with, for instance, the addition of other ions is expected to result in other degradation characteristics and also different bone bonding properties[2].

The aim of the present study is twofold. First, it serves as a general assessment of the biocompatibility of the materials under study. Second, it should provide data as concerns the interactions between the biomaterials and the host tissue without a predominating wound reaction. The choice of the peritoneal cavity as implantation site in combination with the administration of the biomaterials in the form of an injection with a granulate suspension allows such an evaluation as demonstrated by several authors[3-5].

Five calcium phosphate ceramics were investigated: Hydroxyapatite, tricalcium phosphate, tetracalcium phosphate, fluoroapatite, and magnesium whitlockite.

MATERIALS & METHODS

Ceramics: Granulates of hydroxyapatite, tricalcium phosphate, tetracalcium phosphate, fluoroapatite, and magnesium whitlockite were used. The stoichiometry, calcium phosphate ratio and particle diameter are expressed in table 1. An example of the appearance of the granulates as seen by scanning electron microscopy is shown in fig. 1.

TABLE 1

Ceramic characteristics

name	formula	Ca/P ratio	diameter
hydroxyapatite	$Ca_{10}(PO_4)_6(OH)_2$	1.67	40.5 ± 18.8
tricalcium phosphate	$Ca_3(PO_4)_6$	1.5	11.9 ± 4.2
tetracalcium phosphate	$Ca_4(PO_4)_2O$	2.0	9.7 ± 3.4
magnesium whitlockite	$Ca_{2.63}Mg_{0.37}(PO_4)_2$	1.32	9.8 ± 3.8
fluoroapatite	$Ca_{10}(PO_4)_6F_2$	1.67	0.7 ± 0.3

Injection experiment: The granulates were suspended in phosphate buffered saline (PBS)(10 mg/ml). Each mouse (Swiss SPF female mice) received an intraperitoneal injection with 1 ml of the suspension. Three mice were used for every interval and material. The animals were sacrificed at 4, 16, 24, 48, and 72 hours, 2 wks, 1 and 2 months. At these intervals the peritoneum was lavaged and the fluid retrieved. Furthermore, the peritoneum was carefully searched for particle aggregates.

Quantification: Immediately after harvesting, the total cell number of the peritoneal cavity was determined by pooling the cells of three animals and counting in Türks fluid using a Bürker chamber.

Light microscopy & electron microscopy: Cell suspensions and particle concentrations were processed for light microscopy, scanning and transmission electron microscopy according to routine procedures published in an earlier publication[5].

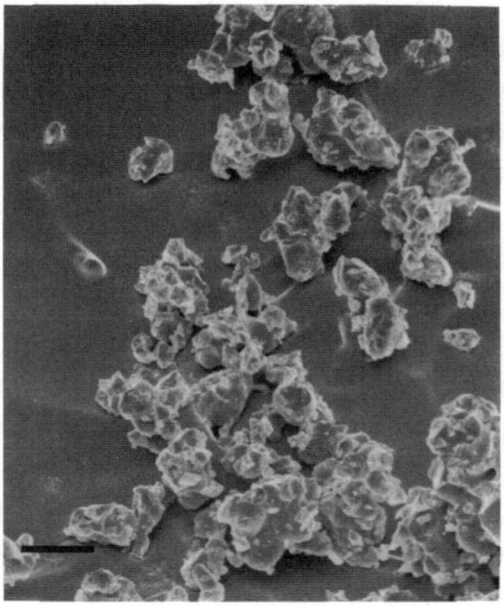

Fig. 1: Scanning electron micrograph of a magnesium whitlockite granulate. Bar: 10 µm.

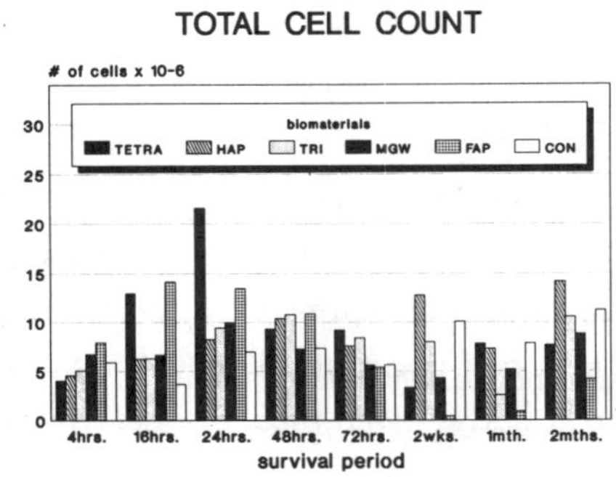

Fig. 2: Graph showing the total peritoneal cell number as a function of time and ceramic.

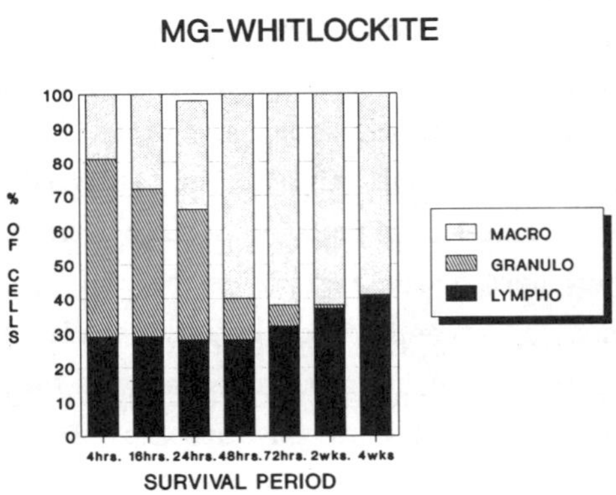

Fig. 3: Graph showing the differential cell count for magnesium whitlockite as a function of time.

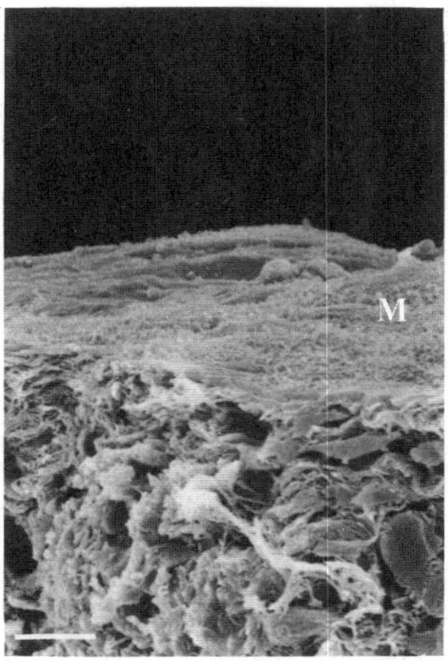

Fig. 4: Scanning electron micrograph of the tissue covering a magnesiumwhitlockite granuloma. Bar: 10 µm. M=mesothelium.

Differential cell count: For each material and time interval three specimens of the peritoneal population were sectioned, stained with toluidine blue and counted. The differential cell count focussed on three cell types: Lymphocytes, neutrophils, and macrophages. A total of 100 cells was counted for each time period per material.

RESULTS

Peritoneal cell population: The total cell count per material as a function of time is shown in figure 2. The materials generally did not deviate from the PBS control, with two exceptions. Tetracalcium phosphate and fluoroapatite showed a relatively high cell count at 16 and 24 hrs, and fluoroapatite was characterized by a cell count distinctly lower than the control from 2 wks on.

The differential cell count revealed the same order of events for all materials including the control. An example is shown in figure 3 which reveals the percentage of the three cell types (macrophages, neutrophils, and lymphocytes) as a function of time. Initially neutrophils were very prominent but their number gradually decreased and had almost diminished after 2 wks. Parallel to the decrease of the neutrophils the number of macrophages and lymphocytes increased. The macrophage was the most prominent cell type from 2 wks on. Transmission electron microscopy and light microscopy showed that phagocytosis of all biomaterials occurred. The number of phagocytes containing endocytosed particles decreased with the increase of time.

Particle aggregates: Already after 4 hours aggregates of biomaterial particles were observed by scanning electron microscopy on the peritoneal viscera. Initially these aggregates were covered with fibrin strands and cells. After 48 hours light microscopy showed that most materials were covered with fibrous tissue, and after 1 month the aggregates were completely covered with mesothelium (fig. 4). The center of the aggregates was composed of closely packed biomaterial granules with very little cells in the interparticle spaces. Towards the periphery of the aggregates the cell number increased and macrophages and foreign body giant cells frequently surrounded the individual particles. With the increase of time vascular ingrowth together with fibrous tissue growing into the aggregates was observed for all materials, and the inflammatory response, based on the number of inflammatory cells associated with the biomaterial granules decreased. Fluoroapatite elicited the highest inflammatory response in all time intervals as shown by light microscopy.

DISCUSSION

As concerns the reactions of the peritoneal cell population versus the injected biomaterials it can be said that these are not in conflict with data described by other authors on various materials[3-6]. The inflammatory response, based on cell numbers was less intense than that found for the well known inflammatory agent crocidolite asbestos[5] and was rather similar to that found for an injection of phosphate buffered saline into the peritoneal cavity[5]. Of the five calcium phosphate granulates investigated in this study only tetracalcium phosphate and fluoroapatite showed a divergent behavior. Both showed a distinctly higher cell count as compared to the control at 16 and 24 hours and in addition fluoroapatite was characterized by a very low cell count from 2 weeks on.

All materials gave rise to the formation of aggregates composed of densely packed biomaterial granules. Especially after longer implantation intervals (ca. 1 month) these aggregates resembled granulomas. As regards the response of macrophages and multinucleated cells fluoroapatite gave the fiercest inflammatory response, which might have been caused by the small size of the granules causing a higher surface area/mass ratio[1,7].

In conclusion it can be stated that the materials under study did not cause a severe inflammatory response when injected into the peritoneal cavity. Furthermore, the formation of granuloma-like biomaterial aggregates offers an interesting possibility to investigate tissue/biomaterial interactions without an intervening surgical intervention and an associated wound reaction.

REFERENCES

1. van Blitterswijk, C.A. and Grote J.J., Biological performance of ceramics during inflammation and infection. CRC Critical Reviews in Biocompatibility, 1989, 5, 1, 13
2. Klein, C.P.A.T., Patka, P., van der Lubbe, H.B.M., Wolke, J.G.C. and de Groot K., Plasma-sprayed coatings of tetracalcium phosphate, hydroxylapatite and ß-whitlockite on titanium alloy. An interface study. J. Biomed. Mater. Res., submitted
3. Pizzoferato, A., Vesputti, A., Ciapetti, G., Stea, S. and Tarabusi C., the effect of injection of powdered biomaterials on mouse peritoneal cell populations, J. Biomed. Mater. Res., 1987, 21, 419
4. Harms, J. and Mausle E., Tissue reaction to ceramic implant material, J. Biomed. Mater. Res., 1979, 13, 67
5. Koerten, H.K., van Blitterswijk, C.A., Grote, J.J. and Daems, W.Th., Accumulation of trace elements by macrophages during degradation of biomaterials, In Implant Materials in Biofunction, eds. de Putter, C. et al., Elsevier Science Publ., 1988, 8, 43
6. Daems, W.Th. and Koerten, H., The effects of various stimuli on the cellular composition of peritoneal exudates in the mouse, Cell Tiss. Res., 1978, 190, 47
7. Behling, C.A. and Spector, M., Quantitative characterization of cells at the interface of long-term implants of selected polymers, J. Biomed. mater. res., 1986, 20, 653

3.16

APATITE CERAMICS WITH TAILORED MICROSTRUCTURES FROM HYDROTHERMALLY-PREPARED ULTRA-FINE HYDROXYAPATITE CRYSTALS

Masahiro YOSHIMURA, Koji IOKU and Shigeyuki SŌMIYA
Research Laboratory of Engineering Materials,
Tokyo Institute of Technology,
4259, Nagatsuta, Midori, Yokohama 227, Japan.

ABSTRACT

The ultra-fine hydroxyapatite single crystals were synthesized by a hydrothermal treatment of the precipitate from the solution of $Ca(NO_3)_2$ and $(NH_4)_2HPO_4$. The hydroxyapatite single crystals obtained at 200 °C under 2 MPa for 10 h had hexagonal prismatic shape of about 25 nm × 90 nm in size from TEM observation. These fine single crystals had high sinterability. The apatite ceramics sintered normally at 900 °C for 3 h showed a porous structure with homogeneous pore distribution. The apatite ceramics post-sintered by HIP at 1000 °C under 200 MPa of Ar for 1 h after normal sintering at 1050 °C for 3 h in air brought about densification up to 99.9 % showing transparency. Further, the apatite ceramics with tailored microstructures, i.e. dense/porous layered apatite ceramics and the apatite ceramics with ZrO_2 particles or α-Si_3N_4 whiskers dispersion having high toughness ($K_{IC} \fallingdotseq 3$ MPa·m$^{1/2}$) have also been prepared.

INTRODUCTION

Hydroxyapatite $Ca_{10}(PO_4)_6(OH)_2$:(HAp), is known to be one of the most biocompatible materials with human bones and teeth. Not only biocompatibility, but also microstructure designing, i.e., grain size, pore size and porosity et al. is necessary to be tailored in the application as implant materials. The authors have presented the preparation and characterization of ultra-fine HAp single crystals [1, 2]. The ultra-fine HAp single crystals synthesized hydrothermally had high sinterability [3, 4]. They could yield a wide variety of ceramics with controlled pore shape, size and porosity or with full-density [4, 5] or with dense/porous layered structures [6, 7] or with zirconia dispersion [8, 9] and/or with whisker dispersion [10] by choosing starting materials and sintering conditions. The present work deals with the preparation of the microstructure-tailored HAp ceramics starting from the ultra-fine HAp single crystals.

MATERIALS AND METHODS

Starting HAp Powders

HAp Ultra-fine Single Crystals: 0.1 M $(NH_4)_2HPO_4$ aqueous solution was added to the 0.167 M $Ca(NO_3)_2$ aqueous solution controlled to the pH 10 to yield white precipitates. The precipitates were treated hydrothermally at 200 °C, under 2 MPa for 10 h in an 5 dm^3 autoclave with stirring to crystallize the HAp.

HAp Powders Dispersed with ZrO_2 Particles or α-Si_3N_4 Whiskers : ZrO_2 particles (3 mol% Y_2O_3 doped ZrO_2; TZ3Y, ToSo Co., Ltd., Japan) or α-Si_3N_4 whiskers (SNW-#10, Tateho Chemicals Co., Ltd., Japan) were dispersed in the 0.1 M $(NH_4)_2HPO_4$ aqueous solution to be the volume ratio of HAp : ZrO_2 or α-Si_3N_4 = 90 : 10. Then the 0.167 M $Ca(NO_3)_2$ aqueous solution was added to that solution with stirring with the pH 10 to yield precipitates. The precipitates were treated hydrothermally at 200 °C, under 2 MPa for 10 h to crystallize the HAp in the autoclave with stirring.

Preparation of HAp Ceramics

The HAp powders obtained were pressed isostatically under 200 MPa for 5 min. by CIP'ing into disks of 6 mm diameter and 3 mm height. When the dense/porous layered HAp ceramics were prepared, the obtained HAp single crystals and the commercial HAp coarse powders (BN grade, Central Glass Co., Ltd., Japan) were molded in layers, then CIP'ed into disks. The disks were sintered under several sintering conditions. Hot-pressing was carried out at the temperatures from 900 to 1100 °C under 30 MPa for 1 h in an argon atomosphere. Post-sintering by HIP'ing without any capsules was carried out at a certain temperature under 200 MPa of Ar for 1 h.

Characterization

The produced phases were identified by XRD. The lattice parameters were determined by the precise angle-measurements corrected by the lattice parameters (a =0.54301 nm) of standard silicon. The crystallite size was caluculated by the Sherrer's formula. The morphology of the particles was observed by TEM. The Ca/P ratio of the HAp crystals was analyzed by a standard EDTA titration for Ca^{2+} and phosphomolybdate techniques for PO_4^{3-} . The sinterability of the powders was evaluated by dilatometry. The bulk density of the compact was measured by Archimedes' method using liquid Hg and then the relative density of the compact was calculated against the theoretical density (d=3.16 g/cm^3). The grain shape of the sintered pellet was observed by SEM. Vickers hardness, fracture toughness were estimated by the indentation microfracture techniques [11] .

RESULTS AND DISCUSSION

Starting HAp Powders

HAp Ultra-fine Single Crystals: The XRD pattern indicated the precipitates prepared at room temperature to be incompletely crystallized HAp, while the HAp treated hydrothermally were fully crystallized. The lattice parameters of the HAp synthesized at 200 °C, under 2 MPa for 10 h (a = 0.9420±0.0001 nm, c = 0.6880 ±0.00005 nm) are in good agreement with the values by previous investigators [12]. The TEM observation indicated the product to be uniform and nonagregated particles consisted of hexagonal prism-shaped ultra-fine single crystals with the length of about 90 nm (Fig.1) and with the aspect ratio of about 3.2. The sizes of the crystals agreed very closely with the crystallite sizes caluculated from XRD peaks, the particles can therefore be regarded as well-crystallized single crystals. The chemical analysis gave a Ca/P ratio very close to the correct HAp stoichiometry (Ca/P = 1.67).

HAp Powders Dispersed with ZrO_2 Particles or α-Si_3N_4 Whiskers : No other phase than HAp and ZrO_2 or α- Si_3N_4 were detected by XRD in any products studied. The lattice parameters of HAp were in good agreement with those of stoichiometric HAp, thus it can be concluded that no reaction occurred both between HAp and ZrO_2, and between HAp and α-Si_3N_4 during preparation in the autoclave. The TEM observation demonstrates that the homogeneous mixture of ultra-fine HAp single crystals and ZrO_2 particles with about 70 nm (Fig.2) or α-Si_3N_4 Whiskers with length of about 10 μm can be obtained by these hydrothermal tequniques.

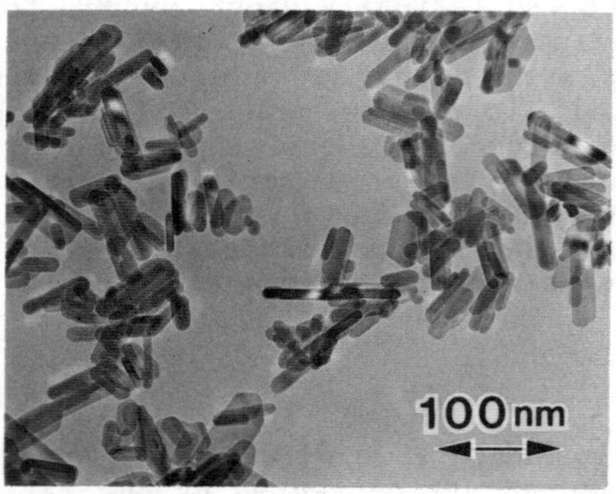

Fig.1 TEM Photograph of ultra-fine HAp single crystals synthesized hydrothermally at 200 °C under 2 MPa for 10 h.

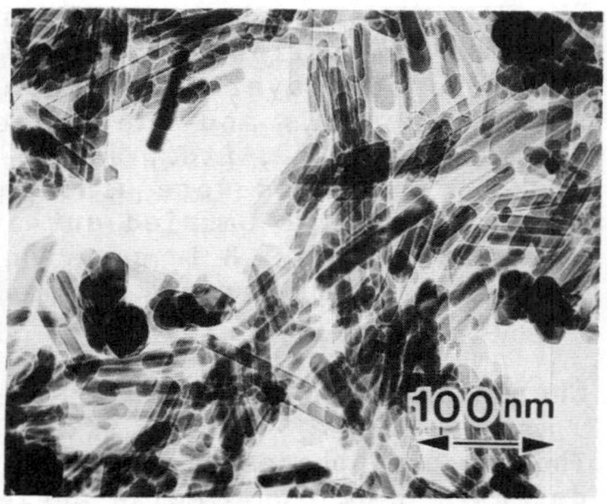

Fig.2 TEM Photograph of well-dispersed ZrO_2 + HAp powders synthesized hydrothermally at 200 °C under 2 MPa for 10 h.

HAp Ceramics with Tailored Microstructures

Porous HAp Ceramics and Transparent HAp Ceramics: The ultra-fine HAp single crystals synthesized hydrothermally had high sinterability [3, 4]. They could yield a wide variety of ceramics. The HAp ceramics normally sintered at 900 °C for 3 h showed 60 % relative density of a porous structure with homogeneous pore distribution. The grain size was about 0.5 μm, which was almost same as that of pores. Those porous ceramics may apply to the adsorption column and/or the filter. The HAp ceramics sintered at 1050 °C for 3 h had more than 90 % density with few pores and the grain size of about 0.6 μm. The post-sintering of these ceramics at 1000 °C under 200 MPa of Ar for 3 h brought about the densification up to 99.9 % density to yield transparent ceramics (Fig. 3). Transparent HAp ceramics can be applied to the terminal for human skin [13].

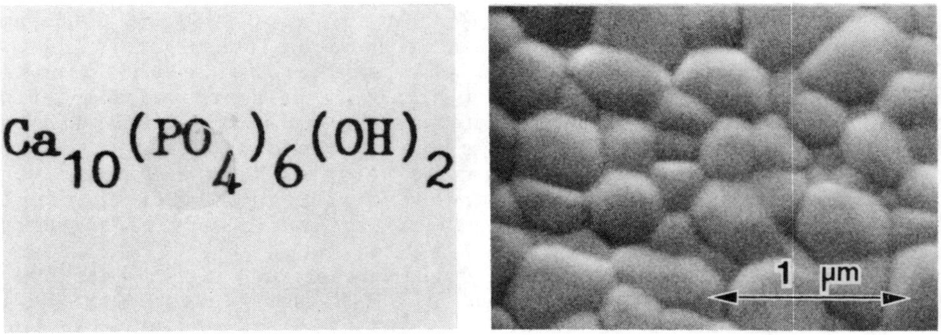

Fig.3 (a) Transparent HAp ceramics post-sintered by HIP at 1000 °C under 200 MPa of Ar for 1 h, after normal sintering at 1050 °C for 3 h. (b) SEM photograph of the polished and thermally-etched surface of the transparent HAp ceramics.

Dense/Porous HAp Ceramics : Implant materials require not only biocompatibility but mechanical strength and porosity to promote the connection with tissues. The starting samples of two types of HAp powders with greatly different sinterability yielded the dense/porous layered HAp ceramics by a normal sintering. The hydrothermally synthesized ultr-fine HAp single crystals with high sinterability provided dense part of the ceramics, and the commercial HAp coarse powders with lower sinterability provided porous part of the ceramics. The post-sintering at 1000 °C can bring about further densification up to 99.9% density of the dense layer without changing the microstructure of the porous layer (Fig.4). These methods can provide biomaterials having both certain strength and biocompatibility [6, 7] .

HAp Ceramics with ZrO_2 Particles Dispersion : In the case of ZrO_2 dispersed HAp, a higher temperature was needed to sintering. It caused the decomposition of HAp into $Ca_3(PO_4)_2$:(TCP) by the reaction with ZrO_2 [8,14] . The HAp ceramics hot-pressed at 1050 °C under 30 MPa for 1 h in Ar, then post-sintered at the same temperature under 200 MPa of Ar for 1 h had almost pore free microstructures consisted of about 3 μm grains of tetragonal ZrO_2 (Fig.5). This sample had over 99 % density in comparison with the calculated one (3.44 g/cm^3) for 10 vol% ZrO_2 : 90 vol% HAp. The XRD showed that this ceramics had no decomposition of HAp into TCP, which has not been reported in the previous works. It showed 3 times as high K_{Ic} as that of the transparent HAp ceramics without ZrO_2 dispersion. This HAp ceramics must be toughened by dispersed ZrO_2 particles due to the transformation toughening mechanism [15, 16] . ZrO_2 particle reinforced HAp ceramics may be used as a tooth root or as a substitute for the cortical bone.

HAp Ceramics with α-Si_3N_4 Whiskers Dispersion: In the case of α-Si_3N_4 whiskers dispersed HAp, normal-sintering could not make dense ceramics. It caused the decomposition of HAp into TCP at the temperature above 900 °C by the reaction with α-Si_3N_4 whiskers. Therefore dense ceramics dispersed with α-Si_3N_4 whiskers were prepared by hot-pressing. The ceramics hot-pressed at 1000 °C under 30 MPa for 1 h in Ar had almost pore free microstructures consisted of HAp and TCP matrix and α-Si_3N_4 whiskers. It showed 3 times as high K_{Ic} as that of the transparent HAp ceramics. This ceramics must be toughened by the crack deflection and/or pullout toughening mechanism [17, 18] due to dispersed α-Si_3N_4 whiskers.

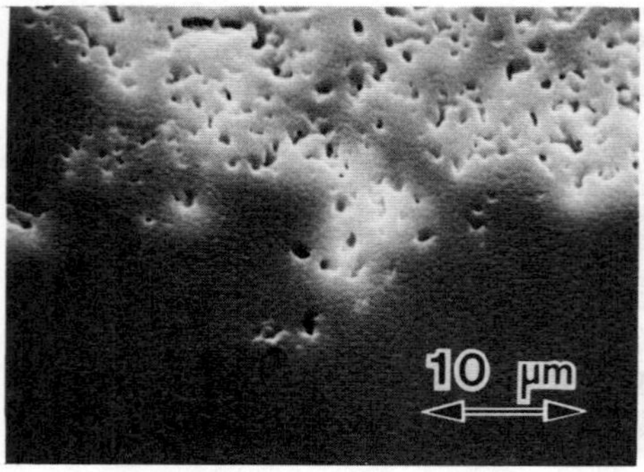

Fig.4 SEM photograph of a cross section of the dense/porous HAp ceramics post-sinterd by HIP.

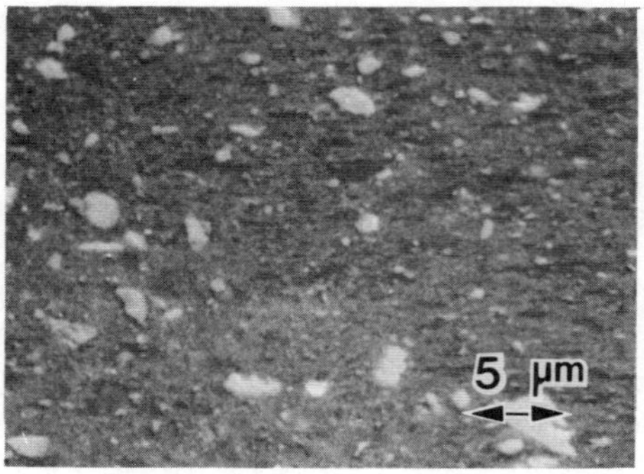

Fig.5 SEM photograph of the post-sintered ZrO_2+HAp ceramics by HIP after hot-pressing at 1050 °C.

REFERENCES

1. Ioku, K., Yoshimura, M. and Sōmiya, S., Nippon Kagaku Kaishi, **1988**, 1565-70.
2. Sōmiya, S., Ioku, K. and Yoshimura, M., Materials Science Forum Vol. 34-36, Trans Tech Publications Ltd., Switzerland, 1988, pp. 371-78.
3. Ioku, K., Yoshimura, M. and Sōmiya, S., Sintering '87, Vol. 2, Elsevier Applied Science, London, New York and Tokyo, 1988, pp. 1308-13.
4. Ioku, K., Yoshimura, M. and Sōmiya, S., Seramikkusu Ronbunshi (formerly Yogyo-Kyokai-Shi), 1988, **96**, 109-10.
5. Ioku, K., Yoshimura, M. and Sōmiya, S., Bioceramics, Vol. 1, Ishiyaku EuroAmerica, Inc., Tokyo and St. Louis, 1989, pp. 62-67.
6. Ioku, K., Sōmiya, S. and Yoshimura, M., Seramikkusu Ronbunshi, (formerly Yogyo-Kyokai-Shi), 1989, **97**, 566-70.
7. Ioku, K., Sōmiya, S. and Yoshimura, M., J. Mater. Sci. Letter, 1989, in press.
8. Ioku, K., Yoshimura, M. and Sōmiya, S., Proc. '87 Fall Meeting of The MRS, Boston, Dec. 2, 1987.
9. Ioku, K., Yoshimura, M. and Sōmiya, S., Biomaterials, in press.
10. Ioku, K., Ishizawa, N., Sōmiya, S. and Yoshimura, M., submitted to Funtai Oyobi Funmatsu Yakin.
11. Niihara, K., Ceramics Japan, 1985, **20**, 12-18.
12. Eysel, W. and Roy, D.M., J. Crystal Growth, 1973, **20**, 245-50.
13. Aoki, H., Akao, M., Shin. Y., Tsuji, T. and Togawa, T., Medical Progress Through Technology Vol. 12, 1987, pp. 213-20.
14. Wu, J-M. and Yen T-S., J. Mater. Sci., 1988, **23**, 3771-77.
15. Evans, A.G., Science And Technology of Zirconia II, Advances in Ceranics Vol. 12, Am. Ceram. Soc., 1984, pp. 193.
16. Claussen, N., *ibid.*, 1984, pp. 325.
17. Faber, K.T. and Evans, A.G., Acta Metall., 1983, **31**, 565-76.
18. Faber, K.T. and Evans, A.G., *ibid.*, 577-84.

THE IMPACT OF THE CLINICAL ENVIRONMENT ON THE SERVICE LIFE OF DENTAL CERAMICS

P.M. MARQUIS,
School of Metallurgy & Materials, University of Birmingham,
P.O. Box 363,Birmingham B15 2TT, UK

ABSTRACT

Most investigations of physical properties of dental ceramics have been undertaken in air and compared relative strengths. In contrast in clinical service the environment is created by saliva and cements and a key factor is the incidence of failure.Results of strength measurements undertaken in environments, including a series of cements and saliva are reported. The impact of the different environments on the performance of dental ceramics is discussed and an explanation proposed for the unexpected high survival rate of dental veneers.

INTRODUCTION

In recent years a number of new ceramics have been introduced for use in clinical dentistry. Whilst traditional glass based materials, such as dental porcelain are still widely used, alternative glass ceramics [1] and reactive ceramic mixes [2] are also in practical use. In addition the forms of dental ceramic restoration are being expanded. A recent development has been the porcelain veneer, a thin shell of porcelain which is cemented to the surface of a discoloured or diseased tooth. Whilst a number of studies of the relative properties of the new materials have been published there is little consensus as to whether any material offers significant improvements in clinical performance. For example, based on strength alone the thin porcelain veneer would be expected to fail under very modest loads [3]. However, in clinical service this type of restoration is proving remarkably resilient. One problem with most previous studies of strength is that the experimental work has been undertaken primarily in air, with a limited number of studies including the impact of moisture.

In clinical practice most dental ceramics survive in an environment created by saliva and the cements which attach them to the remaining tooth. These cements can vary in type including glass ionomer and resin based systems. A clinical environment for a dental ceramic is thus either a buffered pH7 fluid of saliva or a cement. In addition relative strength measurements of ceramics, even if undertaken in a more representative environment, only establish an average failure stress, the point at which fifty percent of a range of samples have failed. In ceramics the distribution about the average can be significant and in clinical terms failure of half of a group of restorations placed is unacceptable. What is more clinically relevant is to establish the levels of applied load at which acceptable survival rates can be achieved and further to determine if strengths degrade in the clinical environment . In this paper a series of strength measurements in different environments and using different strain rates are reported. The aim of the work has been to establish how environment affects performance and in particular to establish the key factors that govern the clinical lifetimes of the dental porcelains used to construct porcelain veneers.

EXPERIMENTAL

Test samples were made using a procedure which reflects commercial practice in the manufacture of jacket crowns. Slurries of Vitadur dentine or aluminous porcelain were condensed into a perspex mould with an aluminium base. Excess moisture was removed using a tissue and vibration and the aluminium foil base then removed. The samples were subsequently fired on a ceramic tile following the manufacturers recommended firing schedule. Strengths of the fired samples were determined using a standard ball on ring test, to reflect the volume to surface ratios appropriate to jacket crowns. The discs were loaded to failure with rates of 0.5, 1 & 10 mm/min and the strength calculated using the following relationship.

$$\sigma = P/h[0.606*\ln(a/h)+1.13]$$

where σ is the strength, a is the radius of the support, h the thickness of the test disc and P the load to failure. To simulate the impact of saliva and other fluids in clinical practice a series of samples were tested surrounded either by natural saliva or buffered solutions at set pH values. A further series of samples also had thin coats of resin, glass ionomer and zinc phosphate cements applied to them. These latter samples were not allowed to dry but kept and tested in saliva.In all cases minimum groups of ten samples were tested for each environment.

RESULTS AND DISCUSSION

As established by O'Brien [4] dental porcelain in common with other glasses is weaker in an aqueous environment. it is therefore encouraging to note as can be seen in figure 1. that the reduction in strength is less when the porcelain is tested in saliva compared to water. This behaviour is related to the fact that saliva maintains a pH of seven, is more viscous than water and also contains proteins. The importance of the glass component in dental porcelains was also reflected in the results obtained from testing in solutions of different pH values, shown in figure 2.. In these tests it was found that for pH values between four and twelve the measured strengths showed no significant fluctuation. For very acidic conditions a significant reduction in strength of 30% was observed.

In clinical practice it is possible for highly acidic conditions to be created by certain cements, notably glass ionomer systems. As can be seen in figure 3 the effect of the presence of a cement layer is generally to reduce the measured strength, reflecting an attack on the porcelain. An exception to this behaviour is the resin cements used for placing

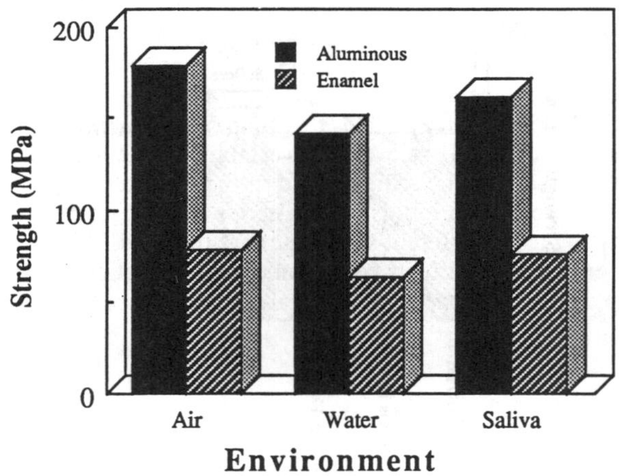

Figure 1. bar chart showing the variation in strength of aluminous porcelain as a function of the test environment

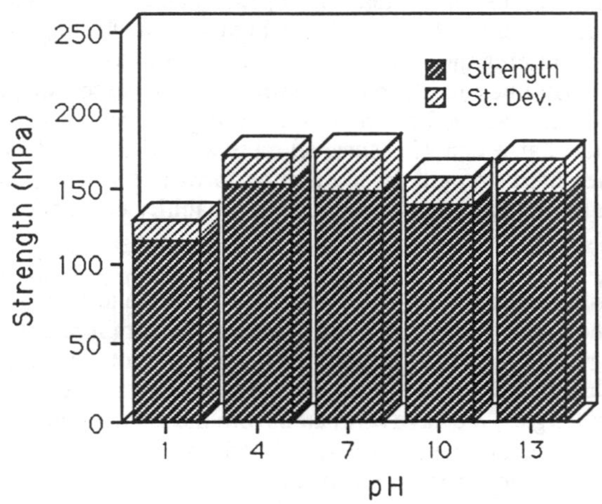

Figure 2. Bar chart showing the variation in the strength of aluminous porcelain tested in a range of buffered water environments

veneers. In this environment not only is the strength not reduced but rather increased above that of the value determined in air. Since the failure of porcelain is normally initiated at surface flaws it appears that the resin cements are able to flow into the surface flaws and effectively heal them, whilst the other cements act to increase the number and sizes of the flaws present at the surface.

In assessing the performance of a glass based material such as porcelain the variability of flaw content is important. If the size and number of flaws varies between samples then their

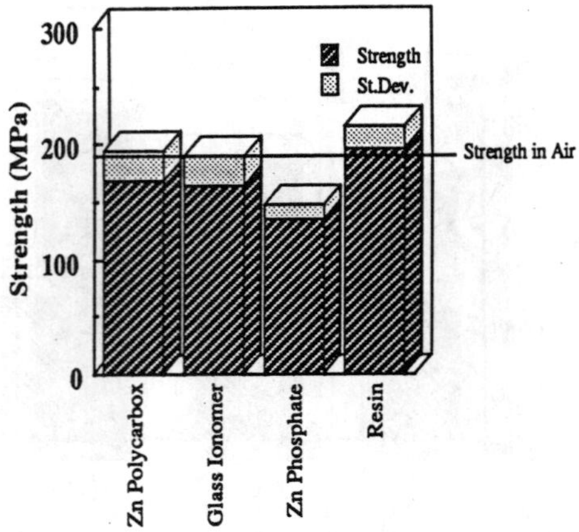

Figure 3. Bar chart showinghow the strength of aluminous porcelain with thin coats of cement depends on the nature of the cement

measured strength values will also fluctuate. The degree of consistency in a set of test samples is reflected by the 'Weibull Modulus'[5], a high value reflecting uniform characteristics. After determining the modulus it is also possible to use a 'Weibull plot' to estimate the survival probabilities at different stress levels. For the sets of samples tested in this study Weibull moduli averaging 5.6 were obtained. A practical consequence of this result is that the stress level at which 95% survival rates will be achieved will be in the region of 71% of the measured strength. In addition performance will be better for samples of smaller volume than those tested due to a reduced probability of a critical flaw being present.

The analysis can be further extended by using variable strain rate tests to generate a survival/probability/time graph [5]. Figure 4 shows that as the strain rate increases so does the measured strength, reinforcing the impact of environment on the strength. An additional conclusion of this result is that the stress levels for a fixed survival rate will decay with time, basically by static fatigue. We have estimated from the results obtained in the present study that the impact of static fatigue on very thin (<0.5mm) porcelain veneers is to reduce their 95% survival stress to below normal masticatory loads within a few seconds whilst for thicker samples (>0.8mm) the time for the same reduction is measured in years. The absolute times at this stage must be viewed with caution but they indicate major differences in survival times for thin porcelain sections.

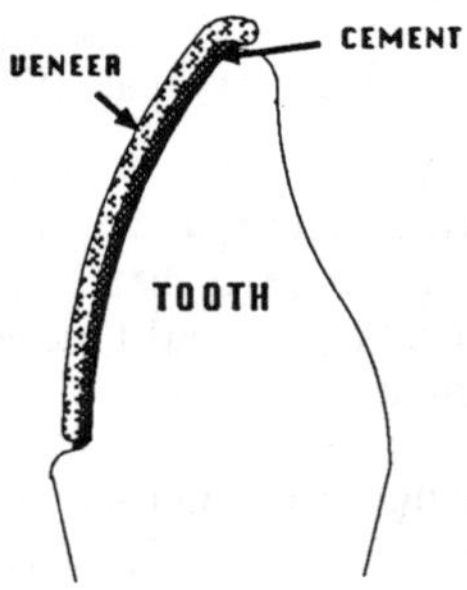

Using these observations it is possible to explain the excellent performance of the porcelain veneer, shown schematically opposite. These restorations are between 0.6 and 0.8 mm thick and applied to the labial, front, surface of a tooth. The masticatory loads in this region are much lower than at the back of the tooth which in a conventional jacket crown is also under

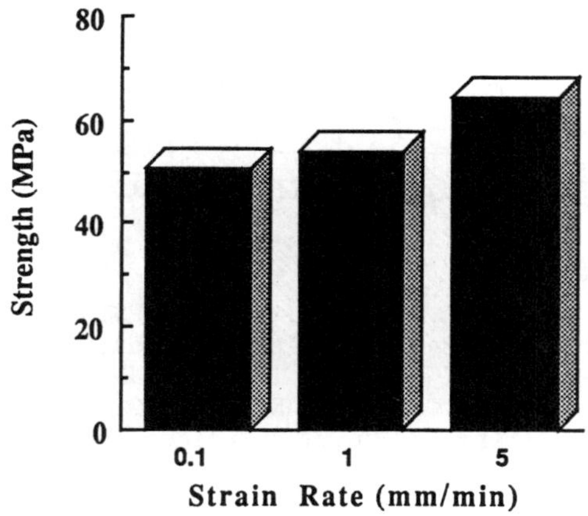

Figure 4. the variation of measured strength of dentine porcelain as a function of the test strain rate.

higher bitting loads. In addition veneers are fitted using resin cements which creates the surface environment where the maximum tensile streeses are likely to occur. The performance of the veneer restoration will therefore be better than a conventional jacket crown because of it placement and clinical choice of cement. In contrast normal all ceramic crowns are placed using cements which weaken them and enhance fatigue. Thus whilst a jacket crown is made of basically stronger materials than a porcelain veneer the lifetime of both restorations are likely to be comparable.

CONCLUSIONS

It can be concluded that the majority of cements used in the placement of jacket crowns have a deleterious effect on their performance. In contrast the effect on strength of saliva is less than water and as a result the impact of static fatigue of the oral environment may be less than anticipated from other studies. Variable strain rate tests confirm the impact of the environment and open up the possibility of using survival/probability/time graphs to compare the potential performance of different dental ceramics.

REFERENCES

1. Adair, P.J. and Grossman, D.G., Castable ceramic crown, Int. J. Peridont. Res., 1984, 2, 33.

2. Sozio, R.B. and Riley, E.J., The shrink free crown, J. Pros. Dent., 1983, 49, 182.

3. Marquis, P.M., Dental Ceramics, Metals & Materials, 1989, 3, 145.

4. Sheril, C.A. and O'Brien, W.J., Transverse strength of aluminous porcelain, J. Peridontal. Res., 1974,53, 683.

5. Davidge, R., Mechanical Behaviour of Ceramics, Academic, 1974

PREPARATION ROUTES OF $Ca_{10}(PO_4)_6(OH)F$ FOR BIOCERAMIC APPLICATIONS

G.J.J. BECKERS, M.J.A.A. GORIS, R.A. TERPSTRA, K. ZEILSTRA
Netherlands Energy Research Foundation, ECN
P.O. Box 1, 1755 ZG PETTEN, the Netherlands
J.G.C. WOLKE, K. DE GROOT
Dept. of Biomaterials, Univ. of Leiden, the Netherlands

Recently we have started a new project in which some calciumphosphates, like fluorhydroxyapatite (FHA) and magnesium containing whitlokite, will be prepared and studied. These calciumphosphates are expected to have interesting properties as materials for bioceramic implants but have up to now received little attention for this purpose.
In this paper we will discuss four different preparation routes for one of these calciumphosphates, i.e. calciumfluorhydroxyapatite, $Ca_{10}(PO_4)_6(OH)F$.
Three preparation routes that concern the mixing of β-$Ca_3(PO_4)_2$, $CaCO_3$ and CaF_2 are:
Dry-mixing, reacting.
Wet-mixing/milling, spray-drying, reacting.
Wet-mixing/milling, slip-casting, reacting.
(The dry-mixed and the spray-dried powder are reacted as a powder as well as after pressing into pellets.)
The fourth preparation route concerns the spray-roasting of a solution containing the appropriate concentration of the necessary ions.
Purity of the FHA-phase is determined with X-ray diffraction.
In addition, we used FHA-powder for plasma spraying.

INTRODUCTION

This study is part of a project on forming of bioceramics using calciumphosphate powders (like fluorhydroxyapatite and magnesium containing whitlokite) which have up to now received little attention as implant material. Hydroxyapatite and whitlokite will be used by ECN as reference materials. These reference materials are obtained commercially but the fluorcontaining apatites and magnesium containing whitlokites are to our knowledge not commercially available and so they are synthesised by ECN.
There is solid solubility in $Ca_{10}(PO_4)_6F_x(OH)_{2-x}$ for the whole range between x = 0 and x = 2, and the solubility product of the apatite is known to decrease with increasing fluoride content [1].

Both the strong crystallographic resemblance with the mineral phase of the hard tissue in man (i.e. hydroxyapatite, HA) and the possibility of decreasing the solubility to a certain (wanted) extent make fluorhydroxyapatite, FHA an interesting candidate as a powder for the processing of bioceramic implants. One of the critical factors in obtaining one phase powders is the mixing of the starting powders and the segregation which may occur during processing.

In this paper four different preparation routes are discussed.

In these preparation routes dry and wet mixing are compared. Also a slip-cast material is compared to a spray dried product, to see whether demixing occurs during slip casting. The fourth route is concerned with spray roasting of a solution of the appropriate ions, yielding the apatite stoichiometry.

It is known [2] that hydroxyapaptite can be synthesized by spray roasting of a solution containing $Ca(NO_3)_2$ and $(NH_4)_2HPO_4$ as starting materials. However, addition of fluorine ions to this solution leads to precipitation of either CaF_2 or $Ca_2(PO_4)_3$ depending on the pH of the solution. To avoid this precipitate to be formed, the calcium ions had to be complexed with citric acid.

MATERIALS AND METHODS

For the synthesis of FHA in the first three preparation routes we have used "trocken reinst" β-$Ca_3(PO_4)_2$, "zur analyse" $CaCO_3$ and "gefällt rein" CaF_2, all from Merck. The dry mixing was performed by shaking the powder in a polyethene jar in a Turbula (W.A. Bachofen, Basel) for 1, 3, 5 and 8 hours. A small amount of Al_2O_3 balls was added to facilitate the mixing. The wet mixing and milling was performed in an attritor (Wieneroto, W.1.S.E.) for 2.5 and 8 hours. As milling media 5 mm Al_2O_3 balls were used. The resulting suspension was either spray-dried using a Büchi 190 Mini spray-dryer, or directly slip cast on plaster of Paris or dried under laboratory conditions (~ 20°C, 50% RH). Part of the resulting dry powder was pressed into pellets using an uniaxial press (Busmann Simeteag, HPM 60). The pellets, the dry powder and the slip cast material were reacted in air at 920°C for 1 hour in an oven (Linn Electronic HT 1800). The pellets and powder obtained from the dry mixing experiments were also reacted for 5 hours at the same conditions.

The spray roasting experiment was carried out in a home made apparatus. For this experiment a solution was prepared containing calcium, phosphate and fluorine ions in a concentration of 0.5, 0.3 and 0.05 mole per liter respectively.
The solution was prepared by dissolving 0.50 mole of $CaCO_3$ with 1 mole of citric acid in 500 g of water. When the $CaCO_3$ is dissolved completely 0.3 mole of $NH_4H_2PO_4$ is slowly added. Finally 500 g of water containing 0.05 mole of HF is slowly added, yielding a clear solution. (All reagentias from J.T. Baker).
This solution was atomized in an air stream and slowly transported through a hot furnace. In this way the particles, that result after evaporation of the water, are heated to 950°C for about 5 sec.
The plasma spraying experiments were performed, using N_2 or Ar with H_2 as a carrier gas, applying an arc voltage of 40-80 V and an arc current of 400-500 A. The gun to substrate distance was between 8 and 12 cm and the translation speed between 10 and 20 cm/s.
The reacted materials were analysed with a Guinier-De Wolf X-ray camera using Ni-filtered CuKα radiation. The reflections were compared with JCPDS-cards no. 15-876 for FA and no. 9-432 for HA.
Scanning electron microscopy (JEOL JXA-840) was used to study the powder morphology after spray roasting.

RESULTS AND DISCUSSION

For all the apatite samples which were synthesized, we determined qualitatively by comparing the (004) and (410) reflections with those of HA and FA, that it was fluor-containing hydroxyapatite. We have not determined the amount of fluoride quantitatively.
All experiments performed with the dry mixed powder yielded FHA and a variable amount of β-$Ca_3(PO_4)_2$. The largest amount was found in the sample that was reacted as a powder.
In the pelletised product the amount had clearly decreased, while after reacting for 5 hours only a trace of β-$Ca_3(PO_4)_2$ could be detected. No influence of the mixing time could be observed. Probably the mixing is not ideal due to of some large β-$Ca_3(PO_4)_2$ particles which are not broken up during mixing.

All experiments performed with the wet mixed and milled powders yielded FHA with small traces of α-Al_2O_3 present, probably due to the wear of the milling media. Also the slip cast material was FHA with no second phase present, showing that there was no significant demixing during the slip casting process.
The spray-roasting experiment yielded particles (Fig. 1) with an average diameter of 1.5 μm consisting mainly of FHA with a minor amount of β-$Ca_3(PO_4)_2$. Probably the residence time in the spray-roaster (≈ 5 sec) is too short to complete the reaction.

Figure 1. SEM-picture showing spray-roasted fluorhydroxyapatite particles.

The FHA powder produced could not be fed into the plasma gun, probably due to a non ideal particle size distribution. However, using the conditions mentioned before, it proved possible to produce 50 μm layers of fluorapatite and hydroxyapatite onto metallic substrates. So, no chemical limitation is set to the production of FHA layers.

CONCLUSIONS

In all experiments it proved possible to synthesize fluorhydroxyapatite. However, when the starting powders were mixed in the dry state, the reaction time had to be increased to over 5 hours. By wet mixing in an attritor, reaction time can be decreased to less than one hour. When a suspension of the starting powders is prepared in the attritor and thean used for slip casting, no segregation is observed.
The spray-roasting experiment yields spherical particles with an average diameter of 1,5 µm. However, the production capacity of a spray-roaster is limited, leading to an expensive product. So if the specific particle size and morphology is not essential, spray-roasting seems the least attractive of the preparation routes studied.

ACKNOWLEDGEMENT

Financial support by the Dutch Ministry of Economic Affairs through the National Programme on Technical Ceramics (IOP-TK) is gratefully acknowledged.

REFERENCES

[1] Mineral Aspects of Dentistry; Driessens F.C.M., Karger, Basel, New York (1982).

[2] Properties of hydroxyapatite prepared by Spry-Pyrolysis Technique; Itatani, K., Takahashi, O., Kishioka, A., Kinoshita, M., Gypsum and Lime, No. 213, 1988, pag. 77-85.

POROUS BIOCERAMIC OBTAINED FROM GLASS POWDER OF CaO, MgO, P_2O_5 SYSTEM SEALED BY DIAMIDOPHOSPHATE

H. BOUTIGNY*- E. DELCOURT-DEBRUYNE*- G. PALAVIT**
P. VAST**- Y. PARENT**

*Lab. de Biologie du Parodonte - U.F.R. Odontologie - Université de LILLE II du Droit et de la Santé - Place de Verdun - 59 045 LILLE Cedex - FRANCE.

**Lab. de Chimie Appliquée - Université des Sciences et Techniques de LILLE - FLANDRES - ARTOIS - 59 655 VILLENEUVE D'ASCQ - FRANCE.

ABSTRACT

One of the metaphosphate glasses used in the field of bioceramics concerns the system Na2O, CaO, P2O5. Obtained by sol-gel or sol-coacervate glass process, this glass is easily corroded in vivo. By an exchange ion reaction with the initial coacervate, we can obtain the system Na2O, CaO, MgO, P2O5 glass. Mg-Na ratio variations permit the modulation of glass corrosion in vivo. By heating at 770°C. a mixing of glass powders and sodium diamidoorthophosphate, we obtain a porous ceramic due to the loss of the main part of the nitrogen in ammonia form from diamidophosphate. It's possible to control the porosity of the ceramic so obtained. We are testing in vivo the tissue behaviour within as well as around the material.

INTRODUCTION

The substitutive therapies aimed at the repairing of osseous defects, particularly in the field of periodontal intra-osseous defects, involve among other things the use of biomaterials as space fillers able to further the osseous reconstruction. We can list the following bioceramics as examples of biomaterials used in the osseous reconstruction: the hydroxylapatite (1)(2)(3), the tricalcium phosphate (4)(5), the calcium carbonate (6)(7). These materials come in the form of block, granule or powder with variable porosity and variable resorbability.

The rapid expansion of biomaterials in the domain of the osseous surgery comes from the fact that these materials are good palliatives for the autogenous and the allogenous bone grafts and for the xenografts.

Several factors are necessary in order to facilitate an

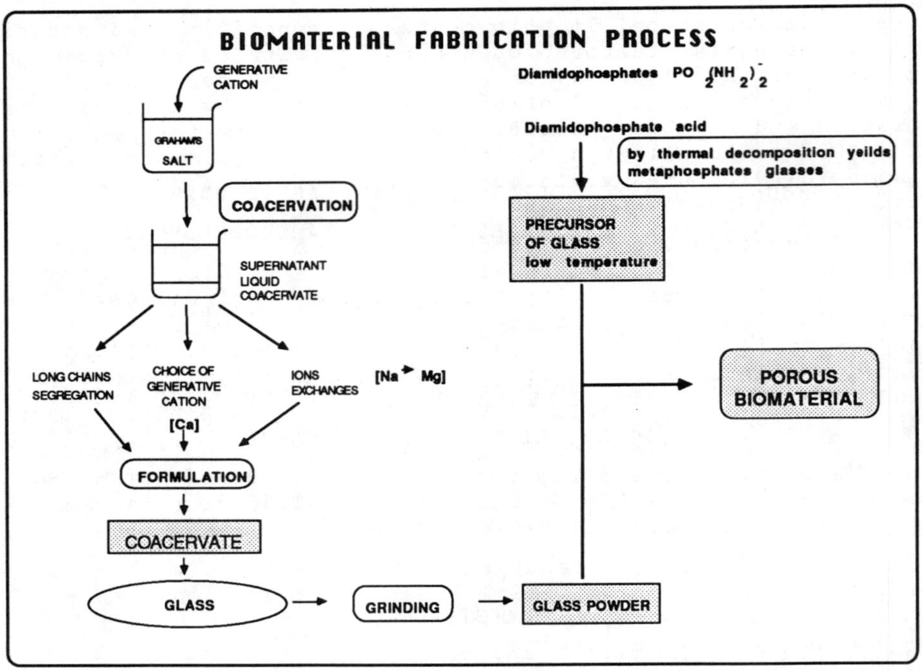

Fig 1 New process of biomaterials

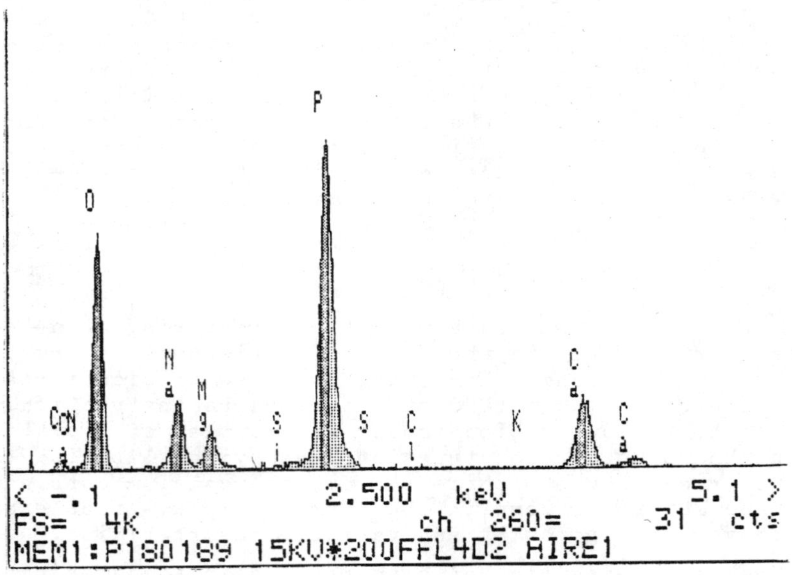

Fig 2 Elemental analysis by X ray microprobe under S E M

osseous neoformation. In this context, composition and porosity are two essential factors. Open porosity with an average diameter greater than 100µ (8) or greater than 150 to 200µ (9) would further the colonization of biomaterial pores by a neovascularization and new bone tissue. Pores with a diameter smaller than 100µ would allow the colonization by a fibrous connective tissue (8)(9). Pores would be used for guiding the osteogenesis acting as an osteoconductor.

Osteoconduction and osteoinduction are also dependent on the composition of biomaterials. Indeed, after implantation the material interacts with the biological environment and does not lead to an acute or chronic inflammatory response; it does not result in any adverse tissue reactions and it does not prevent a proper differenciation of tissues surrounding the implant. In other words, a material must be biocompatible (10). As well as this biocompatibility, a calium phosphate or a calcium carbonate-based intrinsic composition should provide a calcium reserve to the surrounding environment. Also, magnesium and sodium ions release from the material could be a favourable factors for the colonization of the pores by a new bone tissue.

From materials already biocompatible (11), we are trying to obtain a porous biomaterial whose structure would resemble cancellous bone and would further the osteogenesis in periodontal intra-osseous defects.

NEW KINDS OF BIOMATERIALS CONCEPTION

In view of their biocompatibility (11), polyphosphate and diamidophosphate would be good precursors to biomaterials. We used these two kinds of precursors to obtain an heterogeneous glass ceramic. The figure n°1 shows the process used. The first step consists of a polyphosphate glass elaboration obtained after coacervation process in adding calcium ions to sodium polyphosphate (Graham Salts) in acid environment (12). It's possible to formulate this coacervate before vitrification with an exchange of the sodium ions with the magnesium (12). By heating at 850°C. we obtain a glass. Mg-Na ratio variations permit the modulation of glass corrosion in vivo.

This based polyphosphate glass is used after grinding as the main part of biomaterials. This powder is sealed by a low temperature melting (770°C.) polyphosphate glass obtained by thermal decomposition of sodium diamidoorthophosphate (11). The ammonia exhaust producted by thermal decomposition of Na PO2 (NH2)2 permits to control the shrinkage of the composite material. This, conducts of a controled porosity about 100µ to 300µ determined by the glass granulometry powder.

MATERIAL CHARACTERIZATION

- S.E.M. study

The study of fractured material under scanning microscopy shows at lower magnification (x100)(Fig.n°3a) a honeycomb

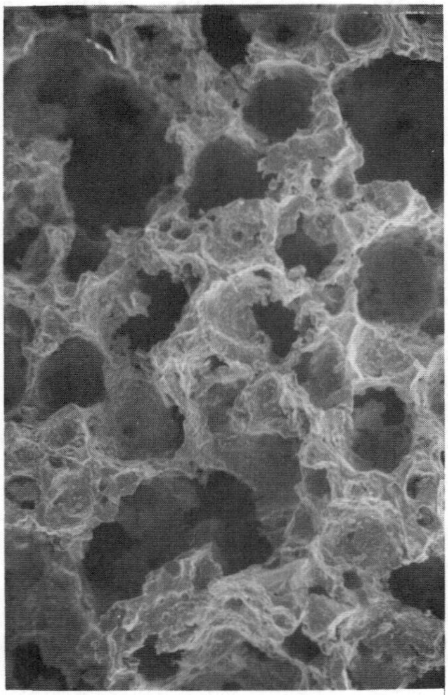

Fig. 3a: S.E.M. (x100) Material

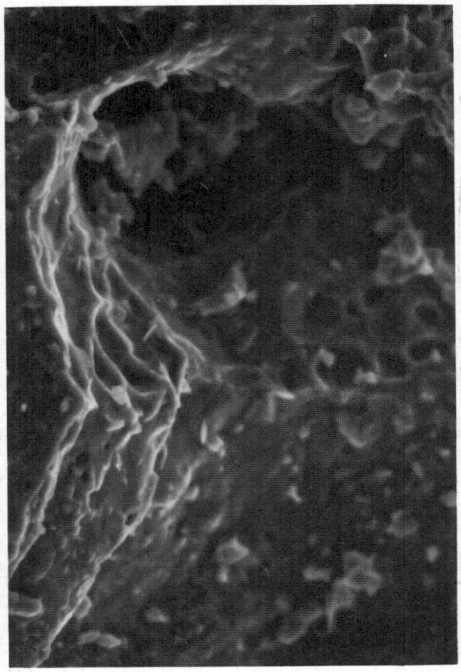

Fig. 3b: Higher magnification

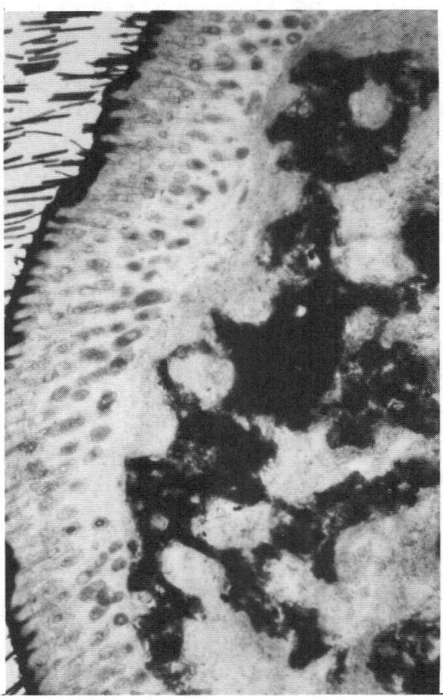

Fig.3c: Tissue surrounding materials(x 16)

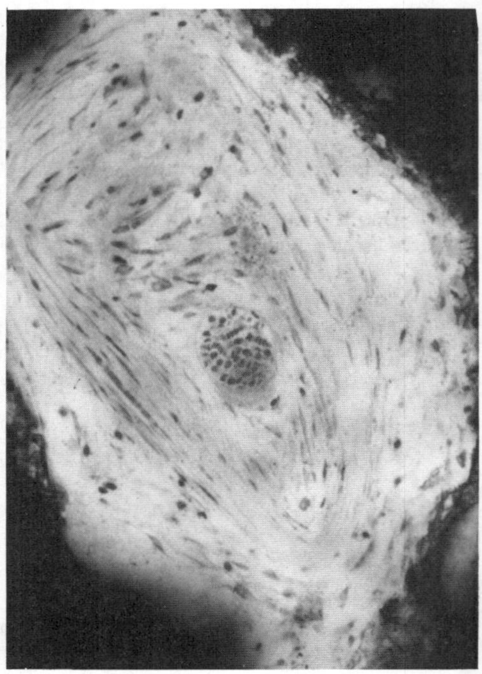

Fig.3d. Inside of a pore (x 40)

stitch like structure. This structure resembling cancellous bone, presents non spheric open pores with irregular edges, random orientation and a 100µ to 300µ diameter. At the bottom of the pores, we can see the opening of other pores, testifying to the presence of interconnections between the pores.

At higher magnification (x2000)(Fig.n°3B), the inside of a pore has a coral like aspect. The pore is demarcated by melted regular leaf like structures with 3µ diameter micropores.

- Elemental analysis

An elemental analysis under S.E.M. with X ray microprobe of three samples made up according to the same procedure, has been performed. The analysis is carried out on an 25µ² area and 1µ thichness. The figure n°2 shows the relative elemental composition of one of this three samples. We obtain a good reproductibility of oxygen, sodium, magnesium, phosphorus and calcium content.

- Biological applications

In order to study the tissue behaviour within as well as around the material, we are implanting this ceramic in subcutaneous, supraperiosteal and supracranial position of Swiss Mice. An histological study was performed on animals killed after a uniform period of 3 months. After fixing, dehydrating and embedding, sections about 5µ thick were cut and stained with Toluidin Blue. The material is surrounded by a rich fibroblastic connective tissue (Fig.n°3c) well organized and highly vascularized without extensive inflammation. The figure n°3d shows the inside of a pore at higher magnification. The pore is completely invaded by a highly vascularized loose fibroblastic tissue.

CONCLUSIONS

This new process permits the obtention of reproductible porous materials. The formulation and the porosity of this bioceramic induce a new well organized vascularized tissue suggested that this material is well accepted. You will improve this kind of porous bioceramic in osseous defect to study the osseous behaviour within as well as around the material.

REFERENCES

1. BEIRNE O.R., GREENSPAN J.S.: Tissue response to hydroxylapatite placed in humans. J. Dent. Res. 63: 324, 1984.

2. BEIRNE O.R., GREENSPAN J.S.: Histologic evaluation of tissue response to hydroxylapatite implanted on human mandibles. J. Dent. Res. 64: 1152-1154, 1985.

3. BENQUE E.P., GINESTE M., HEUGHEBAERT M.: Etude histologique de la biocompatibilité des cristaux d'hydroxyapatite en chirurgie parodontale. J. Biol. Bucc. 13: 271-282, 1985.

4. BHASKAR S.N., BRADY J.M., GETTER L., GROWER M.F., DRISKELL Th.: Biodegradable ceramic implants in bone-Electron and

light microscopic analysis. Oral Surg. 32: 336-346, 1979.

5. FROUM S., STAHL S.S.: Human intraosseous healing responses to the placement of tricalcium phosphate ceramic implants II 13 to 18 months. J. Periodontol. 58: 103-109, 1987.

6. OUHAYOUN J.P., ISSAHAKIAN S., PATAT J.L., GUILLEMIN N., SHABANA H., FOREST N.: Histologic evaluation of alloplastic grafting materials in an animal "closed" model. IADR, Louvain, Abstacts booklet, 275, 1988.

7. GUILLEMIN G., PATAT J.L., FOURNIE J., CHETAIL M.: The use of coral as a bone graft substitute. J. Biomed. Mater. Res. 21: 557-567, 1987.

8. HULBERT S.F., YOUNG F.A., MATHEWS R.S.: Potential ceramic materials as permanently implantable skeletal prostheses. J. Biomed. Mater. Res. 4: 433, 1970.

9. DE GROOT K.: Ceramics of calcium phosphates: preparation and properties. in "Bioceramics of calcium phosphate" Ed. K. De Groot, CRC Press. Inc. Boca Raton, 1983.

10. ALBREKTSSON T.: General biocompatibility. in "Definition on Biomaterials", Proccedings of a consensus conference of the European Society for Biomaterials, Chester, England, Ed. Williams, Elsevier, Amsterdam, 1987.

11. PALAVIT G., LAFFARGUE P., VAST P.: A new family of phosphate biomaterials. Transaction of the Fifth European Conference on Biomaterials, Paris, Paris, 4_6 Sept. 1985, p.139.

12. DRAOUI M., VAST P., PALAVIT G.: Préparation de gels de polyanions phosphoriques à partir de métaphosphates. Rev. Chim. Min. 22: 256-267, 1985.

SINTERING OF HYDROXYLAPATITE-GLASS COMPOSITE MATERIALS

E. TKALČEC, N. VRBOS and D. NAVALA
Favulty of Technology and Faculty of Metallurgy,
University of Zagreb, 41000 Zagreb, Yugoslavia

ABSTRACT

The effect of calcium phosphate glasses on sintering of hydroxylapatite prepared by hydrothermal synthesis from aragonite shells of ARCA NOAE has been studied. The increased compressive strength was achieved when BaO and Al2O3 partialy substituted CaO in the glass composition, decreasing its softening temperature. Phase composition of sintered composites determined by XRD has revealed that β-whitlockite formed during sintering can be partially or completely dissolved in the glass phase. The positive influence on the retaining of grain growth has been determined by SEM.

INTRODUCTION

Among a great number of papers on apatite bioactive ceramics only few ones are dealing with the hydrothermal synthesis of hydroxylapatite (HAP) from calcium carbonate skeletal structure of the sea invertebrates (1,2) or of the algae (3). D. M. Roy et al. (1,2) have reported about hydrothermal synthesis of HAP from coral skeletons, considering that HAP is formed from aragonite, while β-whitlockite is formed from calcite. However, mechanical strength of this material was very low. Kasperk et al. (3) reported about microporous implants of HAP ceramics prepared from calcified algae with specific surface of more than 50 m^2/g.

HAP is one of the best biocompatible materials, but with insufficient mechanical strength. Therefore, attemps have been made to get stronger HAP ceramics by sintering with additives like glasses (4), ZrO_2 (5,6), etc.

The paper presented deals with the effect of calcium phosphate glasses of the compositions very similar to the ones reported in (4) on the sintering of hydrothermally prepared HAP from shells of Arca Noae.

MATERIALS AND METHODS

Starting materials for hydrothermal synthesis were pulverized shells (grain size < 60 μm) preheated at 450°C and at 500°C and 0.1 ML^{-1} $(NH_4)_2HPO_4$ aqueous solution, pH = 11. Hydrothermal synthesis was performed at 200°C (1.6 MPa) and at 230°C (2.8 MPa) in the period from 4 hours to 10 days.

Glasses A, B and C with various softening points were prepared by melting of the homogenized mixture of raw materials in Pt crucible at 1300°C for 2 hours. The molten glasses were water-quenched and pulverized into a powder with grain size < 60 μm.

Mixtures of hydrothermally synthesized and at 700°C calcinated HAP powder and 5 wt. % of glasses were homogenized and compressed at 100 MPa into pellets of 30 mm diameter and 4mm thick. The compositions of glasses are shown in Table 2. The pellets were sitered at 900, 1000, 1100, 1150 and 1200°C. The sintering temperature was reached at the rate of 4 °C/min and maintained at it for 2 hours. Hydrothermally prepared HAP was analysed by XRD, IR and DTA methods. HAP lattice parameters a_o and c_o were determined on 002, 211, 112, 300 and 202 lines by the precise angle measurments corrected by means of Si standard. The crystallite size was calculated by Scherrer formula. Bulk density of sintered compacts was measured by Archimedes method. Compressive strength was measured on Instron 4302 with a crosshead speed of 0.5 mm/min. Phase analysis of compacts was carried out by XRD. The microstructure was investigated by SEM on fractured surfaces etched with 0.1 M acetic acid.

RESULTS AND DISCUSSION

XRD analysis of Arca Noae shells preheated at 450°C confirmed aragonite structure of $CaCO_3$. In shells heat treated at 500°C aragonite has already been transformed into calcite. XRD patterns of one incompletely reacted sample and of the one hydrothermally prepared HAP are given in Fig.1. Contrary to (1) it has been noticed that the formation of hydroxylapatite is not conditioned by aragonite structure since calcite formed during the preheating of shells at 500°C was also converted into HAP and not into β-whitlockite. For all further investigations HAP was prepared from

Table 1 Synthesis conditions, lattice parameters a_0, c_0 and, crystallite sizes (D_{002}) of hydrothermally prepared HAP

Sample	Hydrothermal synthesis Temp /°C, time/h		a_0/nm, c_0/nm, D_{002}/nm	Crystal phases at 900°C	Ca/P
1	200	24	a_0=0.9439 (4) c_0=0.6880 (3) D_{002}=79 ± 10	β-$Ca_3(PO_4)_2$ β-$Ca_2P_2O_7$	1.60
1a	200	24	a_0 = 0.9437(4) c_0 = 0.6880(3) D_{002} = 95 ± 10	HAP β-$Ca_3(PO_4)_2$ CaO	1.69
*2	230	24	a_0 = 0.9430(5) c_0 = 0.6879 (4) D_{002} = 115 ± 10	HAP β-$Ca_3(PO_4)_2$ CaO	1.68
4i in reference 1	260	24	a_0=0.9435(1) c_0=0.6893(1)		
reference 5	200	1	a_0=0.9418(2) c_0=0.6879(1)		1.67

*The content of β-$Ca_3(PO_4)_2$ β-whitlockite and CaO is smaller than in the sample 1a

shells preheated at 450°C. On the basis of XRD analysis (Fig.1c) the hydrothermal synthesis at 200°C and 230°C for 24 hours have been chosen as optimal. Characteristics of the prepared hydroxylapatite are given in Table 1. Hydrothermally prepared HAP was micro crystalline with lattice parameters greater than the ones given for stoichiometric HAP (5), but very near to the ones given in (1). Unfortunately we couldn't get stoichiometric HAP under the chosen experimental conditions (Table 1.). For the preparation of sinterd compacts the HAP samples No.1 and No.2 were used. The compositions of glasses used as additives for sintering are given in Table 2. Compressive strength and density (%) of sintered compacts are given in Fig.2.

TABLE 2
Composition of HAP-glass compacts

Sample	HAP	Glass				
		Composition (mol %)				Softening point, °C ($\eta = 10^{6.6}$ Pas)
		CaO	P_2O_5	Al_2O_3	BaO	
A	1	-	-	-	-	
A_2	2	53.1	46.9	-	-	1229
B_1	1	51.0	45.1	1.0	2.9	755
B_2	2	"	"	"	"	
C	2	48.5	42.9	5.7	2.8	750

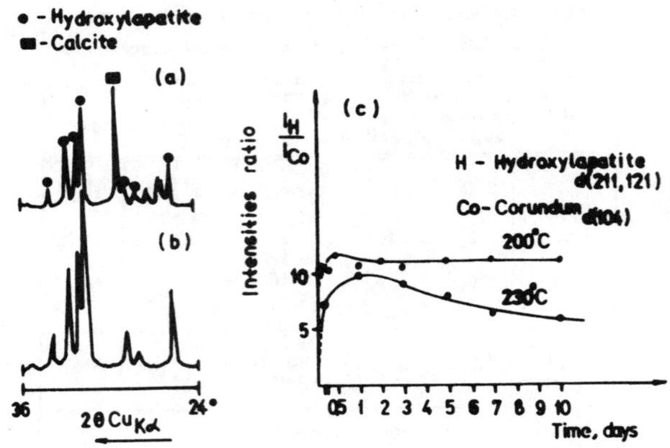

Figure 1. XRD patterns of (a) incompletely reacted aragonite, (b) HAP obtained by hydrothermal reaction of aragonite, previously transformed into calcite, at 200°C, 24 h: (c) intensities ratio I_H/I_{Co} versus temperature: I_H -intensity of 121, 211 line of HAP, I_{Co} - intensity of 104 line of corundum added as standard

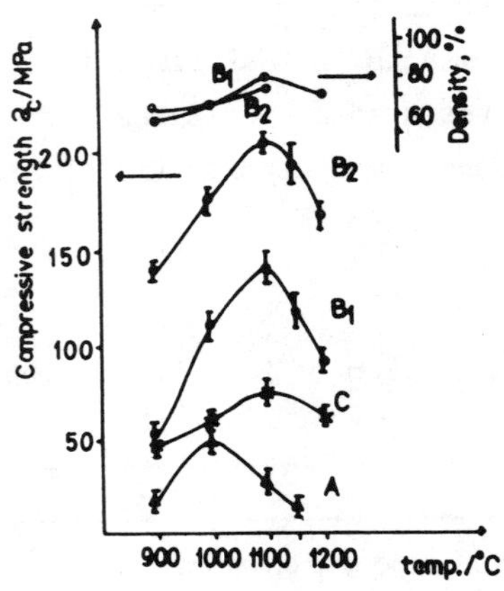

Figure 2. Compressive strength and density (%) of sintered compacts. Denotations are the same as in Table 2

The results obtained are in accordance with the results previously published (4) and show that glass B is the most effective with the samples containing β-whitlockite (B_1) as well as with the samples containing hydroxylapatite (B_2) as the main crystalline phase.

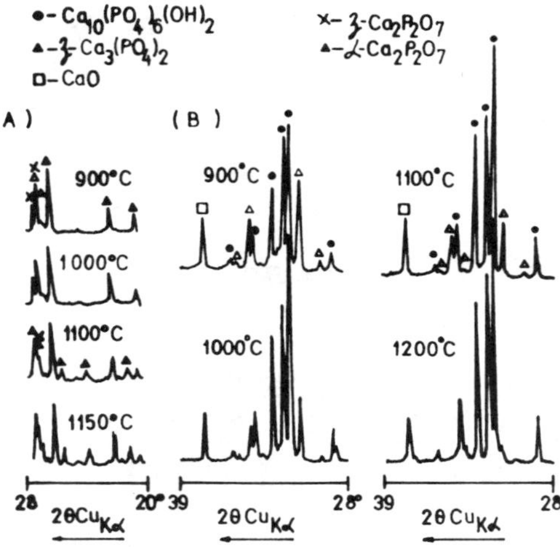

Figure 3. XRD patterns of sintered compacts: (A) series B_1, (B) series B_2

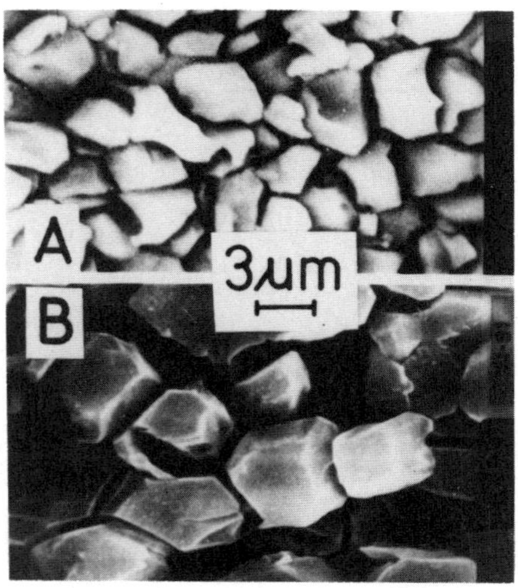

Figure 4. SEM micrographs of etched surfaces of (A)-compacts B_2 and (B)-compact A at the maximal strength temperature

Because of its low softening temperature (Table 2), glass B is in the liquid state at the sintering temperature and reacts with the surface of hydroxylapatite particles resulting in the dissolution of β-whitlockite (Fig.3B). Lower effectiveness of glass B in the compacts series B_1 can be explained by the transformation of β-$Ca_2P_2O_7$ with higher density into α-$Ca_2P_2O_7$ with lower density (Fig.3A). Unlike glass B, glass A with very high softening temperature is not effective. The explanation of the behaviour of glass C still has to be found. The positive influence of glass B on the retaining of grain growth is depicted in SEM micrographs (Fig.4.).

REFERENCES

1. D. M. Roy, Nature, **247** (1974), 222.
2. W. Eysel and D. M. Roy, Z. Kristallogr. Mineral., 141, (1975), 11.
3. Ch. Kasperk, R.Ewers, Z. Zahnarztl. Implant. **2**, (1986), 234.
4. K. Kondo, M. Okyuama, H. Ogawa and Y. Shibata, J. Am. Ceram. Soc., **67**, (1984), 11, C-222.
5. S. Somiya, K. Ioku and M. Yoshimura, Materials Science Forum, **34-36**, (1988), 371.
6. Jenn-Ming Wu, Tung-Sheng Yeh, J. Mater. Sci., **23**, (1988), 3771.

SLIP CASTING OF HYDROXYAPATITE FOR BONE REPLACEMENT

C. Galassi, E. Roncari, A. Ravaglioli, R. Martinetti
Research Institute For Ceramics Technology - CNR
Faenza, ITALY

ABSTRACT

Aim of the work is the optimization of the processing parameters for the production of parts made of hydroxyapatite to be proposed for bone replacement. Slip casting on plaster moulds is the shaping method used for the preliminary production of several prototypes. Solid phase content, pH effects, deflocculant type and concentration, rheological characteristics are considered as well as the complexity and the dimensions of the chosen shape in order to obtain high density and defect free green bodies. Microstructure, green density, pore size distribution were evaluated on green bodies, final density, microstructure were evaluated on the fired bodies in order to optimize the processing parameters and to meet the requirements in view of biomedical applications of this material.

INTRODUCTION

Ceramic materials in massive form, coatings or fillers are now under investigation for the replacement of human bone tissue. Most of studies are devoted to the knowledge of the chemico-physical and biological interaction with the surrounding tissues; in the literature there is a lack of knowledge about the processing parameters and material characteristics of hydroxyapatite, a material of great interest for bioactive applications. Assessed the potential good compatibility with the human tissues, the studies are now focussed to improve the mechanical properties that showed too scarce in samples produced by conventional powder compaction and sintering technique (1,2). Aim of this study is to produce simple but net shaped massive manufacts of hydroxyapatite using a slip casting route. This technique is useful to obtain small batches of components like bone replacement, surgery ear, etc.

TABLE 1
Properties of the as received (HA) and calcined (HAC) hydroxyapatite.

Powder	S.S.A.BET m^2/g	Equivalent spherical diameter μm	crystalline phase	Chemical composition %							
				$Ca_3(PO_4)_2$	H_2O	As	Fe	Pb	Cl	F	SO_4
HA	61.2	0.032	Calcium Hydroxyde Orthophosphate $Ca_5(PO_4)_3OH$	97	2	.0002	.02	.0003	.1	.005	.5
HAC	4.9	0.39	Calcium Hydroxyde Orthophosphate $Ca_5(PO_4)_3OH$	–	–	–	–	–	–	–	–

MATERIALS AND METHODS

A commercial hydroxyapatite $Ca_5(PO_4)_3OH$ powder (Riedel de Haen) was employed as received (HA) and after calcination (HAC), (1h - 1000°C). The powders characteristics are reported in Tab.1; the X-ray diffraction pattern is the same for HA and HAC powder; the particle size distribution is reported in Fig. 1. The HA powder resulted not suitable for suspensions castable with conventional casting parameters, due to the too high fraction of fine particles (40 mass% < 0,2μm), while satisfactory results were obtained after the thermal treatment of the starting powder in the following used for all experiences. From electrophoretic mobility measurements on dilute suspensions of the HAC, it was found

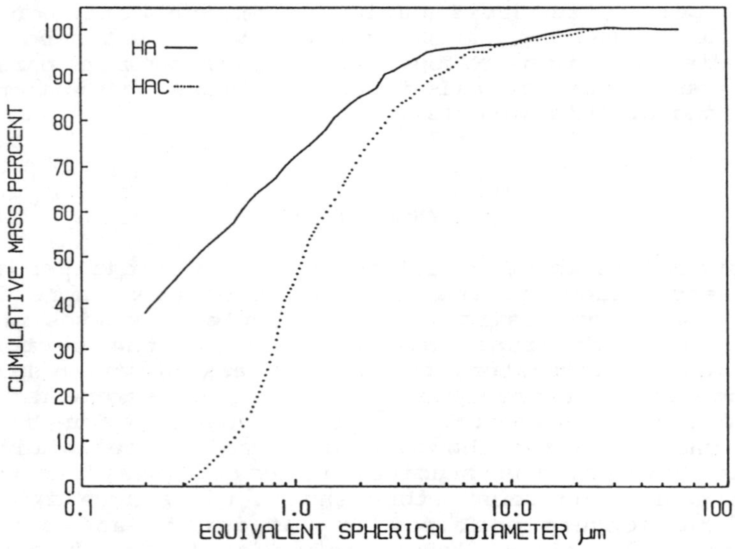

Fig.1 Particle size distribution of the powder as received (HA) and after calcination (HAC).

TABLE 2
Suspension composition, viscosity, green and sintered density.

Sample	Solid Phase wt%	vol%	Defloc. wt%	$\eta_{D=10\ s^{-1}}$ (Pas)	Green density %	Final density %
HAC1	66	38.1	0.83	—	44.0	89.6
HAC2	68	40.2	0.65	0.13	47.4	—
HAC3	69	41.3	0.32	0.44	49.7	94.2
HAC4	70	42.5	0.50	0.87	52.9	94.3

that the electrophoretic mobility increases significantly at high values of pH, so the pH = 11 was chosen for the stabilization of the suspension and ammonium ligninsulphonate was used as deflocculant. The suspensions are prepared adding the HAC powder to the water and deflocculant, adjusting the pH and homogenizing in a ball mill. Rheological measurements were performed on the evacuated suspensions that result very stable and green bodies of different shapes were produced trough solid casting on the plaster moulds. On the green bodies density, pore size distribution and morphology were tested. The samples were fired 1 h at 1300°C (slope 200°C/h); final structure, and density were measured. In Tab. 2 the processing conditions and green and fired properties are reported.

RESULTS AND DISCUSSION

The preparation of the HAC slips takes long times and the powder is added in several steps resulting the 40 vol.% a critical value (maximum 42,5 vol.%), over that the slip changes rapidly from a fluid to a solid state. For all the samples tested a dilatant behaviour was found (Fig.2), typical of the systems where aggregation arises with the increase of the shear rate. The suspensions (mainly HAC3) resulted stable for weeks; the green bodies produced are weak and the relative densities are near to 50%; the pores size range is 100-400 nm, the sample HAC3 present the finest pores (100-200 nm) (Fig.3); the green texture (Fig.4-a) results in a uniform distribution of the particles (Ø< 0.5 μm). In the sintered body the X-ray diffraction pattern reveals only the presence of calcium hydroxyde orthophosphate; the samples are not fully dense and, comparing the SEM morphology of the green (Fig.4-a) and sintered body (Fig.4-b) it is evident a relevant grain growth with net grain boundaries. The soaking time as well as the temperature influences strongly the grain growth as shown by the fracture surface in Fig.4-c (0,5h) and in Fig.4-d (1h); from the same pictures the fracture results transgranular.

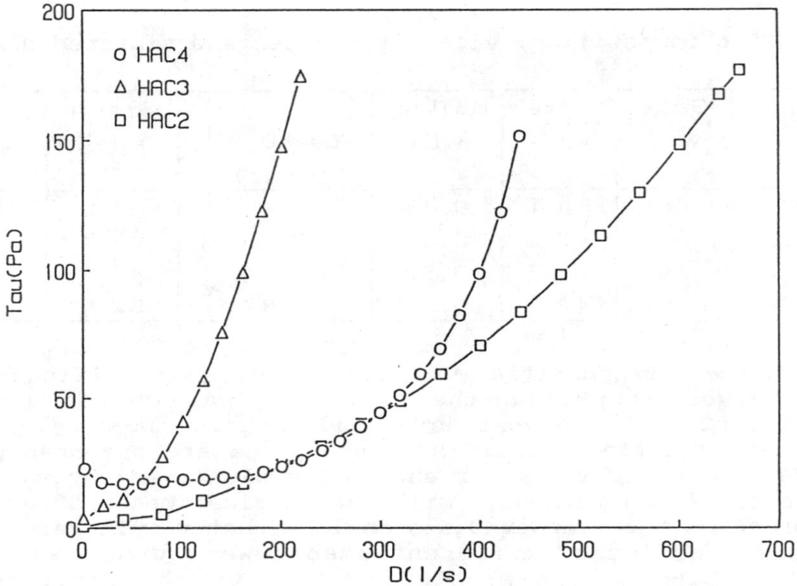

Fig. 2 Rheological behaviour of the HAC slips (HAC4 70 wt%; HAC3 69 wt%; HAC2 68 wt% solid phase).

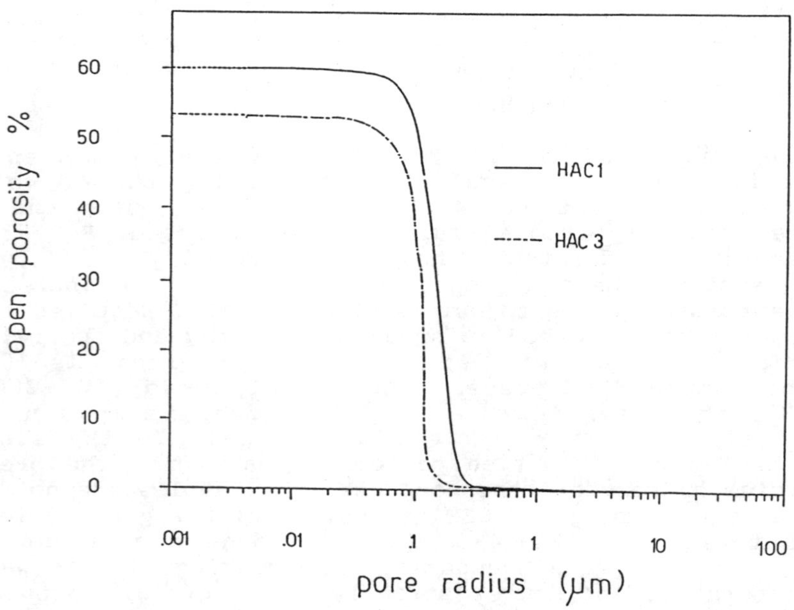

Fig.3 Pore size distribution of the green bodies.

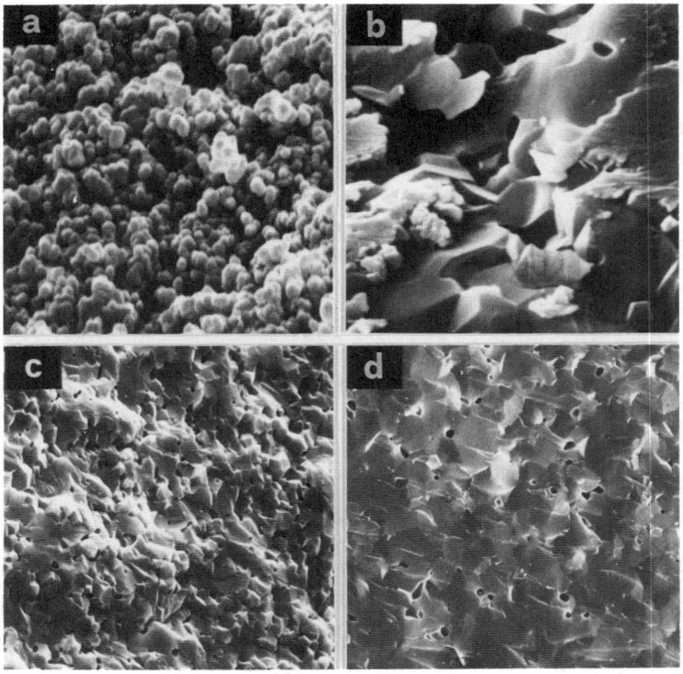

Fig.4 SEM morphology of the green (a) and sintered (b) 1300°C 0,5h, (c) 1300°C 0,5h, (d) 1300°C 1h samples.

CONCLUSIONS

The treatment of hydroxyapatite is quite complex because of the changes in the concentration of the hydroxilic groups on the surface due to the suspension parameters or to the thermal treatment, thus further investigations are needed for a better understanding of the phenomena involved. In this study a thermal treatment was necessary to reduce the fine fraction of the starting powder and improve the castability. The suspensions resulted very stable but with a dilatant behaviour. Green bodies free of macroscopic defects are obtained, but the sintering cycle has to be optimized in order to produce dense samples, preventing an excessive grain growth.

REFERENCES

1. Thomas, M.B. and Doremus, R.H., Fracture strength of dense hydroxyapatite, Am. Ceram. Soc. Bull. 1981, **60**, 258-259.

2. Akao, M., Miura, N. and Aoki, H., Fracture toughness of sintered hydroxyapatite and β-tricalcium phosphate. Yogyo-Kyokai-Shi, 1984, **11**, 672-674.

IS THE SOLUBILITY PRODUCT OF SYNTHETIC CALCIUM PHOSPHATES A GOOD PREDICTOR FOR THEIR BIODEGRADABILITY?

FCM DRIESSENS
Department of oral Function and dental Prosthetics,
Catholic University, P.O. Box 9101, 6500 HB Nijmegen, the Netherlands

ABSTRACT

The following calcium phosphates were synthesized according to the usual methods of ceramic technology and their solubility product was determined by equilibrations in buffers at room temperature: hydroxyapatite, oxyhydroxyapatite, octocalcium phosphate, brushite, β-tertiary calcium phosphate and magnesium whitlockite. The solubility studies indicate that the resorbabilities for implants of these materials should be in the following order: magnesium whitlockite < hydroxyapatite < oxyhydroxyapatite < β-tertiary calcium phosphate. Comparison with biological studies in which these materials were implanted and studies for loss of material, indicate that under in vivo conditions the loss of material is determined not only by a physicochemical process like dissolution but also by biological processes like the scavenging of mineral particles by macrophages, as has also been found with metallic implants.

INTRODUCTION

Many manufacturers and reseachers in the field of implantology distinguish between only two calcium phosphates which might be suitable for implantation, namely β-TCP and so-called "hydroxyapatite". In general both these products are produced by sintering procedures and offered on the medical market as blocks or granulates with a certain particle size, both with various degrees of porosity. Also, metallic implants are available which are coated with so-called hydroxyapatite by a plasma spray technique. In a previous paper it has been made clear that many more calcium phosphate formulations might be applicable in implantology (1). Due to the fact that, besides calcium and phosphate also ions like fluoride, chloride, carbonate, zinc, magnesium, potassium and sodium occur normally in the body fluids, calcium phosphates containing those ions might also be of potential value for implantation purposes. In this way the solubility behaviour of calcium phosphate implants and, hence, their reactivity with the body fluids might be varied over a much broader range than that applied hitherto. An important question in this respect is whether we can predict the biodegradability or the relative rate of biodegradation of a calcium phosphate implant, when we know the solubility product of that calcium phosphate.

On the other hand one must know what the solubility behaviour of the biominerals of e.g. bone is in order to enable a comparison with the synthetic calcium phosphates. It is most appropriate to use as a measure for the solubility of a biomineral the logarithm for the ionic product of hydroxyapatite log I (OHA) of an aqueous solution in physico-chemical equilibrium with that biomineral. Due to the fact that the biominerals of the calcified tissues are not always hydroxyapatite, their log I (OHA) may be pH dependent. Therefore, their log I (OHA) is plotted in Fig. 1 as a function of pH. The appropriate expression to calculate log I (OHA) is:

$$\log I\ (OHA) = 10 \log (Ca^{2+}) + 6 \log (PO_4{}^{3-}) + 2 \log (OH^-)$$

in which (X) means the activity of ion X.

It is also important to know the log I (OHA) and the pH of body fluids. This has been dealt with more extensively in some previous communications (2, 3). It suffices here to summarize the main result as given in Table 1. The biological range of pH variations relevant to implants is from about 5 to 8 and with these variations in pH very large alterations occur in the body fluids surrounding implants. This should be kept in mind when in vivo evaluations are made of the behaviour of calcium phosphate implants.

MATERIALS, METHODS AND RESULTS.

Hydroxyapatite ceramics (Ca/P ratio 1.67). The only way to make pure hydroxyapatite is by precipitation from aqueous solutions at a high pH under exclusion of carbon dioxyde from the air. Such products show a pH-independent solubility product log K (OHA) of -117.2 (4). In contrast, ceramic products having a Ca/P ratio of 1.67 are not hydroxyapatites, but rather oxyhydroxyapatites (5). These have a log K (OHA) of about -70. Upon equilibration of hydroxyapatite ceramics in contact with aqueous solutions they are covered rapidly by a layer of calcium deficient hydroxyapatite DOHA (6), of which the approximate solubility product K (DOHA) equals that of bulk enamel. It is to expected that also hydroxyapatite ceramic implants behave after a short time in contact with body fluids as if they were calcium deficient hydroxyapatite DOHA. But this has never been checked by surface analysis of such implants after implantation and recovery.

β-TCP or "whitlockite" ceramics (Ca/P ratio 1.50). This compound can also be made by ceramic techniques, but only by heating somewhere under 1180°C. Its solubility behaviour is very closely described by the line for dentine in Fig. 1. Hence, it is more soluble than hydroxyapatiteceramics in contact with in vitro aqueous solutions. Recently, it has been proven that upon implantation in the bone of the forehead of the domestic pig it becomes covered at least partially with calcium deficient hydroxyapatite DOHA (7). Nonetheless, it is expected that this coverage is not complete in contrast with that of hydroxyapatite ceramic implants, because the rate of biodegradation of β-TCP ceramics is larger than that of hydroxyapatite ceramics under similar in vivo conditions (8, 9, 10). During in vivo resorption some particles loosen

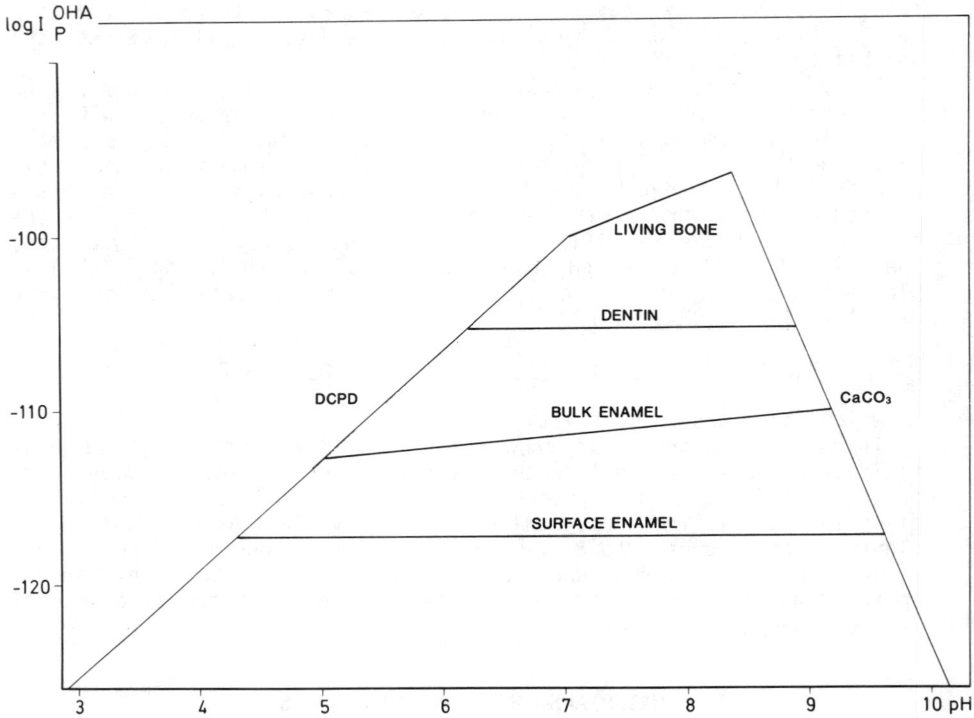

Figure 1. Solubility behaviour of the biominerals of calcified tissues expressed as their logarithm of the corresponding ionic product for hydroxyapatite as a function of pH. DCPD means dicalcium phosphate dihydrate.

TABLE 1.
Log I (OHA) and pH estimated to occur in body fluids averaged over diurnal rhythms

Body fluid	log I (OHA)	pH
Bone extracellular fluid	- 99	7.6
- near osteoblasts	- 97	8
- near osteoclasts	-122	5
Near macrophages	-117	5-6
Blood serum and extracellular fluid	-100	7.4

and are phagocytosed and transported to lymph knodes (9, 11). The rate of biodegradation of β-TCP increases with increasing macro- and microporosity (12, 13).

Several products on the market are not a single-phase hydroxyapatite ceramic nor a single phase -TCP ceramic, but have a composition with a Ca/P ratio somewhere between 1.50 and 1.67. It will be clear that their in vivo behaviour depends primarily on factors like (a) the type of phase which is the continuous one (b) porosity (14, 15).

α-TCP (Ca/P ratio 1.50). This form of TCP is stable above 1180°C and below that temperature it transforms into the β-form. However, it can be obtained at room temperature by quenching from high temperature. This means that the free energy of α-TCP and hence its solubility is larger than that of β-TCP at room or body temperature. Indeed it has been found that the rate of biodegradation of α-TCP is larger (16, 17).

Rhenanite $CaNaPO_4$(Ca/P ratio 1). The solubility of this compound is not known exactly, but it must be high because it has been used since long as a fertilizer. Upon implantation in a porous form in the bone of the forehead of the domestic pig it is tranformed completely into a mixture of the apatites $Ca_{8.5}Na_{1.5}(PO_4)_{4.5}(CO_3)_{2.5}$ and $Ca_9(PO_4)_{4.5}(CO_3)_{1.5}(OH)_{1.5}$ which occur normally in bone mineral (7).

CONCLUSION

The solubility behaviour of calcium phosphates is, in general, not determined by their solubility product, but rather by transformation of the surface layer (in the case of ceramics of hydroxyapatite, β-TCP and probably also α-TCP) or even complete transformation (in the case of rhenanite). Hence, the solubility product is not a good measure for the in vivo behaviour of calcium phosphate implants.

REFERENCES

1. Driessens, F.C.M., Formation and stability of calcium phosphates in relation to the phase composition of the mineral in calcified tissues. In Bioceramics of calcium phosphate, ed. K. de Groot, CRC Press, Boca Raton Florida, 1983, pp. 1-36.

2. Driessens, F.C.M., Physiology of hard tissues in comparison with the solubility of synthetic calcium phosphates. Ann. NY Acad. Sci., 1988, **523**, 131-136.

3. Driessens, F.C.M. and Verbeeck, R.M.H., Relation between physico-chemical solubility and biodegradability of calcium phosphates. In Implant materials in biofunction, Advances in Biomaterials, Vol. 8, eds. C. de Putter, G.L. de Lange, K. de Groot and A.J.C. Lee, Elsevier, Amsterdam 1988, pp. 105-111.

4. Driessens, F.C.M., Mineral aspects of dentistry, S. Karger, Basel, 1982.

5. Verbeeck, R.M.H., Heijligers, H.J.M., Driessens, F.C.M. and Schaeken, H.G., Effect of dehydration of calcium hydroxyapatite on

its cell parameters. Z. anorg. allg. Chem., 1980, **466** , 76-80.

6. Verbeeck, R.M.H., Thun, H.P.T. and Driessens, F.C.M., Effect of dehydration of hydroxyapatie on its solubility behaviour. Z. physik. Chem. NF, 1980, **119** , 79-84.

7. Ramselaar, M., Driessens, F.C.M. and Stols, A., Reactions of some implanted calcium phosphates in vivo, to be published 1989.

8. Klein, C.P.A.T., Patka, P. and den Hollander, W., Macroporous calcium phosphate bioceramics in dog femora: a histological study of interface and biodegradation. Biomaterials, 1989, **10** , 59-62.

9. Renooij, W., Hoogendoorn, H.A., Visser, W.J., Lentferink, R.H.F., Schmitz, M.G.J., van Ieperen, H., Oldenburg, S.J., Janssen, W.M., Akkermans, L.M.A. and Wittebol, P., Bioresorption of ceramic strontium - 85 - labeled calcium phosphate implants in dog femora. Clin. Orthop. Relat. Res., 1985, **197** , 272-285.

10. de Groot, K., Die klinische Anwendbarheit von Calciumphosphat-Keramiken. Zahnärztl. Mitteil. 1985, **75** , 1938-1940.

11. Klein C.P.A.T., de Groot, K., Driessen, A.A. and van der Lubbe, H.B.M., Interaction of biodegradable -whitlockite ceramics with bone tissue: an in vivo study. Biomaterials, 1985, **6** , 189-192.

12. Hollinger, J.O., Schmitz, J.P., Mizgala, J.W. and Hassler, C., An evaluation of two configurations of tricalcium phosphate for treating craniotomics. J. Biomed. Mater. Res., 1989, **23** , 17-29.

13. Zöllner, C., Strutz, J., Beck, C. and Binsing, C.M., Ist die poröse Trikalziumphosphatkeramik als Ersatz von knöchernen Wänden in der Ohrchirurgie geeignet? Laryng. Rhinol., 1982, **61** , 667-673.

14. Köster, K. and Heide, H., Bioaktive Calciumphosphatkeramik für den Knochen- und Zahnersatz, Biotechnische Umschau, 1978, **2** , 226-228.

15. Weinländer, M., Plenk, H., Halwax, E. and Nikiforov, A., In vitro Untersuchungen verschiedener Hydroxylapatitmaterialien, Z. Stomatol 1988, **85** , 399-404.

16. Jacobs, H.G., Luhr, H.G., Krause, A. and Überall, H., Knochendefektfüllung mit granulärer Kalziumphosphatkeramik. Dtsch. Z. Mund Kiefer Gesichts Chir., 1984, **8** , 38-42.

17. Krause, A., Wehrbein, H., Jacobs, H.G. und Morich, S., Trikalziumphosphatkeramik der -Modifikation zur Auffüllung von grossen Knochendefekten nach Zystektomien im Oberkieferfrontbereich, Dtsch. Z. Mund Kiefer Gesichts Chir., 1986, **10** , 108-112.

THE BONDING OF ALUMINOUS DENTAL PORCELAIN TO PLATINUM FOILS

HUAXIA JI and P. M. MARQUIS
School of Metallurgy and Materials, P. O. Box 363
University of Birmingham, B15 2TT
England

ABSTRACT

The bonding of aluminous dental porcelain-to-platinum foils produced at 1100°C for 20 min in vacuum, with or without tin oxide coatings, has been studied by analytical electron microscopy. Two distinct bonding microstructures have been identified. It has been shown that tin oxides between aluminous dental porcelain and platinum are stannic oxide and also dissolve into aluminous dental porcelain. Also atomic interdiffusion has been observed to occur at the platinum porcelain interface. The impact of the different structures on the strengths of resulting restorations are discussed.

INTRODUCTION

In metal based ceramic jacket crowns, platinum has been successfully employed as an alternative substrate to other metals[1] and is well established as a clinical system. The use of tin oxide as an intermediate layer gives a significant improvement in adherence[1][2] between porcelain and platinum and increases the strength of the restoration. It has been suggested that wetting of metallic substrates by dental porcelain leads to the formation of chemical bonds and also that metal ion bridges can be formed at the bonding interface in the presence of stannous ions (Sn^{+2}) or stannic ions (Sn^{+4})[3]. However, there is a lack of the direct observation of bonding microstructures using analytical transmission electron microscope which would lead to a better understanding of the mechanism involved in the formation of aluminous dental porcelain-platinum bonds. In particular it is not clear why thermally precleaned platinum substrates produce a weaker composite system compared to that based on tin oxide coatings.

In the present study the bonding of aluminous dental porcelain to platinum foil was studied using transmission electron microscopy with the aim of understanding the bonding mechanism. Energy dispersive X-ray analysis was also employed to study compositional variations occurring across thin sections through the bonding interface.

EXPERIMENTAL PROCEDURES

To simulate a dental jacket crown structure for the electron microscopy studies pure platinum foil (25 μm thick) was used to make discs 16mm in a diameter. Part of the discs were coated with a thin layer of tin and then oxidised. The rest were thermally cleaned in vacuum at 1050°C for 3 min. Aluminous dental porcelain was applied as a slurry to one side of a platinum disc and then fired at 1100°C for 3 min in vacuum. A further addition of the aluminous dental porcelain was placed on the reverse side of the platinum disc and the assembly was then fired at 1100°C for 20 min in vacuum forming a fired sample 3 mm thick. Thin cross-sectional samples were cut from these samples using a diamond saw and prepared for electron microscopy using mechanical polishing, followed by ion beam thinning. After a thin coat of carbon had been applied, the specimens were examined in an analytical electron microscope (JEOL 4000FX) equipped with an X-ray detector and analyser

RESULTS AND DISCUSSION

A typical bright-field transmission electron micrograph, as shown in figure 1a reveals the bonding of aluminous dental porcelain to thermally cleaned platinum. It is very clear that the aluminous dental porcelain is directly adherent to the platinum and that the interface is abrupt and straight.

In contrast Figure 1b shows a transmission electron micrograph of an aluminous dental porcelain-tin oxide coated platinum interface. It is worthy of note that small tin oxide grains whose average size is approximately 150 nm exist between the aluminous dental porcelain and the platinum. These tin oxide grains are uniformly distributed and tightly attached to the surface of platinum. The surface of the platinum has also become very rough and jagged during fabrication, in comparison to that smooth surface shown in Fig 1a. The presence of the jagged platinum surface will improve the bonding strength due to the increase in the interfacial area. Convergent beam diffraction patterns, typical examples of which are shown in Fig. 2, were taken from tin oxide grains. The indexing of the diffraction patterns confirms that these tin oxides are stannic oxide (SnO_2) which have a tetragonal structure. The unit cell dimensions for SnO_2 are a=4.7378 Å and c=3.1864 Å respectively.

The oxidation potential of platinum is much lower than that of other elements in aluminous dental porcelain. The fact that the interface in the aluminous dental porcelain-thermally cleaned platinum bonds is abrupt and smooth indicates that no further oxidation of platinum has taken place at the interface in the case of aluminous dental porcelain mounted directly onto the platinum. Thus, when a good direct contact between aluminous dental porcelain and platinum has been formed before a sample is fired the aluminous dental porcelain will wet the face of the platinum at a relatively high temperature. The driving force for wetting is associated with the magnitude of the contact angle, a smaller contact angle creates a greater driving force for efficient wetting. The observations made show that efficient wetting has been generated by thermal precleaning and contributes to producing such a strongly adherent interface.

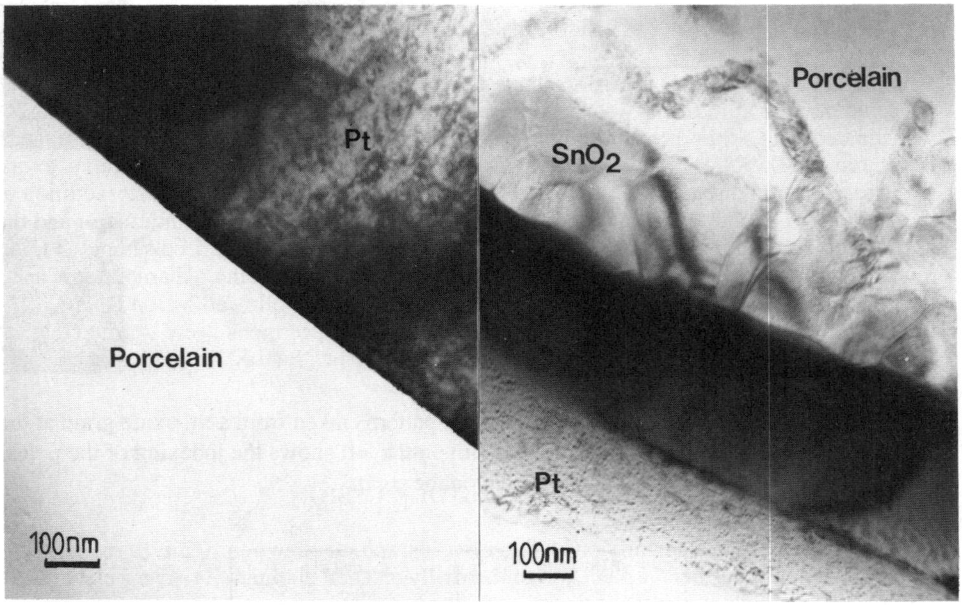

a **b**

Figure 1. Bright field electron micrographs of bonding of aluminous dental porcelain to a) thermally precleaned platinum and b) tin oxide coated platinum

It is possible that platinum could be oxidised to produce platinum oxide at relatively high temperatures. However, such platinum oxides are very unstable. Instability of these platinum oxides also explains the inability in the present study to detect their presence at interfaces. The rough and jagged surface of the platinum in the tin oxide coated samples could therefore be created by preoxidation generating platinum oxides which then decomposes during the oxidation of the tin in the early stages of fabrication..

A number of tiny particles located within the aluminous dental porcelain adjacent to the stannic oxide grains were also observed, as shown in Fig. 1b. It appears that the tin oxides formed at the platinum interface can be dissolved into the aluminous dental porcelain. The dissolution of stannic oxides into the aluminous dental porcelain can be represented by

$$SnO_{2\,(interface)} \longrightarrow SnO_{2\,(porcelain)}$$

This process generally depends on the oxidation potential of the tin. Stannic oxide can be spontaneously dissolved into the aluminous dental porcelain because its standard free energy of its formation is negative (-124.36Kcal/mol).

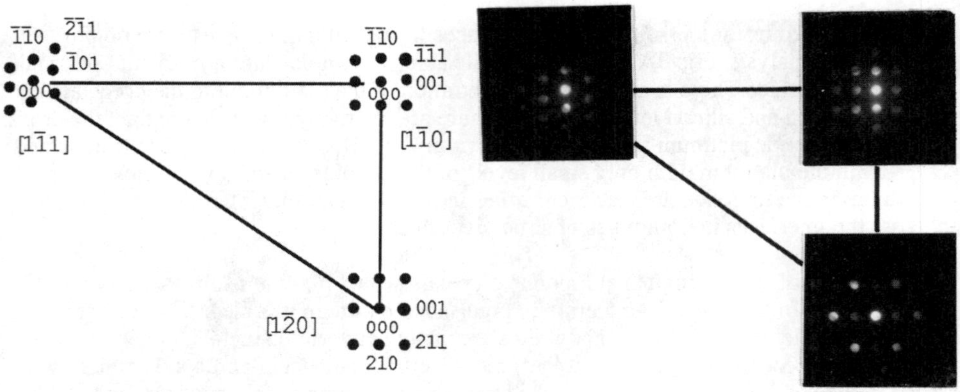

Figure 2. Three convergent beam diffraction patterns taken from a tin oxide grain at the platinum interface. The schematic diagram on the left shows the indexing of the poles shown on the right.

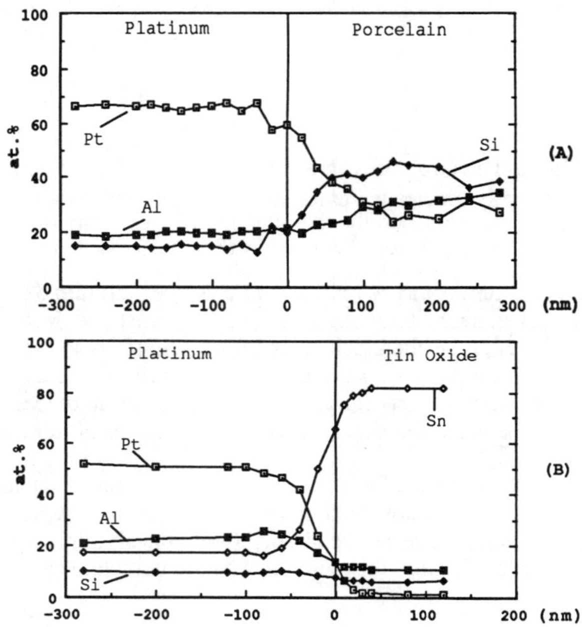

Figure 3. Composition profiles obtained by energy dispersive analysis across A) the platinum-porcelain interface and B) the platinum-tin oxide interface

Elemental composition profiles across interfaces from different samples were obtained using EDX analysis. Fig. 3A shows the profile across a simple aluminous dental porcelain platinum interface.There is a significant penetration of the platinum into the porcelain and the aluminium and silicon levels in the platinum are relatively lower. In contrast the profile across a tin oxide platinum interface, as shown in Fig. 3B, reveals aluminium, silicon and tin within the platinum with only small levels of the aluminium and silicon plus traces of platinum in the tin oxide area. These profiles indicate that atomic interdiffusion is occurring across the interfaces in both types of structures studied.

The benefits of supporting the aluminous porcelain with a platinum substrate rely on a strong bond. In the case of the thermally precleaned platinum it is clear that the bond depends on elemental diffusion and intimate contact between the metal and porcelain. In this case if processing is faulty then inefficient wetting may occur and bond strength will be lost. In the case of tin oxide coatings the strength of the bond is enhanced through the preoxidation generating a rough surface which not only increases the surface area but also forms a mechanical key. Some bonding between tin oxide and porcelain will also be created as the porcelain partially dissolves the tin oxide. The critical stage in this approach is therefore the oxidation of the initial tin coat, which if incomplete will not generate a sufficiently rough surface and result in a loss in strength. It is clear that to create a strong restoration therefore needs good manufacturing with a clear perspective of the required structures.

CONCLUSIONS

In typical bonding situations used in the manufacture of jacket crowns an abrupt and smooth interface is created in aluminous dental porcelain-thermally cleaned platinum bonding, with a chemical bond formed by atomic interdiffusion. In contrast, a stronger bond is produced in aluminous dental porcelain-tin oxide coated platinum bonds because of the presence of a rough and jagged surface of the platinum increasing the surface area and creating a mechanical key. Stannic oxide grains are uniformly distributed between the aluminous dental porcelain and the platinum and a number of particles of tin oxides exist in the aluminous dental porcelain. In addition atomic interdiffusion takes place at the interface. The presence of tin oxide coatings and a rough and jagged surface of platinum play an prominent role in the development of adherence between metal and porcelain.

REFERENCES

1. John W. Mclean and I. R. Sced, The Bonded Alumina Crown. 1.The Bonding of Platinum to Aluminous Dental Porcelain using Tin Oxide Coatings, Australian Dental Journal, 1976, **21**, 119-127.

2. V. Piddock, P. M. Marquis and H. J. Wilson, The Role of Platinum Matrix in Porcelain Jacket Crowns, Br. Dent. J., 1984, **157**, 275-280.

3. J. W. Mclean, A New Method of Bonding Dental Cements and Porcelain to Metal Surfaces,Operative Dentistry, 1977, **2**, 130-142.

DISSOLUTION OF DENSE HYDROXYAPATITE FOLLOWED BY SURFACE ROUGHNESS EVOLUTION.

F. BISSON, P. GOHAR, D. BERNACHE-ASSOLLANT

Laboratoire de Céramiques Nouvelles (CNRS UA 320)
Faculté des Sciences, 1223, Avenue Albert Thomas,
87060 LIMOGES Cédex (FRANCE)

ABSTRACT

Due to their good biocompatibility, calcium phosphates are used as cement for filling cavities or dense implants for the replacement of bone in unloaded parts (1,2). Consequently a perfect knowledge of their reactivity in vivo and in vitro, particularly the mechanisms of their degradation and the relationships with microstructure are needed. Two kinds of dense H.A.P. wer prepared. Powder of H.A.P. was heated at 800°C in the first case, spray-dried before calcining at 900°C in the second case. Dissolution of different dense samples was studied in buffered water at pH = 3.4. The evolution of the surface roughness was then followed with the aid of a rugosimeter apparatus. The experimental results confirm that dissolution always occurs through grain boundary corrosion, resulting in the decohesion of particles from the sample surface.

INTRODUCTION

Bioceramic degradation occurs at the beginning within the grain boundaries. First of all a decohesion of particles from the the sample surface is experienced, these particles can be dissolved or brought away in other parts of the living organism. For the same service conditions the implant resorption rate is then controlled by its microstructure : porosity, average grain size repartition...

The following study consists in determining the roughness evolution with time, for two dense samples of hydroxyapatite (H.A.P.) kept in a water buffered solution at pH = 3.5. The main difference between the two samples lies in the cold forming process of the raw powders.

PREPARATION OF DENSE SAMPLES

Powder morphology

Two batches of H.A.P. powder, containing less than 0.3% tricalcium phosphate, were provided by Prof. Heughebaert (Laboratoire de Physico-chimie Toulouse). The first one (H.A.P. + 3% TCP) was heated at 500°C during 3 hours and 800°C during the same time. The second one (pure H.A.P.) was spray dried from a water suspension and heated at 900°C for 3 hours. In this last case the granulates were sieved through a 60 µm sieve, and granulate size repartition determined in alcohol with the aid of a Sedigraph 2000 apparatus. The average diameter was 30 µm.

Grain surface area of the calcined powders, measured with a Micromeritics 2205 analyser, was about 18 $m^2\ g^{-1}$. Taking the theoretical density of H.A.P. equal to 3.16 $m^2\ g^{-1}$, the value of the surface area makes possible the determination of the mean grain diameter : 0.1 µm. From these results it is obvious that the first batch is an agglomerated powder composed of small grains (0.1 µm) and that the second one a granulated powder (30 µm) composed of small grains.

Green body morphology

These two powders were cold pressed in a graphite die, protected with a boron nitride coating. Mercury penetration was used to determine their pore size distributions (Fig. 1).

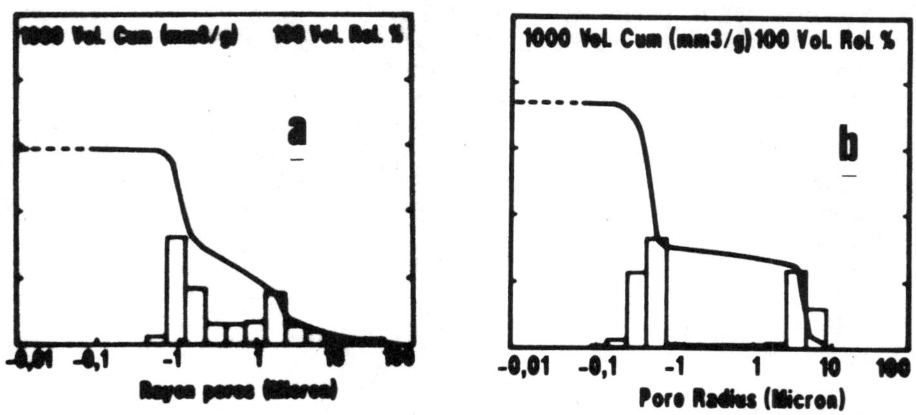

Figure 1. Pore size distribution of H.A.P. (a), and spray dried H.A.P. (b).

One can see that the non granulated powder leads to compacts with pores distributed between 0.1 µm and 2 µm. The granulated powder leads to compacts with a bimodal pore size repartition. The distribution reveals two peaks, the first at 40 µm and the second at 0.06 µm. Such distribution is due to the strong bonds between the grains within the granulates achieved during the thermal treatment, the granulates maintain their rigid structure during the compaction process.

Sintering
In order to achieve closed porosity, the hot pressing method was used. The samples were sintered under nitrogen, at 1150°C and 25 MPa during 15 minutes. Different sintering cycles were tested, but the most efficient was the following : application of a cold pressure of 10 MPa on the raw powder without additives, temperature rate 100°C/min between 20°C and 1150°C, and temperature decrease 10°C/min due to the low toughness of H.A.P.. The high temperature rate to get 1150°C allows the preservation of a small grain size (3). The obtained relative densities were 96% for the non granulated powder and 93% for the spray dried powder. The sintered specimens were used for the corrosion tests.

EXPERIMENTAL RESULTS

Medium and samples
The two batches of HAP powder, having thickness of 5 mm, obtained after sintering appear to be particularly brittle. Nevertheless, the study of the degradation process was achieved on sample fragments. The aqueous medium (200 ml) is constituted by a buffer solution (CH_3COO^-/CH_3OOH) of pH = 3.42 and temperature of 37°C and is maintained homogeneous by mean of a magnetic stirrer. The evolution of the pH is about 0.1 pH unity after 24 hours.

Study of the surface roughness : the experimental technique
The surface state (roughness) is obtained by mean of a non destructive method. An opto-electrical pick-up stylus in mechanical contact with the surface gives the z coordinate corresponding to each position (x, y). The results are numerically treated providing a three-dimensionnal representation of the surface. The stylus displacement (1 µm step) is achieved on an area of 250x250 µm. The acquisition and the treatment of the results are automatically performed. The rugosity is quantified by a set of parameters, for example :the arithmetical mean rugosity Ra and the total vertical deviation Rt.

$$Rt = \frac{|z1| + |z2| + \ldots + |zn|}{n}$$

Rt = difference between the highest pic and the lowestvalley

z1, z2, ..., zn are the deviations of the rugosities from the least square plane position.

Results
Pure HAP
An EBM view of the initial state of the surface allows us to observe the microstructure of the sample. Large agglomerates (about 45 µm in diameter) can be distinguished, some red-colored inclusions of about of few ten micrometers in size can be observed. The composition of these entities

obtained by secondary electrons dispersion spectroscopy (SED) seems to be strictly identical with the matrix. The time evolution of the morphologies which develop while the sample being immersed is issued from rugosimetry analysis realized at regular intervals of time after washing and drying. Then the mass variation is determined and the dissolution kinetic as a function of time is obtained as can be seen in Figure 2a. The curve clearly indicates that the kinetic of dissolution is well fitted by a parabolic law (correlation coefficient = 0.99). The values of rugosity parameters raise until 20 hours of immersion is attained. At this time the mass variation is about 50 mg/cm2. The rugosity profil after 40 hours immersion is depicted in figure 3.

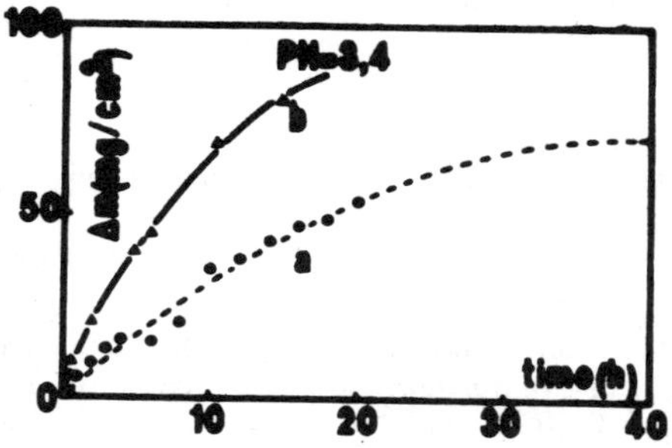

Figure 2. Dissolution kinetic of H.A.P.

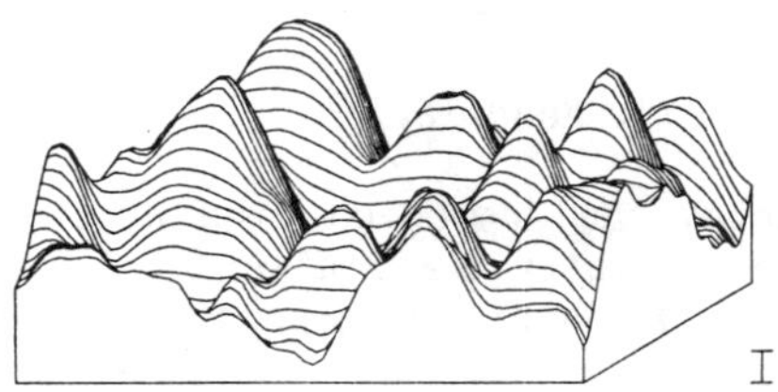

Figure 3. Rugosity profil of spray dried H.A.P. after 40 h. immersion.

At initial time (t = 0) two major kinds of defects characterize the morphology of the surface : the grooves due to polishing and some hollows stemming from the pulling out of agglomerates of about 50 m in diameters, probably the agglomerates that has been previously described. On close inspection the results can be interpreted as a preferential corrosion concerning the grooves in the initial period of immersion (about 1 hour), then in a second time the morphological changes are attributed to the disparition of the grooves and dissolution that occurs through grain boundary until the decohesion of these entities is achieved. At this stage the rugosity is rather high. After 20 hours the morphological parameters take up a constant value ; the mechanism of agglomerates decohesion exibits a stationnary trend which affects all the surface. One can observe a few agglomerates in relief just after the decohesion and some hollows that are due to the decohesion.

HAP + 3% TCP

Some red inclusions were also observed within these samples. The kinetic law describing the mass evolution as a function of time is parabolic (correlation coefficient = 0.99). The dissolution rate is however higher : the mass loss is 50 mg/cm2 after 6 hours (Fig. 2b) whereas this value is obtained after 18 hours in the case of pure HAP. The evolution of the parameters describing the morphology is analogous to the case of pure HAP. Nevertheless, the mechanism of surface degradation is quite different.

At the initial state (t=0), only some grooves can be observed, the rugosity is less dispersed in the precedent case (from -0,4 μm to +0,5 μm). This can be attributed to the homogeneous microstructure of the sample.

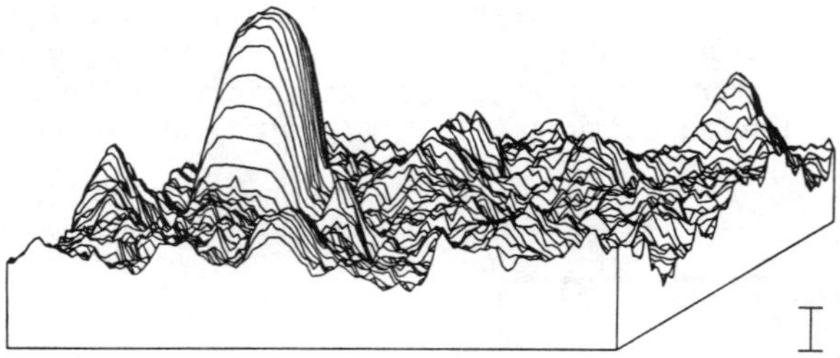

Figure 4. Rugosity profil of H.A.P. (+ 3% T.C.P.) after 14 h. immersion.

During the immersion, the grooves disappear after one hour of immersion. One can observe a preferential corrosion around certain species of about 50 m in diameter. A microscopic observation confirms that the entities in question are the red coloured inclusions already quoted. For more longer time of immersion the degradation of the surface is uniform and concerns preferentially the red inclusions. The roughness enhances little because of the small number of inclusions.

CONCLUSION

The morphology changes of the surface of the sintered H.A.P. sample during the degradation process reveal the relation between batch preparation and corrosion properties. It has been shown that the surface of the spray-dryed samples evolves through a cooperative process of corrosion at grain boundaries and decohesion of agglomerates. This lead to a constant but important rugosity after certain time of immersion.For the non granulated samples (HAP + 3% TCP) the microstructure rather more homogeneous induce a less pronounced evolution of the surface relief.

Acknowledgment
The authors thank C.E.N.G. (Grenoble) for supplying spray dried powder.

REFERENCES

1. De Groot K., Bioceramics of calcium phosphate. <u>CRC Press</u>, 1983.
2. Metals and Ceramic Biomaterials, Ed. Ducheyne P. and Hastings G.W., <u>CRC Press</u>, 1980.
3. Harmer M., E.W. Roberts, Brook R.J., Rapid sintering of pure and doped alumina, <u>Trans J. Br. Ceram. Soc.</u>, 1979, 78(1),22-25.

REVIEW OF THE NATIONAL AND INTERNATIONAL STANDARDIZATION OF ADVANCED CERAMICS.

GERALD C PADGETT
British Ceramic Research Limited
Queens Road, Penkhull, Stoke-on-Trent, ST4 7LQ
United Kingdom

ABSTRACT

The review is confined to the standardization of advanced ceramics as practised in Europe, the United States of America and Japan. The general concept of standardization will be described from an historical point of view. The standardization of advanced ceramics is examined under the headings of terminology, sampling, test methods, product standards and specifications. The most important of these initially is methods of test, which will facilitate the evaluation of ceramic products on an international basis. It will concentrate mainly on Europe as the role to be played by standards in the European Community will become more important when the completion of the single internal market is achieved at the end of 1992. The paper concludes by discussing the attitudes taken by the main National Standards Organizations from USA, Japan and Europe particularly with regard to their international outlook.

INTRODUCTION

Standardization is a means whereby materials, products and systems are described and evaluated in a standard or specified manner. Standards themselves, whether national or international, must conform to two working rules. They must firstly not inhibit progress and the development of new products and secondly, they should not prevent healthy competition. This latter point emphasises the possibility of using National Standards to protect home markets and to frustrate imports.

Standardization itself is a relatively new concept and can be considered as one of the consequences of the Industrial Revolution. It started around the beginning of this century with almost simultaneous activity in the USA and Europe. The leader in the race was the American Society for Testing Materials (ASTM), which was founded in 1898. ASTM's first standard called, "Standard Specification for Steel Rails", was published in May 1900. Within Europe, the first official standards body was in the United Kingdom, where in 1901 the original Engineering Standards Committee was formed as the forerunner of the British Standards

Institution (BSI) its first terms of reference being the standardization of steel sections. In Germany, the Standards Committee of German Industry, (now the Deutsches Institut fur Normung - DIN), was founded in May 1917. In France, the creation of the Permanent Standardization Committee in 1918 preceded the foundation of the Association Francaise de Normalisation, (AFNOR), in 1926. It is perhaps no coincidence that the French also started work first on the standardization of rails and steel sections.

In Japan, industrial standardization started rather late compared with both Europe and the USA. The concept started with Government standards for the procurement of commodities by the army and navy during the Meiji Era (1868 - 1912), and standard specifications for steel water pipes at the beginning of the Taisho Era, (1912 - 1926). The Japanese Engineering Standards Committee (predecessor of JISC), was founded in 1921 and this committee established 520 Japanese Engineering Standards, (JES), by April 1941. During the second World War, the committee set up Temporary JES with simplified contents and procedures. Also during the war, 660 Japanese Aircraft Standards were established under the Aircraft Manufacturing Service Law. After the war, the existing JES were studied and revised and a start was made to establish new standards. This culminated in the formation of the Japanese Industrial Standards Committee (JISC), in 1949. This committee deliberates on JIS and is controlled and supported by the Government Agency of Industrial Science and Technology, (AIST). AIST forms part of the Government Ministry of International Trade and Industry (MITI).

The start of international standardization was brought about by the electrical industry, a comparative newcomer to the industrial scene. That industry provided the first real step in the promotion of international standardization as we now know it, in the founding between 1904 and 1906 of the International Electrotechnical Commission (IEC). In April 1926, the 18 countries which had then set up national standards bodies met together to consider the extension of international collaboration to other fields. This resulted in the formation of the International Federation of the National Standardising Associations (ISA), with most of its strength coming from Europe. ISA was not particularly effective and it ceased to exist when war broke out in 1939. After the war, a new standards co-ordinating committee was set up under the United Nations banner. A full scale conference was held in London in October 1946, at which representatives of 25 standards bodies agreed to set up the International Organisation for Standardization, (ISO). The IEC became its electrical division, though having full technical and financial antonomy. ISO has proved to be a success and now has members comprising the national standards organizations of 90 countries.

European standardization was initiated in 1960 when a meeting of the West European standards bodies agreed that the then Six and Seven should actively collaborate in unification of their standards within the wider ISO framework. The outcome of this decision was the creation of CEN (European Standards Coordinating Committee), and CENELEC, its counterpart in the electrotechnical field. Co-operation agreements between CEN/CENELEC and the Commission of European Communities drawn up in 1984 enabled the commission to give mandates to the joint European Standards Institute for specific projects.

STANDARDIZATION OF ADVANCED CERAMICS

Certain difficulties arise due to terminology as to what is meant by "advanced" ceramics. For the purpose of this review it will refer to those ceramics which are suitable for high performance application. There already exist applications in the electrotechnical field which are already covered by standards. These exist in national standards and also within IEC.

The first country to standardize these ceramics as materials in their own right has been Japan. Beginning in 1981, they have published five standards and these are listed below:

JIS R 1601	- 1981	Testing Method for Flexural Strength, (Modulus of Rupture) of High Performance Ceramics.
JIS R 1602	- 1986	Testing Methods for Elastic Modulus of High Performance Ceramics.
JIS R 1603	- 1987	Methods for Chemical Analysis of Silicon Nitride Powders.
JIS R 1604	- 1987	Testing Method for Flexural Strength (Modulus of Rupture) of High Performance Ceramics at Elevated Temperature.
JIS R 1605	- 1988	Method for Elastic Modulus of High Performance Ceramics at Elevated Temperature.

The JIS work is concentrating on the standardization of test methods and has an on-going programme of 15 separate items which is supervised by the Japan Fine Ceramics Association, (JFCA).

BSI formed its "engineering" ceramics committee in 1985. Its initial terms of reference were to develop standard methods of test and currently has seven standards which are close to publication. Current work now included in the BSI work programme is the preparation of a glossary of terms.

The creation of the BSI committee was very closely followed by the setting up of ASTM Committee C-28 on Advanced Ceramics in the USA. This committee has a comprehensive work programme which is broken down into the following areas:- Performance, Properties, Processing, Design & Evaluation and Characterisation.

ASTM will shortly issue a standard "Test Method for Flexural Strength of Advanced Ceramics at Ambient Temperature", which is essentially an up-date of an earlier Military Standard MIL-STD-1942 (MR). Other work which is close to publication is a comprehensive document on nomenclature.

Other national standards organizations which are known to be active with regard to advanced ceramics include AFNOR (France) and DIN, (FRG). A summary of an on-going activities, prepared by a European Ad-Hoc Committee, is given in Table 1.

TABLE 1

On-going Activities in Standards for Advanced Ceramics

General Area	Specific Area	D	F	UK	US	J
Nomenclature				+	+	
General textural properties	cracking			0	+	
	density/porosity	0	*	0	+	
	grain size	Δ		+	Δ	
	surface texture	Δ	*	+		
Specimen preparation	specimen shape		*			
	surface preparation	Δ	*			
Mechanical properties room temperature	short term strength	+	*	+	+	0
	elastic properties	+	*	+	Δ	0
	fracture toughness	+	*	Δ	Δ	+
	fatigue	+				
	static fatigue			Δ	Δ	
	hardness	+		+	Δ	+
	residual stress	Δ				
Mechanical properties high temperature	short term strength:					
	bend/tensile	Δ	*	Δ	Δ	0
	elastic properties	Δ	*	Δ	Δ	0
	impact					
	fracture toughness	Δ	*			+
	creep	Δ		Δ	Δ	+
	fatigue	Δ				
	low load deformation			0		
	crack growth					
	thermal shock resistance	0				Δ
Physical properties high temperature	thermal expansion	0		0		Δ
	thermal diffusivity		*	0		+
	thermal conductivity	Δ				+
	specific heat			+		+
	permanent change in dimensions			Δ		
Electrical properties	dielectric constant	0	*			
	electrical resistance	0				
Corrosion	oxidation			0		+
	aqueous electrolytes	0		0		
Erosion						
Wear						
Adhesive joints		0				
Powders	particle size		*		Δ	
	specific surface		*		Δ	
	compressibility	0	*		Δ	
	rheology		*		Δ	
Processing	green body density	0	*		Δ	
	sinterability		*		Δ	
Analysis	structural		*		Δ	
	NDE		*			
	chemical		*			0
	statistical		*			

0 completed standard + activity in progress Δ future activity
* under consideration

At present there is no official standardization of advanced ceramics under the framework of ISO. There is, however, certain international work in VAMAS and also in a separate tripartite USA-Sweden-FR Germany agreement. VAMAS is the Versailles Project on Advanced Materials and Standards, the member countries being - Canada, France, FR Germany, Italy, Japan, UK, USA and CEC. The work on ceramics is in Technical Working Area 3 under the chairmanship of Prof P Boch of France.

There has been much interest in the standardization of advanced ceramics within Europe and within the CEC in particular. This has culminated in a mandated request from the Commission to both CEN and CENELEC for the establishment of a comprehensive programme for setting up European prestandards (ENV) and European Standards (EN) in the field of advanced industrial ceramics. It further requests that the programme shall be elaborated taking into account international standardization activities.

The Technical Board of CEN has acted very quickly and has agreed to create a new Technical Committee CEN/TC 184 with the provisional title of "High Performance Ceramics". Its proposed scope is - standardization in the field of high performance ceramics with specific initial tasks being terminology and classification; sampling; methods of test (including physical, chemical, mechanical, thermal, textural, electrical etc) for monolithic ceramics, ceramic composites, ceramic coatings, ceramic powders and ceramic fibres. As a material-related TC, it is expected that the TC will liaise closely with function-related TC's and standardizing bodies working in such fields as eletrotechnology, biomedical (products), nuclear, optical, aerospace, construction etc. The secretariat of the new TC has been allocated to BSI. In view of the urgency to provide a work programme for the CEC by the end of the year, BSI are now preparing to host the inaugural meeting of TC 184 in September 1989 at the Manchester office of BSI.

CENELEC have also been responsive to the mandated request from the Commission. They have called a meeting of experts from the various national bodies to determine whether a possible separate CENELEC work programme is required in the field of Advanced Ceramics. It is anticipated that potential work might belong to the fields of interest of a number of technical committees of the IEC.

THE PRESENT POSITION REGARDING ADVANCED CERAMICS STANDARDIZATION

The development of standards tends to follow the market need and usually starts with the standardization of test methods. However, for the purpose of this review, it is the intention to use a more logical order. This will start with terminology or definitions followed by sampling and methods of test. Once test methods are agreed, it is then possible to proceed to classification product standards and specifications for use. Standardization and its progress or lack of it in these areas is reviewed below.

Terminology

Before any standardization is possible, it is necessary to define the terms to be used. For these "new" ceramics, the main obstacle is to decide on a suitable adjectival description. Possible contenders, (in alphabetical order), are - advanced, engineering, fine, high performance, industrial, special, structural and technical. The United States has opted for "advanced" and Japan for "fine". At present there is no consensus in Europe and this needs to be resolved at the forthcoming meeting of CEN/TC 184. With regard to the bulk of the terminology, good bases will be available from the completed work in ASTM C-28 and the work in progress in BSI.

Sampling

At present, no national standards body is currently working on this subject specifically for advanced ceramics, although, it is on the provisional work programme of CEN/TC 184. Standard sampling plans for inspection by attributes are already available as ISO 2859, IEC 410 and BS 6001. Plans for inspection by variables are given in ISO/DIS 3951 and BS 6002. The Electronic Components Committee of CENELEC, (CECC), has also produced sampling plans for inspection of electronic components by attributes as part of its 9000 series on assessed quality. It is anticipated that CEN/TC 184 may decide to develop specific sampling plans for such advanced ceramics as composites, coatings, powders and fibres.

Test Methods

The standardization of test methods is the most advanced of the standardization subjects. However, despite this, ther is much work to do especially in the field of mechanical and thermo-mechanical behaviour. The situation is reviewed below under seven headings.

1. Chemical and Mineralogical Analysis

Conventional chemical analysis methods are standardized for oxide ceramics. Standardization also exists for methods involving physical methods of analysis such as X-ray fluorescence. These are mainly intended for oxide ceramics. Generally speaking, the chemical analysis of non-oxides in isolation presents no problem. Difficulties can arise, however, in the speciation of mixtures which can contain one or more of the following: - oxides, carbides, nitrides, metallic elements, free carbon and oxynitrides. This is a problem which is international and could possibly be resolved by international co-operation.

2. General and Textural Properties

Subjects under this heading include methods of test for the determination of the presence of cracks, density and porosity, grain size and surface texture. Of these, surface texture is an important property as it is used to characterize test pieces for mechanical testing. It is normally measured by the stylus method and the equipment is fully standardized. However, this equipment is principally designed to measure the surface roughness of metals and it may be necessary to set out different procedures for ceramics.

3. Mechanical Properties at Room Temperature

This is the area which is receiving the greatest attention. Property measurements which require to be standardized include - short-term strength, modulus of elasticity (and Poisson's ratio), tensile strength, fracture toughness, fatigue, delayed failure, hardness and wear resistance. Much work has been done on flexural strength and standards are available. It is important in the international sense that these methods are directly comparable. There are many test methods which are standardized for the determination of fracture toughness. These are mainly intended for metals and are difficult to adapt for ceramics. It is anticipated that hardness and wear resistance will be resolved through the VAMAS programme.

4. Thermo-Mechanical Properties

This includes some of those properties which are to be standardized at room temperature. In addition it also includes the determination of creep (and sagging) and the resistance to thermal shock. Creep resistance is an important engineering parameter, particularly in the selection of materials for turbine blades. The philosophy of testing thermal shock resistance should be similar to that for wear testing i.e. to try and simulate practice.

5. Thermo-Physical Properties

This includes the determination of thermal expansion, thermal conductivity, thermal diffusivity and specific heat. The favoured way of measuring diffusivity is by the Laser flash method.

6. Corrosion and Oxidation Resistance

Because of the wide range of chemical environments which may be used to contain ceramics, it would seem sensible to standardize a general guidance on appropriate corrosion test methods. It is, however, appropriate to have a specific standard test for the determination of oxidation resistance.

7. Characterization of Fine Powders

The main characteristics are particle size and its distribution. These are largely standardized both in ASTM and ISO. However, difficulties may be found with ultra-fine powders and the particle morphology. This may require resolution by further study and work.

Classification

Once test methods are established, it is then possible to classify the various ceramic products. Classification is of commercial importance as it enables comparisons to be made between products from different suppliers. The need for classification has been recognised by the VAMAS Steering Committee, who have approved the initiation of a pre-standards activity to support the development of a unified classification system for advanced ceramics. The objective of this work programme is to identify and assess the issues inherent in developing a unified classification system for advanced ceramics; establish a building block structure featuring critical elements necessary for international use and establish mechanisms and institutional links as needed and appropriate, between national standards bodies for further system development and refinement to meet individual national and international industrial needs.

A working party, representing participating countries and standards groups will concentrate on three areas: (1) Identification of existing classification schemes for parallel, similar or other materials classes amenable to advanced ceramics, assessing attributes and difficulties; (2) Establishment of a priority hierarchy of development pathways; and (3) Development of a conceptual classification and terminology critical structure, by adaption or through new approaches and determination of the feasibility of a single system for both market indicators and technical elements, considering the following classification factors:

A. Organization by end product and use categories.
B. Categorization by major chemical components.
C. Sub-grouping to infer functional attributes.
D. Coverage of major product forms.
E. Use of consistent terminology.
F. Incorporation or property/performance regimes and validation procedures.
G. Compatibility with computerized data bases.

A two/three year effort is envisaged with the work carried out in serial fashion, roughly divided according to the techical approach elements given above.

Specification and Product Standards

Classification is established to provide the broad framework for the detailing and setting up of specifications for use and product standards. It is anticipated that the standardization of these specifications will be the responsibility of user groups rather than material groups. Standard specifications already exist in the electrotechnical field and the concept is being examined in other areas.

CONCLUSION

The commercial exploitation of the new advanced ceramics is poised to take off, and this has stimulated a need for product standards. This need is on an international basis led from three view points, Europe, Japan and USA. There are dangers of duplication of effort and also of national prejudice. It is essential to have openness of discussion and good international co-operation to ensure that positive progress is made.

Acknowledgement

The author is pleased to thank Dr D W F James, Chief Executive, British Ceramic Research Limited for his permission to present and publish this paper.

ADVANCED CERAMICS STANDARDS DEVELOPMENT

SAMUEL SCHNEIDER, JR.
Institute for Materials Science and Engineering,
National Institute of Standards and Technology,
Gaithersburg, Maryland 20899, United States

ABSTRACT

Advanced ceramics, because of their unique properties, are being extensively researched, developed and brought to market as rapidly as possible. Currently there are no associated consensus standards that allow national or international comparisons and this lack represents one of the more important technical unknowns in the commercial market equation. While the needs are diverse and product specific, there is a singular need for a unified classification system as it sets the basis for unanimity in information transfer and coherent standards development. Advanced ceramics development is gaining momentum with independent efforts now underway in several countries. However, early international collaboration is needed before conflicting national standards emerge. This paper presents a perspective on advanced ceramics standards needs, current activities and necessary future directions required for equivalence in data between groups and nations.

PERSPECTIVE ON STANDARDS

Much has been written and said about the importance and potential of advanced ceramics for a host of new or improved industrial applications, particularly in the high technology areas. Indeed R&D is on the upswing and more and more products are becoming commercial realities. In tandem with this notoriety and commercialization, there has been a recognition of the need for standardization. Basically, commercial standards equate to the rules and terms of information transfer among designers, manufacturers, and product users; in matters of commerce they often provide the basis for legal agreements between buyers and sellers on product quality, properties, performance, and the like. Moreover, with a plethora of new materials available for the same application, standards allow comparisons of attributes on a rational basis, and hence, provide a vehicle for product identity, promotion and choice.

Advanced ceramics standards development now is underway, though with considerably less voracity and many steps behind current technological achievements. Significant, but beginning, efforts have started under the auspices of standards groups, including ASTM, BSI (British Standards Institution), DIN (Deutches Institut für Normung) and VAMAS (Versailles Project on Advanced Materials and Standards). Reference [1] provides more complete information on these and other organizations that are currently, or should be, involved in standards work on advanced ceramics. While most of these standards groups foster active participation by industry in standards development, greater involvement is essential. More efforts to this end are required, as commercial standards, for and by industry, are integral to successful business and research. Indeed the standard setting process is complicated, time consuming and often expensive. For advanced ceramics the process is at the early stages with many issues and technical problems to be addressed. The following sections of this report briefly summarize some of these.

ADVANCED CERAMICS-WHAT ARE THEY?

The term "advanced ceramics" is a nebulous descriptor, needing better definition to set the framework, boundaries and directions for associated standards development. Advanced ceramics in the main do not constitute a homologous materials class, but do have some general crosscut characteristics, including sophisticated processing, controlled microstructures and a special property set that facilitates "designed in" high service performance. As such they encompass an enormous array of product types and forms (e.g. films, powders, fibers, monoliths, composites) for multivariant applications. Some have been in production for many years, as for instance the ferrites in use as ceramic magnets, or the glass ceramics used extensively as lamp envelopes and cookware; others like turbine blades for heat engines are in the proto-type stage and still others, such as the high Tc superconductors, are on the scientific drawing board.

Accordingly a first level definition is suggested that includes the more mature engineering/technical ceramics product lines as well as the new high technology types; namely, "an advanced ceramic is a highly engineered-high performance, predominately non-metallic, inorganic, high value added (ceramic) object having unique or superior functional attributes". Needed however is a next level description with the key being rigorous specificity in defining the unique/superior functional attributes. Here advanced ceramic products generally separate along the lines of primary physical functions like mechanical, thermal, electrical, magnetic, optical and chemical. It is at this level that standards differ, with each having separate test methodology and associated varying degrees of test precision and bias, even for the seemingly same test, like mechanical strength.

UNIFIED CLASSIFICATION SYSTEM

Materials producing and using industries in general use some form of system of classification and terminology that uniquely categorize product characteristics by a combination of "set apart" features, such as regimes for composition and properties and for product form and intended use. In essence the classification system describes an array of like products in an orderly fashion so that one can discern similarities and differences in makeup, character and application. In simple terms, the classification system tells what a product is and what it is good for, and when specific limits are imposed, is the basis for specifications. It is intended to facilitate information transfer among diverse interests and should service multi-purpose needs, including industrial statistical codes and trade schedule listings, computerized materials databases, technical literature compilation and sorting, and categorization of standards, testing services and laboratory accreditation.

Currently there is no accepted classification system in place for advanced ceramics among worldwide producers and users and what is evolving through common practice is happenstance and discordant. In recognition of this VAMAS [2] recently has initiated a classification project, in cooperation with major national standards bodies. While this work is just beginning the following skeletal framework is envisioned:

1. Organization by primary end-use application divided along major functional lines, including:

   a. Electrical Components
   b. Mechanical Components
   c. Thermomechanical Components
   d. Optical Components
   e. Chemical Components
   f. Magnetic Components

   Subdivision of a-f above may be required where specific types are recognized products of commerce, as for instance category (a) into conductors, semiconductors and insulators.

2. Designation of a specific property or performance range for each type application component (a-f).

3. Identification generic chemical class, name and formula.

4. Identification of validation test methods and standards.

5. Indication of structural class.

6. Indication of product form and generic fabrication process.

7. Identification of manufacturer and product lot.

Of the above, items 1-3 constitute primary classification building block elements. Item 4 permits product class verification while the remainder facilitate product tracking.

STANDARDS NEEDS

Standard requirements for advanced ceramics are diverse and inherently product specific. For each of the major component application classes identified above (mechanical, electrical, etc), they differ in intent, type and complexity at different stages of the innovation process; from idea-to design-to manufacture-to service use, as generalized in Table 1 [1]. Moreover, development and adoption of standards for the various advanced ceramic classes vary in degrees of advancement.

TABLE 1
Advanced ceramics standards hierarchy

Innovation Stage	Test Standard Category	Purpose and Use
		Invention
Idea generation Technical feasibility	Basic Research Directed basic research	Obtain intrinsic/basic materials character for functional attributes. Obtain property data for materials behavior for application.
		Translation
Product design and development Prototype/interim manufacture	Development	Obtain reliable property database; predict performance for design methodology. Statistical process control.
		Commercialization
Manufactured products	Materials/device acceptance	Purchase classifications and specifications.

Obviously many standards are already in place, at least on a national basis for the more mature products, as for instance multilayer capacitors or chip substrates in the electrical and electronic areas. Whether these are adequate and current for open market international trade is a moot question and a surveillance, harmonization and update process must be mounted and maintained.

Most certainly commercial type standards are required for the new emerging products, i.e. structural (mechanical) ceramics. These require attention and this process is underway. The JISC (Japanese Industrial Standards Council), MITI, has conducted perhaps the most extensive standards assessment available to date. Their summary report [3] covers the spectrum of advanced materials (metals, polymers, ceramics and glasses); 219 items for advanced ceramics and 203 for new glasses were identified as needing standardization within a 10 year period. Greatest needs center on thermal, mechanical and chemical properties, powder properties and processing and optical fiber characteristics. Similar listings and critiques are under consideration by others [1], [2], [4], and associated activities have been started. ASTM Committee C-28 on Advanced Ceramics, for example, considers mechanical property and performance tests developments as up-front standards problems with classification and terminology identified as a generalized need. Already C-28 has in the ballot stage a test method standard on "Flexural Strength of Advanced Ceramics at Ambient Temperatures" and a terminology standard containing several hundred defined ceramic words and phrases. DIN, BSI and JFCC (Japan Fine Ceramics Center) also are addressing mechanical testing issues and this apparently is a major crosscut need recognized internationally, as assured mechanical integrity in service environments is an implicit requirement for all types of advanced ceramics. Morrell [5] and Loveday and Morrell [6] have prepared excellent technical review papers on mechanical testing of ceramics, and properly highlight the need for standardization.

While the listing of advanced ceramics standards needs appears lengthy, it should be emphasized that many probably can satisfied by modest revision or straight forward adoption of existing test standards and common practices for material products of the same or similar character and intended purposes. While round robin testing might be required, applicable procedures could include, to mention a few, tests for chemical and phase composition, density, porosity, thermal expansion, electrical conductivity, dielectric constant, optical transmission, nondestructive evaluation, and even some for mechanical properties. This tactic should be pursued with vigor in tandem with the handling of the more troublesome standards problems. The near term objective of advanced ceramics standardization, after all, is to get standards "on the books" so that national and international comparisons can proceed.

REFERENCES

1. Schneider, Jr., S.J. and Bradley, D.R., The standardization advanced ceramics. Advanced Ceramic Materials, ACerS, 1988, **3**, No. 5, 442-8.

2. Schneider, Jr., S.J., A new VAMAS activity on a unified classification system for advanced ceramics. VAMAS Bulletin, 1989, No. 9, 5-6.

3. Japanese Industrial Standards Committee Summary Report, Standardization of advanced materials. Internal Report, MITI, presented at General Assembly Meeting, ISO, at Prague, September 21, 1988.

4. Private communication, Committee 291, DIN, 1988.

5. Morrell, R., Mechanical properties of engineering ceramics-test bars versus components. Presented at the Spring 1988 meeting of the European Materials Research Society, Strasbourg, to be published.

6. Loveday, M.S. and Morrell, R., Standardisation of mechanical testing and quality control. Int. J. High Technology Ceramics, **4**, 1988, 103-122.

Standardization in Soft Magnetic Ceramics leads to interchangeablity and quality assessment.

C. Vlas Philips Components - Certification Department

Within the worldwide Philips organisation, the Philips Components Division is responsible for the development, manufacture and sales of all kinds of electronic components.

This total package of electronic components includes also a wide range of soft magnetic ceramics finding their application as core-material in transformers and inductors in electronic equipments.

The evolution of different technologies and the influance thereof on the electronic equipment, have led to a need for international standardization.

For the standardization of electronic components, international standardization organisations already existed. On European level this was the CECC System for the Quality Assessment of Electronic Components.
This certification system offered us all the possibilities we were looking for.

What is CECC? CECC is the Cenelec Electronic Components Committee, being part of the CEN/Cenelec structure for the production of European Standards (EN's).
CECC has particular responsibility for standards relating to electronic components.

Together with the ECQAC (Electronic Components Quality Assurance Committee), the CECC manages this third party Quality Assessment system.

The challenge of 1992 has placed new demands on governments, commercial organizations and other bodies in Europe, requiring them in a relatively short period to reorganize long-established methods of working in order to remove trade barriers within the European marketplace. The object of the CECC System is to facilitate this proces by the harmonisation and publication of specifications and quality assessment procedures.

The achievement of the Single European Market is in many ways dependent upon the establishment of common specifications and assessment methods to provide for free interchange of goods.

Within the CECC System components are accepted by all member countries without further testing.

This means a continuous control on the conformance to the CECC requirements, in other words Quality Assurance.

This means also a statement by the inspecting body that the product involved, really conforms to these requirements. In the CECC System the inspectorates of ECQAC act as third party inspectors being responsible for the Certification.
Fifteen CEC and EFTA countries are now participating in the CECC System. Each member country is represented in the CECC Management Council. Representatives of the component industry, the equipment industry and government or user organizations, are taking part in the various CECC working groups.
In ECQAC all CECC member countries having an accepted independent inspectorate are full members. The CECC member countries not having such an inspectorate participate in the ECQAC meetings as consulting members.

Within the total field of Standardization and Certification CECC has build up good relations with many other European bodies. Apart from the inputs of members thru national committees, industrial interests and user groups, contacts exist with Cenelec, CEN, AECMA, EUROCAE and ESA.

In the meantime the CECC System has developed itself to The Certification System for electronic components in Europe. As an example over 180 manufacturers are qualified in the System covering over one million qualified component types.

Already more than 70 000 pages of documents have been published. Specifications and procedures in the CECC System are, as a rule, based on IEC and ISO publications. Worldwide standards are used as much as possible.

The well organised CECC documentation system covers Basic Standards, in which the rules and procedures of the System are laid down, and Quality Assessment or Certification Standards, where all criteria, test methods, etc. can be found.
ECQAC has a number of Surveillance procedures, mainly as guidance to the inspectorates.

The technical requirements for CECC components are described in various levels of specifications. Apart from the higher level documents described earlier, the generic specification gives all requirements for a family of components, like e.g. resistors. In the sectional specification, requirements related to a certain technology are listed, like e.g. metal film resistors. Finally in the detail specification, based on the Blanc Detail Specification (BDS), the detailed requirements of a product type are described.

Preparation of specifications in the CECC System is a combined effort of the Component manufacturers, the Equipment manufacturers, National Standards organizations and the National inspectorates. So combining the various interests of industry and end-users. This is extra assured by the input from the User Groups in CECC and from ESA.

Elimination of multiple assessment of manufacturers and suppliers against many similar but varying standards and procedures, such as: AQAP-1, ISO 9000 series, EN 29 000 series, ESA, AECMA, etc. is reached by the full implementation of the EN 29 000 requirements into the CECC documentation.

For the requirements on testing, certification, etc., in other words for the activities of ECQAC and its member inspectorates, the prEN 45 000 series of documents are adopted in the CECC System.

In this way this Single European Specification and Quality Assessment System or Certification System for Electronic Components matches fully with the certification policy of the CEC and EFTA in the context of Europe 1992. This is extra underlined with the decision of CECC taken in April 1989, to introduce the EN status for the CECC Specifications.

EN status of specifications has a number of consequences. All conflicting National Standards have to be withdrawn, is one of the consequences. Increased use of CECC specifications may be expected due to the recognition by e.g. public procurement agencies and others.

If manufacturers of electronic components want to be qualified to the CECC System, a number of requirements have to be fulfilled. Approval can be applied for against the procedures for Qualification Approval or Capability Approval.

Qualification Approval procedures are used for many years already and cover individual components, tested against published detail specifications.

Capability Approval however is the most recent procedure where a component manufacturer obtains approval for a complete technology of which the boundaries are well defined.

Apart from further development of the Capability Approval technique, within the CECC System an extensive programme of work is devoted to related subjects as: Statistical Process Control (SPC), p.p.m. and Assessed Process Average (APA) techniques.

All together we can say that the CECC System covers a Certifiaction system for electronic components based on Qualification Approval or Capability Approval techniques. Further a strict inspection on the certified components, carried out by independent inspectorates against rigid minimum requirements.

This system gives the equipment manufacturer, the user of our products, a number of advantages:

- clear identification of qualified components,
- dependable testresults,
- rapid introduction of new technologies,
- cost reduction,
- the posibllity for participation in the preparation of specifications,
- multiple source supply,
- savings in rework costs,
- improved reliability.

Concluding we can say that the CECC System provides for:

- Product certification to European Standards (EN's)
- A potential means of solving legal disputes; it has already been acknowledged that the use of European Standards and of products independently certified to them may constitute a valid defence in legal cases by providing a demonstration of compliance with the "state of the art".
- Multiple sourcing to the same specification
- Independent certification to harmonized standards.

ENGINEERING CERAMICS

Prof. Dr. F. Thümmler
Institut für Keramik im Maschinenbau
Institut für Werkstoffkunde II
Universität Karlsruhe
Bundesrepublik Deutschland

ABSTRACT

The field of engineering ceramics (structural ceramics) is much more limited in volume than functional ceramics. Engineering ceramics are often subject of high thermal and high mechanical loadings including severe multiaxial stressing. The used materials, their properties and the principle design aspects are outlined. Some examples are given and important testing methods are described. For many actual or perspective applications it is difficult to meet the requirements with respect to reliability and cost. Nevertheless, a lot of successful developmental work occured during the past. A variety of engineering and wear parts for many applications is commercially manufactured. A slow but continous growth can be expected. The introduction of ceramic parts for Diesel and spark ignited road engines, where extremely high reliability is required, occures step by step, especially in Japan and USA. The ceramic gas turbine will be a long range approach, however. Considerable progress in engineering ceramics is expected in future, when several requirements are fulfilled, namely: A thorough application of the design principles for brittle materials; the generation of a data base for more reliable ceramics, obtained by improvement of processing incl. using precisely controlled raw materials; better understandig of long term degradation phenomena; development and use of composites with high fracture toughness and, last not least, to motivate engineers to utilize the technical and economical possibilities on the existing level of materials development.

1. INTRODUCTION

The main applications of high-tech ceramics manufactured in mass production, are in electronic, telecommunication and electroengineering industries.Ceramics for these applications represent about 70 or even 80% of the entire field of high-tech ceramics. The growth rate per year in Japan is claimed to be about as 10% at the time being [1]. Structural ceramics, which are used as components in engines, in chemical devices, as wear parts, high temperature parts etc., represent in the order of 10-20%, depending on the country. The growth rate in Japan is reported as 0.4% [1] in Europe being some what more, may be 5%. This field is normally defined without classical refractories and insulators. Several reviews can be found in literature, e.g. [2, 3].

When we look after the classification of high tech ceramics according Table 1, the engineering ceramics are concentrated in the upper part of the table. They are often subject of high mechanical and high thermal loading. The load mostly leads to multiaxial stresses which are effective for long terms and changing with time. In case of high temperature application, the mechanical stresses are superimposed by thermal stresses, while the materials properties are changing with temperature and time. Problems correlated with complex and severe loadings under long term conditions are difficult to solve. This is one of the reasons, why the progress in introducing engineering ceramics in technology is slower than formerly expected. Furthermore, many possible applications in engineering are not yet thoroughly evaluated, because brittle materials design is by far not as etablished as metallic design with metals and alloys.

TABLE 1

Classification of advanced ceramics

Main function	Properties required	Applications (examples)
thermal	high-temperature and thermal shock resistance, thermal conductivity (high or low, resp.)	high-temp. components, burner nozzles, heat exchanger heating elements, NE-metallurgy, insulating parts thermal barrier coatings
mechanical	long-term-, high temperature resistance fatigue-, thermal shock-, wear resistance	wear parts, sealings, bearings, cutting tools, engine, motor and gas turbine parts, thermal barrier coatings
chemical biological	corrosion resistance, bio-compatibility	corrosion protection, catalyst carriers, environmental protection, sensors, implants (joints, teeth etc.)
electrical magnetical	electrical conductivity (high or low, resp.) semi-conducting, piezo-, thermoelectricity, dielectrical properties	heating elements, insulators, magnets, sensors, IC-packages, substrates, solid electrolytes, piezoelectrics, dielectrics, supra conductors
optical	low absorption coefficient	lamps, windows, fiber optics, IR-optics
nuclear	irradiation resistance, high absorption coefficient, high-temperature resistance corrosion resistance	fuel and breeding elements, absorbers, shields, waste conditioning

2. THE MATERIALS USED

Most of the engineering ceramic parts used at present time are monolithic, either oxidic or nonoxidic. Important oxide ceramics are Al_2O_3 and ZrO_2, for special applications also Al_2TiO_5, while nonoxidic ceramic parts are mainly based on Si_3N_4 or SiC, see Table 2. Each formula in this table represents an own group of materials, there microstructural and mechanical properties depending on composition, consolidation method, porosity, etc. The properties of some of these products have been improved continuously during the last two decades. A big step in strength and fracture toughness, has been achieved by developing composite materials namely transformation toughened ZrO_2 and Al_2O_3, SiC-whisker (and platelet) reinforced ceramics (mainly Al_2O_3) and fiber reinforced products (e.g. C-C and SiC-SiC). The transformation toughened ceramics provide a considerably higher strength and toughness than comparable monolithics, but only at lower temperatures. The continous fiber reinforcement leads to a drastically increased toughness, a non-catastrophic fracture behaviour and to the possibility of application at high temperatures. These materials, however, are in a less developed state and are very expensive, but they provide the highest potential in principle.

TABLE 2

Selection of monolithic and composite advanced ceramics

material or matrix Vol-%	theoretical density [g/cm3]	Young's-modulus [GPa]	bend-strength [MPa]	fracture toughness (K_{Ic}) [MPa $\sqrt{m}$]	
Si_3N_4	3.19	160 - 300	250 - 1000	2 - 8	monolithic
SiC	3.21	300 - 400	400 - 800	3	
Al_2O_3	3.98	400	400 (1000)^1	3 - 4	
Al_2TiO_5	3.77	13	40	-	
ZrO_2	5.56	205^2	600 - 900^2 (1500)^1	3 - 9	monolithic or reinforced
Al_2O_3-SiC (W)20-30	3.6	400	850	8.5	reinforced
C-C (f) 30 (1d)	1.9	70	1000	-	
SiC - SiC (f) 45 (2d)	2.9	250 - 270	580	12 - 18	
Glass-SiC (f) 30-65 (1d)	2.6	120 - 140	600 - 900	10 - 35	

1: peak values
2: partial stabilized
f: fiber w: whisker
1 d, 2 d: one ore two dimensional reinforced

3. PRINCIPAL DESIGN ASPECTS AND PROPERTIES REQUIRED

For manufacturing engineering parts from these materials we have to consider principle design aspects, from which the most important steps are collected in Tab. 3. The more complicated and expensive a part is and the higher the reliability has to be, the more design effort is necessary. Not all the items of this table can be discussed in this paper, however.

TABLE 3

Brittle material design for engineering components

1. **Definition of service conditions**

2. **Basic evaluations**

2.1. Stress analysis in ceramics and ceramic-metal interfaces.
- load stresses
- thermal stresses
- residual stresses

2.2. Multiaxial stress criteria application
2.3. Evaluation of other influences than mechanical stresses
2.4. Geometrical optimisation
2.5. Definition of materials specifications required

3. **Data base for materials**

3.1. Mechanical properties under short term conditions with respect to failure probability
- strength distribution (bending, tensile, ring test)
- fracture toughness (K_{Ic})
- thermal shock resistance

3.2. Materials behaviour and degradation under long term conditions with respect to life time predictions
- Fatigue (sub-critical crack growth)
  - thermal
  - static
  - cyclic
- Creep and creep fracture
- Friction and wear

3.3. Thermophysical and chemical properties

4. **Evaluation of special procedures**
- hard machining, incl. surface finishing
- joining

3.1. Basic evaluations and short term behaviour

At first one needs a complete stress analysis in the ceramic component by finite elements including the joining interfaces. To this end, the service conditions have to be defined as good as possible. For complete estimation load, thermal and residual stresses have to be considered likewise.

A principle aspect is the load stress distribution in contact planes of axial-symmetric parts of materials with different youngs modulus under pressure [4]. Due to the different transverse strain behaviour, radial tensile stresses occur in the ceramic part although the nominal stress is only by pressure. Stress concentrations are observed at the edges of the contact plane. Fig. 1 shows this situation for pressing cylinders of Ti-alloy on Al_2O_3, assuming no sliding in the contact plane. Tensile stresses in the ceramic part can be reduced or even avoided, when the diameter ratio of metal to ceramic part increases from 1 to 2, but in this case high compressive stress peaks occur. They can be reduced by avoiding sharp edges.

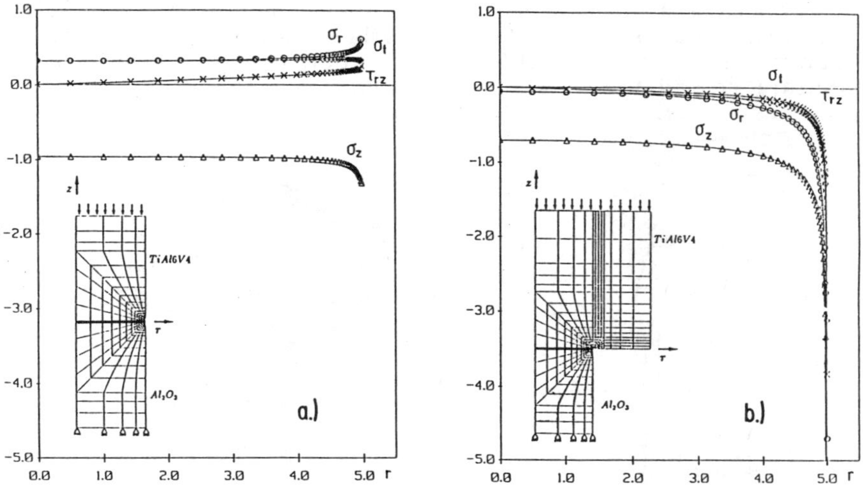

Figure 1: Metal-ceramic contact under pressure; Stresses in the contact plane of the ceramic cylinder (related to pressure of $1 N/mm^2$). Metal / ceramic diameter-ratio: a = 1, b = 2 [4]

In Fig. 2 the FEM-mesh and the load stress analysis is shown as an example with curved contacts for the development of ceramic joint bearing [5]. They have a potential for applications at high temperatures and under severe enviromental conditions. The outer ring is stressed in tension circumferentially and high modulus ceramics (SiC) lead to higher tensile stresses than low modulus ones (ZrO_2). The optimization has to minimize the tensile stress level as well as eventually stress peaks by improving contact geometries with equalizing local pressures and, consequently, local elastic deformation. This is with ceramics, as we know, even more important than in metallic design.

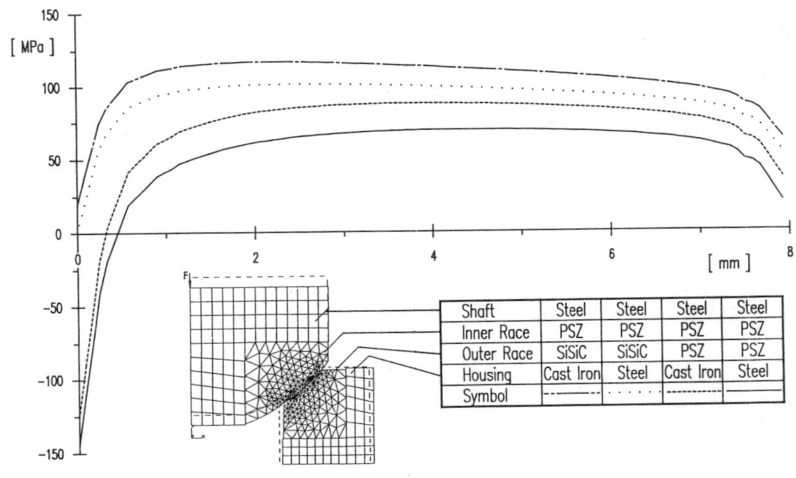

Figure 2: FEM-mesh and circumferential tensile stresses in the outer race contact area of a ceramic joint bearing [5]

Fig. 3 shows, as an example of thermal stresses in the field of turbine combustor development [6], the stress distribution of a flame tube segment. The analysis shows the highest tensile stress values on the outer surface of the sintered SiC part due to the calculated temperature distribution. The highest compressive stresses are occuring in the middle of the inner surface. As a result of these investigations the geometrical dimensions of a ceramic part are of major importance. Thickness, curvature, length to width and radii must be carefully adjusted to the load conditions, a subdividing into segments is advisable.

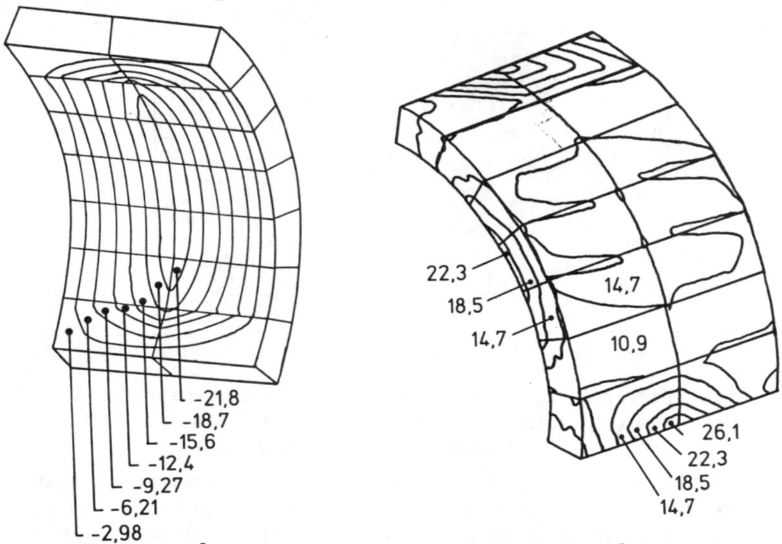

Figure 3: Stress distribution (MPa) in a flame tube segment [6]

Remembering the well known qualitative design rules, namely: avoiding tensile stresses, stress concentrations, thin local cross sections, sharp edges, etc., is has to be stated that it is often impossible to avoid the stresses mentioned. Therefore a quantitative stress analysis is necessary. Residual stresses in ceramics may be a result of manufacturing, machining and joining. Because they can reach considerably high values and superimpose external stresses they have to be considered for strength and life time considerations. Residual stress depth profiles, measured by X-ray analysis are available from several sources [7, 8, 9] and are especially important for machined surfaces and interfaces after joining. In machined surfaces often compression stresses are introduced, but their beneficial effect can be superimposed by increasing the surface flaws, resulting possibly in an effective decrease of strength. Fig. 4 is an example for a soldered ceramic tip on a steel surface for a rocker arm. Measurement as well as calculation [8, 10] show complicated profiles of residual tensile and compressive stresses, which can be controlled by geometrical optimization and by adjusting soldering material and process.

Calculated and measured stresses under service conditions have to be used to define specifications required for the materials and have to be correlated with the properties of the materials available. In case the material response is purely elastic under short term conditions, linear-elastic fracture mechanics and Weibull distribution data of inert strength can be applied for failure probability analysis, where the strength dependence on size has to be considered. However, surface failures often become effective and determine the strength of the part. In order to have full benefit from bulk strength properties, a rigid control of surface quality including grinding or other machining effects is absolutely necessary.

Figure 4: Rocker arm with Si_3N_4 tip, soldered structure (Daimler Benz)

The loading under service conditions is seldom of pure bending, compression or tension, resp. Consequently, the conventional 4-pt. bending test is often of limited value for the design engineer, although it is widely used. Thus, transformation of bending to tensile data [11], and tensile tests are necessary. In many cases, multiaxial stess criteria have to be applied, otherwise the calculation of applicable stresses is too optimistic. Experimentally, the double ring test [12] on disks with biaxial stresses is advisable, resulting in lower strength values than 4-pt-bend tests on bars. (Experimental results with this test are shown in Fig. 7 for the long term strength.)

Based on the ideas of Weibull, Batdorf [13], Evans [14] and in Germany Munz [14a] have developed sophisticated multiaxial failure criteria. The flaws, causing failure are considered as randomly orientated cracks. Local fracture mechanics failure criteria taking into account mixed mode stress-intensity factors are applied. For homogeneous stress distribution the results of these calculations can be plotted in a modified Mohr biaxial stress diagram, where the result depends on the Weibull-parameter m. For inhomogeneous stress states, where the degree of multiaxiality can also vary within a component the principal calculation procedure is shown in Fig. 5. From the external loadings first the multiaxial stress distribution in the components is calculated. For a given crack, which orientation is characterized by two angles ψ and ϕ the normal stress σ_n and the shear stress τ are important. The stress intensity factors K_I, K_{II}, K_{III} for different loading modes are calculated and by applying a local mixed mode fracture criterion an equivalent stress $\sigma_{Ieq.}$ is obtained.

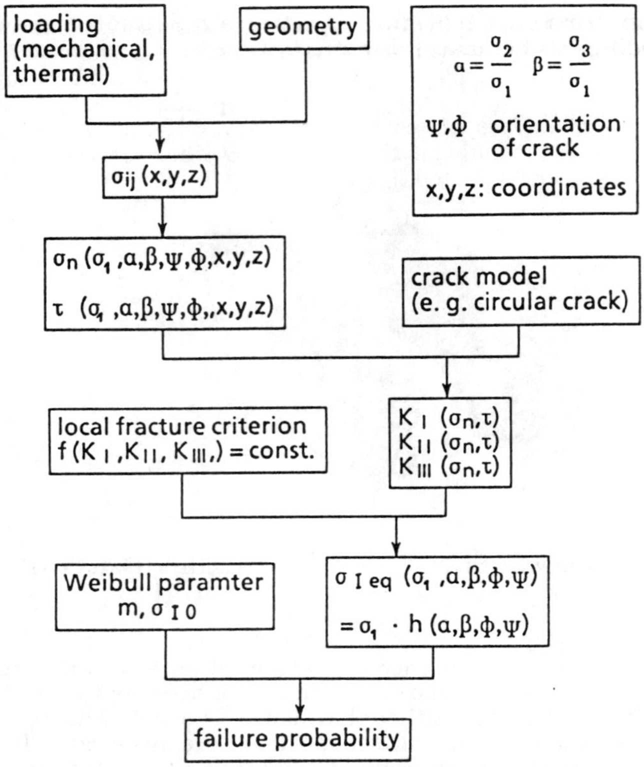

Figure 5: Steps for multiaxial stress design procedure [14a]

Failure occurs for all cracks, for which the equivalent stress exceeds a critical stress. The failure probability is obtained from the two-parametric Weibull-relation with the reference stress σ* and geometrical function g, and the function h.

$$P = 1 - exp \left| -\frac{1}{2\pi} \left(\frac{\sigma^*}{\sigma_{I0}} \right)^m \int_V g^m \int_0^{2\pi} \int_0^{\pi/2} h^m sin\phi \, d\phi \, d\psi \, dV \right|$$

3.2. Long term behaviour

Under long term conditions, a time dependence of strength due to subcritical crack growth is observed in most of the ceramics in a wide temperature range. The laws for these processes are well developed [15, 16] and generally accepted. It seems to be sure that slow crack growth is normally a grain boundary process, occuring preferably, when amorphous layers between the grains are present. Also amorphous material (glasses) undergo these processes, which is strongly influenced by environmental conditions. Different types of stressing, namely by thermal cycling, static, dynamic or cyclic loading lead to similar phenomena and have to be considered for long term applications. In the field of ceramics, they are summarized by the term fatigue.

When in high temperature application no external stresses are expected, thermal fatigue [17] experiments for life time considerations are advisable. (They should be distinguished from thermal degradation effects, where no temperature cycling is involved.) Results of thermal cycling are very dependent on cycling conditions, geometry and materials properties because very different stresses and stress gradients may occur. An example is shown in Fig. 6, where a considerable strength decrease in observed after repeated thermal cycling.

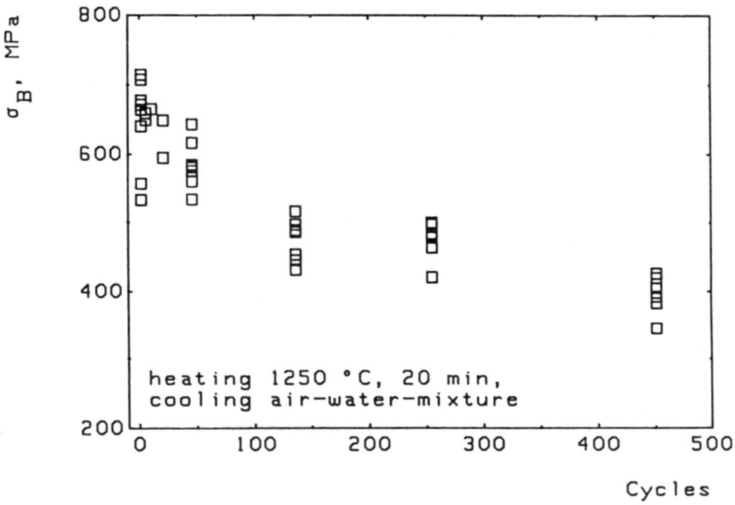

Figure 6: Strength at room temperature of HPSN after thermal cycling [17]

Static fatigue (=delayed fracture) experiments have been performed by many authors normally as bend tests, with most of the interesting advanced ceramics [18, 19, 20]

The straight lines follow the equation

$$t_B \cdot \sigma_T^n = K(T) \cdot \sigma_{RT}^{n-2} = const.$$

with the characteristic parameters n and K(T) and the time at fracture t_B.

A high n value, i.e. a flat line, is a criterion for resistivity against slow crack growth (SCG). Different ceramics may behave very different indeed, mainly depending on state of grain boundaries. Si_3N_4 with cristallized grain boundary phase and some SiC-qualities belong to the more "resistant" ceramics. Materials development during the last years has achieved interesting progress. Thresholds in SCG have been observed in HPSN at certain stresses due to relaxation and creep [19]. Experimental data are shown in Fig. 7 [18a], their main results being the drastically reduced life time, when biaxial testing by ring-on-ring test is used, compared with the conventional bend test. This seems to be extremely important for practice. For theoretical considerations see also [21].
A most challenging field with respect to long term performance is cyclic fatigue, which was investigated in ceramics very little upto five years ago. At the time being many laboratories have entered this field [22-24]. The principle question, if ceramics undergo cyclic effects at all has to be answered positively , but depends

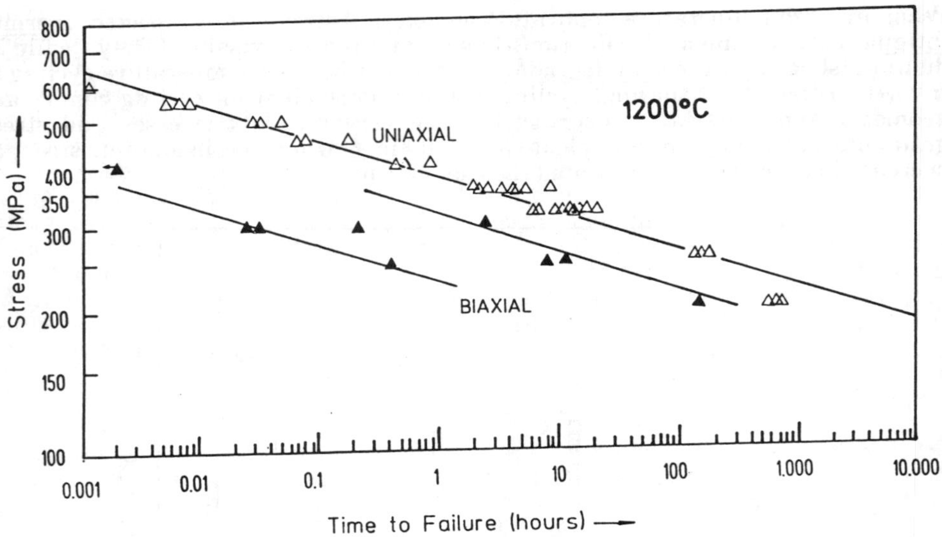

Figure 7: Static fatigue of HPSN in uniaxial and biaxial (ring-on-ring) tests [18a]

strongly on microstructure and crack configuration. Especially some high strength ceramics shows specific cyclic effects due to continuous interaction of crack flanks, formation of micro-debris etc, increasing stress intensity at crack tips. Fig. 8 shows results on cyclic fatigue of ZrO_2 (3% Y_2O_3)- 20% Al_2O_3. Survivors after cyclic tests may exhibit even higher strength than before.

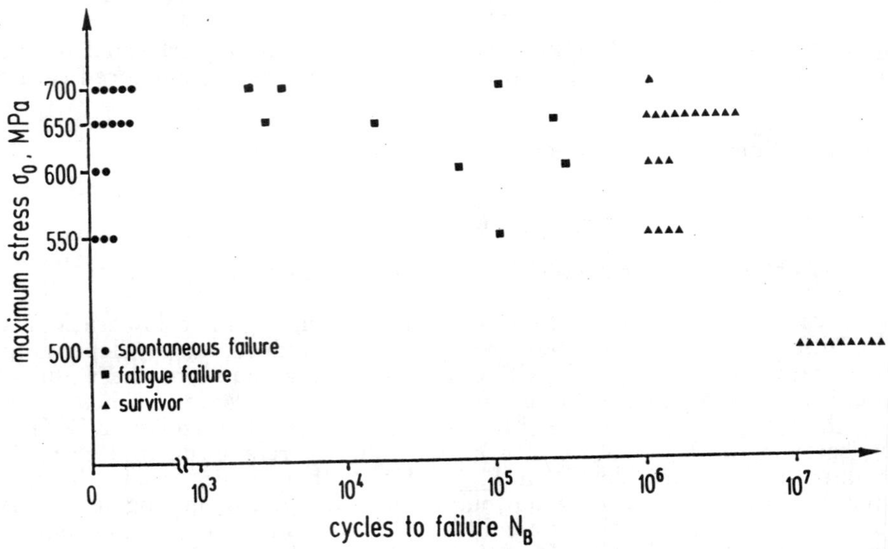

Figure 8. Cyclic fatigue behaviour of TZ (3Y)-20A (200 Hz) [24a]

Creep incl. creep fracture have to be considered as life-time criterion in long-term high-temperature applications, e.g. for gas turbine development. Bend-test creep data have been measured during the last two decades for many ceramics [25-27]. Non-oxide ceramics, esp. high quality RBSN and SiC belong to the most creep resistant materials, ranging between $\varepsilon = 10^{-5}$ to 10^{-6}/h at 1300-1400°C. In these materials creep deformation is hardly a life limiting factor, but possibly creep fracture, because only small creep deformation can be sustained. Oxide ceramics are generally somewhat less creep resistant. Creep properties of dense Si_3N_4-qualities are very dependent on composition, cristalline state and amount of grain boundary phases coming from sintering additives. Especially SSN-qualities, which can be sintered to high densities and homogeneity in larger volumes, are not very creep resistant, unless the glassy phase can be cristallized to a great extent. In nonoxide ceramics it is often not possible to define a wider range of steady state creep because transient creep is very extended [28]. Generally, bending creep data are often not sufficient for design purposes, but tensile creep data are much less available (see chapter 5).

The friction and wear properties are of general importance for the design of components with sliding functions, like bearings, sealing rings, joints etc. Because tribological properties are related to the system and not primarily to the material itself, factors like materials combination, surface finishing, lubrication, sliding speed, and environment, are besides time, temperature and pressure of principal importance. [30] Although friction coefficients and wear have been measured in many ceramic-ceramic and ceramic-metal-combinations [31], each perspective application should be handled as a "new problem". Dry friction between ceramics can lead to desastrous results under high loading conditions [32]. A generally improved behaviour should be achieved, when "internal lubrication" (e.g. graphite-containing SiC) can be applied.

For several applications, esp. at high temperatures and under corrosive environmental influences, thermophysical and chemical properties are necessary to be known including degradation effects during long service. This cannot be discussed here in detail.

3.2. Special procedures

Many applications of ceramics require special procedures like surface finishing hard machining [33, 35], joining [36, 37] etc, (see Table 3). Although hard machining generally increases cost, it is unavoidable, when real net shape manufacturing is impossible or when the required surface quality cannot be achieved by other means. While mechanical surface finishing is (partly) established and is used for a lot of mass produced parts, methods like elektro-erosive or ultrasonic machining are more in a developmental state. Electroerosion with an acceptable speed is only possible when the electrical conductivity exeeds a certain value, being the case at special qualities of SiC [34] or in ceramics with larger additives of high conductivity. Ultrasonic machining is a universal method in principle, but becomes more difficult with ceramics of high toughness and special tooling and processing have to be adapted for complicated geometries.

The reliability of joints is as important as of the ceramics themselves. When joining is necessary for a special design, the problem has to be handled for each geometry and each case separately, although soldering alloys are known in principle and are partly optimized for several ceramic-metal and ceramic-ceramic-combinations. Bonding, thermal expansion misfit, residual stresses and long term stability are of major importance.

4. Engineering ceramics in practice

High hardness, wear and corrosion resistance are inherent properties of ceramics. Consequently, many applications have been realized with this respect. Widely used are alumina as pairs of sealing disks in hot and cold water taps, where low friction has been achieved by specification of surface roughness as low as 0.6 µm or less. Sand-blast nozzles of B_4C or SiC, sealing rings for pumps and equipment for transporting corrosive or abrasive liquids are subject of mass production. Oxide as well as non-oxide ceramics are used. Pump and pipe liners are especially important for transporting abrasive slurries and dry abrasives, SiC seems to be the favorized material.

A field of perspective growth, are roller and ball bearings [38] and shaft protection sleeves. Especially fully dense silicon nitride can obviously improve the performance of antifriction bearings. Ceramic bearings provide the possibility to serve at high temperatures ($\geqq$ 800 °C) and under severe environmental conditions. A most intriguing benefit of ceramic bearings is the possibility to tolerate a starvation of lubrication. A relatively new application are parts for big valves, like cones and ball plugs, e.g. in coal liquefaction plants and for gas-desulfurisation. Products of general interest are knives and scissors manufactured from transformation-toughened zirconia in Japan, Germany [39] and perhaps also in other countries.The perspective importance of these products is in house-keeping hair cutting as well as in craft and industrial applications.

The turnout in heat resistant structural parts is much less than of corrosion and wear resistant parts. Important products are kiln furniture of SiC, a product which requires much less space than conventional kiln furniture and other furnace parts. SiC-burners including heat exchanger and nozzles for gas and oil burners [40] may develop to an interesting market. A commercial product are TiB_2 evaporators [41] and rings of hexagonal BN for horizontal casting. The welding and steel hardening industry perhaps represent a future potential for application of Si_3N_4 materials because of their good thermal shock resistance. In industrial heat exchangers, advanced ceramics permit higher operating temperatures (1300-1350°C) than metallic alloys, resulting in energy saving during heat recovery. Favourized materials for application in recuperators are SiC and perhaps also Si_3N_4.

More than 90% of the metal working tool market is occupied by high speed steels and cemented carbides, to a great deal with coated tips. Ceramic tools materials, especially Al_2O_3, Al_2O_3-ZrO_2, Si_3N_4 (HPSN or SSN) Sialons, whisker-reinforced Al_2O_3, polycristalline diamond (PKD) and cubic boron nitride (CBN) compete with metallic and cemented carbide tools. While Al_2O_3 and Al_2O_3-TiC materials have been used for special applications since about four decades, the others are products of more recent development. Si_3N_4 and Sialons are successful since the 70th in turning and milling of cast iron parts and Ni-based superalloys, with the results of dramatically increased productivity, (upto 200%) [42]. Si_3N_4 tool tips can be used for high speed interrupted cutting operations due to their impressive fracture toughness and "impact resistivity" under these conditions. Whisker-reinforced Al_2O_3 seems to be advantageous for superalloys. Fig. 9 demonstrates the development of toughness of some tool materials since 1957 [43]. The application of PKD is restricted to operation temperatures below 700°C and to materials having no carbon affinity (no steels), while these limitations are not valid for CBN. The excellent properties of advanced ceramic tools do not yet correspond at present to their introduction in practice although for special machining operations in the car and aircraft and industry, ceramics are well established.

The strong efforts to introduce ceramic parts in spark-ignited as well as in Diesel engines during the last 10 years have the goal to increase the performance of these

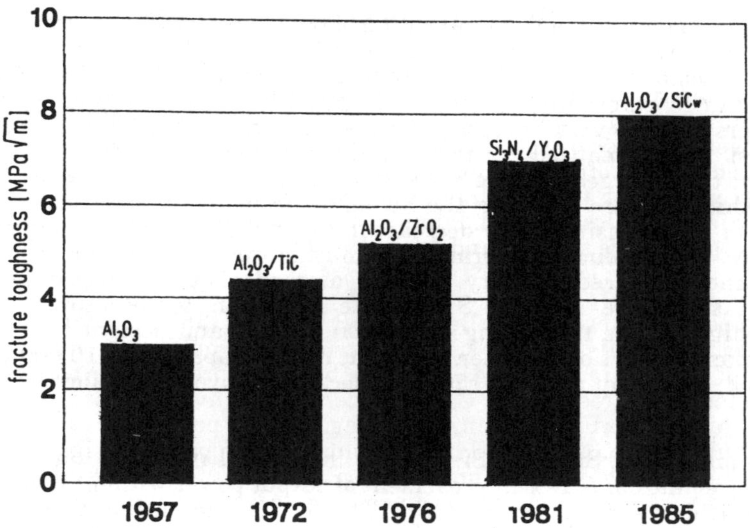

Figure 9: Toughness development in ceramic tools since 1957

engine types. Katz and Lenoe [42] have classified, especially for the Diesel Technology four levels of introduction of ceramics (Tab. 4) in order to achieve step by step benefits, according to the maturity and reliability of the ceramic part mass production.

TABLE 4
Future diesel engine technology development scenario (E. Lenoe, R.N. Katz)

Techn. level	Engine configuration	Potential ceramic components	Potential pay-offs
1	State-of-the-art engine, turbocharged	Turbocharger Valve train components Pre-chamber, glow plugs	Improved performance Reduced cost? Early manufacturing experience
2	Uncooled, non-adiabatic (no water on air cooling) (no turbo-compounding)	Turbocharger Valve train components Piston, cap Cylinders, liners	Reduced weight → efficiency gain Gives option to improve aerodynamics → efficiency gain Reduced maintenance Reduced engine systems cost? Flexibility of engine placement
3	Adiabatic turbo-compound	Turbocharger Turbo-compound wheel Valve train components Piston, cap Cylinders, liners Exhaust train insulation	Very significant reduction in specific fuel consumption Improved aerodynamics Reduced maintenance
4	Minimum friction technology (could be combined with 1, 2 or 3)	Air bearings High temperature rings High temperature bearings Non-galling wear surfaces Low friction liquid, lubricant-free bearings	Lower specific fuel consumption

While the technical and economical realisation of these concepts is to a great deal a future approach, a considerable introduction of ceramics parts was achieved upto now outside the combustion area. Cordierite honey comb catalyst carriers [40] are now widely used in cars with gasoline fuelled spark ignited engines. Ceramic catalyst carriers are also very important for chemical industries. The approach of hotter exhaust gas is realized by the ceramic portliner, consisting of porous Al_2TiO_5. In the turbo-carged Porsche 944 engine, aluminium titanate portliners of about 3 mm thickness are reducing the heat flow from the exhaust port to the cooling by up to 7 kW causing a 13% decrease in cooling efforts [44]. Strong efforts are under way to introduce the ceramic monolithic turbocharger for passenger cars, trucks and armoured military vehicles as well. The favourized ceramic material is gas-pressure sintered Si_3N_4. The operation temperature can be considerably high, at the time being about 800 - 900°C and designed for about 1200°C. The mass production has been settled at first in Japan with 10 000 pieces per month and counts up to 1988 150 000 pieces for Toyota cars for the home market.

The swirl chamber from Si_3N_4 or Sialon was introduced in Diesel cars, e.g. by Isuzu, Toyota and Mazda. A 10% improvement of output power without increase of fuel consumption has been reported [3]. The higher operating temperature compared with metallic swirl chamber may reduce also particle emission. The rocker arm insert is a typical ceramic wear part, obviously introduced as Si_3N_4 tip in Mitsubishi cars. Sealing rings of SSiC, a mass product in conventional pumps, are now used in cooling water pumps due to their superior friction behaviour, combined with less noise generation.

In Germany and - more generally - in Europe, the introduction of ceramic parts into passenger cars and trucks, especially in the hot zone is not very progressed [45], although many R and D activities take place. An unlubricated ceramic intensive 20 kW motor is under development [46].

The ceramic gas turbine, especially the "all ceramic" engine is undoubtly the most challenging project in utilizing high-tech ceramics for industry. The expected benefits are the high turbine inlet temperaturs up to 1350°C, the multi-fuel capability and the potential of low environmental pollution. Most of the experts agree, that the commercialisation of a vehicular ceramic gas turbine (power between, say, 100 and 300 kW) is a long range approach and will occur not earlier than in the year 2000 or even 2015 [47]. Encouraging results have been achieved with a Daimler-Benz engine (100 kW) with a monolithic ceramic Si_3N_4 rotor which is operating at about 1250°C and up to 63000 rpm. The service life at present time correspond to 15000 km on city and country roads [48]. Stators and rotors are components with the most complex geometry. When they are successful under realistic service conditions, the development of the other static parts can be expected being successful as well. The results achieved in the last 15 years, demonstrate in principle the technical feasibility of a vehicular gas turbine. Therefore new R and D programs are sponsored at several countries [49].

5. The lack of knowledge and future requirements

The most essential need for perspective progress is the existance of an appropriate data base for the engineering ceramics, combined with high standard reliable and reproducible manufacturing. Both are by far not yet established at a level we need for larger breakthrough in engineering ceramics. The generation of a data base is only of little value, when the processing technology is in a "preliminary" state and considerable batch to batch variations occur. Thus, a broadly based capability of properties measurement is preferably necessary for materials with a high grade of maturity.For many perspective applications we need to improve the important processing steps, in order to reach clearly defined microstructures, minimized physical and chemical failure and optimized homogeneity. New and optimized starting powders with improved cleanness will help to achieve this goal. Monosized powders, as claimed several years ago, are probably not an appropriate starting material, because they lead to ordered as well as disordered packing in neighboured micro-volumes, leading to different shrinkage behaviour and failure generation. A blend of two monosized powders lead to a controllable disordered, but homogeneous partical distribution with "homogeneous" sinterability [50]. This together with optimized shaping and sintering procedures, e.g. with controlled densification rates [54] could be important steps to reach high strength, high Weibull modulus materials. New possibilities, instead of using prefabricated powders, are opened by reactive processes, especially for manufacturing composite ceramics. Liquid, solid or gaseous precursors are used as starting materials which undergo after shaping a reaction process, resulting simultanously in the formation of the ceramic compounds and their densification, as summarized in [55].

As stated above, several properties are of basic importance for the life time of structural ceramic parts. A strength evaluation has to consider also residual stresses from different sources. Superimposing external stresses, they can initiate subcritical crack growth and possibly lead to catastrophic failure. The investigation and understanding of cyclic fatigue is only at its beginning. This has to be investigated for monolithic as well as for composite materials and has to be considered for long term performance evaluation. It is very important to provide strength data not only by bending, but also by tensile tests, especially for fatigue and creep [51]. Multiaxial tests are of vital importance for practice and may help a lot to the designer. Comparative studies of materials response under bend and tensile stress will provide also a deaper insight into materials behaviour at high temperatures. In Fig.10 a few results for creep are given. As expected, creep strain under tension is generally higher than under bending load at same nominal conditions. For high life time, a continous decrease of creep rate with time, as observed with several Si_3N_4-qualities [28], is favorable, but we cannot clearly define the microstructures to achieve this.

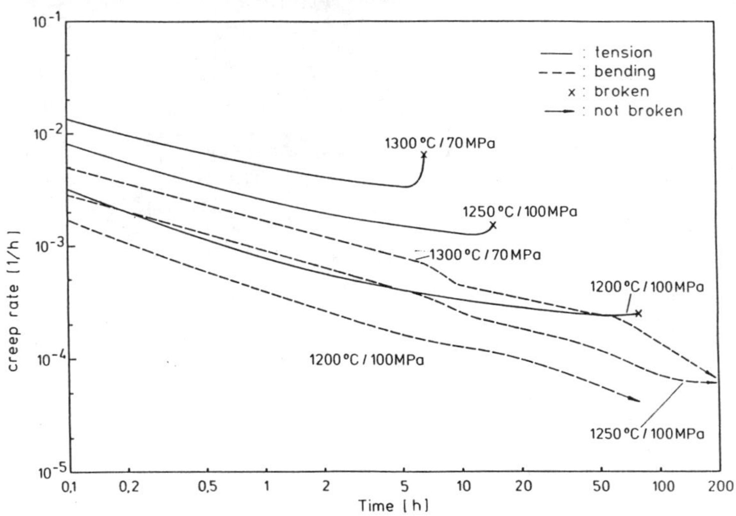

Figure 10: Comparison of creep curves in tension and bending of SSN [29]

There is a principle lack of knowledge in correlations of microstructural parameters with the properties of ceramics. Very little is established in quantitative correlations with respect to mechanical (strength and fatigue) properties, what we know, are mainly tendencies. More effort has to be spent from researchers and manufacturers to determine and to define microstructures, chemically as well as physically, including the state of grain boundaries and to investigate the correlations mentioned above. During a recent conference [52] we have clearly seen, that many analytical methods are well established, but their application on properties and processing problems is missing to a great deal.

Considerable break trough in some "difficult" fields of application, e.g. for car industry or gas turbines could certainly be achieved, when at least three requirements are fulfilled: 1st, the definition of clear and approved specification of properties, to be defined by the user, 2nd, the principal existance of a manufacturing route, which fulfils quality as well as economical criteria, including non-destructive testing methods established, and 3rd, when the manufacturers and the users of ceramic parts are willing to perform extensive long term field tests.

Although there is some potential in improving monolithic ceramics, a drastically improved toughness can be achieved mainly by continuous fiber-reinforcement.For high temperatur applications the solution of the oxidation problems is indispensable. In Fig. 11, a stress-strain diagramm of a "modern brittle matrix material" is shown, where the continuous fibers inhibit catastrophic failure, as demonstrated in a SiC-fiber reinforced glass. Fig. 12 shows a gasturbine rotor [53], manufactured from SiC-fiber-reinforced SiC, exhibiting fracture toughness data which never can be achieved in monolithic SiC (see Tab. 2).

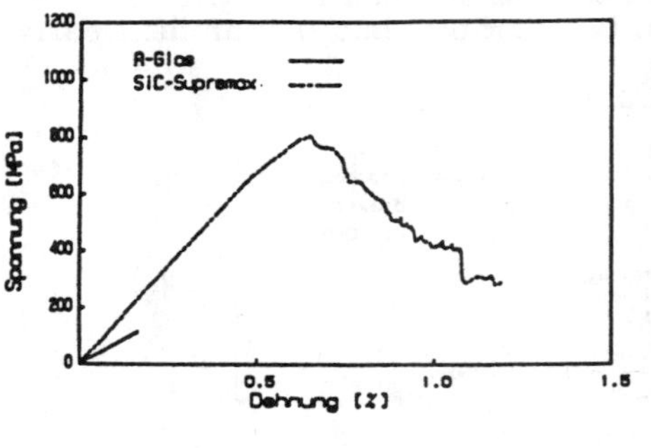

Figure 11. Stress strain diagram of SiC-fiber reinforced supremax glass [24a]

Figure 12. SiC-SiC experimental gas turbine rotor [53]

6. Outlook

The long range perspective for ceramic intensive engines has been assessed by Argonne National Laboratory [47]. Tab. 5 shows some of the data, which reflect the expected step-by-step introduction of structural ceramics in heat engines. The market introduction ranges from 1995 for Diesel engines to bejond 2000 for gas turbines.

Tab.5 Projected market development for ceramic-intensiv engines [47]

Type of engine	Light duty		Heavy duty	
	Introduction (1% market share)	5% market share	Introduction (1% market share)	5% market share
Diesel	1995	2005	1995	2005
Spark ignition	1996	2005	2000	2010
Rotary	2000	2005	2005	2010
Adiabatic	2000	2010	2005	2015
Gas turbine	2003	2025	2005	2015

The success in this field will be closely related to the needs discussed in Chapter 5, focussed in the problems of product reliability and cost. At the time being, the economic question is the crucial point for potential applications in the automotive industry in cases when the reliability is considered as adequate [48].

Not only automotive industry has to be considered, however.There is no doubt that the market in engineering ceramics will grow continously, but it is very difficult, to make future estimates. Ceramics compete with parts manufactured from metals, which may result in special cases even in a replacement of ceramics by metals. (This eventually will take place in the field of catalyst carriers for personal cars). The normal way is, as ceramists hope, the opposite! Many new applications of ceramics can be achieved in future simply due to their specific properties advantages, because many potential applications with expected pay-offs are not yet thoroughly evaluated. Although it is extremely necessary to improve materials quality as pointed out above, engineers should not wait for the "ideal" ceramic material. Even the existing levels of properties in oxide and non-oxide ceramics would enable us to achieve more application of structural ceramics, when the possibilities and principles of designing are properly applied. When material specialists, producers, designers and users will face the technical and economical problems of reliability and cost by an interdisciplinary approach, the field of engineering ceramics will be considerably enlarged in future.

Acknowledgements: The colleagues of the author Prof. Dr. P. Kuhn, Prof. Dr. D. Munz and Prof. Dr. S. Wittig and their coworkers have provided experimental results to this paper. Mrs. A. Gottschalk and Dipl.-Ing. A. Kühne have helped continously in preparing the manuscript. The author gratefully acknowledges this support.

7. REFERENCES

1. New Materials Japan, 5 (1988) 2

2. R.N. Katz in: High Tech Ceramics (ed. Vincencini) Elsevier Sci.Publ., Amsterdam, 1987, 145-161

3. R.N. Katz in: Ceramics Development (ed. C.C. Sorell and B. Ben-Nissan), Materials Science Forum, Vol. 34-36 (1988) Trans.Tech. Publ. Ltd., 9-16, and K. Funatani, 31-38

4. R. Dürr, P. Kuhn in: Institut für Keramik im Maschinenbau, Universität Karlsruhe, Jahresbericht 1987, 109-114 and 1988, 126-130

5. H. Pfeifer, P. Kuhn in: s. [4], Jahresbericht 1986, 61-64 and 1987, 115-122

6. A. Pfeiffer, G. Stürmer, S. Wittig in: s. [4] ,Jahresbericht 1988, 146-152

7. B. Eigenmann, B. Scholtes, E. Macherauch: X-ray stress determination in ceramics and ceramic-metal-composites. Presented at 2nd Int. Conf. on Residual Stresses, Nov. 23-25, 1988, Nancy

8. O. Jancu, D. Munz, B. Eigenmann, B. Scholtes, E. Macherauch: Characterisation of the stress state of brazed ceramic/metal joints by analytical methods and X-ray residual stress measurements. Submitted to J. Amer. Ceram Soc.

9. R. Prümmer: Keram. Z., 38 (1986) 512-515

10. B. Eigenmann, B. Scholtes, E. Macherauch in: s. [6], 105-111 and 112-117

11. H. Cohrt, G. Grathwohl: Festigkeit keramischer Hochtemperaturwerkstoffe, VDI-Berichte Nr. 600.4, 1987, 137-175

12. DIN 52292, Teil 1 "Bestimmung der Biegefestigkeit - Doppelring Biegeversuch an plattenförmigen Proben mit kleinen Prüfflächen", Beuth, Berlin, 1984

13. S. B. Batdorf, H. L. Heinisch, J. Amer. Ceram. Soc., 61 (1978) 355-358

14. A. G. Evans, J. Amer. Ceram. Soc., 61 (1978) 302-308

14a. D. Munz, T. Fett: Mechanisches Verhalten keram. Werkstoffe, Springer-Verlag, in print

15. T. Fett, D. Munz: Subcritical crack extension in ceramics. in: MRS-Internat. Meeting on Advanced Ceramics, Tokyo, 30.5.-3.6.1988, in press

16. H. Riedel, J. Mechanics and Physics of Solids, 29 (1981) 35.

17. K. Keller, Theoretische und experimentelle Untersuchungen zur Thermoermüdung keramischer Werkstoffe, Dissertation Universität Karlsruhe, 1989

18. G.D. Quinn: Review of static fatigue in silicon nitride and silicon carbide; Ceram. Eng. and Sci. Proc., 1-2 (1982) 77

18a. G. Quinn, G. Wirth: Biaxial static fatigue of silicon nitride 3rd Int. Conf. on Ceramics in Automotive, Las Vegas, Nevada, Nov. 1988, Proceedings in print

19. G. Grathwohl in: Creep and fracture of engineering materials and structures (ed. by B. Wilshire, D.R.J. Owen) Pineridge Press, Swansea, UK, 1984, 565-578.

20. S. M. Wiederhorn, E.R. Fuller: J. Mater. Sci. Engin., 71 (1985) 169-186

21. T. Thiemeier, A. Brückner-Foit, D. Munz: Lifetime prediction for ceramic components subjected to multiaxial loading, Proc. ECF7, Budapest, 1988, EMAS Publ., Warley, 476-484

22. R. H. Danskardt, W. Yu, R.O. Ritchie: Amer. Ceram. Soc. Comm., 70 (1987) C-248-C-252

23. T. Kansakubo, K. Komeya: J. Amer. Ceram. Soc., 70 (1987) 400-405

24. G. Grathwohl: Mat.-wiss.u.Werkstofftech., 19 (1988) 113-124

24a. G. Grathwohl et al., unpublished results

25. S.M. Wiederhorn, L. Chuck, E.R. Fuller, Jr., N.J. Tighe in: Tailoring multiphase and composite ceramics (ed. by R.E. Tresler e.a.) New York, Plenum Press (1986) 755-773.

26. D. F. Carroll, R.E. Tressler: J. Amer. Ceram. Soc., 72 (1989) 49-53

27. F. Thümmler, G. Grathwohl: High temperature oxidation and creep of Si_3N_4- and SiC-based ceramics and their mutual interaction in: s. [15]

28. U. Ernstberger, G. Grathwohl, F. Thümmler: Int. J. High Technol. Ceramics, 3 (1987) 43-61

29. M. Gürtler, A. Weddigen, G. Grathwohl: Mechanical testing of high-performance ceramics with tensile specimens. Mat.-wiss. u. Werkstofftech. (1989) in press.

30. K.-H. Zum Gahr, T. Degen: Z. Metallkunde, 79 (1988) 796-805

31. M. Mitwollen, H. Pfeifer: Literaturrecherche über die tribologischen Eigenschaften von Keramik, Fortschrittsber. VDI Reihe 5 Nr. 137, VDI-Verlag Düsseldorf 1988

32. H. Pfeifer, R. Haller in: s. [6], 131-136

33. König, W.: Keramik bearbeiten - aber wie?, VDI-Fachtagung "Neue Werkstoffe erfordern neue Bearbeitungsverfahren, 8./9.6.1988 Düsseldorf, 2.1.-2.32

34. G. Grathwohl, H. Iwanek, F. Thümmler: Mat.-Wiss. u. Werkstofftechn., 19 (1988) 81-86

35. N.F. Petrofes, A.M. Gadalla: Ceramic Bulletin, 67 (1988) 1048-1052.

36. W. Schäfer: Fügetechniken für Bauteile aus technischer Keramik in: Technische Keramik, Jahrbuch, Vulkan-Verlag Essen, Ausg. 1, 1988, 142-149

37. H.W. Hennicke: Keramik/Metall Füge- und Verbindungstechnik in: Technische Keramik, Jahrbuch, Vulkan-Verlag Essen, Ausg. 1, 1988, 136-141

38. R.N. Katz, J. G. Hannoosh: Int. J. High Tech Ceramics, 1 (1985) 69-79

39. Product of Fa. Jaguar, Solingen

40. Products of several ceramic manufacturers, e.g. Hoechst-CeramTec, Selb

41. Product of Elektroschmelzwerk Kempten

42. R.N. Katz in: Treatise of Material Science and Technology, Vol. 29, Structural Ceramics (ed. J. Wachtman), Academic Press 1988, in print

43. M. Fripan, U. Dvorak in: Schneidstoffe, Symposium 3.-4.11.1988, Hagen, 194-214, Verlag Schmidt, Freiburg i.Br.

44. J. Huber, H. Heinrich: Ceramics in internal combustion engines; Proceedings of the 2nd European Symposium on Engineering Ceramics, London, 1987

45. Automobil-Revue, (1987) H. 52, 24, and (1988) H. 27, 27

46. Ficht-Motor, common development of Fa. Ficht and Hoechst-CeramTec

47. L. M. Sheppard: Advanced Ceramic Materials, 3 (1988) 309-315

48. Daimler-Benz AG, Stuttgart, personal communication

49. Eureka-Programm: AGATA, Advanced Gas Turbines for Automotive, in preparation

50. E. Liniger, R. Raj: J. Amer. Ceram. Soc., 70 (1987) 843-49

51. M. Gürtler, G. Grathwohl, A. Weddigen: Mat.-wiss.u.Werkstofftechn., in press

52. Mikrostrukturelle und mikroanalytische Charakterisierung keramischer Werkstoffe, 10.-11. Nov. 1988, Bad Nauheim, Deutsche Gesellschaft für Metallkunde e.V., Oberursel.

53. Experimental product of SEP, Paris, France

54. H. U. Kessel, W. P. Engel: Gasdrucksintern mit kontrollierter Verdichtung, Vortrag Ceramitec 1988, München

55. P. Greil: Powder Metallurgy Int., 21 (1989) 40-46

STRUCTURAL RELIABILITY OF CERAMICS

JACQUES LAMON
Battelle-Geneva Research Centres
7, route de Drize, 1227 - Carouge/Geneva, Switzerland

ABSTRACT

Our approach to the structural reliability of ceramics places emphasis upon the fracture inducing microstructural flaws. This approach uses the Multiaxial Elemental Strength Model for failure probability determination and the CERAM computer code for the analysis of ceramic components.

INTRODUCTION

Structural reliability of ceramics is dictated by microstructural defects. All structural ceramics have various populations of microstructural defects (such as grain boundaries, triple junctions, agglomerates, inhomogeneities, inclusions, cracks, etc.). It is today impossible to prevent the presence of such flaws which appear first on processing and then throughout the lifetime of components: on machining as well as in service in high temperature or hostile environments.

These flaw populations have a fundamental influence upon fracture. Fracture is thus an erratic event, and the fracture strengths vary to such a large degree that a statistical treatment is required.

Several statistical approaches to brittle fracture have been proposed [1]. In recent years, the well-known Weibull model has been the most widely used for the routine analysis of failure strengths, preponderantly in uniaxial stress states. However, this model is essentially a statistical treatment of fracture stress data. The physical process producing fracture is not addressed, and the fracture inducing flaws are neglected. This model has been found inadequate by several authors in multiaxial stress states ([1] and references therein).

A fundamental probabilistic fracture model which considers the fracture inducing flaws as physical entities has been developed by Lamon and Evans [2,3]. This Multiaxial Elemental Strength Model (referred to as the Muest model in the following) proved to be an improvement for treating polyaxial failure. This model is used in the CERAM computer program for the reliability analysis based design of ceramic components.

The purpose of this paper is to emphasize structural reliability dependence upon the populations of fracture inducing flaws and to discuss our approach to ceramic reliability.

INFLUENCE OF THE MICROSTRUCTURAL FLAWS ON FRACTURE CHARACTERISTICS

Although the critical defect is the one which induces the highest stresses locally, defect criticality is not only a matter of defect size, but it is also dictated by defect geometry and nature, stress state and magnitude [1-4]. At given size, surface cracks are more critical than voids and inclusions respectively, whereas silicon inclusions are more deleterious than the Fe and WC ones in silicon nitride matrices [4]. This trend may be affected by the stress state, and specimen dimensions. Figure 1 thus shows an example where the internal defects become preponderant at large component dimensions in the presence of mixed mode loading.

Since the microstructural defects have an undefined distribution in terms of size, nature and orientation, location of the critical defect is a probabilistic event. The critical flaw cannot be identified prior to fracture using non-destructive means. A deterministic-type analysis cannot be used for predicting load carrying capacity by way of fracture mechanics relations. Therefore, fracture toughness is not a fundamental data for reliability analysis.

As a result of the presence of populations of microstructural flaws the fracture strength of ceramics is not characterized by a unique value. Several identical specimens of the same ceramic will fail at different stress levels when tested in identical conditions. Moreover, the fracture strength depends upon several parameters including the specimen size, the stress state and the populations of fracture inducing flaws. Figure 1 thus shows that increasing the specimen size may cause tremendous strength decreases by enhancing sensitivity to the weakest population of internal flaws. A direct consequence of the above-mentioned flaw induced strength effects is that the strength data measured on test specimens do not represent the fracture resistance of components.

Statistical-probabilistic approaches to brittle fracture should allow the use of laboratory strength data to infer the strength and reliability of components under more complex stress states encountered in service. Probabilistic fracture mechanics places emphasis on the microstructural flaws, as opposed to the statistical approaches which consider the macroscopic fracture strengths exclusively. Probabilistic fracture mechanics provide the basic relationships between the three criteria for failure in ceramics: flaw populations, stresses and failure probability. We can go around this triangle in any way. Failure probability can be derived from flaw population characteristics at various applied stresses. Or, for desired component failure probability, design stresses can be evaluated as a function of flaw population characteristics.

THE MULTIAXIAL ELEMENTAL STRENGTH MODEL

The Multiaxial Elemental Strength Model combines fracture mechanics concepts with an elemental strength based statistical approach.

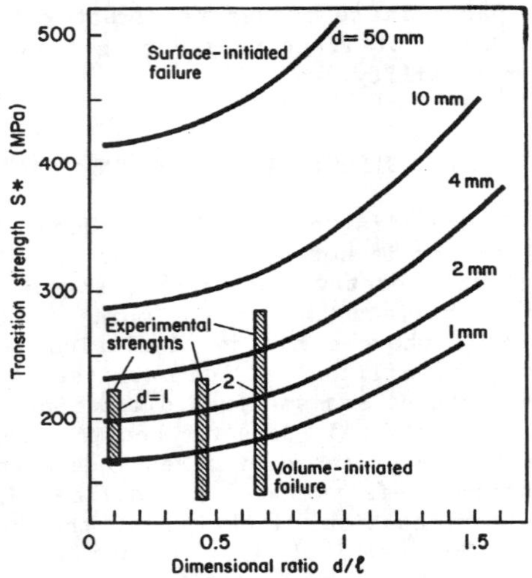

Figure 1. Influence of specimen size upon flexural strengths and fracture origins, for various thickness (d)-span length (l) ratios [3].

The Elemental Strength Approaches are based upon the premise that the distributions of fracture inducing defects can be characterized by a flaw extension stress S. Several approaches have been used to obtain strength failure probability relations from the distribution in S [5-7]. The Multiaxial Elemental Strength model uses the following basic failure probability relation [5]

$$P = 1-\exp \left[- \int_V dv \int_o^S g(S)dS \right]$$

where g(S)dS represents the number of flaws within the material having a strength between S and S + dS.
An explicit form of the flaw density function is determined in the Muest model for the most general multiaxial stress state, based upon recent concepts of non-coplanar crack extension, as detailed in previous papers [2,3]. Therefore only the final failure probability equation is given here for a single population of volume located flaws. Similar equation applies to failure from surface located flaws.

$$P_v = 1-\exp \left[-\int_V \left(\frac{\sigma_1}{\sigma_{OMV}} \right)^{m_V} I_V \left(m_V, \frac{\sigma_2}{\sigma_1}, \frac{\sigma_3}{\sigma_1}\right) dV \right] \quad (2)$$

where m_V is the shape parameter for the volume located flaw population, σ_{OMV} is a scale factor, and I_V characterizes the flaw distribution-stress state relationships. σ_1, σ_2 and σ_3 are the principal stresses. It is important to note that m_V may be similar to the Weibull modulus. σ_{OMV} is different from the Weibull scale factor as it refers to the flaw extension stresses whereas the Weibull scale factor refers to the macroscopic fracture strengths. The flaw strength parameters m_V and σ_{OMV} characterize the distribution of fracture inducing flaws.

APPLICATION TO RELIABILITY ANALYSIS

The Muest model -based CERAM program [8] can solve complex problems involving complicated geometries and multiaxial stress states, unsteady loading conditions (thermal shocks, fatigue), multiple flaw populations, and transient flaw populations in high temperature and corrosive environments.

CERAM is a post-processor to finite element programs. It forms part of a specific methodology for developing reliable ceramic designs.

The Muest model and CERAM have been validated by comparisons of failure probability results with experimental data. Various ceramics including fiber-reinforced composites [9] and involving single or multiple flaw populations [2,3,10] have been considered. Various loading geometries [11,12,15] involving uniaxial [1,11,12] polyaxial [1,3,4,10] and transient stress states induced by thermal shocks [13] and thermal shock heat-ups [14] have been analyzed.

In all cases, the failure probabilities predicted using the Multiaxial Elemental Strength Model compared quite well with experimental data. As an illustration, figure 2 shows failure probability comparisons for silicon carbide C-Rings subject to diametral compression. The experimental strength-failure probability data have been obtained by Ferber and coworkers [16].

Failure probabilities for the C-Rings have been predicted from the flaw strength parameters derived from 4-point bending strength data shown in Figure 2. Failure probability computations with CERAM used various 2D (60 and 1000 elements) and 3D (44 and 300 elements) finite elements meshes. It can be seen that the failure probability predictions are in excellent agreement with experimental results. On the contrast, the predictions by Ferber and coworkers using the Weibull theory exhibited a significant discrepancy with experimental data.

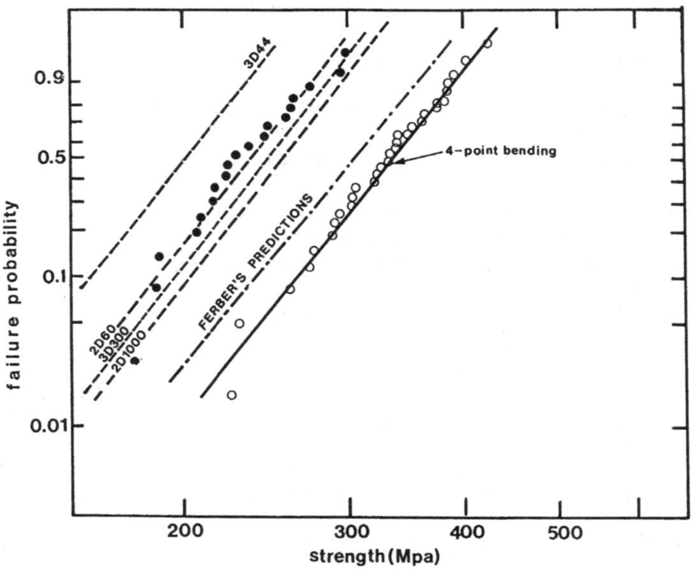

Figure 2. Failure probabilities predicted from 4-point bending strength data for a SiC C-Ring subject to diametral compression. Also indicated in the prediction by Ferber and coworkers using the Weibull model [16].

CONCLUDING REMARKS

Our approach to the analysis of structural reliability of ceramics focusses on the microstructural flaws as they dictate failure.
The Muest model for failure probability determination considers the flaws as physical entities. The CERAM computer code allows the analysis of complex components.
Failure predictions in good agreement with experimental results were obtained.

REFERENCES

1. J. Lamon: "Statistical Approaches to Failure for Ceramic Reliability Assessment".
   J. Am. Ceram. Soc., 71 [2] 106-12 (1988).

2. J. Lamon, A.G. Evans: "Statistical Analysis of Bending Strengths for Brittle Solids: A Multiaxial Fracture Problem".
   J. Am. Ceram. Soc., 66 [3] 177-82 (1983).

3. J. Lamon: "Statistical Analysis of Fracture of Silicon Nitride (RBSN) using the Short Span Bending Technique".
   Gas Turbine Conference and Exbibit, Houston, Texas, March 1985. Am. Soc. Mech. Eng. paper No. 85-GT-151.

4. A.G. Evans: "Structural Reliability: A Processing-Dependent Phenomenon".
   J. Am. Ceram. Soc., 65 [3] 127-37 (1982).

5. A.S. Argon and F.A. McClintock: "Mechanical Behavior of Materials (1966).
   Addison Wesley, Reading, Mass.

6. B.D. Coleman, J. Mech. Phys. Solids 7 (1958) 60.

7. S.B. Batdorf, J. Am. Ceram. Soc. 57 (1974) 44.

8. J. Lamon: "Ceram: A Computer Code for Reliability Analysis and Structural Design of Ceramic Components".
   European Conference Composites-89, Paris, June 1989.

9. J. Lamon: "Fracture of Silicon Carbide Fibers".
   JNC6, 6th National Conference on Composites, Paris, October 1988.

10. J. Lamon: "Ceramics Reliability: Statistical Analysis of Multiaxial Failure Using the Weibull Approach and the Multiaxial Elemental Strength Model".
    Gas Turbine and Aeroengine Congress, Amsterdam, The Netherlands, June 6-9-1988. Am Soc. Mech. Eng. paper No. 88-GT-147.

11. J. Lamon, D. Pherson: to be published.

12. J. Lamon, D. Pherson: "Reliability Analysis of C-Ring Specimens using the Multiaxial Elemental Strength Model".
90th Annual Meeting of the American Ceramic Society, Cincinnati, USA, May 1988. Annual Meeting Abstracts. The Am. Ceram. Soc. Inc 176 (1988) to be published.

13. J. Lamon, A. Grosjean: to be published.

14. J. Lamon, D. Pherson: "Reliability of Brittle Materials in Thermal Shock Heat Up". ibid [10], to be published.

15. E. Amar, F. Gauthier, J. Lamon: "Reliability Analysis of a Si_3N_4 Ceramic Piston Pin for Automotive Engines".
3rd International Symposium Ceramic Materials and Components for Engines, Las Vegas, November 1988.

16. M.K. Ferber, V.J. Tennery, S.B. Waters, J. Ogle: "Fracture Strength Characterization of Tubular Ceramic Materials using a Simple C-Ring Geometry".
Journal of Material Science 21 (1986) 2628-2632.

ASPECTS OF DESIGN AND STRESS CALCULATIONS IN ENGINEERING CERAMICS

S. SINNEMA
Structural Ceramics R & D
Hoogovens IJmuiden BV
P.O. Box 10.000, 1970 CA IJmuiden, The Netherlands

ABSTRACT

Stress calculations using the 'Finite Element Method' have been performed on a ceramic insert in a ring that is used in a process for making cans for beverages and food packaging. With this example, aspects of design and stress calculations in ceramics are illustrated. Conventional design concepts are adapted and the design is such that tensile stresses are avoided.

INTRODUCTION

Since the largest interest in engineering ceramics only has grown over the last decade, there is a short design tradition in these materials. There is a growing awareness that designing and constructing in ceramics is rather different from metal design.

First of all one has to keep in mind that ceramics cannot bear high tensile stresses and reducing of peak stress levels by plastic deformation is impossible. In design calculations it is important to take into account the variation in properties, especially in the strength. Models exist to describe this scatter [1,2]; the Weibull approach is well-known. The use of metal-design conventions is therefore less appropriate for ceramics than for instance the design rules for refractories, concretes and soils. Most designers are taught to think in metal concepts. However, worldwide efforts are made to develop concepts on the basis of probabilistic models [2]; in that case failure is described in terms of failure probability instead of the ratio stress/strength. This approach is superior to the conventonal ones used for metal design, though incorporating it in a standard finite-element method in an appropriate way seems to be a large effort that can take several years.

Apart from statistical considerations, in a failure criterion for ceramics the difference between large compressive strengths and relatively low tensile strengths must come out. For this reason, we make use of the failure criterion of Drücker and Prager [4] that has it origin in soil mechanics. Our approach is illustrated with an example from the process of wall-ironing.

THE DRUECKER-PRAGER CRITERION

The Drücker-Prager criterion can be compared with the more common Von Mises criterion, that is used for metal-design calculations.

Figures 1-3 illustrate both criteria shown for ceramic material and metal, respectively. In figure 1 the stress-strain diagram is shown. Instead of the possibility to deform plastically (which metals have) ceramic material behaves (generally speaking) very brittle.

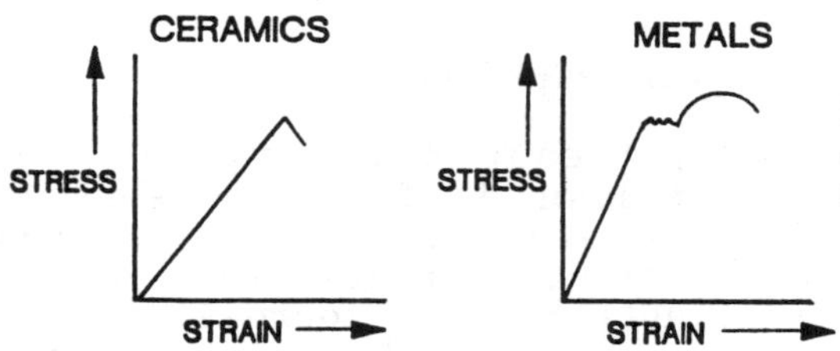

Fig 1. The stress-strain diagrams for ceramics and metals, respectively.

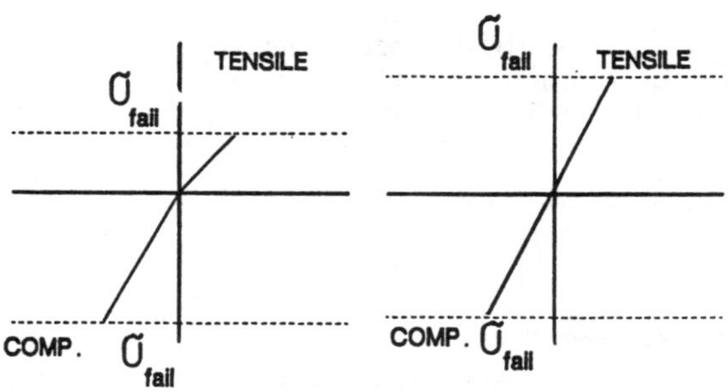

Fig 2. The fail-stresses (compressive and tensile) for ceramics and metals. (schematically)

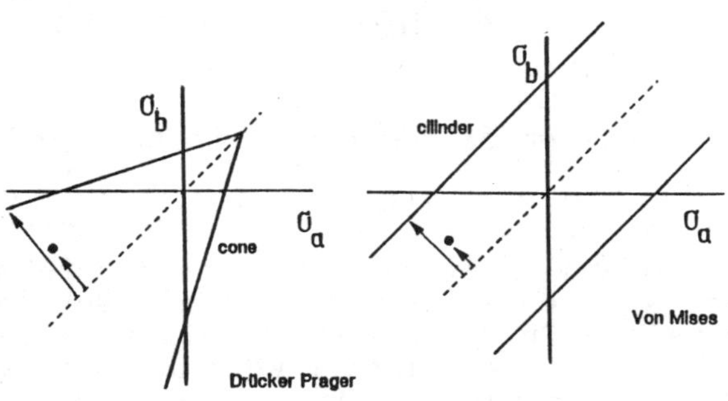

Fig 3. A simplified picture of the Drücker-Prager and the Von Mises criterion.

For both materials a fail-stress can be defined. For metals this value is numerically the same for compressive stresses and tensile stresses. For ceramics, however the uniaxial tensile fail-stress is much lower than the uniaxial compressive fail-stress as illustrated (schematically) in figure 2. A multiaxial stress state can be expressed in principle stresses, only. The material will survive if the stress state, expressed in principle stresses, is between the boundary lines in figure 3. In three dimensions the boundary is formed by a cilinder (Von Mises) or a cone (Drücker Prager [3,4]. The so-called Huber-Hencky stress (or Von Mises stress) is defined by calculating the distance of the point that represents the stress state to the axis of the cilinder or cone, respectively. This value is divided by the radius of the circle that is formed by intersecting the cilinder or cone by the plane (perpendicular to the axis) in wich the point that represents the stress state is lying. For values, so found, between zero (iso-static stress) and 1.0 (maximum stress) the material will, theoretically survive.

DRAWN AND WALL IRONED CANS

To produce the two-piece can, used for beverages and food packaging, a tin plate with a thickness of 0.3 mm is drawn to form a cup. The thickness of the wall of this cup is reduced in three steps by means of three steel rings. This so-called process of wall-ironing is illustrated in figure 4. The steel rings have a hard metal insert. A punch pushes the cup through these three rings; after the process the wall thickness is reduced to 0.1 mm. Since a large amount of cans (240 cans/minute) is produced, interruptions of the process must be avoided as much as possible. A high-wear material for the insert is demanded. To study the possibility of applying a ceramic insert, finite-element calculations were performed.

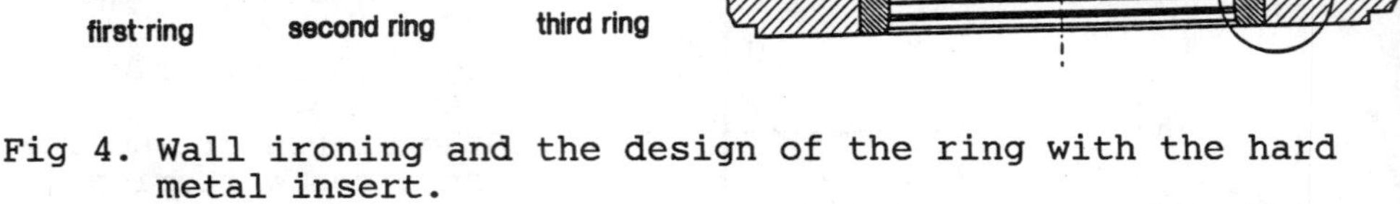

Fig 4. Wall ironing and the design of the ring with the hard metal insert.

The design of the ring and insert is shown in figure 4. To avoid tensile stresses as much as possible, the insert is shrunk in the steel housing. In previous calculations and experiments the forces between can and insert were determined. Using this results, the stresses within the entire ring were calculated. In figure 5 the calculated stress state after applying the load (without the effect of shrinking) is shown for sialon.

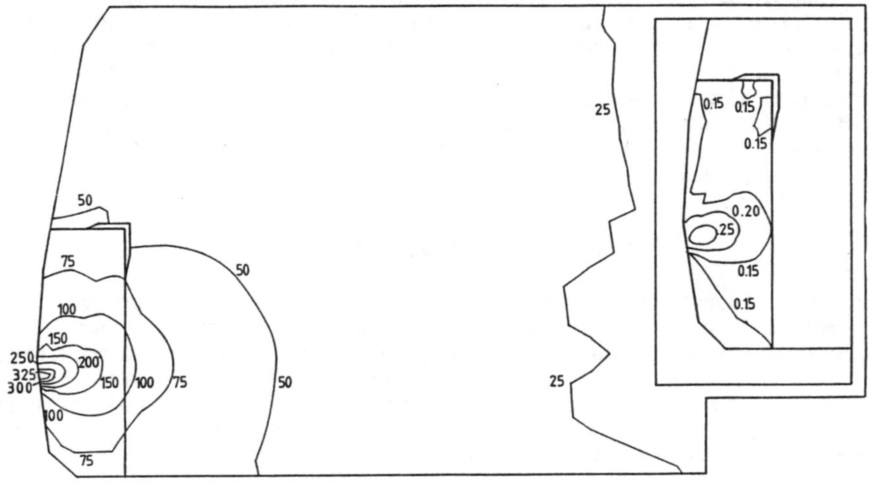

Fig 5. Huber-Hencky stresses (N/mm^2) after load. The values of the stress/strength ratio according to the Drücker-Prager criterion are given in the insert.

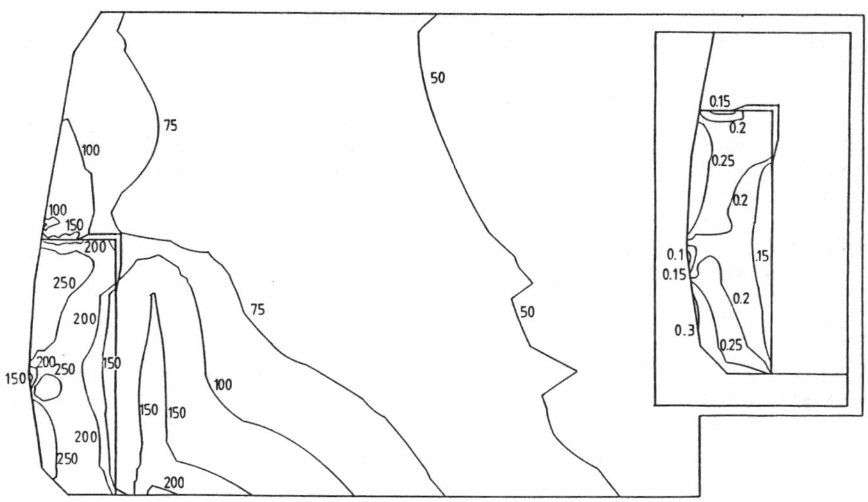

Fig 6. Huber-Hencky stresses (N/mm^2) after load and shrinkage. The values of the stress/strength ratio according to the Drücker-Prager criterion are given in the insert.

The effect of shrinkage (thermal stresses) also has been taken into account in calculating the stresses as shown in figure 6. To have an impression of the stresses related to the strength, the Drücker-Prager criterion was used (inserts in figure 5 and 6).

For the optimal shrinkage conditions, the stresses at the most important area (where the can has first contact with the ring) have largely been reduced. The stress/strength ratio even drops more pronounced. Apart from this, in our calculations it came out that no tensile stresses appeared anymore. This is very important, because machining can cause small cracks and locally the tensile strength can appear to be much lower than the value that was given as a result of flexure or tensile tests.

CONCLUSIONS

Using the finite-element method, it was possible to calculate the optimal pre-stress conditions for a ceramic insert in a steel ring that is used for wall-ironing of cans. According to the calculations tensile stresses can be avoided by pre-stressing the insert by shrinkage of the steel housing. Also in the crucial part of the ring the stresses were drastically lowered by this mechanism.

REFERENCES

1 Weibull W.A., Statistical distribution function of wide applicability. J. Appl. Mech., 1951, **18**, 293-97

2 Lamon J., Statistical approaches to failure for ceramic reliability assessment. J. Am. Cer. Soc., 1988, **71** [2], 106-12

3 Butter J.A.M., Rengersen J.,Temperature distribution and thermal stresses in refractory material. Proceedings, mathematical models for metals and materials applications, 1987, preprint p. 26.1 -26.6.

4 Drücker D.C., Prager W.,Soil mechanics and plastic analysis or limit design. J. Appl. Math., 1952, **10**, 157-65.

5 Ras H.B., Van den Hoeven J.A., Jansen E., A numerical calculation of the stress distribution during wall-ironing. Proceedings of the 2nd International Conference on Numerical Methods in Industrial Forming Processes, 1986, p. 299-304.

FRACTURE OF COMPOSITE CERAMICS*

R.G. Cooke
School of Materials Science,
University of Bath,
Bath BA2 7AY, UK

**Extended Abstract. Full paper to be submitted to British Ceramic Transactions.*

INTRODUCTION

Fibre reinforcement of brittle matrix systems offers potential improvement in toughness (ie resistance to crack propagation). One feature of such materials, and many other composites, is acoustic emission which occurs at stress levels very much below those that may be identified with ultimate failure processes (1). Similarly, heterogeneous ceramic and graphite systems show such activity (2). It has also been found that, for a very large range of composites, there appears to be a linear relationship between the strength, σ_f, and fracture toughness measured as critical stress intensity factor, K_{Ic}(3). In this paper, the relationship between toughness and strength is presented, together with acoustic emission result for a fibre reinforced systems is presented and the extent to which 'critical value' theories of strength are applicable. Some unusual Poisson ratio effects that may be due to sub-critical fracture activity are also discussed.

Acoustic Emission and Fracture Results

Results for Nicalon SiC fibre reinforced borosilicate glass (4) and carbon fibre reinforced carbon (5) show strong sub-critical acoustic activity, especially in materials where the microstructure has been 'optimized' to produce the toughest structure. Figure 1 presents information on a carbon fibre reinforced borosilicate glass as a recently determined example of this behaviour. Figure 2 presents direct (strain gauge measurements) of longitudinal versus transverse strains for such material. This behaviour, ie a change from negative to positive Poisson's ratio, has been observed in other systems (6).

Where quoted values of K_{Ic} and strength have been presented which contain data obtained on the same batches of materials, the linear relationship between their values that was observed for polymeric composites has been confirmed for the results that have been presented for ceramic matrix composites by Hasson and Fishman (7) and for carbon-carbon composites by Ford (5).

DISCUSSION

On the basis of linear analysis, the theories of fracture mechanics have predicted that failure will occur at some externally imposed stress level, the strength, when the stress intensity, K, or crack extension force, G, reach some critical value in front of a well-defined sharp flaw. In an attempt to justify the use of the measured values of these quantities for non-linear (plastic) systems the concept of the f-integral was developed. However, in all cases the form of the prediction is that linear elastic fracture mechanics (LEFM) i.e.

$$\sigma_f = YK_{Ic}\ C^{-\frac{1}{2}}$$

where YU is a geometrical constant and C is the crack size. For materials that are heterogeneous there are a number of difficulties with such analysis. Considering the specific case of fibrous composites, the following points need to be considered. Firstly, LEFM assumes the sharp crack to be immersed in a uniformly homogeneous elastic body. Clearly, the highly heterogeneous nature of a composite is specifically designed to produce uneven distribution of the external load. Secondly, the acoustic activity shows that many sub-critical events occur and these are generally associated with fracture events of matrix, interface or fibres. It is clear that the overall development of failure is a combination of very many such events. It is also true that the identification of a uniquely specified individual flaw cannot usually be made from microstructural examination and, furthermore, the fracture

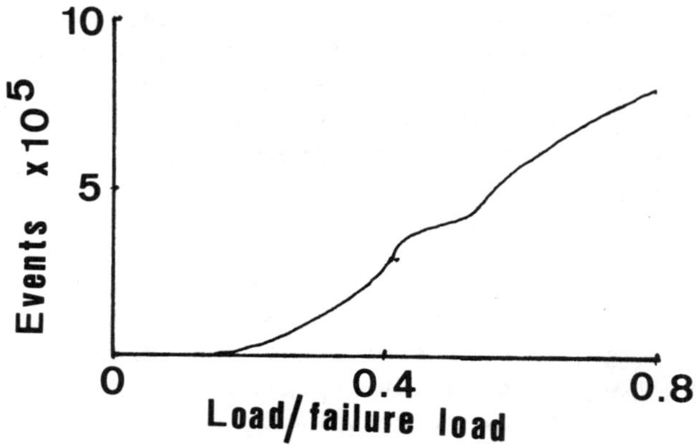

FIGURE 1. Acoustic emission

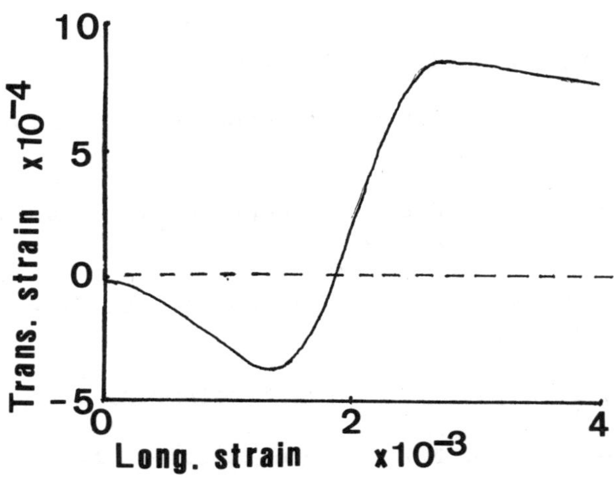

FIGURE 2. Transerse vs. longitudinal strain.

surfaces are extremely complicated, especially in optimized materials where large amounts of pull out occur. Of particular interest is the observation of changes in Poisson's ratio. At low strains, the systems behave conventionally, but at higher strains the transition to the opposite type of behaviour can only be explained by sub-critical matrix cracking. Therefore, analysis is being undertaken to examine the tolerance of such systems to the possible forms of damage . Analysis of fracture processes using microstructural input heterogeneous systems (8) may be developed but this type of approach considers the build up of separate sub-critical fracture events that combine to produce a flaw that becomes critical at a given level of stress intensity. In view of the correlation between K_c and σ_f, it is proposed that such a critical condition be replaced by a summation of microevents to a level that becomes unstable.

REFERENCES

1. Harris, B., Phillips, M.G., Guild, F.J. and Ackerman, J., Proc. 37th Ann. Conf. S.P.I., 1982, Paper 32-D.

2. Pickup, I.M., Cooke, R.G. and McEnaney, B., Science of Ceramics, 1984, **12**, 523-527.

3. Harris, B., Dorey, S.E. and Cooke, R.G., Composites Science and Technology, 1988, **31**, 121-141.

4. Ford, B., Cooke, R.G. and Newsman, S., Proc. Brit. Ceram., 1988, **39**, 229-234.

5. Ford, B., PhD Thesis, University of Bath, 1987.

6. Harris, B., Habib, F and Cooke, R.G., *to be published.*

7. Hasson, D.F. and Fishman, S.G., Proc. 9th Risø Symposium on Metallurgy and Materials Science, 1988, 391-396.

8. Cooke, R.G., Proc. Brit. Ceram., 1982, 171-180.

SEM IN-SITU BENDING EXPERIMENTS ON HIGH PERFORMANCE CERAMICS

H. Frei, C. Plappert, G. Grathwohl
Institut für Keramik im Maschinenbau,
Institut für Werkstoffkunde II,
Universität Karlsruhe, Haid-und-Neu-Str. 7, D-7500 Karlsruhe

ABSTRACT

A new developed 4-point bending device was designed for testing high-strength-ceramics in the vacuum chamber of a scanning electron microscope (SEM). Simultaneous SEM-observation of ceramic specimen during crack propagation under various loading conditions is possible and typical results are presented on a video-tape.
Controlled crack propagation processes and their dependece on the microstructure are studied on a modern sintered silicon nitride (SSN), a fine-grained HIP-alumina, a SiC-whisker reinforced alumina and a transformation toughened zirconia.

INTRODUCTION

The progress in the development of advanced structural ceramics is characterized by a remarkable increase in their strength and fracture toughness. Further improvement of these essential mechanical properties is still desirable and requires a fundamental understanding of the crack propagation process. In the new types of ceramic microstructures, e. g. in whisker-, particle-, or platelet-reinforced ceramics the relevant crack growth processes are not adequately understood. These processes are responsible, for example, for the R-curve behaviour which may be due to the formation of a process zone around the crack tip, or by a wake effect of interacting forces between the crack surfaces. Furthermore, fatigue in ceramics is a problem in toughened ceramics in particular and relies directly on the various mechanisms of increased crack resistance.
As in metals it will certainly be important to understand these effects in order to investigate the influence of crystal defects on these processes as is possible by TEM studies. In order to understand the formation and extension of the relevant micro- and macrocracks, SEM is a powerful tool because of its ample range of magnification and large depth of focus.

DESIGN OF THE TEST DEVICE

A complete description of the bending device used is given elsewhere [1], [2] so that only the main features will be mentioned here.
Using a very stiff frame and a position controlled piezo translator it was possible to obtain controlled fracture of brittle ceramic materials. This means that a crack is not spontaneously propagated through the specimen, but slowly advances micrometer for micrometer.

RESULTS

The fracture experiments are recorded by a video recorder directly connected to the SEM. At a magnification of 100x the naturally sharp pre-crack comes into view. This crack was introduced by the bridge method [3] and is about 3mm long. A magnification of more than 5000x is necessary to see the microstructural details. Some ceramic materials need thermal etching methods to reveal their microstructure (e. g. alumina or zirconia), some do not. Their microstructure is visible due to material contrast. The secondary electron yield depends on the atomic number, so that for example in a SSN material the ytterbium-rich phase brightly appears between the often needle like silicon nitride grains (Figure 1).

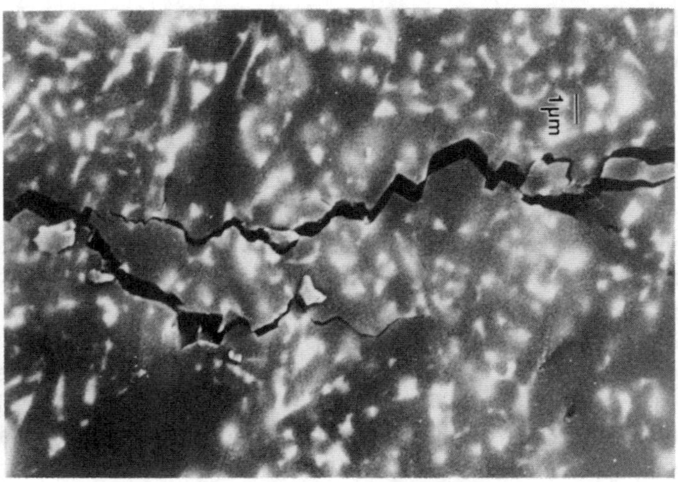

Figure 1. Microstructure of Sintered Silicon Nitride (SSN) during controlled fracture experiments.

By applying a voltage to the piezo translator the load on the specimen is slowly increased. As soon as the stress intensity factor K_I reaches its critical value K_{IC} crack propagation starts. By quickly reducing the load,

acceleration of the crack can be avoided resulting in controlled fracture. The measurement of the actual crack length *a* and the respective load *F* enables a crack resistance curve, commonly known as R-curve, to be drawn [2]. The high measured value of 7 $MPam^{\frac{1}{2}}$ for the SSN in Figure 1 can be explained by observing the fracture process. The crack propagates partly inter- and partly transcrystalline with extensive crack bridging in the crack wake.
Single large grains (Figure 2) or whole regions of the microstructure (Figure 1) bridge the crack. This results in the crack walls being under stress as far as 500 μm behind the crack tip. Therefore the stress at the crack tip is lower than calculated from the applied stress by the K-formulations.

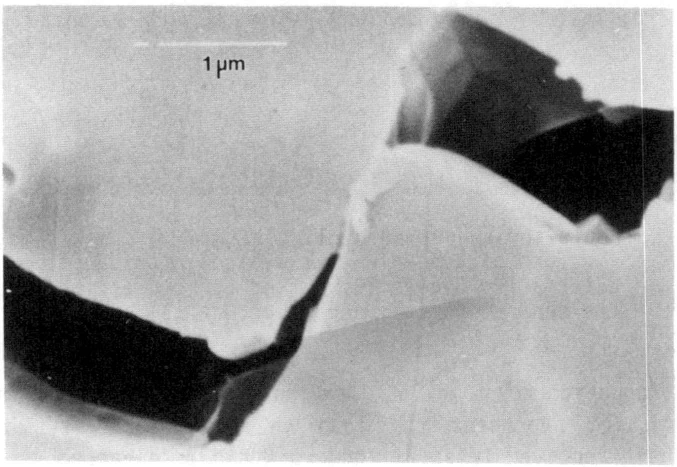

Figure 2. Heavy friction due to geometrical misfit in the crack wake of SSN.

The observed crack branching and crack bridging is not specific to silicon nitride, such effects were also found in other ceramics which have been examined. For instance SiC-whisker reinforced alumina which shows similar crack bridging effects.
This behaviour was observed to a lower extent in fine-grained alumina and even in transformation toughened zirconia.
Another advantage of the device is the possibility of direct measurement of crack velocities from 10^{-9} m/s to 10^{-4} m/s; thus v-K-curves can be directly obtained. These curves are fundamental to life time prediction of ceramic components.
Another question concernes fatigue of ceramics during cyclic loading. Almost any desired loading cycle can be realized by the used device with

frequencies up to 30 Hz.
It was shown that a specific cyclic fatigue effect does exist in SSN (Figure 3).

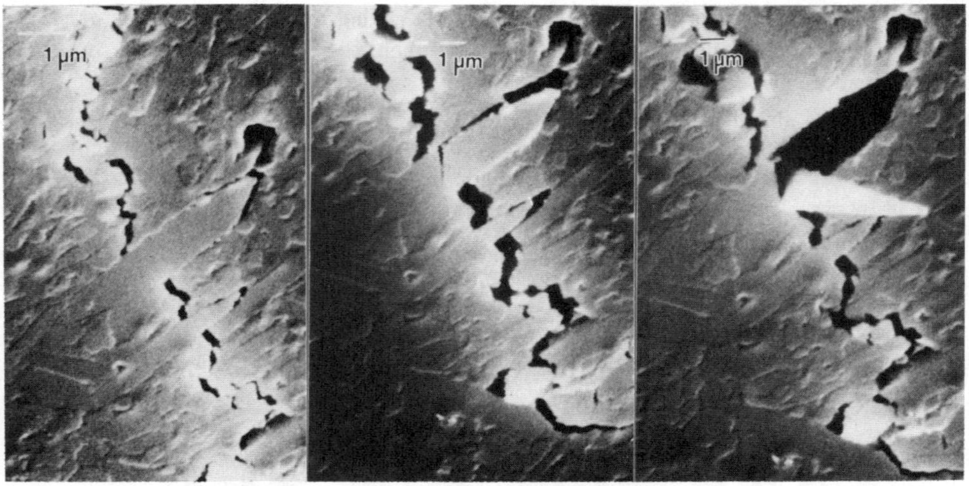

Figure 3. Photo series during cycling of SSN. A crack bridge (1) in form of a needle like silicon nitride grain is cracked after a few cycles (2). After 10^5 cycles the grain has lost its contact to the microstructure (3).

Due to the reduction of friction and interlocking effects through wear and microcracking processes the load on the crack walls is reduced. Therefore the effective stress at the crack tip is enhanced.
This means that a previously stable crack can grow and the component may fail at loadings which are only about 70 - 80 % of the statically tolerable loading.
Besides the device presented here, which is designed for swelling bending and simultaneous observation of the crack walls of long cracks, other rigs were designed and produced.
For example a device by which the tensile surface of a bend specimen can be observed in both, optical and scanning electron microscopes.
Without artificial precracking it is possible to observe the formation of a crack out from an inherent or machining flaw. With this device crack resistance values for short cracks and R-curve behaviour are unequivocally detectable.

SUMMARY

A recently developed 4-point bending device for in-situ experiments in the SEM is used to obtain controlled fracture of ceramic materials.

The experiments reveal no frontal microcrack cloud in the field of the primary crack proposed by [4] but a wake effect of interacting forces between the surfaces of the crack [5].
A specific cyclic fatigue effect could be established for SSN due to microstructural observations.

REFERENCES

1. Frei, H. and Grathwohl, G., Development of a piezo translator based bending device for in situ SEM investigations of high-performance ceramics. In Journal of Physics E: Scientific Instruments 1989, in press.

2. Plappert, C., Frei, H. and Grathwohl, G., Controlled fracture experiments on SiC-whisker reinforced alumina. In this issue.

3. Brugger, N., Zum Verhalten von Rissen in keramischen Werkstoffen unter statischer, langsam ansteigender und schwingender Belastung. Dissertation Universität Karlsruhe 1986.

4. Evans, A.G. and Faber, K.T., Crack Growth Resistance of Microcracking Brittle Materials. In J. Am. Ceram. Soc., 67 (1984), 255-60.

5. Swanson, P.L., Fairbanks, C.J., Lawn, B.R., Mai, Y. and Hockey, B.J., Crack-Interface Grain Bridging as a Fracture Resistance Mechanism in Ceramics. In J. Am. Ceram. Soc., 70 (1987), 279-89 and 289-94.

FRACTOGRAPHIC STUDY OF A SILICON NITRIDE CERAMIC

M. K. FERBER and V. J. TENNERY
OAK RIDGE NATIONAL LABORATORY
Oak Ridge, TN 37831-6064 USA

ABSTRACT

A commercially available Si_3N_4 ceramic was fractured in four-point flexure at room temperature as part of a round robin study involving 13 laboratories in the United States, Federal Republic of Germany, and Sweden. A minimum of 60 samples were fractured by each participant. For each specimen set tested, approximately 15 samples representing the five highest strength bars, the five lowest strength bars, and five bars nearest the mean of the strength distribution were chosen for fractographic examination. The nature, location, and size of the defects responsible for failure were determined. The resulting information was used to examine the applicability of strength-flaw size relationships.

Research sponsored by U.S. Department of Energy, Assistant Secretary for Conservation and Renewable Energy, Office of Transportation Systems, as part of the Ceramic Technology for Advanced Heat Engines Project for Advanced Materials Development Program under contract DE-AC05-84OR21400 with MARTIN MARIETTA ENERGY SYSTEMS, INC.

INTRODUCTION

This paper summarizes the results of fractography studies of a GTE-Wesgo SNW-1000 Si_3N_4. This work was conducted as part of an International Energy Agency (IEA) agreement between the United States, Federal Republic of Germany, and Sweden. One objective of this research was to compare the strength distributions measured on a particular material in multiple laboratories. The fractography studies were used to supplement these comparisons. The United States participants included Sohio Engineered Material Company, NASA Lewis, Garrett Turbine, Allison Gas Turbine, and GTE Laboratories. The participants from Federal Republic of Germany supplying data were ESK, KFA, MAN Technologie, KFK-University of Karlsruhe, Bosch, IWM Freiburg, and Daimler-Benz. The participating laboratories in Sweden were Swedish Silicate Research Institute, Asea Cerama, and Sandvik.

All flexure bars tested in this study had dimensions of 3.5 by 4.5 by approximately 50 mm. The inner and outer spans of the four-point bend fixture were 20 and 40 mm, respectively. Each of the 13 participating laboratories fractured a minimum of 60 samples for a total of 877. For each of these 60 specimen sets tested, approximately 15 samples representing the five highest strength bars, the five lowest strength bars, and five bars nearest the mean of the strength distribution were chosen for fractographic examination (a total of 126 samples were examined). The general location of the fracture (with respect to the loading points) was initially determined for each bar in the three groups using low power microscopy. The fracture surface associated with each bar was then examined using scanning electron microscopy (SEM).

The primary objective of these observations was to identify (1) the flaw position with respect to the load points (Fig. 1a); (2) the location of the defect with respect to the tensile surface (Fig. 1b); (3) the flaw type; and (4) the flaw dimensions including size and depth below the tensile surface (Fig. 1c). The flaw types were classified using the following designators: (1) POROSITY (including void and void clusters); (2) INCLUSION: defect associated with foreign material; (3) AGGLOMERATE: flaw attributed to differential shrinkage or exaggerated grain growth; (4) MACHINING DEFECT: critical flaw associated with surface preparation process; and (5) DEFECT: exact nature of flaw uncertain.

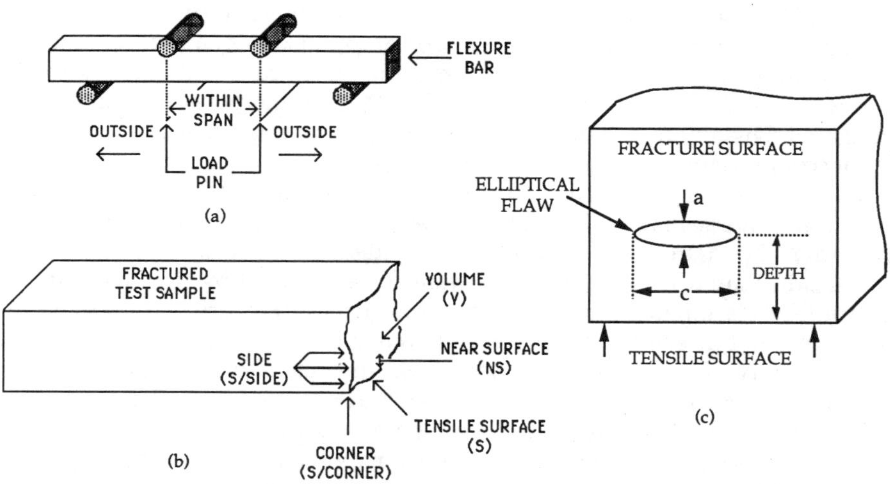

Figure 1. Schematic illustration of the designators used to describe (a) the flaw position, (b) the flaw location, and (c) the flaw size.

The resulting data were used to examine the applicability of Griffith equation relating fracture strength, σ_f, to flaw size, a. By assuming a two-dimensional elliptical flaw geometry, the Griffith expression could be represented as,

$$\sigma_f=(\phi/Y)\,K_{IC}\,a^{-1/2}, \qquad (1)$$

where K_{IC} is the fracture toughness; Y is a dimensionless term that depends upon the flaw depth and test geometry [1]; and ϕ is a dimensionless flaw shape parameter which depends only upon the a and c values (Fig. 1c) and is given by an elliptical integral [2]. Based upon information given in [2], the value of Y was taken as 1.94 and 1.77 for surface and volume flaws, respectively. In the case of volume defects, the corresponding values of flaw depth were used to correct the fracture strength quantities. In order to calculate the fracture toughness, the quantity, $(\phi/Y)\ a^{-1/2}$, was first determined for each sample. The slope of the $(\phi/Y)\ a^{-1/2}$ versus σ_f plot was then used to estimate K_{IC}. A fracture toughness value was also calculated for each sample by dividing $(\phi/Y)\ a^{-1/2}$ by the fracture strength. These data were used to examine the dependence of fracture toughness upon flaw size, flaw depth, and flaw type. Finally, the calculated K_{IC} numbers were compared with the values measured experimentally.

RESULTS AND DISCUSSION

Although three materials were examined as part of the IEA agreement, only the results for the GTE-Wesgo SNW-1000 silicon nitride will be discussed here. Data obtained for ESK SiC and ASEA silicon nitride are presented elsewhere [3].

Most fractures for the GTE material occurred within the gauge section of the bar. The low strength specimens generally broke into two pieces while high strength specimens shattered. Of the 126 samples examined, approximately 92% failed from single pores or pore clusters which were randomly distributed throughout the volume of the test sample. Most of the pores (Fig. 2a) contained elongated Si_3N_4 grains which may have formed during sintering by a vapor/condensation process. Other less predominant defects included surface damage, presumably caused by the machining process, and metallic-like inclusions. Elemental analysis of these inclusions revealed the presence of Fe, Cr, and Y. The latter element was probably derived from the Y_2O_3 sintering aid.

Another interesting microstructural feature revealed by the SEM study was intermittent dark patches along the fracture surface (Fig. 2b). Although the dark areas were not directly responsible for specimen fracture, they were often located in the vicinity of the failure initiation sites. In such cases, the corresponding fracture strength was generally lower than that obtained for a flexure bar having a similarly sized critical defect but having no dark phase present.

The development of these dark regions may have been caused by localized variations in the crystallography associated with the grain boundary phase. A previous TEM study [4] of this silicon nitride revealed both crystalline and amorphous phases in the grain boundary region. The crystalline phase apparently nucleated at isolated points in the microstructure and then grew as a single crystal over a fairly large region containing numerous silicon nitride grains. Consequently, the dark phase observed in the present study may have formed via this crystallization process.

The application of Eq. 1 to the experimental data is illustrated in Fig. 3. The slope of the $(\phi/Y)\ a^{-1/2}$ versus σ_f plot, which was determined using a linear regression analysis, gave a fracture toughness value of 6.6 MPa $(m)^{1/2}$. Due to scatter in the data, the 95% confidence interval was fairly large [4.5 to 15 MPa

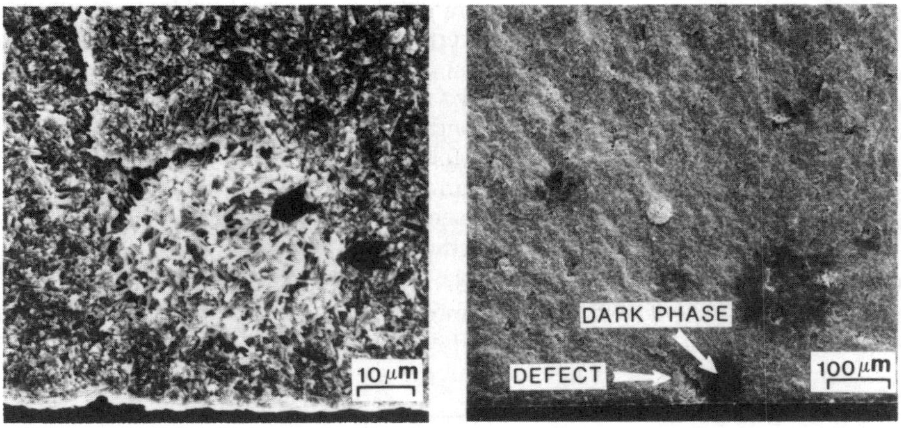

Figure 2. Typical failures in GTE silicon nitride generally originated at large pores containing silicon nitride crystals (a). Fracture origins were often located in the vicinity of dark regions in the microstructure (b).

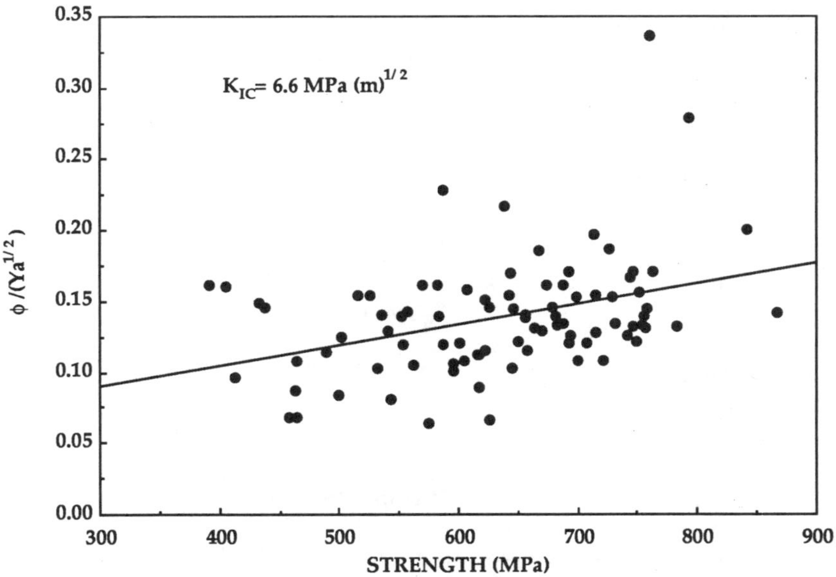

Figure 3. The relationship between flaw size and fracture strength was used to estimate fracture toughness.

(m)$^{1/2}$]. The fracture toughness determined from indentation-crack methods [5,6] was 8.8 ± 2.0 MPa (m)$^{1/2}$. The uncertainty associated with the calculated toughness value could be attributed to several factors. First, there was some uncertainty associated with the flaw size measurements particularly when failure originated at pore clusters. Secondly, the presence of the dark phase noted previously was apparently responsible for variations in the local fracture resistance. Assuming that this phase formed from a crystallization process, one might expect residual stresses to be present. Such stresses were not accounted for in the fracture model. Finally, the fracture toughness calculated for the individual samples was found to increase with increasing flaw size (Fig. 4). This behavior suggests that either the flaw model (Eq. 1) was inadequate or that K_{IC} exhibited a real dependence upon defect size.

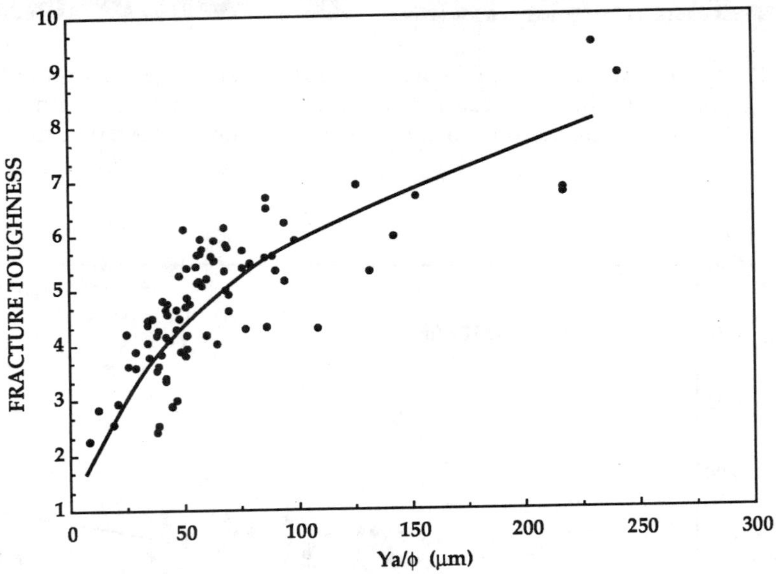

Figure 4. The calculated fracture toughness for the GTE material was a function of the defect size.

CONCLUSIONS

The most common defects associated with the GTE silicon nitride consisted of 20-100 μm diameter pores containing elongated silicon nitride crystals. These pores were distributed uniformly throughout the bulk of the material. The calculation of the fracture toughness from the $(\phi/Y)\ a^{-1/2}$ versus σ_f plot gave an average value of 6.6 MPa (m)$^{1/2}$. However, the K_{IC} values determined from the individual fracture strength and flaw size data were found to increase from 2 to 9.2 MPa (m)$^{1/2}$ as the effective defect size [$(Y/\phi)\ a^{1/2}$] increased from 10 to 250 μm. The toughness determined from direct indentation-crack measurements [8.8 ±

2.0 MPa $(m)^{1/2}$] was comparable to the K_{IC} values associated with the large critical flaws. Such behavior suggests that the effective fracture resistance decreased as the defect size became smaller. Reasons for this relationship are unclear. A second possibility is that the flaw model was inadequate.

ACKNOWLEDGMENTS

This research was conducted under Subtask 4, Mechanical Properties of Structural Ceramics, of the International Energy Agency (IEA) Annex II agreement entitled,"Implementing Agreement for a Programme of Research and Development on High Temperature Materials for Automotive Engines." Laboratories in the United States, the Federal Republic of Germany, and Sweden participated in this joint effort. The organization in each country responsible for the research was the Department of Energy in the United States, the Kernforschungsanlage Jülich GmbH (KFA-PLR) for the Bundesministerium für Forschung und Technologie (BMFT) in the Federal Republic of Germany, and the Styrelsen für Teknisk Utveckling (STU) in Sweden. The person and organization in each country responsible for organizing and overseeing the research was Dr. V. J. Tennery at the Oak Ridge National Laboratory in the United States, Dr. D. Munz at the Universität Karlsruhe (Institut für Zuverlässigkeit und Schadenskunde in Maschinenbau) in the Federal Republic of Germany, and Dr. R. Pompe at the Swedish Institute for Silicate Research in Sweden. Special thanks are also expressed to P. F. Becher and J. I. Federer for reviewing the manuscript and D. D. Conger for assembling the final version for printing.

REFERENCES

1. Evans, A. G. and Tappin, G. , Proc. Br. Ceram. Soc., 1972, **20**, 275-97.

2. Sung, J. and Nicholson, P. S., Strength improvement of yttria-partially-stabilized zirconia by flaw elimination. J. Am. Ceram. Soc., 1988, **71**, 788-95.

3. Ferber, M. K., Fractography analysis of silicon nitride and silicon carbide structural ceramics. ORNL Technical Report, Oak Ridge, TN, June 1989.

4. Nolan, T. A., Microstructural characterization of ceramic materials. Presented at the DOE/ORNL Advanced Materials Bimonthly Meeting, Washington, DC, June, 1988.

5. Cook, R. and Lawn, B. R., A modified indentation toughness technique. J. Am. Ceram. Soc. Comm, 1983, **11**, 200-1.

6. Evans, A. G., Fracture toughness: the role of indentation techniques. In Fracture Mechanics Applied to Brittle Materials, ed. S. W. Freiman, ASTM Spec. Tech. Publ. No. 678, 1979, pp. 112-35.

ITERATIVE STRENGTH DEVELOPMENT OF SLIP CAST Si_3N_4

K.M. LINDE, M. PERSSON, R. POMPE, S. KARLSSON AND R. CARLSSON
Swedish Ceramic Institute
Box 5403, S-402 29 Göteborg, Sweden

ABSTRACT

The mechanical properties of four batches of slip cast silicon nitride were evaluated. Iterative development of the powder processing, slip casting and sintering techniques led to an increase in average strength at room temperature from 570 MPa for the 1st batch to 790 for the 4th. Fractographic studies showed how the type and size of fracture origins changed with the fracture strength. For high strength specimens (>800 MPa) the fractures mainly originated from Si_3N_4-agglomerates (20-70 µm), but also from spherical pores. None of the fracture causing defects were smaller than 20 µm. Elimination of defects larger than 40 µm would probably be sufficient to give strength values above 800 MPa for all the specimens.

INTRODUCTION

To obtain the strength, reliability and reproducibility required for ceramics in advanced structural applications, an overall view of the fabrication procedure, from powder manufacturing to mechanical testing is necessary. Since every fabrication parameter has to be optimized a certain level of knowledge and experience is required in each fabrication step. One single mistake in one of the subprocesses might have strongly detrimental consequences for the material properties. Technology development for fabrication of reliable ceramics has been successfully achieved by an iterative approach (1, 2, 3). In this paper progress in the iterative process development for slip cast silicon nitride is described.

EXPERIMENTAL

Powder Processing and Slip Casting: Two different commercial silicon nitride powders were used in this study: LC12, H C Starck for sample A and E10, UBE Industries for samples B and C. As sintering aids 5.56% yttrium oxide (Finest, H C Starck) and 1.85% aluminium oxide (A16SG, Alcoa) were used.

The powder batches were mixed and homogenized in a two step process, by ball milling in a polyethylene jar with silicon nitride milling media. First, the powder mixtures were milled in ethanol for 70 hours. After evaporation of the solvent the powders were dispersed in water using lignosulphonate (Wanin, Holmens Bruk, Sweden). The highly concentrated slips (65 wt-%) were homogenized overnight.

Sample A can be considered as a baseline material since none of the processing steps have been optimized in order to minimize the defect size. The fabrication method for LC12 seems to yield a powder of less suitable morphology for slip casting and of too high specific surface area (approx 20 m^2/g). The E10-powder was used for samples B and C, to minimize the defects by giving a more dense and uniform green body microstructure. For sample B the ball milled slurry was sieved through a 10 µm cloth prior to the evaporation of the solvent. Plates measuring 50*50*5 mm^3 were produced by solid casting. The processing of materials B and C differed both in the sieving step and the casting technique. To avoid contamination after sieving, slip C was sieved immediately before casting. However, in this fabrication step, the slip is highly concentrated, which made it necessary to change from 10 µm to 20 µm sieves to enable the slip to pass easily through the sieve. When solid casting is practised, planar cavities may occur in the centre of the plate caused by two consolidating layers growing together. This type of large defect was eliminated when fabricating material C using drain casting. Circular plates with a diameter of 90 mm and a thickness of 5 mm were drain cast. Two batches, C1 and C2, were produced in this way.

Sintering: The issues addressed in optimizing the sintering procedure were concerned with the control of sintering atmosphere, selection and handling of the protective powder bed and handling, pretreatment and control of the dimensional stability of the green bodies. All materials were sintered in a horizontal graphite resistance furnace (Balzer, Pfeiffer).

Thermogravimetric studies (Harrop TG-716 thermobalance) have shown that both the green bodies and the Si_3N_4 protective powder reabsorb a considerable amount of moisture during storage. A degassing step at 800°C for 2 hours in vacuum has proved necessary. Also, a separate heat treatment of the Si_3N_4 protective powder has been needed in order to avoid attack on the specimen surface. A low quality Si_3N_4 powder has been used and recycled with only a minor loss of bed material. A smooth sintered surface could be obtained by coating the green bodies with BN powder and by suitable addition of SiO_2 to the powder bed. By optimizing the packing density and thickness of the powder bed the slip cast circular discs could be densified without deformation. A typical sintering cycle involves a degassing step at 800°C and densification step at 1820°C. The hold time at temperature depends on the amount of material sintered which will control the build-up of temperature gradients.

Mechanical Testing: Mechanical tests were performed with respect to fracture strength, hardness and fracture toughness at room temperature. Modulus of rupture bars were diamond sawed and polished (3 µm cloth) from the densified shapes, most of them to measure 3.5*3.0*50 mm^3. The samples were tested in 4-point flexural mode with a crosshead speed of 0.5 mm/min and a 40/20 (mm) fixture. The modulus of rupture data were analysed with Weibull statistics. To study the nature of the fracture origins, all fracture surfaces were examined by scanning electron microscopy (SEM). Hardness and fracture toughness were measured by Vickers indentation at a load of 10 kg. The surfaces were polished to a 1/4-µm diamond cloth finish to obtain strain free surfaces with easily measured indents and cracks. The fracture toughness was calculated according to a method described elsewhere (4). Six to ten indents were measured in each material.

RESULTS AND DISCUSSION

An increase in the average strength of about 100 MPa was obtained for each new material generation (Table 1). Comparison of samples A and B shows that the inferior powder morphology and the improved sintering technique have resulted in a denser material with increased strength. Elimination of defects by sieving and optimization of the slip casting led to a further increase in the average strength for sample C.

TABLE 1
Results from mechanical testing and density measurements

Material	A	B	C1	C2
Average strength [MPa]	572 ± 32	673 ± 198	793 ± 47	789 ± 118
Weibull Modulus	20 ± 6	3 ± 1	17 ± 6	8 ± 2
Number of Samples	10	13	8	22
K_{IC} [MPa $m^{1/2}$]	6.6 ± 0.3	5.9 ± 0.1	6.2 ± 0.1	6.5 ± 0.5
Hardness (HV_{10}) [GPa]	12.8 ± 0.1	14.8 ± 0.3	14.4 ± 0.3	15.5 ± 0.3
Number of indents	8	9	6	10
Relative Density [%]	92.7	99.4	99.5	99.4

The Griffith-Irwin fracture equation: $\sigma_c = K_{Ic} / (Y\ c^{1/2})$ (1)
relates the fracture strength σ_c to the fracture toughness K_{Ic} and the crack radius c. The location and shape of the crack determine the constant Y. As the size of the processing related flaws decreases, the strength increases and approaches a maximum level where it is controlled by the grain structure. At this strength level the grains themselves may act as critical flaws (5). The fracture toughness was approximately the same for all the materials. The highest strength values for materials B and C were also similar (1038 and 995 MPa respectively). Since the grain structures are similar, fracture strengths above 1000 MPa must be obtainable for both material B and C. The increase in average strength for material C was caused by elimination of relatively large defects, which was also shown by the fractographic examination of the samples.

The strength was generally high for both material B and C in relation to the measured defect sizes. Calculation of the critical flaw size for a specific fracture strength and toughness, in accordance with equation 1, provides that the fracture origin can be referred to as a crack of a certain size and geometry. The real flaws are of all shapes from sharp to spherical and are randomly located throughout the structure. Even though the defects in most cases are easily identified by SEM it is seldom obvious which is the fracture initiating crack and how to make an accurate measurement of its radius. However, the flaws can be divided into different categories, as the critical flaw size differs between the defect types. The different flaw types have to be distinguished to understand the reason for their appearance and to determine which flaws are the most detrimental to the fracture strength. The fractographic study showed that the fractures were caused by three main types of defects which could be related either to contaminants, directly to the slip casting procedure or to density variations in the green body microstructure. The latter was by far the most common and can be related to various fabrication steps from the manufacturing of the powder to the drying of the slip cast shapes. An inhomogeneous density of the powder compact results in the formation of pores or porous regions during sintering. Differential sintering of Si_3N_4-agglomerates relative to their surrounding causes voids and internal cracks (5,6).

The fracture behaviour for material A was controlled by the porous structure of the material. Pores could be seen all over the fracture surfaces and the fractures in all cases originated from voids with diameters ranging from 50 to 100 μm. These caused low strength with little scatter in the strength values (Table 1) due to the uniform pore distribution.

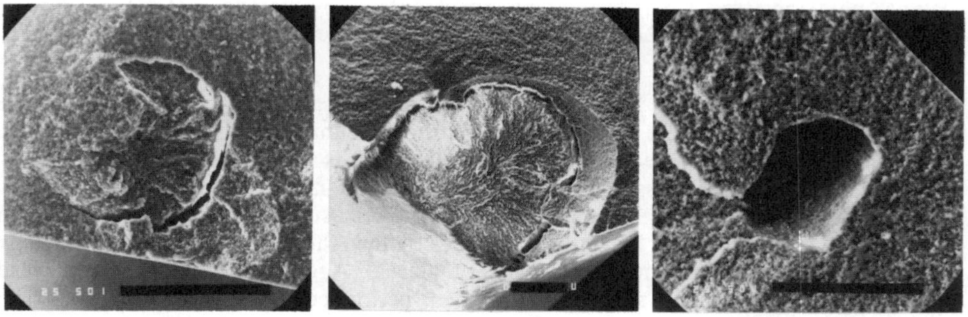

a. B, σ_F=503 MPa Si_3N_4-granule

b. B, σ_F=267 MPa Fe-rich inclusion

c. B, σ_F=659 MPa Void caused by organic particle

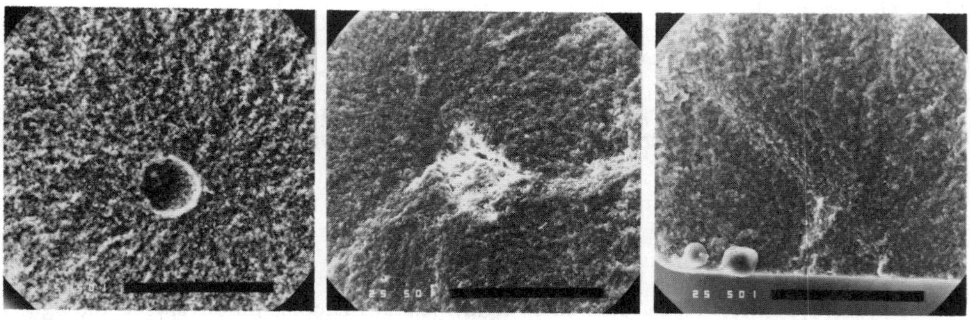

d. B, σ_F=1038 MPa Spherical pore 100 μm from the edge

e. C1, σ_F=795 MPa Si_3N_4-agglomerate 150 μm from the edge

f. C2, σ_F=995 MPa Si_3N_4-agglomerate

Figure 1. Some fracture origins for materials B and C, (bar = 100 μm).

For material B the strength values were scattered from 267 to 1038 MPa. For low strength specimens (<700 MPa) most of the fractures were caused by Si_3N_4-granules or by contaminants (Figure 1a-c). The 10 μm sieving must have been followed by contamination during the subsequent processing steps. Voids formed during combustion of organic particles and fibres were the most common among the defects related to contamination but metal inclusions and other inorganic inclusions also occurred. The high strength specimens of material B (>700MPa) failed because of agglomerates (40-100 μm) or spherical voids (40-50 μm) caused by entrapped air in the slip (Figure 1d).

For material C, an increase in average strength of 120 MPa was obtained and the scatter in the strength was smaller than for material B. However it was still unacceptably high, particularly in sample C2 where a number of voids formed by combustion of organic fibres and particles were found to be responsible for fractures at low stresses. Since the slip was sieved immediately prior to slip casting, contamination must have occurred during this operation. A further development of the procedure prior to slip casting will be required in the next iteration. More than 80 % of the fractures originated from voids and internal cracks caused by agglomerates (Figure 1e-f). None of the fracture causing defects were smaller than 20 μm in diameter even when located in the tensile surface or very close to it.

CONCLUSIONS

Strength values above 1000 MPa are obtainable in slip cast Si_3N_4-bodies. None of the fracture causing defects were smaller than 20 μm and elimination of defects larger than 40-50 μm would probably be sufficient to get 800 MPa as a minimum strength value.

Fractures at high stresses (>800 MPa) are caused mainly by Si_3N_4-agglomerates. Differential sintering of agglomerates relative to their surrounding causes voids and internal cracks (defect sizes: 20-70μm). Fractures at low stresses (<600 MPa) are mainly caused by contaminants and large Si_3N_4-granules. Agglomerates are formed and contamination occurs after sieving even when performed immediately prior to slip casting. A further development of the slip casting procedure is required.

In summary it has been shown that an iterative approach involving all processing steps is essential in the development of brittle materials.

ACKNOWLEDGEMENTS

This work was supported financially by the Swedish Board for Technical Development. The authors also express their gratitude to Dr. Ian Brown for revision of the English text.

REFERENCES

1. Richerson, D.W., Smyth, J.R. and Styhr, K.H., Material improvement through iterative process development. Ceram. Eng. and Sci. Proc., 1983, **4**, 841-52.

2. Levine, S.R., Dutta, S., Freedman, M.R., Sanders, W.A. and Shaw, N.J., Improved processing of SiC and Si_3N_4. Proc. 24th Automotive Tech. Dev. Contractors, Coord. Meeting, Dearborn, MI, October 27-30, 1986, pp. 299-311.

3. Yeh, H., Fang, H7. and Teng, K., Process improvement for Si_3N_4 for heat engine applications. Ceram. Eng. Sci. Proc., 1988, **9**, 1333-42.

4. Nihaara K., Morena R. and Hasselman P.D.H., Indentation fracture toughness of brittle materials for Palmqvist cracks., Fracture Mechanics of Ceramics, 1984, 5, pp. 97-105.

5. Pasto A.E., Neil J.T. and Quackenbush C.L., Microstructural effects influencing strength of sintered silicon nitride., Ultrastructure Processing of Ceramics Glasses and Composites, ed. L.L. Hench and D.R. Ulrich, John Wiky & Sons, New York, 1984, pp. 476-89

6. Lange F.F., Processing-related fracture origins I-III., J. Am. Ceram. Soc., 1982, **66**, pp. 396-408.

STRENGTH - VOLUME - GEOMETRY: QUANTITATIVE RELATIONS FOR VARIOUS COMPONENT DERIVED STRENGTH TESTS

LUDWIG WEILER, VOLKER HOFFESOMMER
Asea Brown Boveri, Corporate Research Heidelberg
P.O.Box 101332, 6900 Heidelberg, FRG

ABSTRACT

Strength of ceramics is determined by pecularities of the production process (resulting in a particular size distribution of large microstructural inhomogeneities) and it depends on volume. For extrapolation of component strength from practical test data the 'effective volumes' and 'effective surface areas' are needed. These figures are calculated for strength tests on the prototype component 'tube', the hoop test, the C-ring test and the Cyl-Seg (cylinder segment) bend test on the basis of the Weibull theory. The ratio 'wall thickness/radius' and the size are taken as free parameters. Experimental strength data on Na-beta-alumina tubes by the above methods are in excellent agreement with the theoretically derived values.

INTRODUCTION

Strength is inversely proportional to the square root of the size of large microstructural inhomogeneities. The frequency distribution of the size of these flaws determines the scatter of the strength data and the volume dependence of strength. Size and size distribution of microstructural inhomogeneities are determined by particularities of the production process, i.e. the powder preparation, shaping and sintering conditions. Reliable strength data for design and for process development are at best obtained from tests on specimen, which have run through this particular process, i.e. on components or parts of components. For design strength tests should further be close to loading in service which may involve tensile stresses throughout the bulk or only parts of the surface. In order to correlate strength data from different tests and to extrapolate the component strength from test data, the volume and surface area dependence of the particular test data are to be known.

We are concerned with the component prototype 'tube' and the thus derived strength tests hoop test (1), C-ring test (1) and Cyl-Seg (cylinder segment) bend test (2). The hoop test in principle is a tensile test, the strength being determined by bulk flaws. The other tests are bend tests, the strength being determined by surface flaws and/or bulk flaws near the surface.

METHODS AND EXPERIMENTAL

The base of the calculations is the weakest link theory according to Weibull: The failure probability, normalized to σ_o (a strength value independent of volume and loading geometry) and to the volume of the test specimen V (3):

$$P = 1 - \exp\left[- \left(\frac{\sigma_{max}}{\sigma_o}\right)^m V \int \left(\frac{\sigma(V)}{\sigma_{max}}\right)^m \frac{dV}{V} \right],$$

σ_{max} being the maximum tensile stress and $\sigma(V)$ the stress distribution in the specimen. The integral is referred to as the relative effective volume 'V_{eff}/V'. The dependence of V_{eff}/V on the Weibull modulus is obvious. The strength is inversely proportional to $(V_{eff}/V)^{1/m}$. Concerning the 'effective surface area' and the surface strength the volume related terms are simply to be replaced by surface related terms.

For the calculation of the integrals the main tensile stress (uniaxial) is considered only. An effect of flaw orientation is neglected, because nearly all microstructural inhomogeneities have threedimensional extensions of the same magnitude. Details of the solution of the integrals are not discussed.

The experiments are done on Na-beta-alumina tubes, r_o = 12.5 mm, r_i = 11.2 mm, produced by dry powder preparation. The hoop tests were done on the whole tubes and on 45 mm long parts of the tubes. The specimens for the C-ring test had a width of 10 mm. The Cyl-Seg bend tests were done in 3-point loading using span widths of 10 and 20 mm and specimen thickness h of 0.3 - 1 mm.

RESULTS AND DISCUSSION

V_{eff}/V of the tube derived tests are compared to those of the pure tensile test (of constant cross section between the grips) and of the worldwide 'standard' bend test on bars of rectangular cross section: V_{eff}/V of the hoop test is close to that of the tensile test. V_{eff}/V of the C-ring tests, in the compression and in the tension version being slightly different due to the nonlinear stress distribution along the wall thickness, lie between the 'standard' 4- and 3-point bend test. This is due to the variation of the bending moment along the specimen length between the grips being in the same order. V_{eff}/V of the Cyl-Seg 4-point bend test is only a little lower than the C-ring test, but destinctively lower than the 'standard' 4-point bend test; the difference to the 'standard' bend test is due to the circle segment cross section.
The V_{eff}/V ratio of the extremes, the tensile test and the Cyl-Seg 3-point bend test, increases from ~100 at $m = 4$ to ~10000 at $m = 30$.
V_{eff}/V is an important item as it indicates the representitiveness of the strength data with respect to specimen volume. The tensile and the hoop test include at least nearly the whole volume, the Cyl-Seg 3-point bend test at $m > 5$ less than 1 %, at $m > 12$ less than 0.1 % of the specimen volume.

The effect of the different tests on the extrapolated strength of $V_{eff} = 1$ (corresponding to a uniaxial tensile test on a specimen of $V = 1$), which is

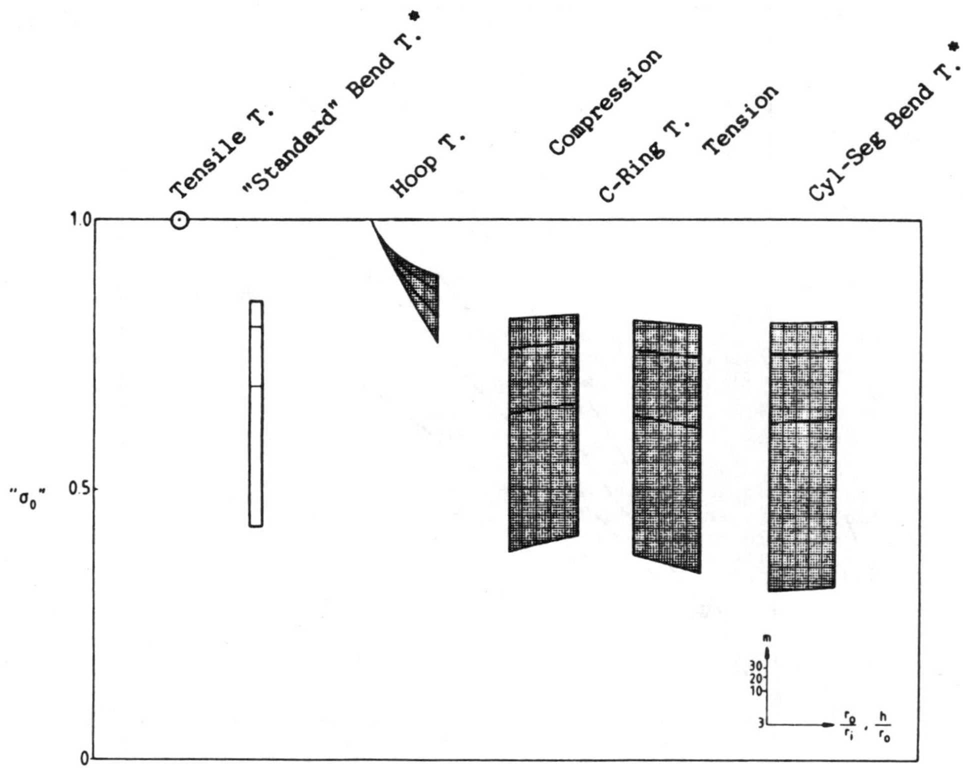

Figure 1. $(V_{eff}/V)^{1/m}$ or σ_o of the specimen unit volume (V=1): value fields as functions of m (vertical axis of the value field; lines for m = 3, 10, 20, 30 from the bottom to the top) and r_o/r_i, h/r_o (horizontal axis; r_o/r_i for hoop and C-ring tests: 1.01 - 1.50 from left to right; h/r_o for the Cyl-Seg bend test: 0.01 - 1.0); * 4-point loading, span ratio 1:2.

proportional to $(V_{eff}/V)^{1/m}$, is shown in Fig. 1; the value fields of each test include the influence of m (vertical axis of the field) and r_o/r_i or h/r_o (horizontal axis). The σ_o of the hoop test is equally affected by the variation of m and the variation of the ratio r_o/r_i. This is in contrast to the bend tests, C-ring test and the Cyl-Seg bend test (and the 'standard' bend test), in the case of which the Weibull modulus has a far more pronounced effect on σ_o.

Experimental strength data of Na-beta-alumina tubes, measured by the hoop test on the whole tubes and on parts of the tube, by the C-ring test and by the Cyl-Seg 3-point bend test of variable length and thickness are compared to the above (theoretical) results. In Fig. 2 the logarithms of the characteristic strength of each test are plotted vs. the logarithm of the ratio 'V_{eff} (hoop test, whole tube) / V_{eff} (actual test)' using the V_{eff} on the basis of the actual tests. The σ_c values do not lie on a straight line as would have been expected on a simple 'strength - effective volume'

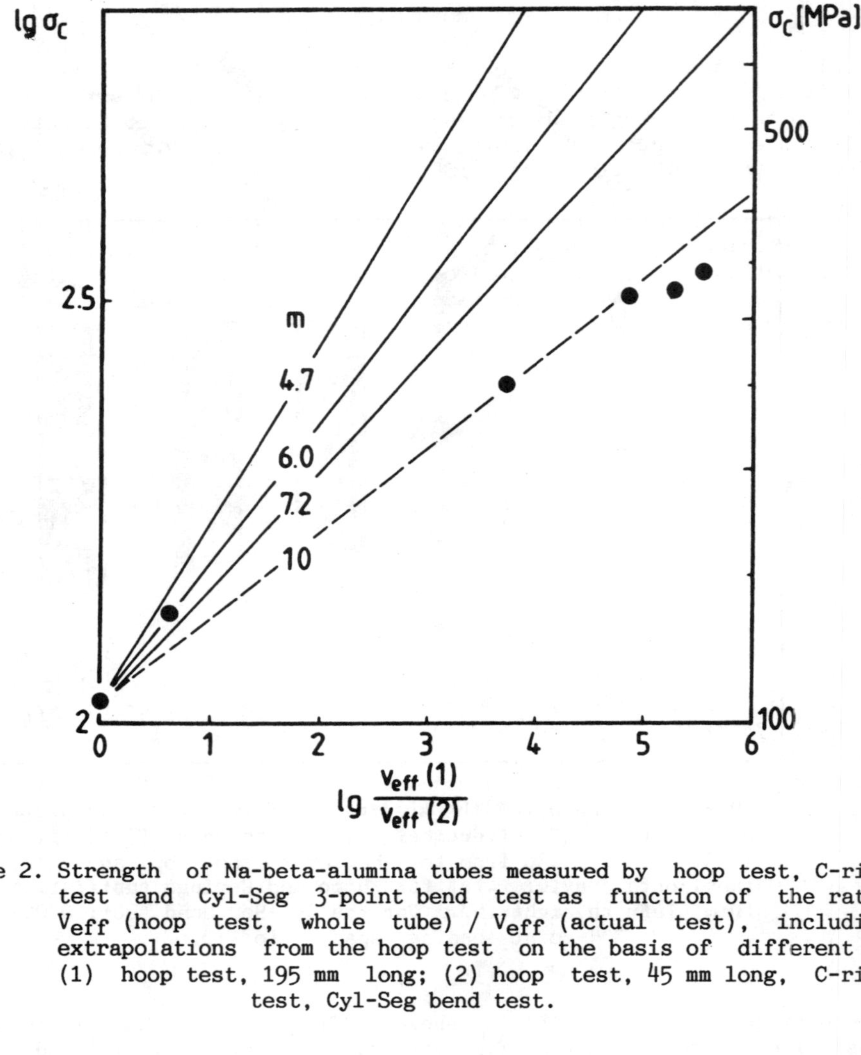

Figure 2. Strength of Na-beta-alumina tubes measured by hoop test, C-ring test and Cyl-Seg 3-point bend test as function of the ratio V_{eff} (hoop test, whole tube) / V_{eff} (actual test), including extrapolations from the hoop test on the basis of different m. (1) hoop test, 195 mm long; (2) hoop test, 45 mm long, C-ring test, Cyl-Seg bend test.

relation. The C-ring test and Cyl-Seg bend test data lie far below the lines extrapolated from the hoop test on the basis of the Weibull modulus and its 90 % confidence level values of the hoop test. - The slope of the lines is 1/m. - But by extrapolation using the Weibull moduli of the C-ring and Cyl-Seg bend test data there is an excellent agreement of the extrapolation and the experimental data. This result illustrates the reason for the nonlinear relation of the lg σ_c and the lg (V_{eff} ratio): different m in hoop tests and bend tests. The different m indicate a nonlinear size distribution, more precisely a nonlinear decay of the size distribution towards the large size end, of the large microstructural inhomogeneities.

CONCLUSIONS

Excellent agreement of the calculated 'strength - effective volume' relations of the three different tube based strength tests hoop test, C-ring test, Cyl-Seg bend test and experimental results on Na-beta-alumina was achieved taking the Weibull moduli of the particular bend tests into account; the V_{eff} ratio being > 10^5!

This result confirms the Weibull concept of the strength dependence on volume and loading geometry. The σ_0 value as part of this concept is only a normalization factor without a real counterpart. This is thought to be due to the nonlinear flaw distribution resulting in m variation on a drastic change of effectively loaded volume.

ACKNOWLEDGEMENT

We thank H. Riedel for support and discussion and Ph. Herschel for performing the strength tests. This work was supported by the 'Bundesminister für Forschung und Technologie'.

REFERENCES

1. Tan, S. R., May, G. J., McLaren, J. R., Tappin, G., Davidge, R. W., Strength controlling flaws in beta-alumina. Trans. J. Brit. Ceram. Soc., 1980, **79**, 120-7

2. Weiler, L., Cylinder-segment bend test, a new strength measuring technique for ceramic tubes and cylinders. In Science of Ceramics 14, ed. D. Taylor, The Institute of Ceramics, Stoke-on-Trent, 1988, pp. 621-5

3. Johnson, C. A., Fracture statistics in design and application. 49th Meeting of the AGARD, Koeln, 8.-10.10.1979, 1980, **276**, 20-1 - 20-16

INFLUENCE OF NONLINEAR ELASTIC EFFECTS ON THE CRACK RESISTANCE OF CERAMICS

F.E. BURESCH

IRW/KFA, Jülich, West Germany

Institute for Computer Applications, Stuttgart, West Germany

Abstract

Ceramics with a nonlinear nonelastic deformation during loading show a rising crack resistance vs stable crack propagation. This is due to the residual elastic strain energy which is stored in the damage zone with substantial microcracking. The effects are explained theoretically and experimentally.

1. Scope of the presentation

Crack growth in materials is governed by damage which takes place in front of a critical crack due to stress redistribution processes [1]. In the case of elastic damage which arises in brittle materials such as ceramics or rocks it was recognised that microcracking is the main damage mechanism. Thus a damage zone is built up in front of a stationary as well as a propagating crack during loading a body.

Analytical modelling of the crack front phenomena were carried out in comparison with the Dugdale modell [1]. The size of the damage zone and the cohesive strength can easily be measured via the dependence of the stress intensity factor (SIF) on the notch root radius. In addition experimental observations with photoelastic coatings [2], small angle x-ray scattering [3], residual stress analysis [4] and microcrack decoration [5] makes evident that damage arises ahead or at the crack front and produces residual stresses due to a density reduction of the material. Thus radial compression stresses arises inside the damage zone and reverses tangential tension stresses on the surface including the fracture surface. It was found experimentally that the inner surface of the damage zone is also free from normal tension stresses [1,2].

It is the aim of the present paper to show that the self consistent residual stress state of the damage zone is the effective driving force of crack propagation in brittle materials. Especially in the case of remote microcracking and a large damage zone the work to drive the frontal damage zone through the body is substantially converted in residual strain energy. It is recognized that this energy characterizes the load bearing capacity and the flow tolerance of a high tough ceramic. This is confirmed experimentally.

2. Energy release rate with elastic damage

We will start with considerations about the residual strain energy in the dilated damage zone which arises in the outer layers of a bend bar if the local SIF on microcrack nuclei reaches critical values [1]. We assume a constant reduced Young's modulus E_m in the microcracked damage zone with a constant cohesion strength S_m which corresponds to a constant yield strength in plastically deformed metals. Then the strain energy density is constant whereas in the elastically deformed core the strain energy density is inhomogeneous distributed. Thus these two quantities are given as (Fig. 1)

$$\frac{S_m^2}{2E_m} \quad \text{and} \frac{S_m^2}{2E} \quad \frac{y^2}{\xi^2 h^2} \tag{1}$$

respectively, where $2h$ is the height of the beam with $0 \leq \xi \leq 1$. Then the total stored elastic strain energy of the beam of thickness B and length a which is inelastically loaded up to a constant load at point G in Fig. 2 is given after integration as

$$U_{inel} = \frac{BS_m^2 ha}{3E}(1 + \frac{\psi}{h} \quad \frac{3E - E_m}{E_m}) \tag{2}$$

where the size of the damage zone is given as $2\psi = 2h(1 - \xi)$.

Contrary after pure idealistic elastic loading of the beam up to the constant load at point E, the stored elastic strain energy is given as

$$U_{el} = \frac{BS_m^2 ha}{3E}(1 + 2\frac{\psi}{h}) \tag{3}$$

Thus the elastic strain energy of the inelastically loaded beam is higher by the residual strain energy which is still stored in the beam after unloading and is given with eqn. (1-3) (Fig. 1-3) as

$$U_r = U_{inel} - U_{el} = \frac{BS_m^2 a}{E} \quad \psi \quad \frac{E - E_m}{E_m} = BS_m a\psi(\epsilon_m - \epsilon) = \frac{BaS_m}{2}(u_m - u) \tag{4}$$

Deformation of an elasto-plastic beam

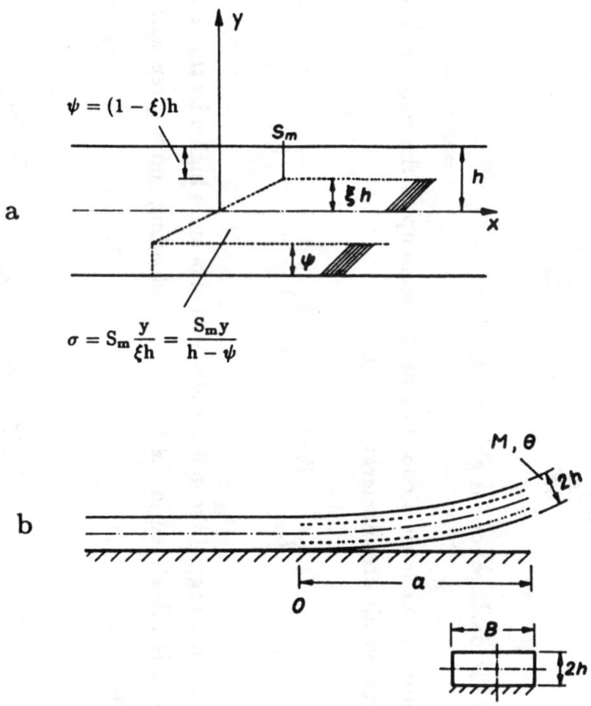

a Stress distribution across the beam depth with the regions of elastic and plastic bending
b Rotation of an elasto-plastic beam

Fig. 1

Load-displacement curve with incremental crack growth Δa at constant load

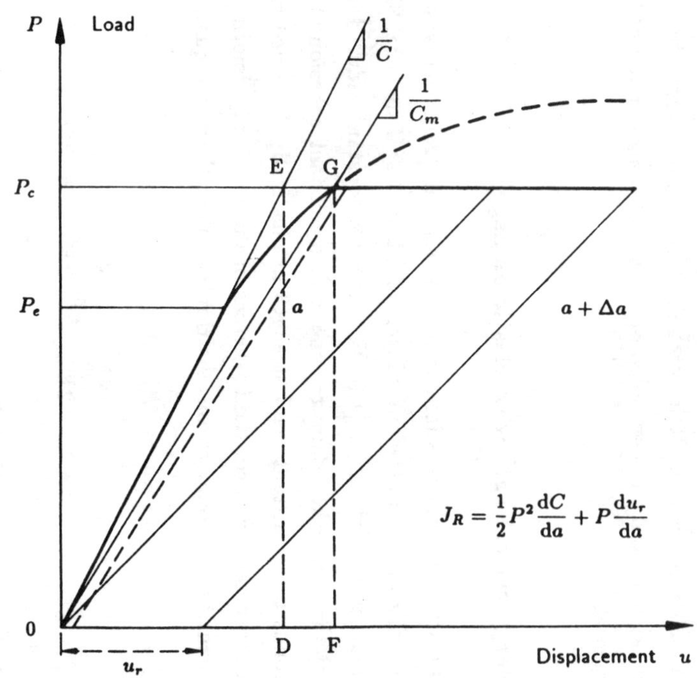

Fig. 2

This quantity is approximately given by the areas OEG or $DEFG/2$ in Fig. 2.

During unelastic loading of the beam, energy is dissipated due to microcracking, the energy is given as

$$U_{\mathrm{diss}} = B\frac{S_m^2 a}{hE_m}\psi^2 \tag{5}$$

Thus during bending of the beam the stress concentration at point 0 (Fig. 1) can reach a critical value with respect to incremental growth Δa of the beam and elastic energy is released with eqn. (1-4) and $U = U_{el} + U_r + U_{diss}$ by the amount

$$\tilde{G}_R = \frac{1}{B}\ \frac{dU}{da} = \frac{S_m^2}{3E}\ (1 + 2\frac{\psi}{h}) + \frac{S_m^2}{E}\ \frac{E - E_m}{E_m}\psi + \frac{S_m^2}{Eh}\psi^2 \tag{6}$$

Cracking occurs if the rate of $\tilde{G}_R$ and of the materials crack resistance R with respect to a equals each another. The derivative of eqn (6) contains a local and a global criterion. As a first approximation the local criterion is assumed to be the energy rate determining process which arises at the root of the beam during an incremental growth of δa. Thus eqn. (6) yields

$$\tilde{G}_R = \tilde{G}_r = \frac{S_m^2}{E}\ \frac{E - E_m}{E_m}\psi \tag{7}$$

This equation defines the release rate of residual elastic strain energy (eqn 4). The residual elastic strain energy is stored in the damage zone during each unloading process which arises subsequently and locally at the crack front during each stepwise incremental jump of crack growth δa as observed experimentally [2]. Eqn (7) follows also from the J-integral formulation which will be shown in the following.

As shown by Bui and Ehrlacher [6] the energy release rate in elastic-plastic damage is governed by the effective strain energy density which is available after some deformation of a cracked body. In the case of elastic damage the effective strain energy density w after loading a beam up to point G (Fig. 2) is given by that strain minus the strain at point E which is lost in the body due to microcracking which generates the change of Young's modulus from E to E_m. Thus the J-integral for crack initiation in elastic damage yields

$$J = \int_{-\psi}^{+\psi} w(\epsilon_m - \epsilon)dy = \frac{S_m^2}{\mathbf{E}} \quad \frac{\mathbf{E} - \mathbf{E}_m}{\mathbf{E}_m}\psi \tag{8}$$

This is equivalent to the elastic strain energy release rate of a bend beam due to the stored residual strain energy density as a consequence of microcracking in a dilated damage zone (eqn 7). The same results are shown in foregoing works [1].

3. Effective crack resistance in elastic damage

It was proposed in foregoing works that the release of strain energy which arises in the front of the damage zone of size 2ψ during incremental growth equals the sum of all elastic strain energy densities of newly formed microcracks $e_m = (S^2/2E) = (2\gamma/a_m)$ with a volume density β. Thus the crack resistance is given as

$$R = \int_{-\psi}^{+\psi} \frac{2\gamma}{a_m}\beta dy = \int_{-\psi}^{+\psi} \left(\frac{S^2}{\mathbf{E}}\right)_m dy \tag{9}$$

2γ is the specific surface energy, a_m is a characteristic microcrack length. This defines the crack resistance of the damaged body. Thus equivalence of crack resistance with the elastic strain energy release rate yields a formulation for the cohesive strenght of the damage zone which contains a Griffith-term modified due to the interaction of the microcracks of the damage zone. Thus the cohesive strength is given as [1]

$$S_m = \sqrt{\frac{2\gamma\mathbf{E}}{a_m}} I_m = \sqrt{\frac{2\gamma\mathbf{E}}{a_m}} \quad \sqrt{\beta\frac{\mathbf{E}_m}{\mathbf{E} - \mathbf{E}_m}} = \sqrt{e_m\mathbf{E}} \quad \frac{K_o}{K_m} \tag{10}$$

where K_o and K_m are the SIF of cracks in a safe and a damaged material respectively. Using the Dugdale model the effective elastic strain energy release rate of elastic damage for crack initiation can be written as

$$\tilde{G} = \frac{S_m^2}{E}\psi = e_m\psi\frac{K_0^2}{K_m^2} \tag{11}$$

This holds for a stationary crack in small scale yielding. Following Fig. 2 the crack resistance of a quasi static propagating crack is modified due to the work of the external forces P on the damage zone and is given with the offset u_r as

$$\tilde{G}_R = \frac{P^2}{2B} \quad \frac{dC}{da} \quad + \quad \frac{P}{B} \quad \frac{du_r}{da} \tag{12}$$

Displacement at a crack

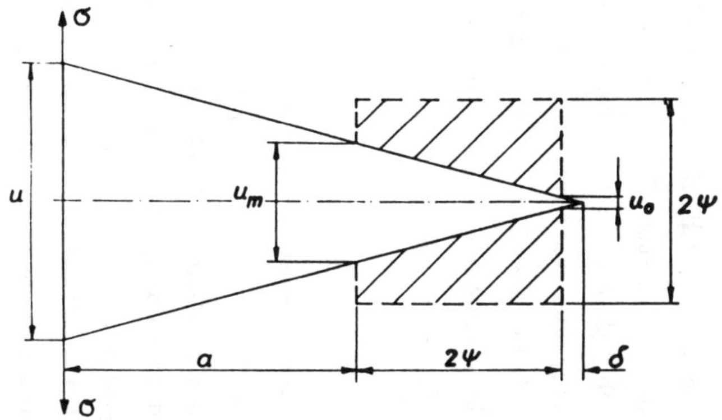

$$\frac{u}{a + 2\psi + \delta} = \frac{u_m}{2\psi + \delta} = \frac{u_0}{\delta}$$

$$\delta < 2\psi < a$$

$$u = u_m \frac{a + 2\psi + \delta}{2\psi + \delta}$$

$$u_m = \epsilon_m 2\psi = \frac{S_m}{E_m} 2\psi$$

$$u = \epsilon_m \left(\frac{a}{1 + \frac{\delta}{2\psi}} + 2\psi \right)$$

$$\frac{du}{da} \approx \epsilon_m$$

Fig. 3

Crack resistance vs crack growth of

HPSN at 1200°C

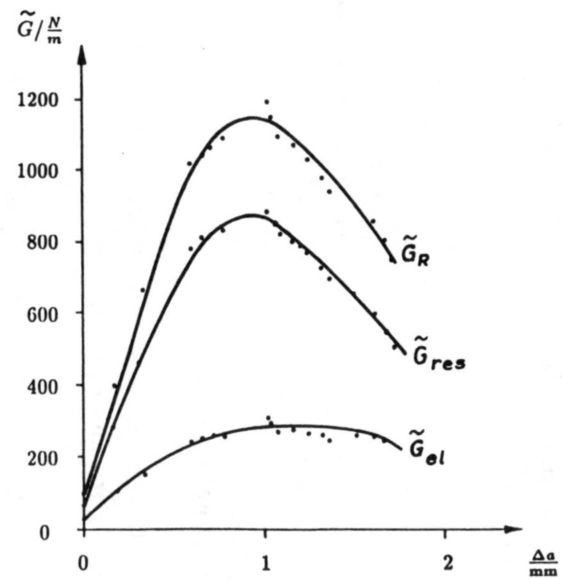

Fig. 4

With eqn (11) the crack resistance can also be written in terms of internal parameters and follows as

$$G_R = e_m \quad I_m^2\psi + \psi\frac{d}{da}e_m I_m^2\psi = e_m I_m^2\psi + \psi T_J \tag{13}$$

T_J is the tearing modulus which is a measure of the residual elastic strain energy which is stored in the body during stable crack growth.

4. Experimental observations

The total residual elastic strain energy which is stored in the body after stable crack growth of δa is given with eqns (11-13) as

$$U_r = \int_0^{\delta a} \tilde{G}_r da = \int_0^{ur} \frac{P}{B} du_r = \psi \int d\left(\frac{2\gamma}{a_m}\frac{K_0^2}{K_m^2}\right) \tag{14}$$

Thus in accordance with observations of Osterstock et al [7] only a fraction of the external energy rate which is spent during stable crack growth is released during crack growth. A great amount of fracture work is stored in the body as residual elastic strain energy which follows from the above mentioned relations.

Fig. 4 shows as an example crack resistance curves for HPSN at 1200° C [8]. The elastic energy release rate reaches a plateau value of about 300 N/m. However, the inelastic rate at change of energy drops sharply after a maximum value at about 900 N/m. The stored elastic residual strain energy after crack growth of 0,8 mm follows from eqn (14) approximately as U_r = 0,3 N. However it must be noticed that the corresponding total elastic strain energy which is spent during fracture is only 0,1 N.

5. Conclusion

It is observed that the crack resistance of a specific ceramic can incrase during stable crack growth in bending [7-10]. To get a high crack resistance during stable crack growth a high amount of residual elastic strain energy has to be stored in the body during monotonic loading. It is assumed that during the rising part of the $\tilde{G}_r$-curve K_m decrease due to an increasing density of short microcracks with a specific orientation [1] whereas a decreasing R-curve is affected by a coagulation of short microcracks to longer microcracks and thus a reduced microcrack density inside the damage zone. A high crack resistance is also responsible for a high thermoshock resistance of a ceramic if a body is elastically damaged as a consequence of thermal cycling. Then residual elastic strain energy is stored in microcracked regions due to the reduction of Young's modulus in comparison to undamaged parts of the body. This holds especially for ceramics with a bimodal microstructure [1]. Thus it would seem that the key of improving the toughness of ceramics could depend primarily on events which occur at or ahead rather than behind the advancing crack tip.

References

[1] F.E. Buresch, Bruchmechanische Aspekte beim Einsatz partikelverstärkter keramischer Bauteile, Materialprüfung 29, 1987, 261-268.

[2] F.E. Buresch, Th. Müller, Einfluß von Kerb- und Probengeometrie auf das Verformungsverhalten sowie die bruchmechanischen Kennwerte eines Reaktorgraphits, Proc. Int. Conf. "Carbon 80", Baden-Baden, AK Kohlenstoff der DKG 1980, 56-60, Jül.-Conf.-36, ed. W. Delle, Mai 1980, 22-26.

[2a] F.E. Buresch, H. Nickel, Mechanische Untersuchungen an keramischen Werkstoffen für Komponenten von Hochtemperatur-Reaktoren, DVM, Festigkeit keramischer Werkstoffe, Abschlusskolloquium im Schwerpunktprogramm der DFG, 1984, 123.

[3] E. Babilon, G. Kleist, F.E. Buresch, H. Nickel, Characterisation of damage in alumina ceramics by small angle x-ray scattering, Science of Ceramics 14, 1987, 665-669.

[3a] this conference

[4] T. Mishima, Y. Nanagama, Y. Mirose, K. Tanaka, X-ray fractography of fracture surfaces of alumina ceramic, Advance in X-ray analysis 30, 1987, 545-552.

[5] O. Buresch, M. Müller, K. Kromp, F.E. Buresch, Crack resistance of a glass ceramic and direct exposure of the microcrack zone at the crack front, ECF 7, Vol. 1, 546, 1988.

[6] H.M. Bui, A. Ehrlacher, Propagation of damage in elastic and plastic solids, Advance in Fracture Research, ICF 5, Vol. 2, 1981, 533-551.

[7] F. Osterstock, On the Graphical Evaluation of Forcedisplacement Curves to Determine Toughness Parameters of Ceramics, Fortschrittsbericht der DKG, Bd 2, 1986/87, Heft 3, 1977.

[8] C.T. Bodur, K. Kromp, F.E. Buresch, erscheint demnächst.

[9] A.G. Atkins, Y.W. Mai, Elastic and plastic fracture, Ellis Horwood Ital, Chichester, 1985.

[10] C.T. Bodur, K. Kromp, Investigation of the sintering behaviour of HPSN with ytria at high temperature, Fortschrittsbericht der DKG, Bd 3, 1988, Heft 3, 109-136.

PROOF TEST FOR ASSURING THE STRENGTH OF CERAMIC MATERIALS

ICHIRO TAKAHASHI
Department of Mechanical Engineering, Kanagawa Institute of Technology
1030, Simo-ogino Atugi-shi 243-02, Kanagawa, JAPAN

ABSTRACT

A test technique for loading the arbitrary stress and a method for strength evaluation were studied to develop a reliability testing method. (1) The test technique for loading arbitrary stress was developed by using thermal stress. (2) The thermal stress reached value in a short time, after cooling the specimen, and then decreased monotonically. (3) The maximum thermal stress increased with an increase of both temperature and thickness of specimen. (4)The strength of the ceramic materials was evaluated by using a relationship between temperature and the maximum stress.

INTRODUCTION

The major difficulty in using ceramics or other brittle materials as strength members such as machine parts is the larger vaiation in strength as compared with other structural materials. When the fracture of ceramic material is observed, surface scraches, inclusions, large grains, cavities and other minute flaws are found at the starting point of fracture. Structural ceramics have fracture toughness about one tenth that of structural steel, and the allowable flaw size of ceramics under identical stress is one hundredth to one thousandth that of structural steel. For ceramics, therefore, minute flaws which would pose no problem with steels govern the strength, leading to large variations in strength. Therefore, the large variation in strength for ceramics depends upon the flaw distribution rather than the statistical characteristics of strength which are inherent in the material.

Accordingly, many studies have been conducted on the strength based on the flaws[1]-[12] and the techniques of nondestructive examination[13]-[16]. It is, however, difficulty to detect flaws of the order of $10\mu m$ in machine parts with X-ray or ultrasonic test equipment. For rotating parts, the over speed spin test method is used to load stresses to assure the reliability of actual machines[17]-[18]. For other structural parts, however, there is no method suitable for loading the necessary stresses.

This report presents a technique for loading an arbitrary stress to establish a proof test method for strength of parts and a method for strength evaluation of ceramic materials containing flaws. The same problem of smooth brittle materials was also presented in reference [19].

EXPERIMENTAL PROCEDURE

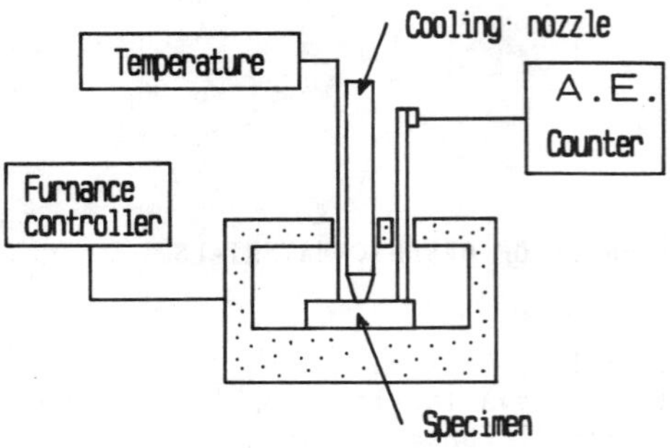

Figure 1. Scheme of Proof test apparatus.

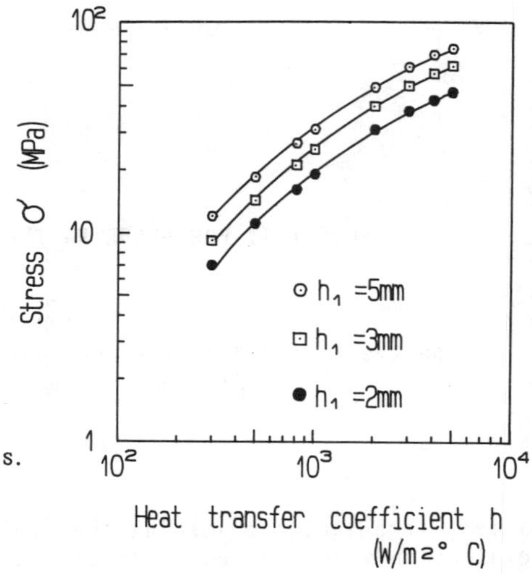

Figure 3. Relationship between heat transfer coefficient and maximum stress of various specimens (heating temperature θ =300℃).

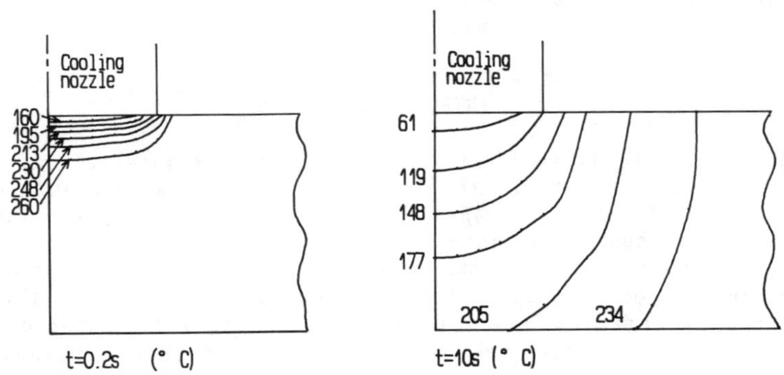

Figure 2. Contour map of temperature inside a specimen (heating temperature θ =300℃, thickness of specimen h1=3mm).

The material tested was float glass (soda-lime glass) an amorphous ceramic material. The mechanical properties of the glass were listed in reference [19]. The sizes of the three types of specimens were 60mm long and 60mm wide, with thicknesses of 5, 3 and 2mm. The cut sections were finished with #80-1000 silicon carbide sand paper, while the other sections were as received. Flaws were artificially introduced in the specimen surface. Semi-circular controlled surface flaws, of 30-1600μm in diameter were introduced by Vickers-indentation.

Figure 1 is the scheme of the proof test apparatus. The specimen was placed in a heating furnace using kanthal wires, and heated to the test temperature. The heating time was 30 to 40 min. After holding at the test temperature for 10 to 15 min., a 3mm dia. water-cooled cooling nozzle was brought into contact with the specimen to generate thermal stress . The tip of the cooling nozzle was made of tough pitch copper with a relatively high thermal conduc-

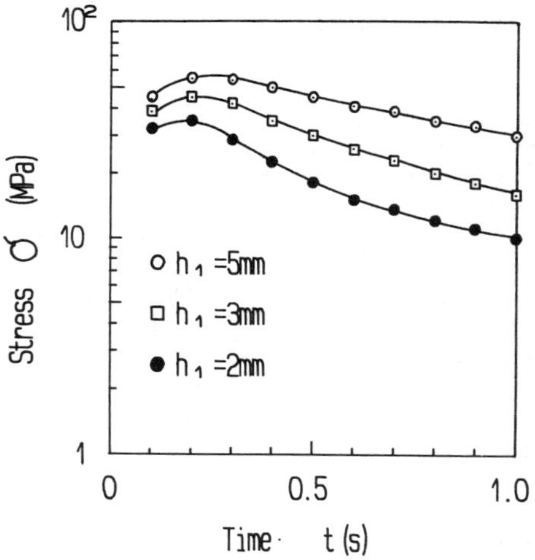

Figure 4. Relationship between time elasped and maximum stress of various specimens (heating temperature θ =300℃).

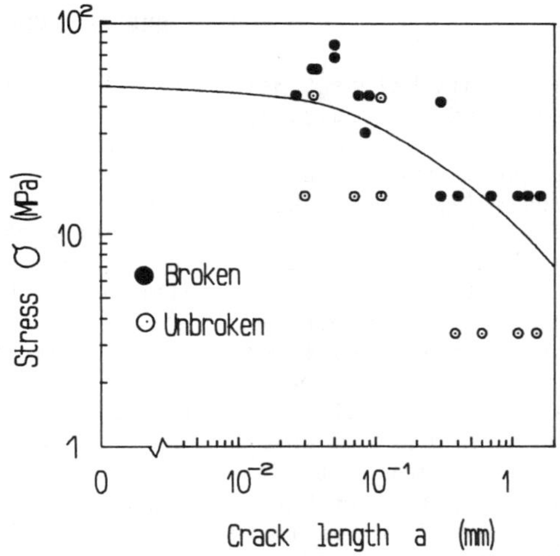

Figure 6. Relationship between crack length and maximum stress (thickness of specimen h1=3mm)

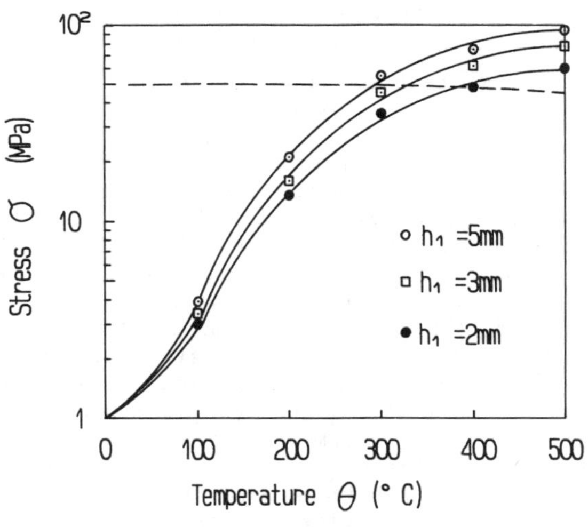

Figure 5. Relationship between heating temperature and maximum stress of various specimens.

tivity. The cooling nozzle was cooled by water instead of direct cooling by gas[20] because the gas cooling method causes variable heat transfer coefficient. Tap water of about 15℃ was used as the cooling water with the flow rate varied from $5*10^{-6}$ to $1.4*10^{-4} m^3/s$. While the specimen surface temperature was measured, the presence of cracks due to thermal stress was checked by Acoustic Emission (A.E.). The A.E. signals were sent out of the furnace through a silica glass rod installed on the specimen, and counted by an A.E. counter.

EXPERIMENTAL RESULTS AND DISCUSSION

The finite element method ("ANSYS-PC/THERMAL, LINEAR", Cybernet System, Ltd.) was used for analyzing the temperature distribution and thermal stress distribution produced by the contact of the cooling nozzle with the specimen.

The analysis was performed using the isoparametric element, and the mesh model (288 nodes and 255 elements)[19] was used for calculating non-steady temperatures and stresses. Part a where the specimen surface is in contact with the cooling nozzle and part b where the surface is in contact with the air have heat transfer coefficients of h and h', respectively. These coefficients were estimated from the temperature measured and the calculation result described later, in the range of approximate values for flowing water (290-5816W/m2℃) and still air (1.16-23W/m^2℃)[21], respectively. For analysis, assuming the heat transfer coefficients for part a and b, the temperature distribution for each elasped time from the start of cooling of a specimen heated uniformly was determined by using the non-steady temperature analysis program (ANSYS-PC/THERMAL).

Figure 2 shows temperature contour maps of the inside of the specimen measured 0.2s and 10s after the start of cooling. It can be seen that the temperature gradient is steep under the nozzle at the elasped time of 0.2s when the stress becomes maximum as described later, while the temperature gradient is slight at the elasped time of 10s, cooling being uniform.

Figure 3 shows the relationship between heat transfer coefficient h (at part a where the specimen surface is in contact with the cooling nozzle.) and maximum stress for various specimens heated to 300℃. As the heat transfer coefficient and thickness of the specimen increase, the stress increases monotonically. Based on the fact that the bending strength of this material is about 50MPa and the test results, the heat coefficient h at the nozzle contact area was estimated to be about 2500W/m^2℃, which is same with value obtained in reference [19].

Figure 4 shows the relationship between elasped time and maximum stress of various specimens. The stress increases for 0.2s after the start of cooling, and afterwards decreases monotonically with time. From this result, it is considered that the time when the maximum stress is produced coincides approximately with the time of crack initiation determined from the experiment.

Figure 5 shows the relationship between heating temperature and maximum stress of various specimens. The dashed line denotes the mean value of four-point bending strength. As the heating temperature and the thickness of specimen increases the stress increases. The crack initiation can be explained relatively well by using this figure on the basis of bending stress. At a heating temperature of 300℃, cracks initiate in some specimens because the stress generated in the 5mm thick specimens exceeds the bending strength. At 500℃, cracks initiate in all specimens because the stress generated in 2 to 5mm thick specimens exceeds the bending strength.

Figure 6 shows the relationship between crack length and maximum stress (thickness h_1=3mm). The solid line denotes the mean value of four-point bending strength. The marks ●(broken) and ○(unbroken) indicate the development and nondevelopment of initial crack due to thermal stress, respectively. The crack development can be also explained relatively well by using this figure on the basis of bending strength of specimen containing a flaw. This explanation can be applied for the specimens with the thicknesses of 2 and 5mm.

As described above, the technique presented in this report can be used for loading an arbitrary stress on an arbitrary location and also for evaluating the strength of a member.

CONCLUSIONS

A test technique for loading arbitrary stress and a method for strength evaluation were studied to develop a reliability testing method, with the following conlusions.

(1) The test technique for loading an arbitrary stress was developed by using thermal stress.
(2) The thermal stress reached a maximum immediately after cooling, and then decreased momotonically.
(3) The maximum thermal stress increased with increases in temperature and thickness of the specimen.
(4) The strength of ceramic materials was evaluated by using the relationship between temperature and the maximum stress.

REFERENCES

1. Kirchner, H.P., Gruver, R.M. and Sotter, W.A., Mater. Sci. Eng., 1976, 22, pp.147-56.
2. Iseki, T., Murayama, T., Hanabusa, K. and Suzuki, H., Yogyo- Kyokai-shi, 1978, 86, pp.47-52.
3. Kawai, M., Abe, H. and Nakayama, J., International Symposium of Factors in Densification and Sintering of Oxide and Non-oxide Ceramics , Japan, 1978, pp.545-52.
4. Bourne, W.C., and Tressler, R.E., Frac. Mech. Ceram., 1978, 3, pp.113-24.
5. Rice, R.W., Freiman, S.W., Pohanka, R.C., Mecholsky, Jr. J.J. and Wu, C.Cm., Frac. Mech. Ceram., 1978, 4, pp.849-74.
6. Mackinney, K.R. and Rice, R.W., Fracture Mechanics Method for Ceramics, Rocks and Concrete, ASTM STP-745, 1981, pp.118-26.
7. Kirchner, H.P. and Isaacson, E.D., Frac. Mech. Ceram., 1983, 5, pp.57-70.
8. Usami, S., Takahashi, I. and Kimoto, H., 33th Ann. Meeting Proceedings, The Society of Materials Science, Japan, 1984, pp.159-61.
9. Yamada, T., Hoshide, T. and Furuya, H., Journal of the Society of Materials Science, Japan, 1984, 33, pp.28-33.
10. Takahashi, I., Usami, S., Nakakado, K., Miyata, H. and Shida, S., Yogyo-Kyokai-shi, 1985, 93, pp.186-94.
11. Kimoto, H., Usami, S. and Miyata, H., Transactions of The Japan Society of Mechanical Engineers (Part A), 1985, 51, pp.2482-88.
12. Usami, S., Kimoto, H., Takahashi, I. and Shida, S., Eng. Frac. Mech., 1986, 23, pp.745-61.
13. Khuri-yakub, B.T., Kino, G.S. and Evans, A.G., J. Am. Ceram. Soc., 1980, 63, pp.65-71.
14. Kozuka, K. and Yamamoto, T., Nondestructive Examination 1982 Spring Time Annual Proceedings, 1982, pp.156-57.
15. Kitadate, K., Tanimoto, Y. and Tanaka, T., Ceramics, 1985, 20, pp.903-13.
16. Helms, H.E., Heitman, P.W., Lindgren, L.C. and Trasher, S.R., "Ceramic Applications in Turbine Engines", Noyes, 1986, pp.106-31.
17. Rottenkolber, P., Langer, M., Storm, R.S. and Frechette, F., SAE No.810523, 1981.
18. Sasaki, M., Izumi, T., Achiha, S. and Ito, T., GTSJ, 1985, 13, pp.28-35.
19. Takahashi, I., J. Ceram. Soc. Jpn. Inter. Ed., 1988, 96, 848-52.
20. Faber, K.T., Haung, M.D. and Evans, A.G., J. Am. Ceram. Soc., 1981, 64, pp.296-301.
21. Kimio, K., Okuno, J. and Makino, S., "Industrial Thermodynamics", Morikita Shuppan, 1972, p.151.

MECHANICAL PROPERTIES OF CERAMIC LINED PIPES PRODUCED BY A CENTRIFUGAL-THERMIT PROCESS

OSAMU ODAWARA
Department of Electronic Chemistry, Tokyo Institute of Technology
4259 Nagatsuta, Midori-ku, Yokohama 227, Japan.

ABSTRACT

A centrifugal-thermit process is characterized by its reaction propagation under the centrifugal force as well as a large amount of reaction heat and the centrifugal force affecting the reaction products. Since the centrifugal-thermit process proceeds along the inner surface of the hollow body first and then into the layer in the radial direction, the temperature increase of the outer metal pipe during the process is delayed compared to the product layers. Due to the different effect of heat removal and time delay in shrinkage of each layer, the outer metal layers contract much more than the produced ceramic layer resulting in high compression stress in the ceramic layer and tensile stress in the intermediate metal layer. The mechanical properties of ceramic lined pipes produced by the centrifugal-thermit process are discussed under taking into consideration a role of the intermediate metal layer .

INTRODUCTION

A new technique has been proposed for ceramic lining to hollow metallic body by means of a thermit reaction taking place under the influence of centrifugal force("Centrifugal-Thermit Process": C-T process)[1]. According to the C-T process, a thermit mixture placed in a rotating metal pipe is ignited, for example, by contacting with an acetylene flame. The thermit reaction propagates under the influence of the centrifugal force so that the molten metal and the molten ceramic produced from the reaction of the thermit mixture are separated into stratified layers by virtue of their density difference with the latter forming the innermost layer and the former forming the intermediate layer between the ceramic layer and the wall of the pipe with strong bonding of the ceramic layer on solidification by cooling.

Main characteristics of the C-T process are a large amount of reaction heat and centrifugal force applied to the reaction products[2]. Through long-sized ceramic lined pipe development, it was confirmed that the behavior of reaction propagation under the influence of centrifugal force was also a significant feature of the C-T process[3]; the thermit reaction proceeds rapidly along the inner hollow surface of the reactant formed under the centrifugal effect first and then into the reactant layer simultaneously in the radial direction resulting in homogeneous quality in the direction of pipe length under the conditions of proper amount of thermit powders and centrifugal force. This is a great advantage in the production of long-sized ceramic lined pipes, which reveals a unique characteristics on the mechanical properties of the present ceramic lined pipes.

EXPERIMENTAL

The C-T process and the measurements of produced pipe properties were carried out in the same manner as the previous work[4]. A reactant mixture was prepared by blending 41.55 kg of the stoichiometric powder mixture of aluminum(~100 μm) and ferric oxide(~5 μm) and 2.91 kg of silicic anhydride powder(~5 μm) as the additives to improve the densification of the produced ceramic layer which is 7 mass% of the total amount. A carbon steel pipe with an outer diameter of 165.2 mm and a wall thickness of 7.1 mm cut in a length of 3 m was mounted on a roller-type centrifuge machine and loosely filled with the reactant mixture. After the rotation of the centrifuge machine had reached to a fixed velocity yielding 130 G of centrifugal force to the inner wall of the steel pipe, the mixture was ignited with the fire of magnesium-barium peroxide mixtures. The thermit reaction propagated rapidly and, after completion of the reaction (ca. 15 s), the rotation of the centrifuge machine was continued for about 20 min. further to cool down the body.

The properties of the produced ceramic lined pipes were investigated through the measurements of compressive strength, compression-shear stress, Young's modulus, etc., which have been described in detail[5]. The properties of the produced ceramic layer were also measured. The change of strain of the outer steel pipe was measured with strain gauges attached on its surface and the residual stress was calculated from its strain data and the data on its Young's modulus and Poisson's ratio. The release of stress was carried out in two processes, i. e. through taking off the ceramic layer and through taking off the intermediate metal layer. In the former process, the ceramic layer was taken off by compressing in a radial plane with a tool attached to the ceramic layer and a tool attached to the metal layers, and in the latter the inner produced metal layer was taken off by grinding the layer.

RESULTS AND DISCUSSION

The typical experimental data on the mechanical properties of the present ceramic lined pipes are shown in the direction of pipe length in Figure 1. Since the differences of these properties in the direction of pipe length are small, the pipe is considered to be uniformly produced in the direction of pipe length.

With respect to the thermal expansion and shrinkage of each layer during the C-T process, some delay is expected in the outer steel pipe layer compared to those of product layers because of the delay in temperature increase; since the melting point of the produced ceramic is much higher than that of the metal and the heat propagation occurs in the radial direction, the outer pipe would be still in expansion when the produced ceramic starts to solidify and shrink. After the temperature of the outer pipe starts to cool down, the metal layer contracts much more than the ceramic with its higher coefficient resulting in the compression stress remaining in the produced ceramic layer(linear expansion coefficient: 1.5×10^{-5} K^{-1}(steel) and 8.6×10^{-6} K^{-1}(present ceramic)). The size of pipe produced by the C-T process was a little shrinked both in diameter and in length. Therefore, it is considered that the expansion of the outer steel pipe would not be enough during its expanding-process affected by the simultaneous shrinking-process of innermetal and ceramic layers compared to that of a pipe expanding without such co- relating layers, which would finally result in a little shrink of the present pipe.

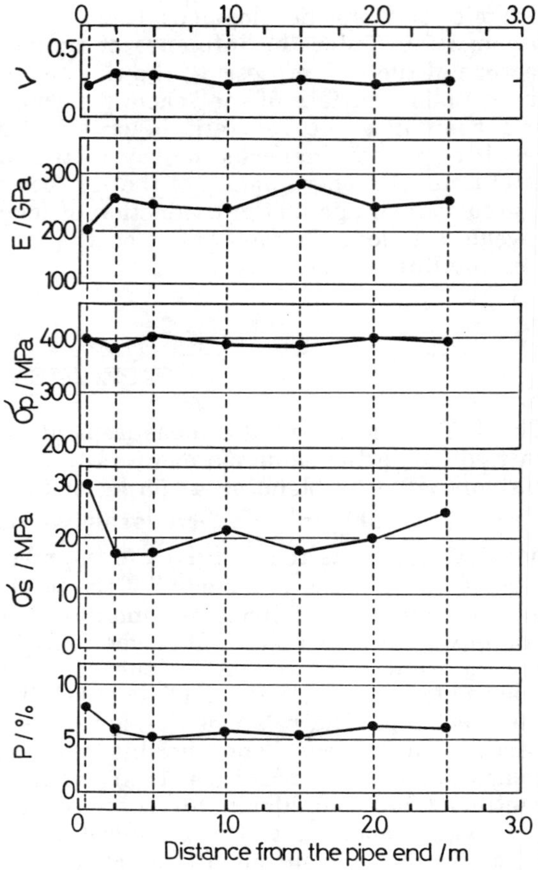

Figure 1 Mechanical properties of a 3 m long C-T ceramic lined pipe.
ν ; Poisson's ratio, E ; Young's modulus, σ_p ; compressive strength, σ_s ; compression shear stress, P ; porosity of the ceramic layer.

Figure 2 shows the residual stress of the outer steel pipe. Although the data include a rather large experimental error part to part of the measurement, the average value of the released stress was about 118 MPa in the direction of pipe length and about 58 MPa in the arc direction of pipe circumference when the ceramic layer was taken off, and about -74 MPa in the direction of pipe length and about -85 MPa in the arc direction when the metal layer was taken off, where the positive value is in tensile stress. In Figure 3, the schematic illustration is shown for the residual stress distribution in each

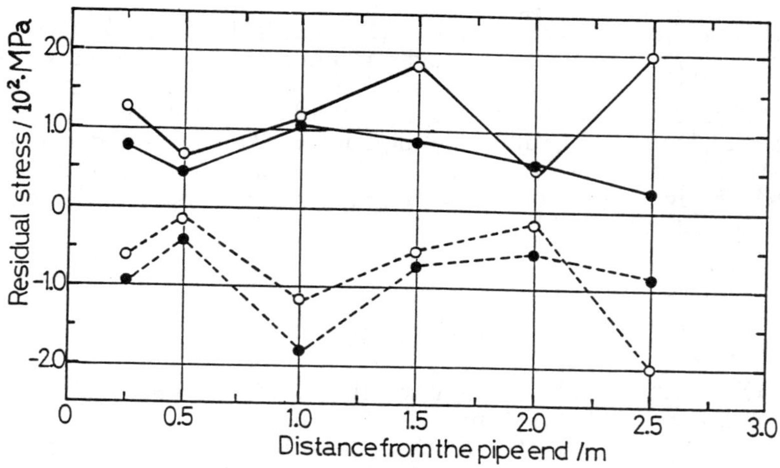

Figure 2 Residual stress of the outer pipe measured with a strain gauge. (positive values refer to tension)
○; in the direction of pipe lengh, ●; in the arc direction
——; ceramic layer taken off, -----; intermediate metal taken off

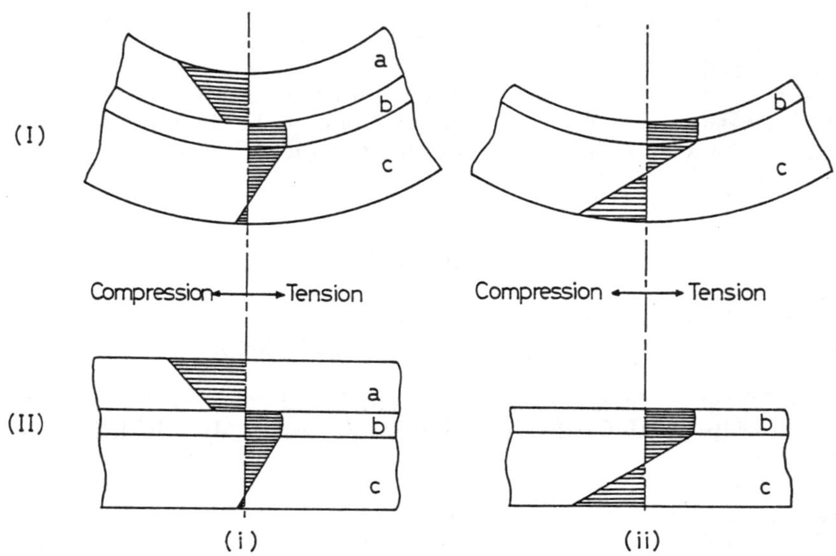

Figure 3 Schematic illustration of an estimated distribution of residual stress in each layer formed by the C-T process.

layer following the previous work[4]. The tensile stress generating in the ceramic lined pipe during these layer formation is considered to mostly remain in the intermediate metal layer. With this intermediate metal layer, the stress affecting on the ceramic layer would be relieved and balanced with the stress remained in the outer steel pipe layer. This kind of distribution of residual stress is also one of the significant features established by this C-T process, which give high potential to the produced ceramic lined pipes in the practical applications.

CONCLUSION

Although the mechanism of thermit reaction is too complex and difficult to make clear in details, the mechanism of the reaction propagation in the C-T process was confirmed that the reaction proceeds in hollow surface first and subsequently in the radial direction simultaneously. With this characteristics of thermit reaction in the C-T process, it could be achieved to produce long-sized ceramic lined pipes of homogeneous quality in the direction of pipe length. According to the present data on residual stress of each layer composing the present ceramic lined pipe, it was estimated that the ceramic layer was compressed by the intermediate metal and outer steel pipe layers and the stress in the outer steel pipe layer graded from tension to compression toward larger radial direction in both pipe circumference and length. With the intermediate metal layer, in which the tensile stress is mainly remained, the ceramic lined pipes produced by the C-T process can reveal high potential compared to those produced by other conventional ceramic lining techniques. The present results obtained would become one of the advantageous guiding principles on the way to further improvement in the C-T process.

REFERENCES

1. Odawara, O., Method for Providing Ceramic Lining to a Hollow Body by Thermit Reaction. US Patent No. 4363832(Dec. 14, 1982).

2. Odawara, O. and Ikeuchi, J., Effect of Centrifugal Force in the Production of Composite Pipes by a Centrifugal-Thermit Process. J. Jpn. Inst. Metals, 49, 801-05(1985).

3. Odawara, O., Shiraishi, M., Ikeuchi, J., Ishii, Y., Yamasaki, H. and Sato, M., Characteristics of Thermit Reaction in a Centrifugal-Thermit Process. J. Jpn. Inst. Metals, 49, 806-10(1985).

4. Odawara, O., Long Ceramic Lined Pipes Produced by a Centrifugal-Thermit Process. J. Am. Ceram. Soc., in review.

5. Odawara, O., Ceramic Lined Pipes Produced by a Centrifugal-Thermit Process. Trans. Jpn. Inst. Metals, 26, 578-86(1985).

TOUGHNESS AND CRACK PROPAGATION RESISTANCE IN TRANSFORMING CERAMIC MATERIALS

M. SAADAOUI*, G. ORANGE, G. FANTOZZI
GEMPPM (UA 341-CNRS), Bat. 502 INSA, 69621 Villeurbanne (FRANCE).
*Ecole Mohammadia d'Ingénieurs, B.P. 765 Rabat (MAROCCO).

ABSTRACT

Ceramic materials reinforced with particles or metastable precipitates can exhibit improved properties due to several toughening mechanisms. The toughening effect can be analyzed in terms of increase of energy at the onset of crack initiation and/or during crack propagation (R-curve).
The dependence of crack resistance with crack extension, or the R-curve behaviour, has been observed in magnesia-partially stabilized zirconia (Mg-PSZ) ceramics. Results show the R-curve dependence on experimental conditions: notched or precracked specimens.
The effect of sub-critical crack growth were also pointed out; this effect is much more pronounced as the material (Mg-PSZ) presents a higher content of monoclinic phase (e.g. microcracks).

INTRODUCTION

The improvement of mechanical behaviour of ceramic materials by the use of phase transformation toughening has considerably increased the interest devoted to these materials and the developement of some potential applications. Partially stabilized zirconia materials containing stabilizing oxide solid solutions (CaO, MgO, or Y_2O_3 additions) present enhanced fracture properties - at room and medium temperature - and a good thermal-shock resistance.

The increase of fracture energy as the crack goes through the material (R-curve effect) has been analyzed according to theoretical models in phase transforming materials [1,2] ; some experimental results are reported in case of Mg- PSZ [3 - 6] . Different mechanisms can explain this effect, which is also observed in some monolithic ceramics [7 - 9] : formation of a damaged zone at the tip of the main crack (crack shielding effect), fritional effect across the newly fractured surfaces (wake effect), crack branching or bridging, and stress - induced phase transformation of metastable zirconia particles (or precipitates) in the case of zirconia-based systems.

The purpose of this work is to observe the effect of experimental conditions on measurement of R - curves on a Mg - PSZ material. Special care has been taken to note the effect of the characteristic of the starting crack as well as the effect of environment.

EXPERIMENTAL PROCEDURE

Material used in this work is an industrial grade of partially stabilized zirconia containing about 9 % mole of MgO as stabilizing agent * (Mg-PSZ). This material is made of a cubic solid solution matrix with inter- and intra- granular precipitates of monoclinic and tetragonal symmetries. The monoclinic content (Vm) measured by X.R. diffraction after annealing treatment (1000°C, 1h) was about 15 % vol. in the considered batch.

Crack propagation resistance curves (R-curves) were determined from 3 points bending tests (span = 35 mm) , on S.E.N.B. type specimens of an overall size of 4 x 6 x 40 mm^3, with cyclic or monotonic loading procedures. A special care has been taken to prepare the notch : a first notch of 0.3 mm width is machined at low speed and a sharp crack (tip radius = 35 μm) is made inside the notch to a total relative depth a/W = 0.6. Annealing treatments (1000°C, 1h) were performed on notched specimens before any test to eliminate any residual stresses and stress induced phase transformations.

All tests were performed on a closed-loop controlled machine (Schenck - Trebel) so as to induce stable crack propagation conditions. The deflection rate used was about 2 μm/min, and the crack lengths were calculated from compliance calibrations.

R-curves were obtained from the calculated toughness K_r, the strain energy release rate G_1, or the total fracture energy R dissipated during cyclic loading experiments (R = G + Øp : elastic + non elastic contributions).

$$K_r = \frac{3\,l\,P\,\sqrt{a}}{2\,B\,\alpha^2}\,Y(\alpha) \quad (1) \qquad G_1 = \frac{P^2}{2B}\,\frac{dC}{da}(a) \quad (2)$$

with α = a/W: relative crack length, and Y : polynomial function [10];
B, W : specimen dimensions ; l = span and P = applied load;
C(a) : compliance calibration of cracked specimens.

The different tests were performed in various environments (air, water, and alcohol) so as to observe the effect of sub-critical crack growth on the experimental R - curves.

RESULTS and DISCUSSION

The load-deflection curves obtained by cyclic loading experiment on notched specimens present a significant deviation from linearity before the maximum load Pmax is reached; residual strain is measured after unloading in this non-linear regime. After Pmax all the loading curves, non linear at the starting point, are straight at the upper part; moreover, extrapolations of these curves intersect at the same point on x-axis(P = 0). Variations of R and G_1 parameters as a function of the crack propagation da are represented in Fig.1: G1 increases at the first stage of crack propagation to a maximum (corresponding to Pmax), and decreases regularly as the crack propagates through the specimen. However, R parameter presents very high values at the onset of crack initiation and decreases from the starting point of the crack (no maximum): after some crack extent, R parameter tends to identical values to that one of G_1 observed after Pmax.

----

*ZFME Grade : C.T.D. , Trappes (FRANCE).

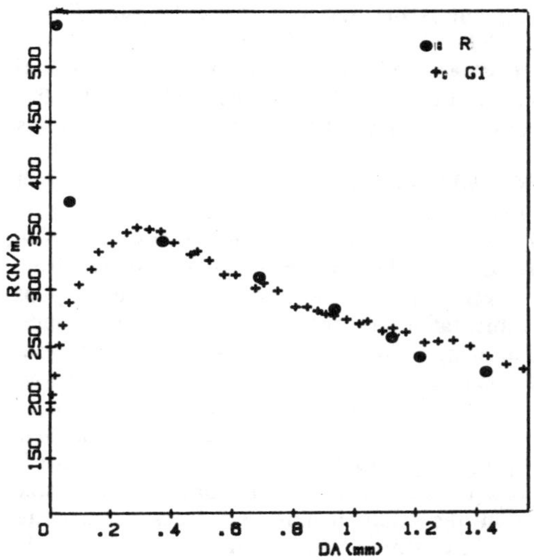

Fig. 1. R and G_1 parameters as a function of da (notched specimens).

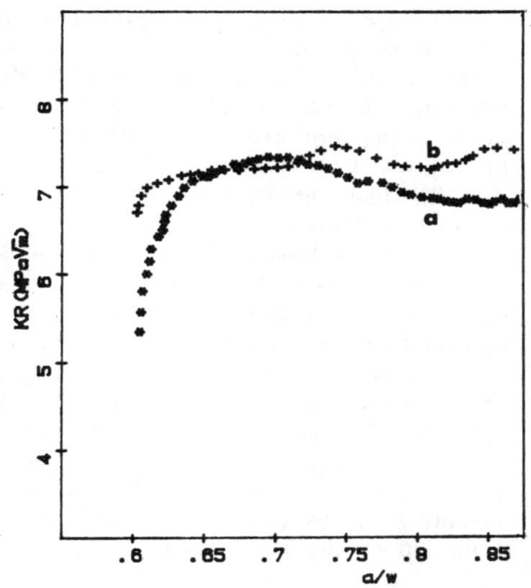

Fig. 2. K_R curves: **a)**notched specimen **b)**precracked specimen

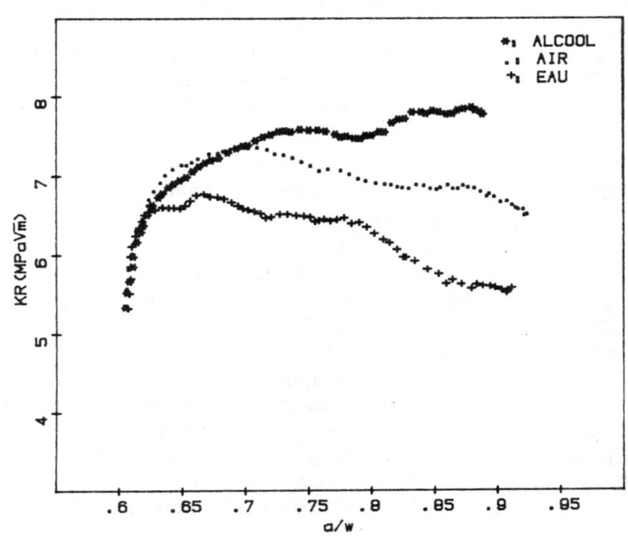

Fig. 3. Environment effect (air, water, alcohol) on K_R curves (notched specimens) - Vm = 15% .

In case of precracked specimens (with the same relative crack length a/W = 0.6), the deviation from linearity of load - deflection curves is very limited: loading curves are identical to that measured after Pmax on notched specimens. The initial curvature of P-δ curves can be correlated to the presence of "debris" and so the general behaviour can be interpreted in terms of Linear Elastic Fracture Mechanics (LEFM).

The variation of toughness values (K_r) with the relative crack length is shown in Fig.2: a large increase of K_r is observed only in case of notched specimens. Precracked specimens present constant Kr values (plateau) of about 7.4 MPa$\sqrt{m}$. Thus, the observed toughening seems to be closely related to irreversible phenomena during initiation of the crack : formation of a damaged zone at the tip of the notch (main crack), and plasticity correlated to some stress-induced phase transformation of tetragonal precipitates. These phenomena control to a large degree the deviation from linearity observed on loading curves and can also explain the divergence between R and G_I parameters during the first crack propagation steps.

The general decreasing tendancy of measured R-curves is analogous to that observed by Liu et al. [11] , but doesn't agree with theoretical models [1, 2] . Such decreasing curves can be interpreted in terms of diminution of the process zone size at the tip of the main crack and probably in the wake behind the crack front. The zone width is dictated by the transformation stress, which in turn is usually determined by the stress induced nucleation criterion [12] . Decrease of R-curves could be explained by increasing stress-induced nucleation conditions, or more probably by coupling and interacting toughening effect to stress-induced phase transformation due to microcrack formation.

Some influence of subcritical crack growth has also to be taken into account in case of R-curve mechanisms. Fig. 3 shows K_r values (notched specimens) obtained in different environmental conditions : air, water, and alcohol. The curves are identical at the beginning of crack propagation (increasing part) but a large difference is observed after crack has developed by some extent. The decreasing rate of the curve observed in air is considerably enhanced in water; moreover, the maximum value of toughness is lower in water. On the contrary, we observe no lowering of the value in alcohol: the toughness values (K_r) increase as the crack propagates through the material, to reach value of about 8 MPa$\sqrt{m}$ at a relative crack length of 0.87. The total stress intensity, K_r, i.e. the experimentally determined toughness, is usually considered as the superposition of a constant crack tip term (K_{tip}) and a crack extension dependent term (K_w). K_{tip} is the stress intensity required to drive the crack through the matrix containing transformed particles while K_w acts to shield the crack tip (wake effect). In fact, K_{tip} term is probably affected by microcrack formation and sub-critical crack growth phenomena, and so the decreasing K_r curve in corrosive environment could be due to a drastic reduction of K_{tip} parameter. Moreover, sub-critical crack growth phenomena promote inter-granular fracture mechanisms. A strong correlation has been established between this crack propagation mode (along grain boundaries), and the presence of small transformation zone leading to lower K_r values [6].

The R-curve dependence on environment is a function of the material microstructure: differences in crack resistance behaviour according to the environmental conditions are much more pronounced as the monoclinic content (Vm) is increased. This means that the presence of microcracks in the material play an important role on the control of the crack propagation mechanisms (R-curve) and specially in presence of sub-critical crack growth phenomena.

CONCLUSION

The dependance of crack resistance with crack extension has been measured on notched and precracked specimens : the increase of toughness observed in the first case is correlated to the non-linearity of P-δ curves before Pmax. The toughening effect can be explained by a stress-induced phase transformation (t m) with the formation of a process zone around the main developping crack. These irreversible phenomena are responsible for the difference between R and G_I curves at the first stage of the crack propagation. Except this non-linear behaviour (in case of notched specimen, with P < Pmax), the fracture mechanisms can be interpreted with the L.E.F.M. concepts.

The decreasing part of R-Curves can be correlated to a decrease of the process zone size. Microcrack formation effect has also to be taken into account. Moreover, we have to consider the effect of sub-critical crack propagation mechanisms: the decreasing profile of R-Curves is considerably pronounced if some sub-critical crack propagation occurs.

In case of Mg-PSZ materials, complex phenomena such as stress-induced phase transformation toughening coupled with other mechanisms (microcrack toughening) on one part and sub-critical crack growth on the other part control the observed fracture behaviour. A great care has to be taken to compare theoretical models with experimental results, as well as in the estimation of lifetime of structural parts (presence of large defects -similar to notch- and corrosive environment).

ACKNOWLEDGMENTS

The authors wish to acknowledge Dr. B. Cales from Céramiques Techniques Desmarquest (F) for supplying materials used in this work.

REFERENCES

1. D.B. MARSHALL, A.G. EVANS, M. DRORY - Fract. Mech. of Ceram., Vol. 6, 289 - 307, 1983).
2. R.M. Mc MEEKING, A.G. EVANS - J. Am. Ceram. Soc., 65 (5), 242 - 246, (1982).
3. M.V. SWAIN, R.H.J. HANNINK - Advances in Ceramics , Vol. 12, 225 - 239, (1984).
4. L.R.F. ROSE, M.V. SWAIN - J. Am. Ceram. Soc., 69 (3), 203 - 207, (1986).
5. A.H. HEUER - J. Am. Ceram. Soc. , 70 (10), 689 - 698, (1987).
6. M.J. READY, A.H. HEUER, R.W. STEINBRECH - Mater. Res. Soc. Symp. Proc. , Vol.78, 107 - 120, (1987).
7. R. STEINBRECH, R. KNEHANS, W. SCHAARWACHTER - J. Mater. Sci. , 18, 265 - 270, (1983).
8. F. DEUERLER, R. KNEHANS, R. STEINBRECH - J. de Physique , 47 (2) C1, 617 - 618, (1986).
9. M.V. SWAIN - J. Mater. Sci. Letters , 5, 1313 - 1315, (1986).
10. J.E. SRAWLEY - Int. J. Fract. Mech. , 12, 475 - 476, (1976).
11. T. LIU, G. GRATHWOHL - Zirconia 88 (7th SIMCER ; Italy), December 88.
12. A.G. EVANS, R.M. CANNON - Acta Met. 34(5), 761 - 800, (1986).

ZIRCONIA TOUGHENED CORDIERITE

I. Wadsworth, J. Wang and R. Stevens

School of Materials, The University of Leeds, Leeds LS2 9JT

ABSTRACT

Cordierite-zirconia ceramic composites were fabricated by hot pressing cordierite and zirconia. Both the fracture toughness and fracture strength have been enhanced by the addition of zirconia. The improvements are due to stress-induced transformation toughening and to the generation of residual stresses, but no evidence of microcracking was found in the composites as a consequence of the large thermal expansion mismatch. The transformability of zirconia inclusions in the cordierite matrix is higher than in the case of an alumina matrix, despite their rounded morphology resulting from the presence of a liquid phase at the hot pressing temperature.

INTRODUCTION

Dispersion toughening of oxide ceramics by a zirconia second phase is a well established process and has been successfully employed to improve the mechanical properties of alumina, mullite and spinel [1-4]. Toughening mechanisms such as stress-induced transformation toughening, microcracking and crack deflection have been found to be responsible for these improvements. Results of studies on this system have previously been published [5-6] but the emphasis was not on the mechanical behaviour. In this study investigations have been carried out to determine the effects of systematic zirconia additions on the mechanical properties of cordierite and to relate these to microstructural observations. It has been shown that both the differences in physical properties and the chemistry of cordierite affect the transformability of the zirconia and hence the mechanisms of toughening.

EXPERIMENTAL PROCEDURE

Baikalox cordierite and Toya Soda zirconia powders were used to fabricate all composites. The constituent powders were ball milled for 24 hours in isopropanol using zirconia media after which, the isopropanol was rapidly evaporated off by means of a hot plate. The dried powders were consolidated by hot pressing in an inductively heated graphite die, 25 mm in diameter, for 10 minutes at 1350°C under a pressure of 20 MPa.

Strength measurements were made on bars machined from the pressed discs using a four point bend rig (outer span 20 mm, inner span 6 mm) in an Instron 1185 testing machine at a cross head speed of 0.5 mm/min. Fracture toughness was measured by the microindentation method using a Zwick diamond indenter with an applied load of 3 kg.

RESULTS AND DISCUSSION

Transformability of zirconia in cordierite

Column 2 in Table 1 displays the amounts of retained tetragonal zirconia detected in composites containing 20 v/o zirconia with varying amounts of yttria stabiliser. The results indicate that the transformability of zirconia inclusions in cordierite is high compared to the Al_2O_3/ZrO_2 system where yttria concentrations in the zirconia in excess of 2 mol % result in the retention of 100% tetragonal ZrO_2 [7,8]. It was also observed that destabilisation increased with increasing time at the hot pressing temperature. The effect of ageing cordierite 20 v/o ZrO_2 2 mol % Y_2O_3 at 1350°C for various times is given in Table 2.

The transformability of zirconia inclusions depends on several parameters including:

1. Zirconia particle size
2. Zirconia grain morphology
3. Stabiliser content
4. Matrix constraint.

1. Particle size

The stability of a small tetragonal zirconia grain can be considered to be due to its low surface energy [9]. The instability of a large tetragonal zirconia grain is due to the increased number of defects in the structure [10-12]. The zirconia inclusions in the cordierite matrix in this work are considered to be below the critical size as a result of the moderate processing conditions used when compared to those used for ZTA. On this basis it is to be expected that the transformability of the zirconia inclusions in the cordierite would be lower than that of those in zirconia ZTA as a consequence of smaller grain size. However, the experimental results in Table 1 show that this is not the case.

Table 1: Tetragonal phase content in cordierite 20 v/o ZrO_2 composites determined on polished and ground specimens.

Stabiliser/mol %	% Tetragonal (polished)	% Tetragonal (ground)
2.0	28	12
2.5	42	20
3.0	50	27

Table 2: The effect of ageing time at 1350% on the amount of retained tetragonal in cordierite 20 v/o ZrO_2-2 mol % Y_2O_3.

Ageing time/min	% Tetragonal
10	28
60	12
300	11

2. Grain morphology

An angular grain of tetragonal zirconia exhibits a higher transformability than a rounded grain of the same size as a result of its increased surface energy and the presence of nucleation sites for the monoclinic phase [10-12]. Fig. 1a shows the rounded morphology of zirconia inclusions in cordierite. This morphology is due to the presence of a liquid phase at the zirconia grain boundaries (Fig. 1b). Their shape suggests that the inclusions are likely to be less transformable. Again, this is clearly not the case. A more dominant process is operative, manifesting itself as an increase in transformability of the zirconia.

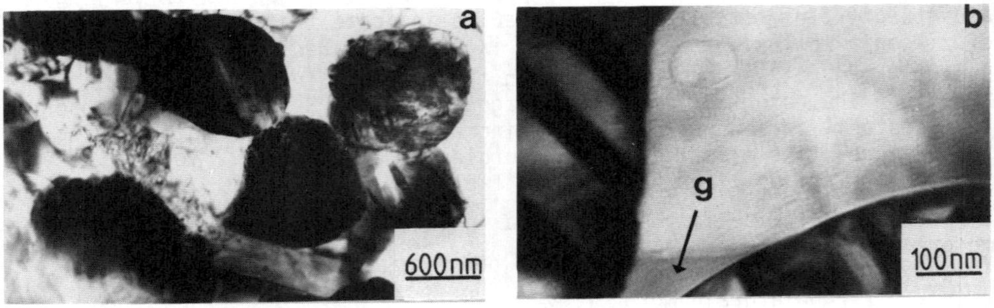

Fig. 1: TEM micrographs of zirconia inclusions in a cordierite matrix (a) illustrating their rounded morphology, (b) showing amorphous region at their intersection.

3. Yttria loss

3 mol % yttria is sufficient to achieve a fully stable tetragonal solid solution [13], the critical size for the tetragonal to monoclinic transformation increasing sharply in the 2-3 mol % yttria range. However, as is shown in Table 1, only 50% of the tetragonal phase is retained in composites consisting of 20 vol % ZrO_2-3 mol % Y_2O_3. Grain growth can therefore be eliminated as a cause of transformation due to the very short times used to densify the composites. The solubility of zirconia in cordierite glass has been determined to be approximately 10 wt% [14]. Dissolution of zirconia into the amorphous phase in this system was also confirmed. Figure 2 shows a transmission electron micrograph of an amorphous region adjacent to a zirconia grain. Microanalysis indicated the presence of zirconia within this phase. It was not possible to detect yttria due to the low overall concentrations present and the overlap of ZrKα and YKα peaks compounded the problem.

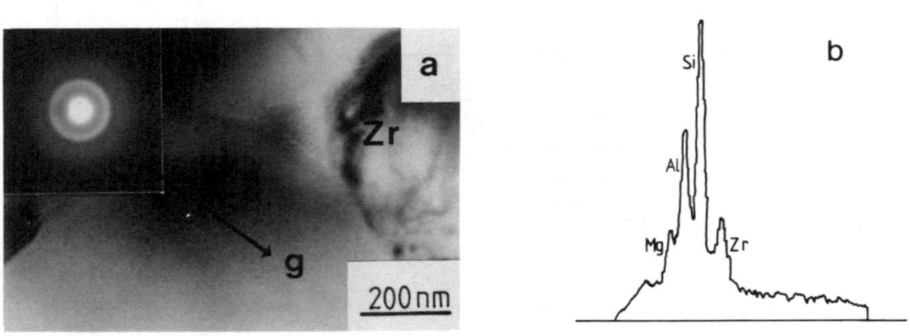

Fig. 2: TEM micrograph of (a) an amorphous region adjacent to a zirconia grain, (b) the corresponding EDX trace.

4. Matrix constraint

The constraint exerted on the zirconia particles by cordierite is lower than that exerted by alumina as a consequence of the large difference in thermal expansion coefficient and lower elastic modulus of cordierite. The lower thermal expansion of cordierite, compared with that of zirconia, leads to tensile stresses being imposed on the zirconia grains during cooling from the fabrication temperature. The presence of such tensile stresses will favour transformation. A relative volume concentration of approximately 3.0% is expected for zirconia on cooling from the fabrication temperature. Thus the volume contraction associated with the thermal expansion mismatch is comparable to the volume expansion associated with the tetragonal to monoclinic transformation.

No evidence of microcracking was found around the transformed monoclinic zirconia inclusions (Fig. 1a) indicating mutual cancellation of elastic strains developed by the two processes. The results, given in Table 1, do indicate that the matrix does prevent about 50% transformation suggesting that the cordierite imposes a certain degree of constraint on the zirconia grains.

Fracture Toughness and Fracture Strength

Fig. 3 shows the variation in fracture strength and fracture toughness as a function of ZrO_2-2 mol% Y_2O_3 content. Their behaviour is not identical as predicted by the Griffith equation. Unlike the relationship between fracture toughness and zirconia content, the strength shows a maximum at 20 vol% ZrO_2-2 mol% Y_2O_3. Composites containing 30 vol% ZrO_2-2 mol% Y_2O_3 show a large reduction in fracture strength. The critical flaw size in these composites is required to be much larger than for the specimens containing less zirconia. It was observed that dispersion of zirconia inclusions in the cordierite matrix is more homogeneous in the specimen containing 10 vol% ZrO_2-2 mol% Y_2O_3 than in the composite containing 30 vol % ZrO_2-2 mol% Y_2O_3 where zirconia agglomerates of 10 to 15 μm existed. It may therefore be concluded that the reduction in fracture strength of the specimen containing 30 vol% ZrO_2-2 mol% Y_2O_3 is due to the heterogeneous dispersion of zirconia inclusions.

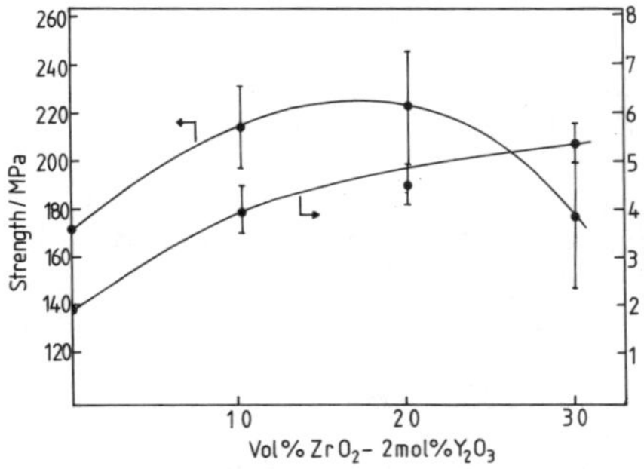

Fig. 3: The variation in fracture strength and fracture toughness with increasing ZrO_2 additions.

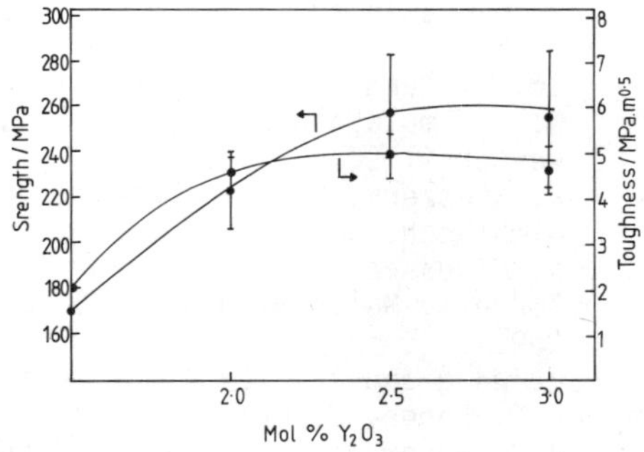

Fig. 4: The variation in fracture strength and fracture toughness in cordierite 20 v/o ZrO_2 as a function of Y_2O_3 content in the ZrO_2.

Figure 4 shows fracture strength and fracture toughness as a function of yttria content in the zirconia inclusions for the composites containing 20 vol% partially stabilized zirconia. The fracture toughness increases sharply with yttria content up to 2 mol% but levels off from 2 to 3 mol%. The result differs from the relationship between the fracture toughness and yttria content observed in ZTA in which a maximum toughness occurs at 2 mol% yttria. This difference is considered to be due to the destabilisation of the zirconia in cordierite composites. It may therefore be inferred that the transformability of zirconia inclusions, originally containing 2.5 to 3 mol% yttria in the cordierite, is similar to that of those containing 2 mol% yttria in alumina. The fracture strength shows a similar trend to the fracture toughness, indicating that there is no change in critical flaw size in the specimens as a result of varying the yttria content of the zirconia.

Observation of cracks around indentations demonstrated that the degree of crack deflection by zirconia inclusions was very limited. Two mechanisms are thus considered to be important in toughening and strengthening of zirconia-cordierite composites in the present work: stress-induced transformation toughening and the presence of residual stresses.

CONCLUSIONS

1. Zirconia particles exhibit unusually high transformability in a cordierite matrix. The evidence collected from this study strongly suggests that this is brought about by the leaching of yttria out of the zirconia into the amorphous phase present in the matrix.
2. The mechanical properties of cordierite are substantially improved by zirconia additions. The improvements are due to stress induced transformation toughening and the presence of residual stresses. No evidence of microcrack toughening or significant crack deflection was found.

REFERENCES

1. N. Claussen, p.325 in Advances in Ceramics, Vol. 12. Science and Technology of Zirconia II, edited by N. Claussen, M. Ruhle and A.H. Heuer, The American Ceramic Society, Columbus, OH (1984).
2. A.G. Evans and R.M. Cannon, Acta Metall., **35** (1986) 761.
3. N. Claussen and J. Jahn, J. Amer. Ceram. Soc., **63** (1980) 228.
4. Y. Kubota and H. Takagi, p.999 in Advances in Ceramics, Vol. 24. Science and Technology of Zirconia III, edited by S. Somiya, N. Yamamoto and H. Yanagida, The American Ceramic Society, Westerville, OH (1988).
5. K. Nieszery, K.L. Weibkopff, G. Petzow and W. Pannhorst, p.841 in High Tech. Ceram., edited by P. Vincenzini, Elsevier, Amsterdam (1987).
6. N. Claussen, Journal de Physique, **47** (1986) C1-673.
7. S. Hori, M. Yoshimura and S. Somiya, J. Amer. Ceram. Soc., **69** (1986) 169.
8. J. Wang and R. Stevens, J. Mat. Sci., **23** (1988) 804.
9. F.F. Lange, J. Mat. Sci., **17** (1982) 225.
10. A.H. Heuer and M. Ruhle, p.1 in Advances in Ceramics, Vol. 12. Science and Technology of Zirconia II, edited by N. Claussen, M. Ruhle and A.H. Heuer, The American Ceramic Society, Columbus, OH (1984).
11. I.W. Chen and Y.H. Chaio, Acta Metall., **31** (1983) 10.
12. I.W. Chen and Y.H. Chaio, Acta Metall., **33** (1985) 1827.
13. H.G. Scott, J. Mat. Sci., **12** (1977) 311.
14. Y. Cheng and D.P. Thompson, Proc. Brit. Ceram. Soc., **42** (1989).

INFLUENCE OF GEOMETRICAL AND MATERIAL PARAMETERS ON THE THERMOMECHANICAL BEHAVIOUR OF CERAMIC COMPONENTS

A. Dutschk
DLR (IBK), Pfaffenwaldring 38-40, D-7000 Stuttgart 80
F.E. Buresch
KFA (IRW), D-5170 Jülich
UNI (ICA), Pfaffenwaldring 27, D-7000 Stuttgart 80

ABSTRACT

The combination of ceramic components in automotive engines induces heavy thermomechanical problems. This work is addressed to characterize and quantify the stress analysis with respect to the material properties of a ceramic tube. The residual stresses as well as the heat flux induced macroscopic stresses will be numerically analyzed with FEM. The results agree with experimental results.

1. SCOPE OF THE WORK

It is proposed that in the future ceramic components should be used in automotive engines. Thus metallic and ceramic parts are intimately connected and serious safety problems arises due to the different thermomechanical properties of these two classes of materials.

This work is addressed to characterize and quantify the stress analysis with respect to the material properties of a ceramic tube which shall be used as a piston chamber in an engine. Especially the thermomechanical stresses will be analyzed if the metal is cast in the mold.

The thermomechanical stress distribution during the casting and subsequent cooling process will be numerically modelled with respect to the statistical integral strength and the local residual stress distribution of the special ceramic component. The experimental and theoretical results show that besides the thermal stresses which arises in the ceramic tube during casting the mold the survival of the tube depends strongly on the inherent residual stresses which are build up during the fabrication process of this ceramic component.

2. MATERIAL PROPERTIES

As a model component two sizes of SSiC tubes are used. They have a diameter of 100 mm and the heights are of 50 mm and 246 mm respectively. The density and the young's modulus are about 3,1 g/cm^3 and 400 GPa respectively. The thermal conductivity and the heat capacity are related to the temperature which are given as polynominal functions of temperature.

It is well known from the literature that ceramic components contain residual stresses due to statistical variations during the fabrication process such as density gradients during forming or thermal gradients during cooling down from sintering temperature. Especially residual stresses are built up in ceramics during cooling down from sintering due to two different shrinkage processes: one is due to the inelastic deformation above and the other is due to the elastic deformation below a material specific temperature which is called the freezing temperature T_c.

Above T_c shrinkage arises due to creep, below T_c the mechanism is linear elastic thermal expansion. Both processes are instantaneous related to the heat capacity C and the heat conductivity K of the material and the environmental cooling rate dT/dt.

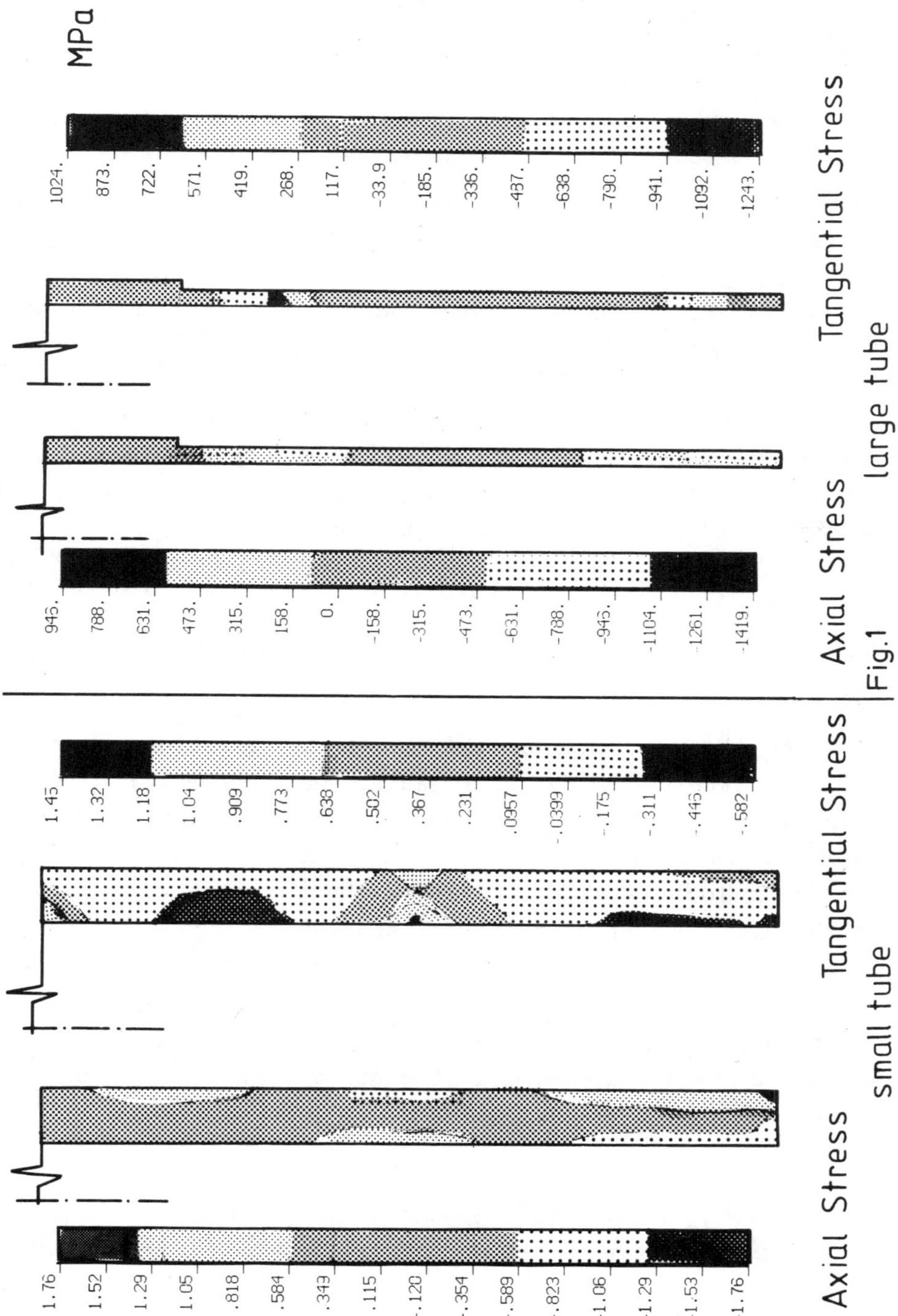
MPa
1024.
873.
722.
571.
419.
268.
117.
-33.9
-185.
-336.
-487.
-638.
-790.
-941.
-1092.
-1243.
945.
788.
631.
473.
315.
158.
0.
-158.
-315.
-473.
-631.
-788.
-946.
-1104.
-1261.
-1419.
Axial Stress
Tangential Stress
large tube
1.45
1.32
1.18
1.04
.909
.773
.638
.502
.367
.231
.0957
-.0399
-.175
-.311
-.446
-.582
1.76
1.52
1.29
1.05
.818
.584
.349
.115
-.120
-.354
-.589
-.823
-1.06
-1.29
-1.53
-1.76
Axial Stress
Tangential Stress
small tube

Fig.1

The processes are related to the differential diffusion equation of the scalar temperature field given:

$$C\dot{T} + KT = \dot{R} \qquad (1)$$

where $\dot{R}$ is the load vector and C and K are the respective matrices.

The thermomechanical coupling relates present stress σ (t) to the integral strain ϵ (t) and the residual strains $\eta = \alpha \Delta T$ with respect to each material point (x,y,z) and the specific shrinkage mechanisms for $T = T_c$ and $T < T_c$ in volume fractions B_1 and B_2 respectively. The thermomechanical coupling is numerically evaluated using the FEM systems SMART 1 and 2 following the equation /1/

$$\sigma = \mathbf{E} \cdot (\varepsilon + \eta_1(B_2) + \eta_2(B_2) + \ldots + \eta_n(B_2)) \qquad (2)$$

The figure 1 shows the local distribution of the residual stress components in axial and tangential direction after rapid cooling of the component, which is taken as worst case. It is obvious that the residual stresses can reach locally critical values where the heat flux due to the distribution of the heat capacity is high. The theoretically evaluated distribution of residual stresses was experimentally verified for another component /2/. The fracture probability of the component was then calculated using the multimodal Weibull strength distribution given as /3, 4/

$$P_{f,tot} = 1 - \exp\left\{ - \left(\frac{1}{m}!\right)^m \left(\frac{1}{\sigma_{fv}}\right)^m \frac{1}{v} \cdot \Sigma \right\} \qquad (3)$$

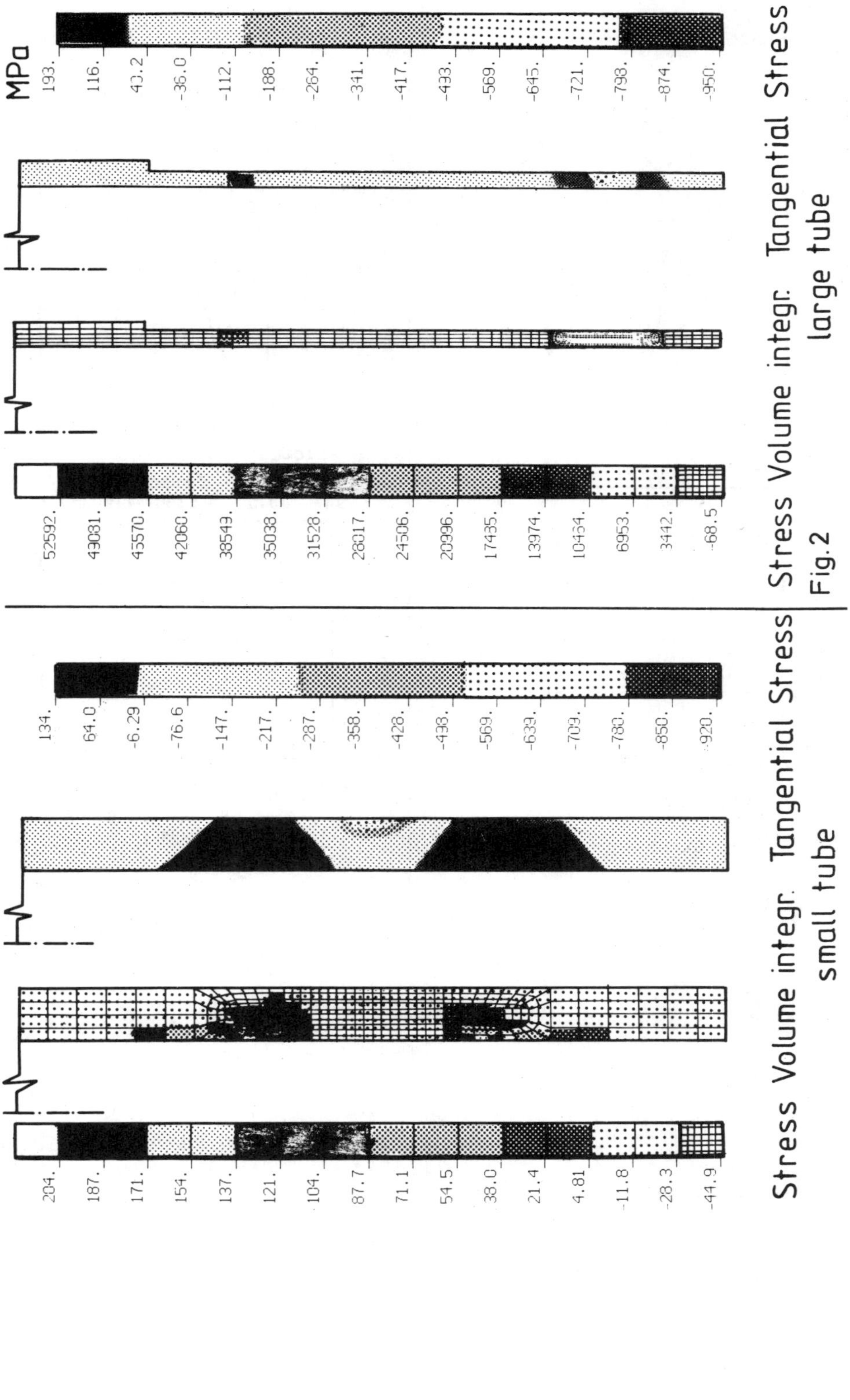
MPa
193.
116.
43.2
-36.0
-112.
-188.
-264.
-341.
-417.
-493.
-569.
-645.
-721.
-798.
-874.
-950.
52592.
49081.
45570.
42060.
38549.
35038.
31528.
28017.
24506.
20996.
17485.
13974.
10464.
6953.
3442.
-68.5
Stress Volume integr.
Tangential Stress
large tube
134.
64.0
-6.29
-76.6
-147.
-217.
-287.
-358.
-428.
-498.
-569.
-639.
-709.
-780.
-850.
-920.
204.
187.
171.
154.
137.
121.
104.
87.7
71.1
54.5
38.0
21.4
4.81
-11.8
-28.3
-44.9
Stress Volume integr.
Tangential Stress
small tube

Fig.2

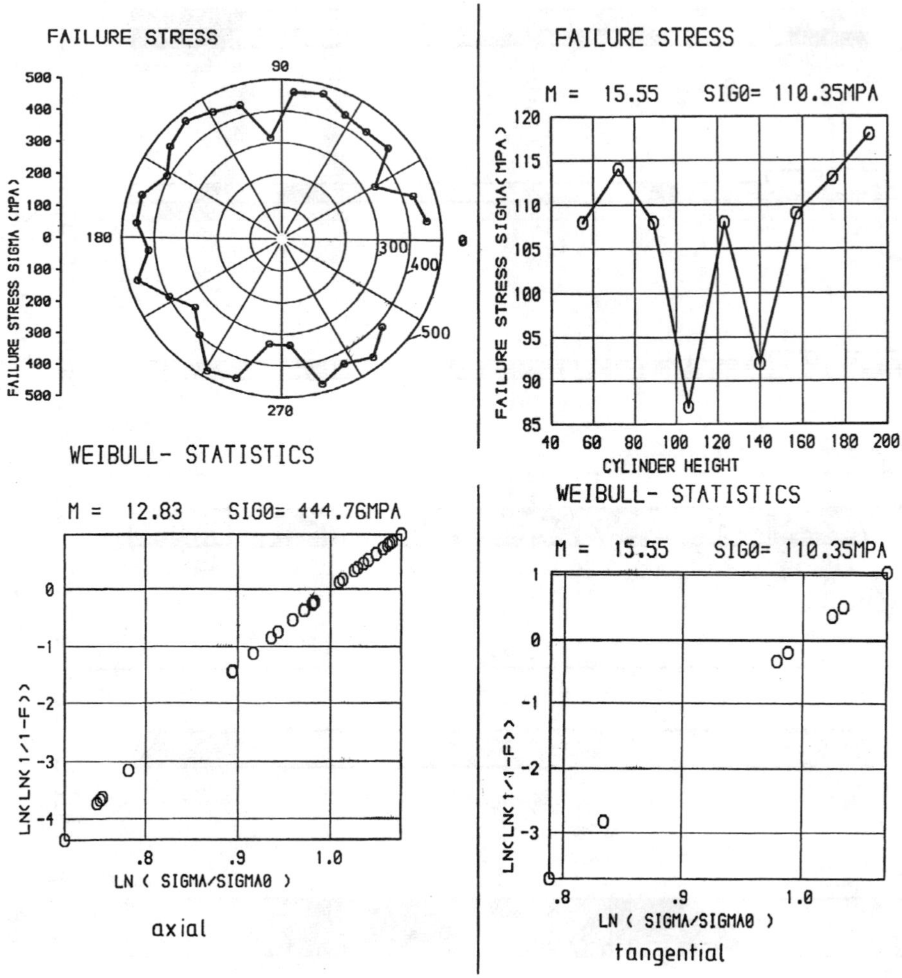
FAILURE STRESS
FAILURE STRESS SIGMA (MPA)
90
180
0
270
300
400
500
FAILURE STRESS
M = 15.55 SIG0= 110.35MPA
FAILURE STRESS SIGMA(MPA)
CYLINDER HEIGHT
WEIBULL- STATISTICS
M = 12.83 SIG0= 444.76MPA
LN(LN(1/1-F))
LN (SIGMA/SIGMA0)
axial
WEIBULL- STATISTICS
M = 15.55 SIG0= 110.35MPA
LN(LN(1/1-F))
LN (SIGMA/SIGMA0)
tangential

Fig.3

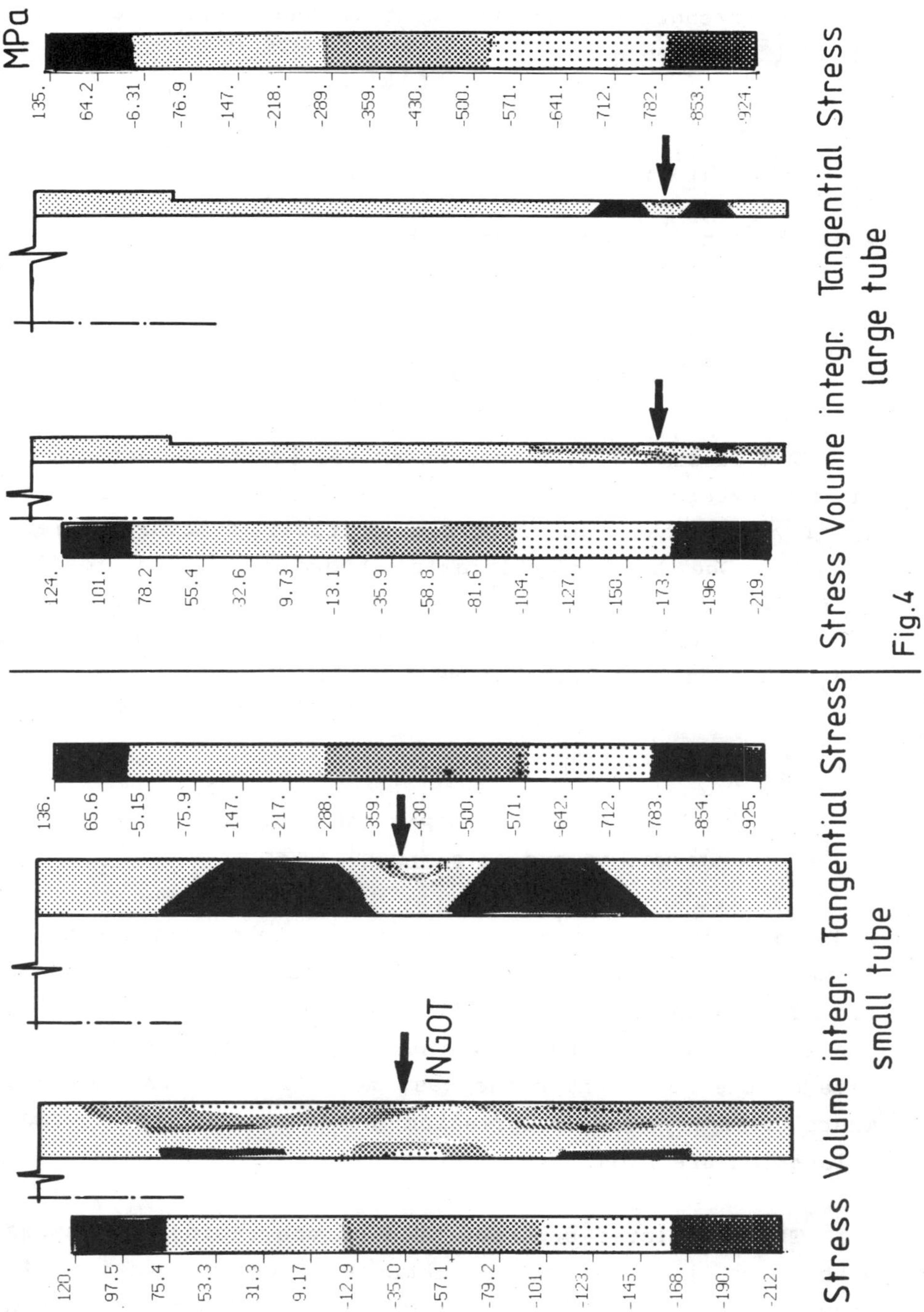
MPa
INGOT
Stress Volume integr. Tangential Stress
large tube
Stress Volume integr. Tangential Stress
small tube

Fig.4

The strength of the component is than calculated using the following equation

$$\sigma_{fv} = \left\{ \frac{1}{v} \int_V \left[\left(\frac{\sigma_1}{H(\sigma_1)} \right)^m + \left(\frac{\sigma_2}{H(\sigma_2)} \right)^m + \left(\frac{\sigma_3}{H(\sigma_3)} \right)^m \right] dV \right\}^{1/m} \tag{4}$$

where Σ is the stress volume integral.

$$\Sigma = \int_V \left[\left(\frac{\sigma_1}{H(\sigma_1)} \right)^m + \left(\frac{\sigma_2}{H(\sigma_2)} \right)^m + \left(\frac{\sigma_3}{H(\sigma_3)} \right)^m \right] dV$$

The failure of a component arises if the superposition of the external load with the residual stresses reaches locally the material specific critical fracture stress (fig.2). Due to the multiaxial thermomechanical loading during the casting process the statistical distribution of the axial and tangential strength are measured using bend and ring specimens which shows fig. 3.

3. INFLUENCE OF THERMOCHANICAL LOADING DURING CASTING ON FAILURE

High local thermal stress arises in the tube when the metal is cast into the mold. The calculated local distribution of the thermal stresses shows fig. 4. The highest tangential and axial thermal tension stresses arises on the opposite site of the point where the cast metal flux meets the tube where contrary the compression stresses due to thermal dilatation are high.

The calculated superposition of the residual stresses with strength values of the components using equation [4] shows fig. 5 which correlates very well with the observed failure which shows fig. 6.

Stress Volume Integral ×10^3

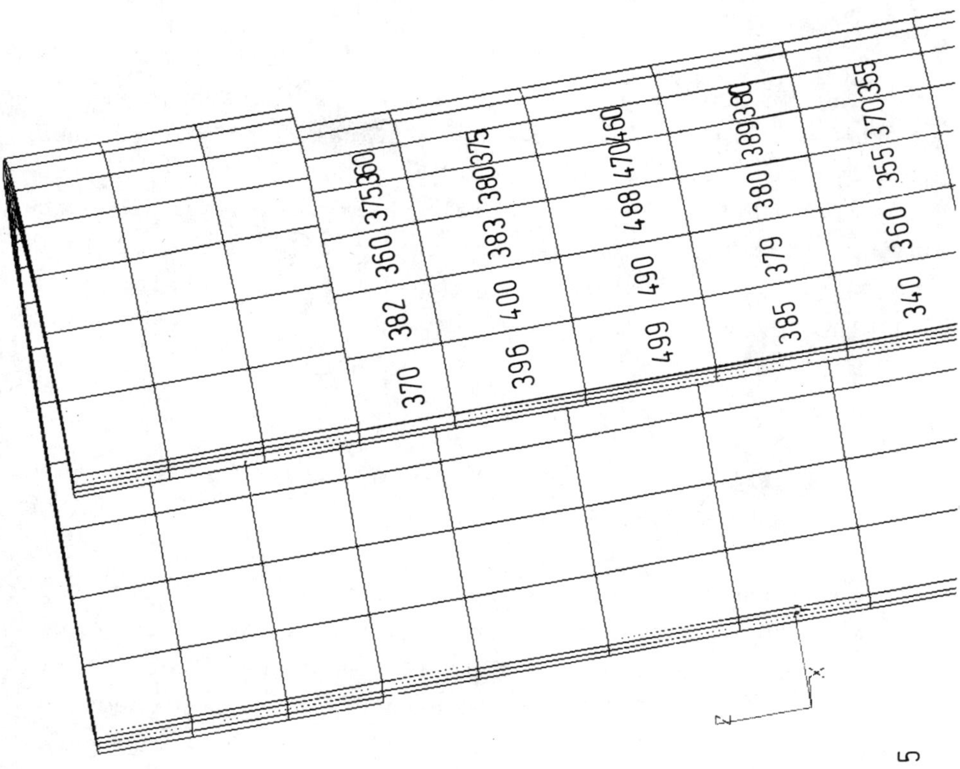

Fig. 5

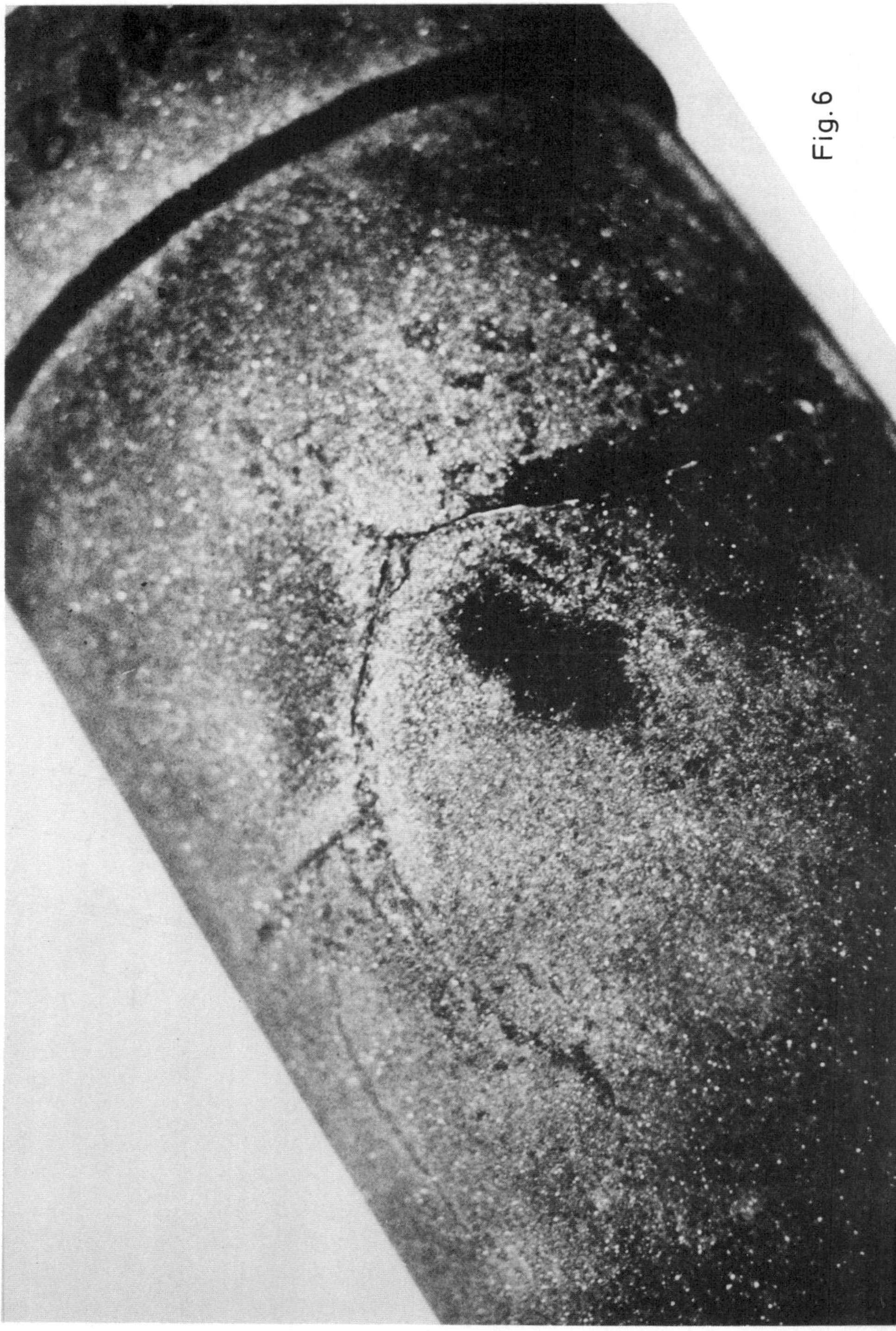

Fig.6

REFERENCES

[1] Szimmat, J.
SMART II,2 - Instationäre Diffusion (Benutzerhandbuch)
ISD-Bericht NR. 192 Revision A,
Universität Stuttgart 1982

[2] Buresch,I., Schubert, H., Petzow, G., Dutschk, A.
Entstehung und Ausbildung thermischer Eigenspannungen
in keramischen Bauteilen
Vortrag DGM Hauptversammlung 1989 Karlsruhe

[3] Stanley, P., Fessler, H. Sivill, A.D.
An Engineers Approach to the Prediction of
Failure Probability of Brittle Components
Proceeding of the British Ceramic Society June 1973

[4] Lamon, J. Evans, A.G.
Statistical Analysis of Bending Strength for
Brittle Solids
Journal of the American Ceramic Society 66, 1983

HIGH TEMPERATURE MECHANICAL BEHAVIOUR OF DENSE ZIRCON BODIES

R. Torrecillas, G. Orange, G. Fantozzi, INSA, 69621 Villeurbanne, FRANCE.

E. Segura, M.A. Rodríguez,* S. de Aza, J.S. Moya, Instituto de Cerámica y Vidrio CSIC, Arganda del Rey, Madrid, SPAIN.
* Cerámicas Tenaces, S.A., Getafe, Madrid, SPAIN.

ABSTRACT

Submicron zircon powders have been used as starting materials to obtain dense compact bodies (99% th) by pressureless sintering at 1570 and 1630º C.
Bending strength, fracture toughness and creeep behaviour have been studied as a function of temperature. The effect of a partial dissociation of zircon on the high temperature mechanical properties is also reported.

INTRODUCTION

It is very well reported in the literature (1-6) that zircon-based materials have excelent chemical stability against melted glasses as well as slags. However no information is available on the high temperature mechanical behaviour of zircon bodies.
The aim of this investigation is to study the bending strength, fracture toughness and creep of dense zircon specimens obtained by two different sintering treatments.

MATERIALS AND METHODS

Fine zircon powder (QUIMINSA, ESPAÑA) with the chemical analysis (wt%) SiO_2, 34.20; ZrO_2, 62.13; H_fO_2, 1.14; Al_2O_3, 0.50; Fe_2O_3, 0.09; TiO_2, 0.20; CaO, 0.17; MgO, 0.07; Na_2O, 0.06; wt loss, 1.42; and 1.3 μm average particle size; 8.3 m^2/g BET specific surface, has been used as starting material.

This powder was isopressed at 200 MPa and the obtained green density was 2.80 g/cm^3.

Two different sintering temperatures were used: 1570ºC 2h and 1630ºC 2h with a heating rate of 5ºC/min.

The bending strength (σ_f) and fracture toughness (K_{ic}) were determined by 3- point bending method using bars of 3 x 4 x 25 mm size and with a loading rate of 0.1 mm/ min., in the temperature interval ranging from RT to 1200ºC

The creep test was done in a special equipement by 4-point bending test with a σ = 30 MPa.

The microstructure was observed by SEM.

RESULTS AND DISCUSSION

In table I, the RT mechanical properties, density and quantitative phases determined by XRD analysis, are reported for the samples sintered at 1570 and 1630º C. As expected from the SiO_2-ZrO_2 system (7) a partial decomposition of zircon took place at 1630º C.

In Fig. 1 the σf and K_{ic} values are shown. As observed the σf and K_{ic} values increase slowly from a T < 600ºC in the sample sintered at 1570ºC and from a T > 600ºC in the sample heated at 1630ºC up to 800ºC.

At higher temperature (T > 800ºC) a decrease in both parameters is clearly detected. However, it is worth to point out that the decreasing rate in both parameters ($\sigma f, K_{ic}$) is significantly higher in the 1570º C sample. This behaviour is in complete agreement with the results obtained in the creep test (Fig. 2) where the creep strain rate ($\dot{\varepsilon}$) is ~10 times lower than in the 1630ºC sample.

TABLE I

RT mechanical properties, density and quantitative phases determined by XRD* analysis for samples sintered at 1570 and 1630º C

	ZS 1570	ZS 1630
Density g/cm3	4.46	4.40
Bending strengh σ_f (MPa)	270± 8%	290± 7%
Fracture toughness MPa m1/2	2.10± 5%	2,00± 10%
Zirconia (Vol %)	1.0	3.0

*Diffractometer Siemens D 500, Cu K and Ni filter

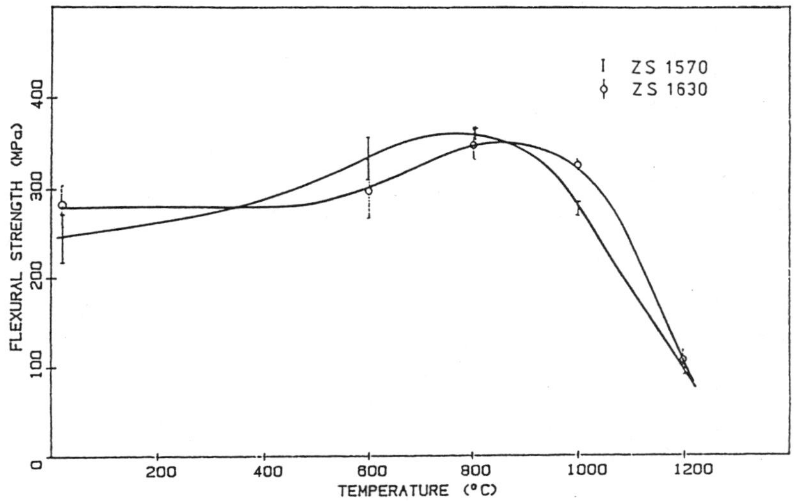

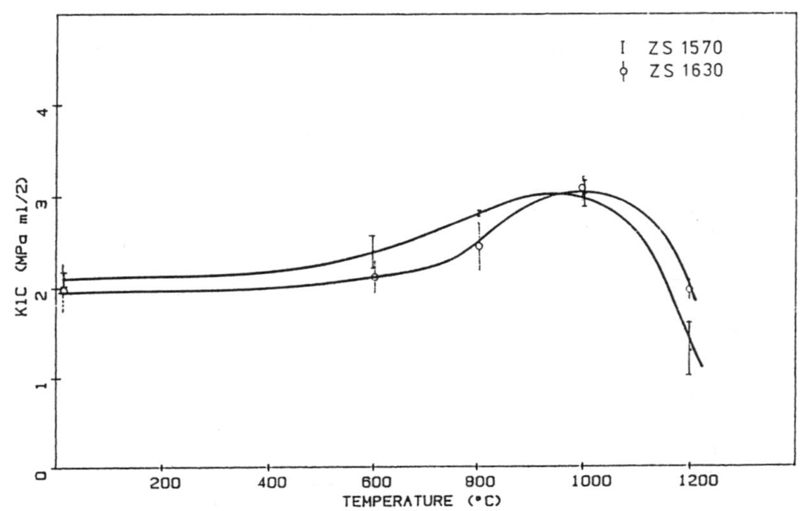

FIG. 1. σ_f and K1c vs temperature for ZS 1570 and ZS 1630 samples.

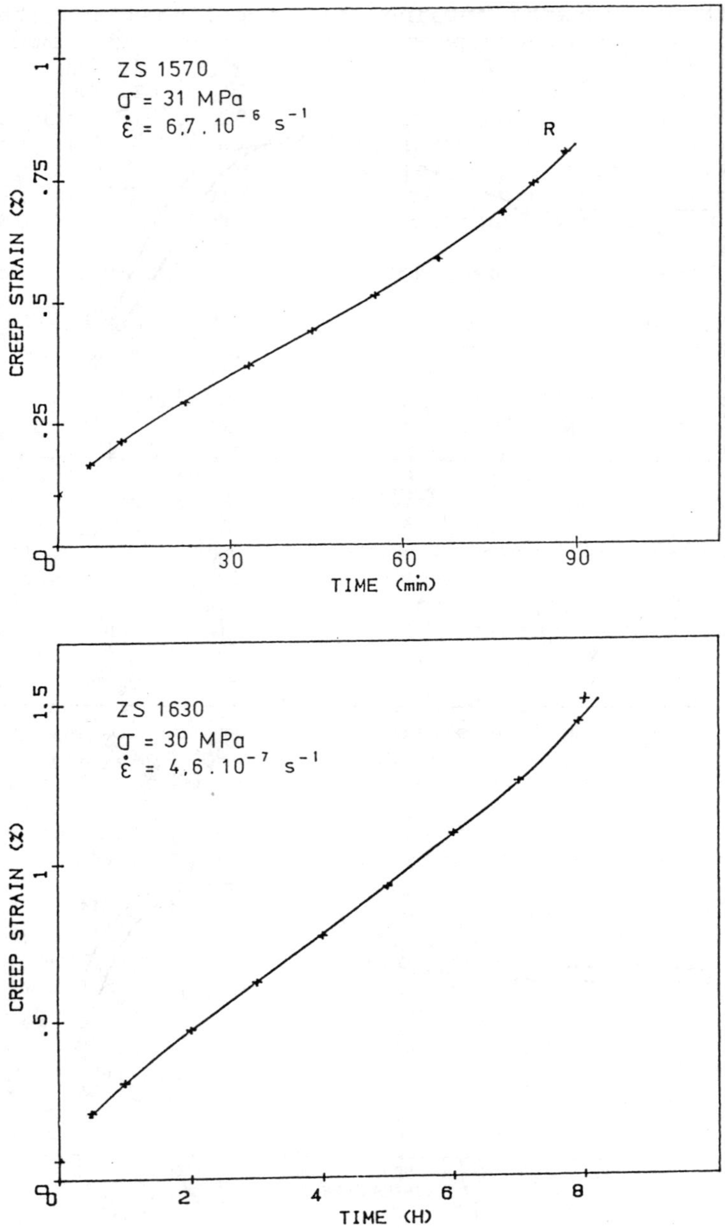

FIG. 2. Creep strain vs. time for ZS 1570 and ZS1630 samples.

The SEM micrographs obtained on as polished and thermally etched surface corresponding to as-sintered samples are shown in Fig. 3.

Fig. 4 shows the SEM fracture surfaces of both samples after the high temperature bending tests these micrographs clearly indicate a progresive change in the fracture mode from complete transgranular and brittle at RT to intergranular and plastic fracture at 1200ºC.

From these results the following points can be stated:

i) No significant grain growth is observed in both sintered samples.

ii) The glassy phase present in both samples is responsible for the strengthening observed in the temperature interval ranging from 500ºC to 800ºC.

iii) The different HT mechanical behaviour observed in both samples have to be related to the nature of the glassy phase present in each sample. That is, in the sample sintered at 1570ºC, the viscosity of this glassy phase is lower than the one corresponding to 1630ºC sample (Fig. 2); in the former case, the liquid completly wet the zircon grains while tend to be located in pochets between aglomerates in the last one. This behaviour have to be associated with a change in the glassy phase composition as a consequence of a partial disolution of the silica glass formed during the partial decomposition of zircon.

    This fact can explain the observed differences in the high temperature behaviour of both materials.

    It is expected that the Tg corresponding to this silica-reach glassy phase will be higher that the one corresponding to 1570ºC samples. Consequently, at 1200ºC higher deformation rates are expected in the speciment sintered at 1570ºC, as has been experimentaly observed (Fig. 2)

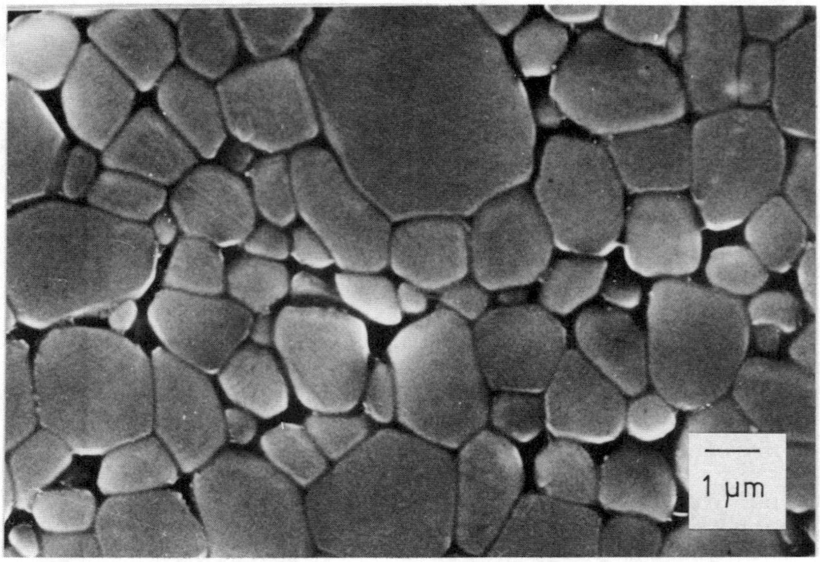

(A)

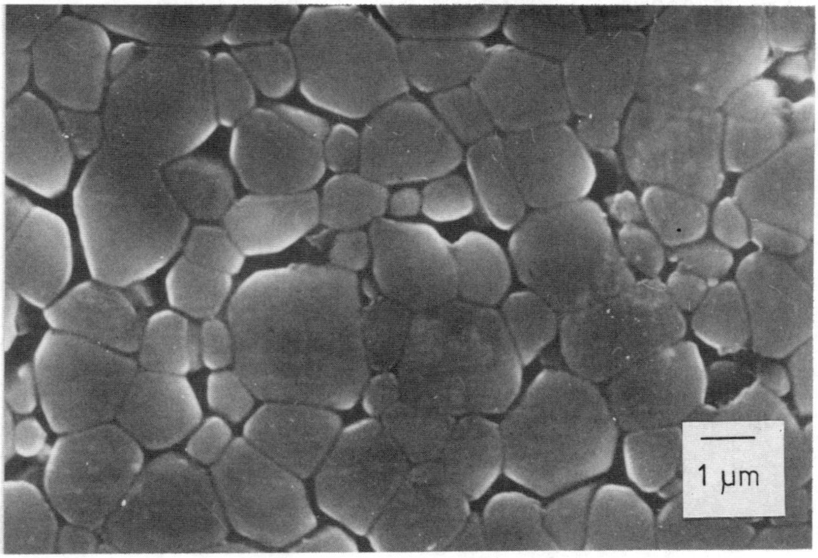

(B)

FIG. 3. SEM Micrographs obtained on polished and thermal etched (1400º C-2h) surfaces corresponding to ZS 1570 (A) and ZS 1630 (B).

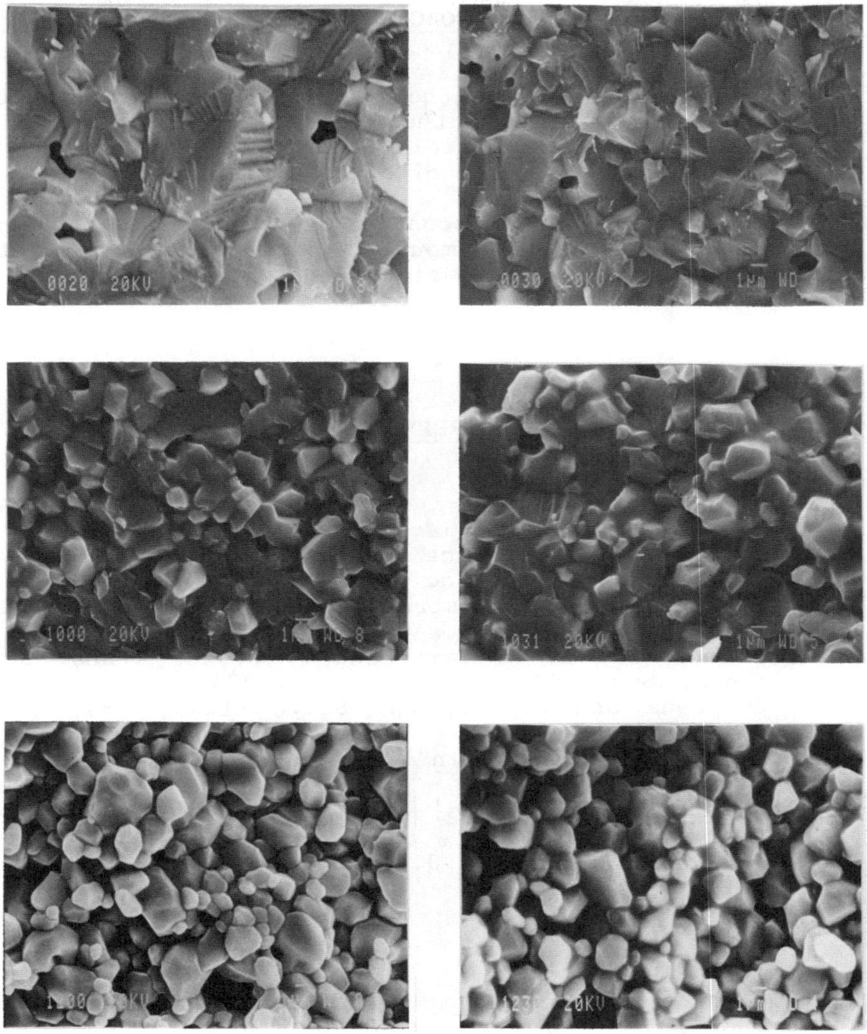

FIG. 4. SEM Fracture surfaces after bending - test at differents temperatures.

CONCLUSIONS

The results obtained in the present investigation clearly prove that by changing the chemical composition of the glassy phase, it is possible to improve the high temperature mechanical behaviour of zircon based materials.

The composition and viscosity of this glassy phase is very dependent on a) impurity present in the starting zircon powders and b) the sintering temperature.

REFERENCES

1.- Aldred, F.H., Shutt, T.C. and Steen, W.J. (1965). Glass. Technol., 6, 14.
2.- E. Fauber, J.V. Peirce and D.N. Clook, J. Austral. Ceram. Soc., 13, (1), 1977, PP. 17-19.
3.- J.A. Thomson, J. Austral. Ceram. Soc., 19 (1), 1983, PP. 5-7.
4.- S. de Aza, C. Richmond and J. White, Trans. J. Br. Ceram. Soc., 73, (4), 109-116, (1974)
5.- P. Pena and S. de Aza, Sci. Ceram., (9), (1977), 239.
6.- R.C. Garvie (1984) In N. Claussen, M. Rühle and A.H. Hever (Eds.) Advances in Ceramics, Vol. 12, Am. Ceram. Soc., Columbus. PP. 465-79.
7.- P. Pena, S. de Aza, J. Mater. Sci., 19, (1984), 135-142.

MEASUREMENT OF FRACTURE TOUGHNESS AND WORK OF FRACTURE OF SINTERED SILICON NITRIDE USING A MODIFIED CHEVRON-NOTCHED SPECIMEN.

F. Merckx[+], B. Fournel[++], P. Vivier[+++], O. Van der Biest[+], M. Boussuge[++], B. Cales[+++]
+ Department of Metallurgy and Materials Engineering, Katholieke Universiteit Leuven, Belgium.
++ Centre des Matériaux, Ecole Nationale Supérieure des Mines,Evry, France.
+++ Céramiques Techniques Desmarquest, Trappes, France.

ABSTRACT

A modified chevron-notched specimen has been evaluated from a theoretical as well as an experimental point of view. Theoretical analysis shows that 3-point bending and a high stifness machine will promote stable crack growth. The specimen can be used successfully to measure fracture toughness from the work of fracture if stable crack growth occurs. Special attention needs to be paid to the procedure of pre-cracking by indentation so that the pre-crack and the fracture surface are co-planar. Toughness values derived from maximum load underestimate toughness.

INTRODUCTION

Toughness measurements of monolithic ceramics are subject to large scatter. Continued development of measurement methodology is needed in order to improve the accuracy and reproducibility with which this important property can be determined.

Use of the chevron-notched specimen has the advantage that a sharp pre-crack should be generated during the loading of the specimen due to the high stress intensity factor at the tip of the V-shaped cross-section. A valid test requires that crack initiation takes place before the maximum load is reached in the load-displacement curve. In practice different types of load-displacement curves are obtained, depending on the details of specimen preparation procedure. A disadvantage of the chevron geometry is that the location of crack initiation is not accessible to assure its sharpness.

A modified chevron-notched specimen has been proposed [1] (Figure 1), in which crack sharpness can be controlled by indentation. In the present work the use of this modified chevron specimen is explored in order to determine the toughness of a sintered silicon nitride.

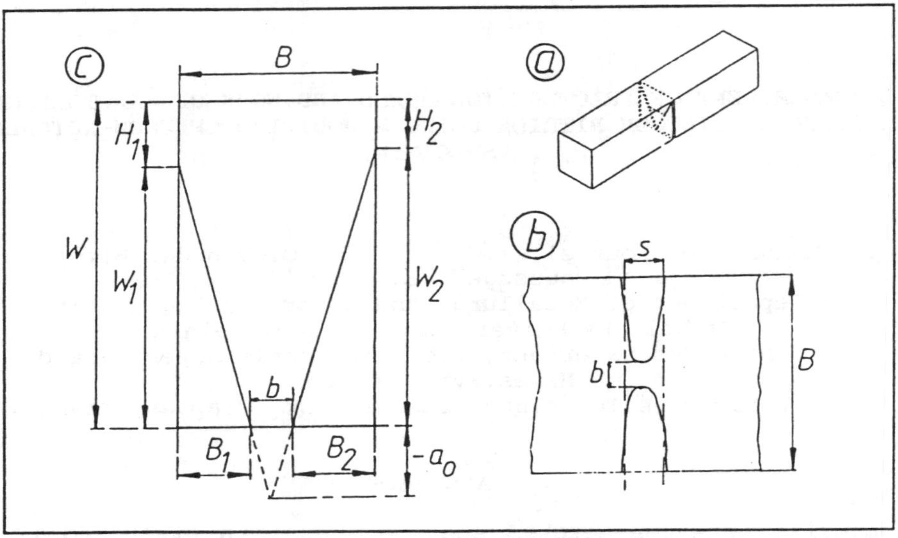

Figure 1 : (a) Overall view of the specimen. The length is 55mm; (b) Bottom of the specimen. Knoop indentations were introduced in the ligament b; (c) Cross section at the notch; Nominal values are :W=5mm; B=3mm ; B1=B2=1.3mm; b=0.4mm ; H1=H2=0.2mm ; s=0.6mm ; a_0/W=-0.1.

EXPERIMENTAL TECHNIQUE

Figure 1 shows the shape and dimensions of the sample used. One or more Knoop indentations with a load of 200N were applied at the ligament b. The material is Kersit 301 (Desmarquest), a pressureless sintered silicon nitride containing also Y_2O_3 and Al_2O_3. Characteristics of this material are : density 3.2 kg/mm^3 ; no open porosity ; grain size in the range 1 to 20 µm ; E-modulus 315 GPa and an average strength of 870 MPa.

The compliance of the specimen as function of crack depth was experimentally determined by measuring the deflection of the specimen with respect to the frame of the machine. Values were corrected for the displacement of the support and loading rods.

Two methods were used to determine toughness : (i) From the maximum load P_{max} as in [1]. (ii) From the work of fracture γ, which was calculated by integration of the load- displacement curve. The toughness is derived from the equation :

$K_{Ic}= \sqrt{(2E'\gamma)}$.

THEORETICAL STUDIES

Compliance of the specimen

The compliance of the chevron-notched specimen of Figure 1 is calculated using two methods. One is based on the straight through crack assumption [2]. For the compliance of the straight through crack specimen, formulas have been given by Chen [3] and Scrawley [4]. Both give numerical results which are very close to each other and both were used as convenience dictated. The other method is based on Bluhm's slice model [5].

The calculations showed that both the straight through crack model and Bluhm's slice model give a good fit to the data at relative crack lenghts α=a/W below 0.7. The experimental curve can be fitted by the equation :
$C = C(\alpha=0) + 1.536.10^{-3}. \exp(9.298\alpha)$.

Calculation of Stability Conditions

In order to achieve a valid test result during toughness testing, it is necessary that the crack grows in a stable manner. The stability factor S as defined by Bluhm and Schimmoeler[5] has been used. S should be positive for stable crack growth. The stability factor depends strongly on the shape of the compliance curve and for this reason the results in this section should not be seen as quantitative predictions but rather as guidelines in the design of experimental conditions which will lead to stable crack growth. The compliance curve calculated with the straight through crack assumption has been used.

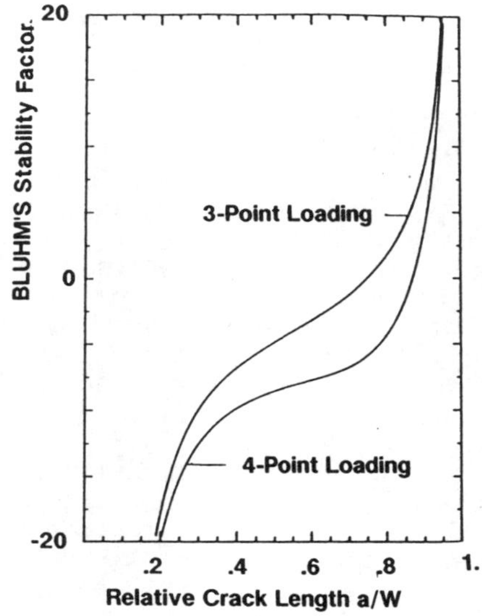

Figure 2 : Bluhm 's stability factor S as function of relative crack length (a/W) for three and four point bending.

Figure 2 shows that 3-point loading is preferrable to 4-point loading. This prediction was confirmed by the experimental results : it was not possible to achieve stable crack propagation using four point bending. This can readily be understood since it is easy to show that for the same stress on the tensile face of a sample, the elastic energy in the sample is twice as high and the elastic energy in the machine is four times higher in 4-point than in three point loading. An analogous calculation showed that use of a stiff machine will promote stable crack growth during testing.

EXPERIMENTAL RESULTS AND DISCUSSION

Stable crack behaviour
Three types of load-displacement curves have been obtained (Figure 5) showing increasing levels of stable crack growth. Stable crack growth could only be achieved by using three point instead of four point bending. It was also found essential to bridge the two notches on the tensile face of the sample by a continuous row of Knoop indentations instead of a single one.

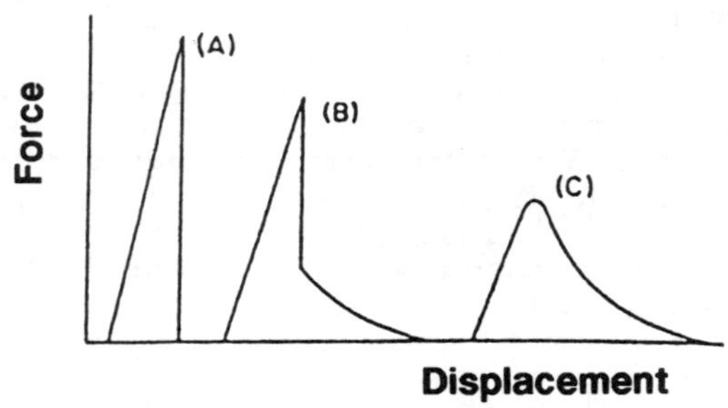

Figure 3 : Three types of load-displacement curves observed.

Figure 4 : Side view of reconstituted samples. Tensile face is on top.

Nevertheless, stable crack growth was not consistently obtained. Systematic comparison of the fracture path with the load-displacement curve shows that a straight planar crack front (Figure 4a) always corresponds to stable crack behaviour. When the crack front changes plane near the tensile surface (Figure 4b), most samples do not show stability. The difference in behaviour is thought to be related to the crack pattern introduced by the indentation and its interaction with the two grooves in the specimen. Depending on the precise position and orientation of the indentation, it appears that the straight radial cracks do not run straight into the specimen, but may become curved, tending to run parallel to the surface near the crack tip. Such a crack orientation is not favorably oriented for further propagation under the applied stress system ,but effectively requires re-initiation into the proper orientation. Further research is required in order to clarify these points and thus increase the reproducibility of the procedure.

Toughness values

Values for K_{IC} were derived from the maximum load $K_{IC}(P_{max})$ as well as from the work of fracture, $K_{IC}(\gamma)$. The values in Table 1 are for five samples which showed stable crack propagation during the test.

TABLE 1 : Toughness values in $MPa\sqrt{m}$

$K_{IC}(dt)$ [6]	$K_{IC}(P_{max})$	$K_{IC}(\gamma)$
6.3	5.0 ± 0.23	5.9 ± 0.18

The value obtained from the work of fracture differs by about 6% from that obtained by the double torsion technique, $K_{IC}(dt)$. $K_{IC}(P_{max})$ is however about 20 % lower. This discrepancy cannot be explained by errors in the parameters used in its calculation. An error analysis indicates that measurement errors could at most give a difference of about 4%. An explanation needs to be sought in the analytical model used to derive the formula for $K_{IC}(P_{max})$. Specifically, since $K_{IC}(P_{max})$ is systematically lower, it is thought that residual tensile stresses induced by the indentation, which have not been taken into account in the model [1] are, the cause for the discrepancy. In contrast, $K_{IC}(\gamma)$ is based on the complete load displacement diagram and will not be sensitive to the residual stresses at the beginning of crack propagation.

REFERENCES

1 Himsolt G., Munz D., Fett T., J. Am. Ceram. Soc., 1987, **70**, C133-135.
2 Munz D., Shannon J.L., Int. J. Fracture, 1980, **16**,R137-141.
3 Chen C., Heng Y., Chin C-Y,ASTM STP 855, 1983, 179.
4 Scrawley J.E., Gross B., ASTM STP 601, 1976,571
5 Bluhm J.I., ICF4 Fracture 1977,p409.
6 Vivier P., Ph.D. Thesis, Ecole des Mines de Paris,1988.

MICROSCOPICAL OBSERVATIONS ON CONTROLLED CRACK PROPAGATION IN POLYCRYSTALLINE ALUMINA

K.K.O. Bär, IRW-KFA, 5170 Jülich (FRG),
R. Mergen, IWW-TU Clausthal, 3392 Clausthal (FRG)
F. Osterstock, ISMRA-LERMAT, U.A. 1317, 14032 Caen Cedex (France)

Abstract

Fracture mechanical specimen have been prepared and tested in conditions of inert environment. Controlled load or displacement tests have been run in conjunction with AE measurements and optical observations and recording using a device with very high resolution. The R-curves depend on the loading conditions and cannot be explained by solely wake effects. The optical observations show damage in the crack tip region in addition to the propagation of a main crack.

Introduction

Some non-cubic polycristalline ceramics exhibit an R-Curve. This means that the resistance of a material against crack propagation increases as the crack extends. Several models propose to describe this effect. In view of thermal miss-match stresses at the grain boundaries of such ceramics, the increase in size of a frontal process zone (1) (2) offers one kind of explanation. Other models propose bridging and/or hooking in the wake of the crack (3) (4) (5). Basic differences can be put in evidence if crack extension is conducted in well defined conditions, i.e. controlled load or controlled displacement, and if stress corrosion is avoided.

Experimentals

Alumina samples (AF 997 from Desmarquest) have been prepared for three point bending (5 x 10 x 105 mm^3) with a span of 80 mm. They have first been furnished with a notch of relative length a/w = 0.4 using diamond fitted copper blades (notch width < 70 um). Then they were heat-treated for 2 hours at 1100°C under dry nitrogen flow (H_2O < 2 ppm), gold sputtered and kept in imersion oil (H_2O < 80 ppm).

The tests have been run with a Schenk-Trebel 100 RMC testing machine of very high stiffness. The crosshead is driven by an electro-mechanical jack. A high resolution optical microscope (magnification up to x 1250) was fixed on the crosshead. It offered the facility to record and display the behaviour of the crack on a TV screen at a maximal magnification of x 5000. The immersion oil used for the optics also protected the crack against air humidity (6).

Results

The bridging models are load, resp. stress, defined criteria. Thus a point of the load-displacement record, sys. R-curve, is not dependent on the control parameter of loading in inert environment. As an example, once the crack has started before maximum load, and load or displacement is held constant, the crack and its bridging zone should be in mechanical balance with the external constant load, i.e. the crack should stop (7).

On the other hand microcracking in a frontal process zone is a strain energy density problem; crack propagation is defined by the ability of the tested sample to absorb the strain energy. Once the crack is forming and at constant load before the maximum, the input of strain energy would still be transformed into microcracks. The crack may thus continue to propagate and the process zone increase to a critical size until unstable failure. At fixed displacement, microcracks could be created at a decreasing rate: the main crack slows down and finally stops.

Figure 1 shows load-displacement records for either constant load (1a) or constant displacement (1b) conditions. In the first case the formation of a crack has been verified by acoustic emission in conjunction with optical observations. Several levels of constant load have been chosen between just observable deviation from linearity and maximum load. Unstable propagation arrived thus in delays between 2 min and 18 hours. Furthermore in comparison with monotonic loading (constant displacement rate), the point of instability is outside the monotonic loading curve. This is the more pronounced, the lower the constant load level.

At fixed displacement, the load decreases at a decreasing rate as well as the crack velocity (Fig. 1b). At the point of arrest the crack is stable and unloading-reloading cycles can be run from this point without further propagation.

R-curves have been worked out using the crack length calculation by the compliance-Method. They reflect the change of the load-displacement-records with loading conditions. The typical R-Curve from monotonic-loading (constant displacement rate) exhibits a concave curvature (Fig. 2). That obtained from constant load is first convex curved (Fig. 3). It becomes concave only at the point of unstable propagation. The R-curves are thus not unique and the equilibrium conditions of the crack depend on the loading conditions. The aim of the microscopical observations was to get better insight of the micromechanical behaviour of the crack and of the experimental difficulties linked with (Fig. 4).

All the events linked to crack extension are very difficult to get. Nucleation, opening and closure of lateral microcracks, as the main crack propagates, could be detected only at a slow display of the video. Furthermore, the closure is such that the microcrack is no longer visible. This is also the case for the very crack tip: If crack branching occurs, it happens in most of the cases that the non-propagating branch recloses. Of course this depends on the resolution of the used optic (Fig. 5).

Conclusion

The R-curves in inert environment depend on the loading conditions and cannot be explained by solely wake effects. Furthermore the optical observations indicate that damage activity takes place in addition to the propagation of the main crack. All events may not have been resolved. These results give evidence that if wake effects occur, additional micromechanisms take also place and influence the fracture process of the investigated alumina (8). More detailed description and quantification are expected from direct crack length and crack velocity measurements which are in progress. They should also help to get better insight into the equilibrium conditions of an arrested or propagating crack.

References

1) F.E. Buresch, Science of Ceramics, Vol. 7, p. 381-398, 1973
2) W. Pompe, H.A. Bahr, G. Gille and W. Kreher, J. Mat. Science, 13, p. 2770-2773, 1978
3) R. Knehans, R. Steinbrech, J. Mat. Science Letters, 1, p. 327-329, 1982
4) C.J. Fairbanks, B.R. Lawn, R.F. Cook, Y.W. Mai Fracture Mechanics of Ceramics, Vol. 8, pp. 23-37, 1986
5) A.G. Evans, K.T. Faber, J. am. Ceram. Soc., 67, p. 255-260, 1984
6) K.K.O. Bär, Dissertation, RWTH, 1989 to be published
7) K.K.O. Bär, G. Kleist, "Festigkeitsseminar des MPI-Stuttgart", 9/10 March 1988, Proc. in Ceram. Forum Int. 3 (3), 1988
8) F. Osterstock, R. Moussa, "Festigkeitsseminar des MPI-Stuttgart", 9/10 March 1988, Proc. in Ceram. Forum Int. 3 (3), 1988

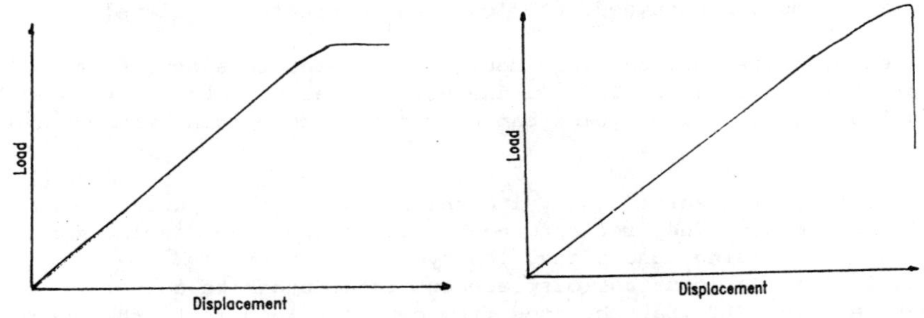

Fig. 1: load displacement records
a) for constant load conditions
b) for constant displacement conditions

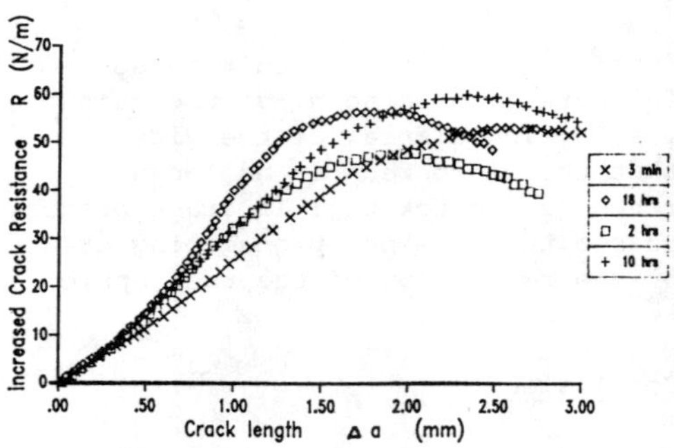

Fig. 3: R-curve obtained from constant load conditions (LEFM assumed)

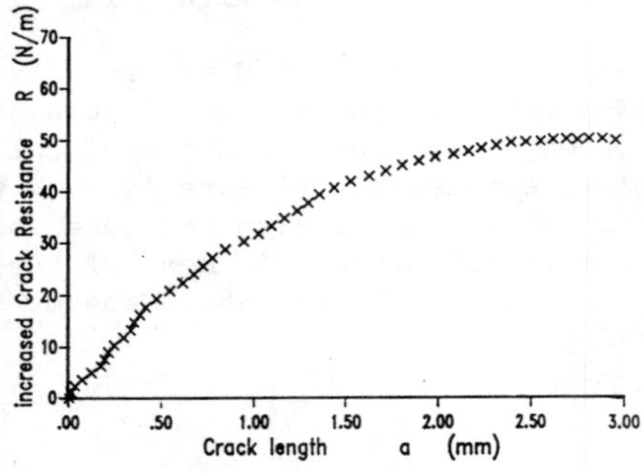

Fig. 2: R-curve obtained from constant displacement rate (LEFM assumed)

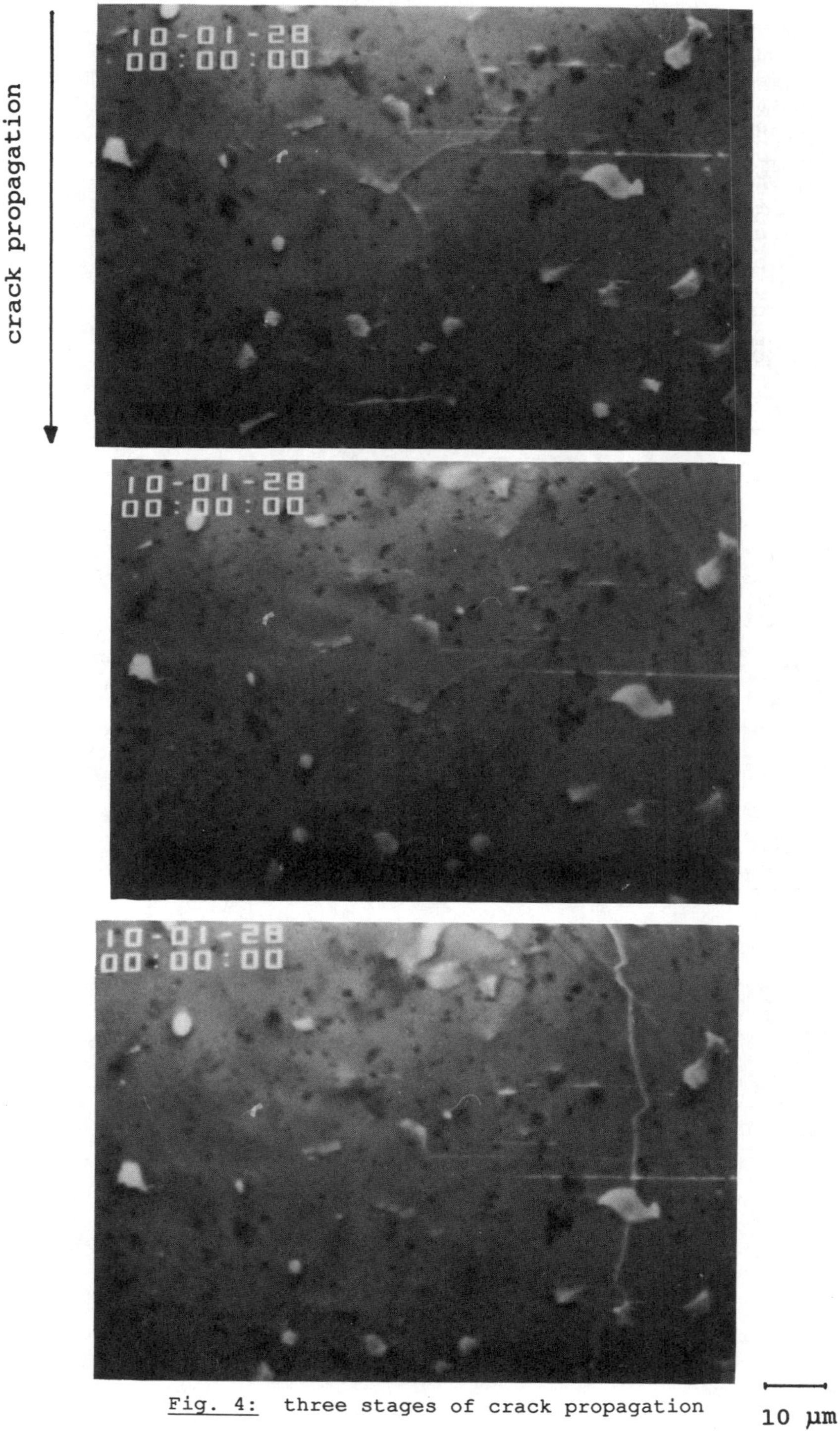

Fig. 4: three stages of crack propagation

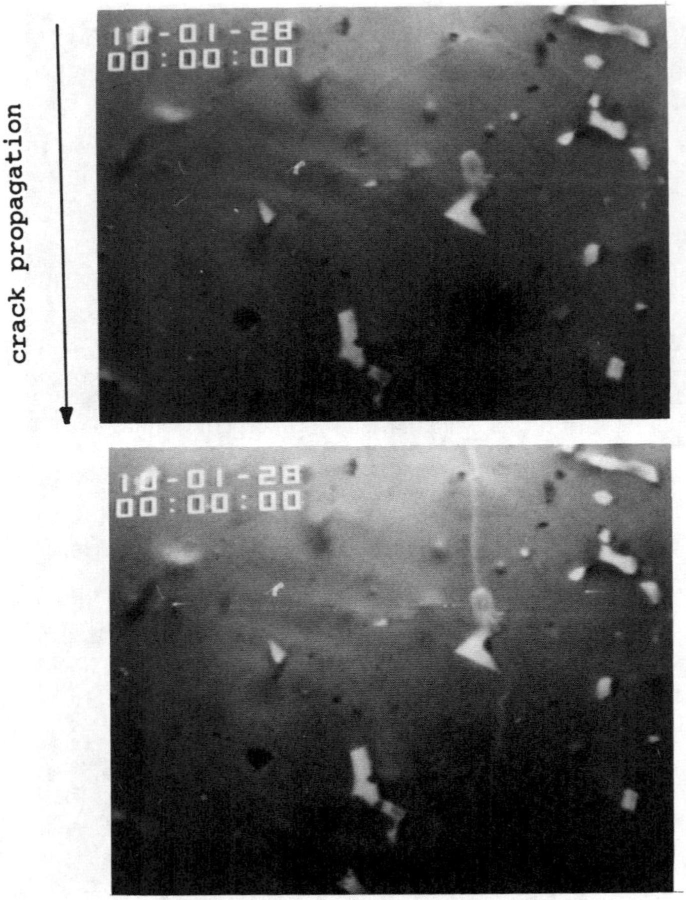

Fig. 5: two stages of crack propagation

10 µm

CYCLIC FATIGUE OF ALUMINUM OXIDE IN BENDING

T. FETT, D. MUNZ

Kernforschungszentrum Karlsruhe,

Institut für Material- und Festkörperforschung IV

and

Universität Karlsruhe,

Institut für Zuverlässigkeit und Schadenskunde im Maschinenbau

ABSTRACT

Delayed failure of mechanically loaded ceramic components at temperatures below the creep range can be caused by subcritical crack growth as well as by a real fatigue damage. In cyclic tests the influence of cycles can be evaluated by comparing cyclic lifetimes from experiments with predictions based on static tests. Experimental results are obtained for alumina in air at room temperature and alumina containing a glass phase at high temperature. It can be concluded from these tests that a real cyclic fatigue effect occurs.

INTRODUCTION

Cyclic fatigue of ceramics with natural cracks can be caused by subcritical crack growth determined from static tests. In addition "real" fatigue damage may occur. This cyclic effect can be proved in different ways. By comparing cyclic lifetimes from experiments with predictions from static tests an effect of the cycles is detectable. A second method is the measurement of cyclic lifetimes with strongly different frequencies but identical upper and lower stresses and identical shape of the cycles. In case of a real fatigue effect the lifetime must be reduced with increasing frequency. In the literature the behaviour of macroscopic cracks is sometimes investigated using fracture mechanical specimens with macroscopic cracks. At least for subcritical crack extension under constant load it is a well-known fact that the crack growth behaviour of natural cracks differs significantly from that of macroscopic cracks, especially for such materials exhibiting a pronounced R-curve behaviour [1]-[3].

For lifetime predictions the failure behaviour of components with natural crack population is of interest.

RELATIONS FOR PREDICTING CYCLIC LIFETIMES FROM STATIC TESTS

To predict the lifetime for pure K_I-controlled subcritical crack growth the special power law is considered:

$$v = AK_I^n \tag{1}$$

K_I is defined by

$$K_I = \sigma\sqrt{a}\,Y \tag{2}$$

where σ denotes a reference stress and a the depth of a crack in a structure, and Y is the geometric correction factor dependent on the shape of the crack and the component. By combining eqs.(1) and (2) one obtains a rather general *lifetime relation*

$$\int_0^{t_f}[\sigma(t)]^n dt = B\sigma_c^{n-2}\left[1-\left(\frac{\sigma_f}{\sigma_c}\right)^{n-2}\right] \tag{3}$$

with

$$B = \frac{2}{AY^2(n-2)K_{Ic}^{n-2}} \tag{4}$$

If $(\sigma_f/\sigma_c)^{n-2} << 1$, a simplified form results

$$\int_0^{t_f}[\sigma(t)]^n dt = B\sigma_c^{n-2} \tag{5}$$

By introducing into eq.(5) a periodical stress with a period T and a mean stress $\overline{\sigma}$

$$\sigma(t) = \overline{\sigma} + \sigma_a f(t) \quad , \quad f(t) = f(t+T) \tag{6}$$

into eq.(5) and by assuming that only the positive stress parts σ^+ cause subcritical crack growth it results for the lifetime in the cyclic test

$$\frac{t_{fc}}{T}\int_0^T (\sigma^+)^n dt = B\sigma_c^{n-2} \tag{7}$$

Tests with R≥0: If the stress ratio $R = \sigma_{min}/\sigma_{max}$ is positive, one obtains the lifetime in a cyclic test t_{fc} from the lifetime of a static test t_{fs} performed at stress σ_s:

$$t_{fc} = t_{fs}\left(\frac{\sigma_s}{\overline{\sigma}}\right)^n \frac{1}{g(\sigma_a/\overline{\sigma}, n)} \quad \text{, with} \quad g = \frac{1}{T}\int_0^T\left[1+\frac{\sigma_a}{\overline{\sigma}}f(t)\right]^n dt \tag{8}$$

Figure 1 shows results of 4-point-bending tests on Al_2O_3 containing 2.7%SiO_2 [4]. The tests are carried out at 1100°C with an elastically calculated mean stress $\overline{\sigma}=60$MPa and R=0.2 at different frequencies. A linear-elastic lifetime prediction was made on the basis of results of static bending tests measured with an upper stress of $\simeq$100MPa. For these values the condition $t_f << t_1$ is fulfilled. Here t_1 is the characteristic time given by Riedel [5] which separates the regions of linear-elastic fracture mechanics and creep fracture mechanics. The predicted lifetimes for cyclic tests based on four experimentally determined lifetimes under constant loading, applying eq.(8) are plotted in the left part of fig.1. There are two arguments for the absence of a cyclic fatigue effect of this material under the chosen test conditions

1. Within the scatter of the lifetimes no significant influence of the frequency becomes obvious.

2. The predicted lifetimes are nearly identical with the measured ones.

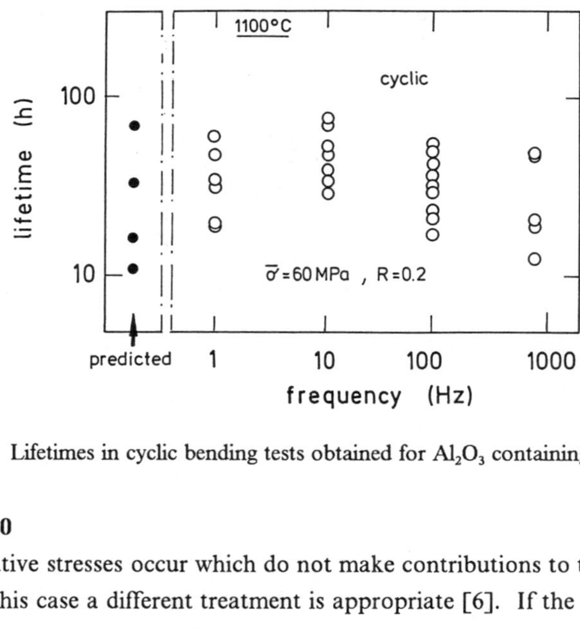

Figure 1. : Lifetimes in cyclic bending tests obtained for Al_2O_3 containing 2.7% SiO_2.

Tests with R<0

this case negative stresses occur which do not make contributions to the integral in eq.(7). Therefore, in this case a different treatment is appropriate [6]. If the stress is sinusoidal

$$\sigma(t) = \overline{\sigma} + \sigma_a \sin(\frac{2\pi}{T} t)$$

it results

$$t_{fc} = t_{fs}\left(\frac{\sigma_s}{\sigma_a}\right)^n \frac{1}{h(\overline{\sigma}/\sigma_a, n)} \tag{9}$$

where

$$h(\frac{\overline{\sigma}}{\sigma_a}, n) = \frac{1}{\pi}\int_{-\alpha}^{\pi/2}[\overline{\sigma}/\sigma_a + \sin\varphi]^n d\varphi \quad \text{with} \quad \alpha = \arcsin(\overline{\sigma}/\sigma_a) \tag{10}$$

If especially the cyclic lifetime is compared with static lifetimes measured with the upper stress t_{fs}^{*} it holds

$$t_{fc} = \frac{1}{h}(1 + \frac{\overline{\sigma}}{\sigma_a})^n t_{fs}^{*} \tag{11}$$

The alternating test (R = -1) It can be expected that the difference between predictions from static tests and cyclic behaviour increases with decreasing R. Therefore, tests with R = -1 are especially useful to detect cyclic effects.
For this case, the function h can be expressed analytically by

$$h(0,n) = \frac{1}{2\sqrt{\pi}} \frac{\Gamma(\frac{n}{2}+\frac{1}{2})}{\Gamma(\frac{n}{2}+1)} \tag{12}$$

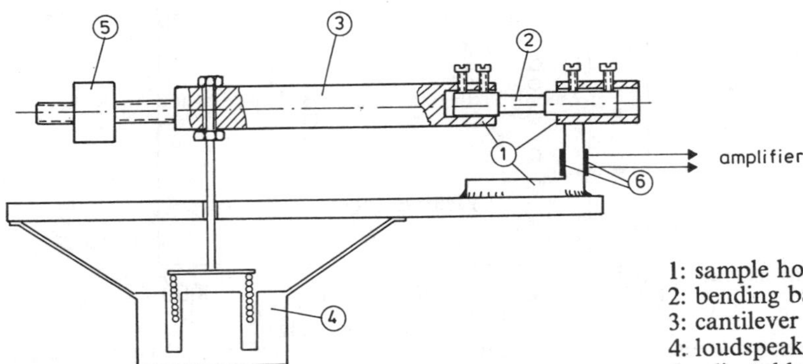

1: sample holder
2: bending bar
3: cantilever
4: loudspeaker
5: adjustable mass
6: strain gauches

Figure 2. : Testing device for alternating bending tests.

Figure 2 shows a simple testing device for cyclic bending tests with R = -1. The specimen is fixed at its ends in brass tubes by an epoxy resin. The cyclic load is generated by the magnet system of a loudspeaker and transferred to the specimen by a cantilever. The bending moment is measured by strain gauges provided on the fixing bracket as well as directly on special specimens used for calibrating. At the moment of failure, the loudspeaker stops working and a time counter is interrupted.
Figure 3 shows the result of lifetime measurements on Al_2O_3 at room temperature in cantilever beam tests performed under pure alternating load at a frequency of 50Hz for speci-

mens with natural cracks as well as artificial Knoop cracks. From the results of static tests the corresponding cyclic lifetimes were calculated using eqs.(11) and (12). Whereas in the static bending tests only one side is under tensile loading, failure can occur on both sides in the alternating bending test, i.e. the effective surface of the specimens in cyclic tests is twice the surface in static tests. This has to be taken into consideration for the failure prediction of the specimens with natural flaws. It can be concluded from these tests that a real cyclic fatigue effect occurs for both types of cracks.

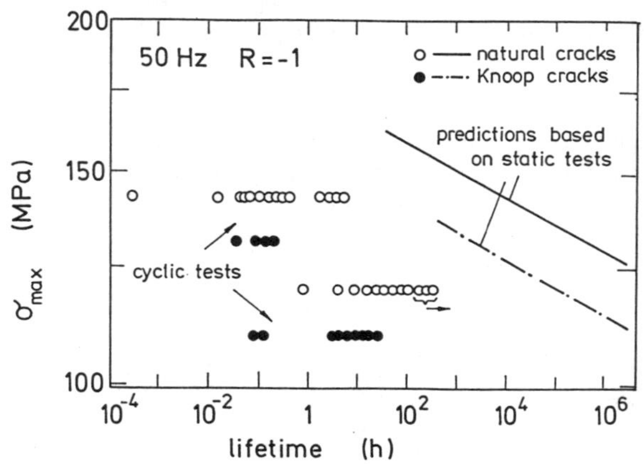

Figure 3. : Predicted and measured lifetimes in cyclic bending tests for Al_2O_3 with natural cracks and Knoop-cracks.

REFERENCES

[1] T.E. Adams, D.J. Landini, C.A. Schumacher, R.C. Bradt, "Micro- and macrocrack growth in alumina refractories", Amer. Ceram. Soc. Bull. **60** 730-35(1981).

[2] K. Chen, Y. Ko, Amer. Ceram. Soc. Bull. **67** 1228-1234(1988).

[3] T. Fett, D. Munz , "Lifetime evaluation of ceramic materials", Symposium on "Reliability of Structural Ceramics", der "Advanced Materials Science and Engineering Society, Japan" 16/17. März, 1989, Tokyo.

[4] M. Mißbach, T. Fett, D. Munz, "Untersuchungen zum Versagen glasphasehaltigen Aluminiumoxids im Kriechbereich" Werkstoff-Kolloquium 5/6 April 1989, Stuttgart.

[5] H. Riedel, "Fracture at high temperatures", Springer-Verlag, Berlin 1986.

[6] T. Fett, D. Munz, "Subcritical crack extension in ceramics", Proceedings of the MRS-Conference, Tokyo 1988.

INFLUENCE OF ATMOSPHERE AND ANNEALING TIME ON MICROSTRUCTURAL AND MECHANICAL PROPERTIES OF MULLITE - ZrO_2-TiO_2 COMPOSITES

M.F. MELO, Dept.Mater.Techn.,LNETI, 1699 Lisboa Codex, Portugal
J.S. MOYA, Inst.Ceram. y Vidrio,CSIC, Arganda del Rey, Spain ,
M.O. FIGUEIREDO, Cryst.Miner,Cent., IICT, 1000 Lisboa, Portugal

ABSTRACT

Annealing effects in mullite/zirconia composites with titania additions (0.25 and 1.0 mol %) have been studied under helium and air atmospheres at sintering temperatures (1500-1550°C). Differences in grain and pore growth, solid solution conditions and mechanical properties, were noticed to depend on the TiO_2 content. The results are explained in terms of changes in grain boundary microchemistry, influenced by distinct P_{O_2} conditions.

INTRODUCTION

Attention has been focused on the effect of sintering atmospheres on grain growth and porosity of composites and the observed behaviour was correlated with grain boundary microchemistry (1). Changes in mechanical properties and microstructure during ageing of mullite/zirconia composites, and the structural role of titanium additions under distinct annealing atmospheres, have been separately studied (2,3). In the present work these features are considered altogether as influenced by air and helium atmospheres during different annealing periods. The effect of titanium additions on oxygen reactivity and migration of impurities to the grain boundaries is also reported.

MATERIALS AND METHODS

Appropriate mixtures of zircon (Opazir-S, Quiminsa S.A.,Spain), alumina (CT 3000 SG Alcoa, USA) and titania (Merck, BRG), were formulated to produce mullite/zirconia composites without and with aluminium titanate according to the stability relations in quartenary system ZrO_2-SiO_2-Al_2O_3-TiO_2 (4). Relevant impurities are Fe_2O_3 (0.1% in both zircon and alumina) and CaO plus Na_2O (0.22% in alumina).

Powders were homogenized by attrition milling in a teflon coated attritor using alumina balls in an isopropyl alcohol suspension. After drying and sieving, the raw composition were isostatically pressed at 200 MPa. The resulting cylindrical green bars were sintered in an electrical furnace (super-kantal elements) at 1500°C/2h (composition x=1.0 mol % TiO_2) and 1550°C /2h (composition x=0.25 mol % TiO_2). Sintered bars were subsequently annealed in air or in helium during selected time intervals - 6, 24 and 48h - at the sintering temperatures in tubular furnaces (silicon carbide or platinium elements).

Phase composition was monitored by X-ray diffraction using single-crystal monochromatized Cu $K\alpha$ radiation. Tetragonal zirconia proportion was calculated by the expression of Garvie and Nicholson (5).

Bulk density of sintered annealed materials was measured by immersion in destilled water. Porosity and average pore size were calculated by the usual linear intercept method over RLOM micrographs of polished surfaces.

Microstructural evolution was observed by SEM and the average grain size of crystalline phases (inter and intra-granular zirconia, mullite and aluminium titanate) was estimated under an image analyser.

Bending strength (σ_f) was determined by the three-point bend method on cylindrical bars with 4mm diameter and ≃ 80 mm length. The indentation method (6) was used to evaluate toughness characteristics (K_IC values) of the samples.

RESULTS AND DISCUSSION

The evolution trends of bulk density, porosity and toughness values (table 1) are similar for both compositions with comparatively increased amplitude for larger titania additions. As usual, density has lower values for these compositions. Porosity and density are quite independent from annealing atmosphere and stabilize for long treatment periods. Although porosity does not increase significantly with annealing time in both atmospheres, an increase in average pore size was detected for long periods possibly due to coalescence (fig. 1). Grain growth of main phases is clearly apparent in SEM micrographs (fig. 2). As expected, intra-granular zirconia remains size constant during annealing.

Ripening is identical for all main phases. An initial acceleratory trend followed by a sort of induction period and ending by an increased rate of ripening (sigmoid type curve) occurs for composites higher in titanium (fig. 3). Stabilization is attained under helium. Comparatively, composition x = 0.25 presents a constant desacceleratory trend whatever the atmosphere.

TABLE 1
Bulk density, porosity and toughness values (a)

Parameter	TiO_2 mol%	0 h air	0 h He	6 h air	6 h He	24 h air	24 h He	48 h air	48 h He
bulk density (g/cm^3)	0.25	3.60	3.60	3.57	3.58	3.52	3.53	3.51	3.54
	1.0	3.57	3.57	3.50	3.56	3.37	3.48	3.40	3.51
porosity (%)	0.25	9.0	9.0	9.0	6.2	10.5	9.0	11.0	7.9
	1.0	8.0	8.0	7.8	7.9	10.3	8.8	9.6	8.5
K_IC ($MPa.m^{1/2}$)	0.25	4.53	4.53	4.83	4.90	4.70	7.31	-	-
	1.0	4.01	4.01	4.22	3.73	-	3.70	-	3.95

(a) Standard deviations range from 0.02 to 0.18 (density and porosity) up to 0.9 (porosity).

Strength degradation during annealing is exemplified in figure 4, the same trend holding for both compositions. However, composites lower in titanium are less sensitive to the atmosphere. Toughness reaches a maximum value after the first hours of annealing independently of composition, and decreases for long-term treatments (table 1). Annealing atmosphere seems to be irrelevant in K_IC evolution and no relationship with tetragonal zirconia content was observed.

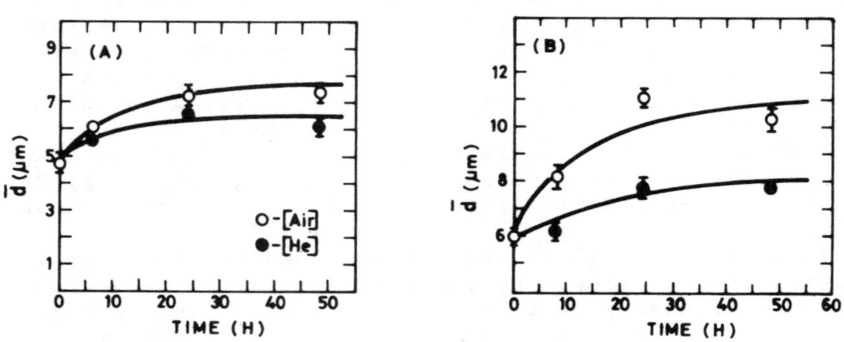

Figure 1. Average pore size evolution with annealing time.
(A) composition x = 0.25.
(B) composition x = 1.0 .

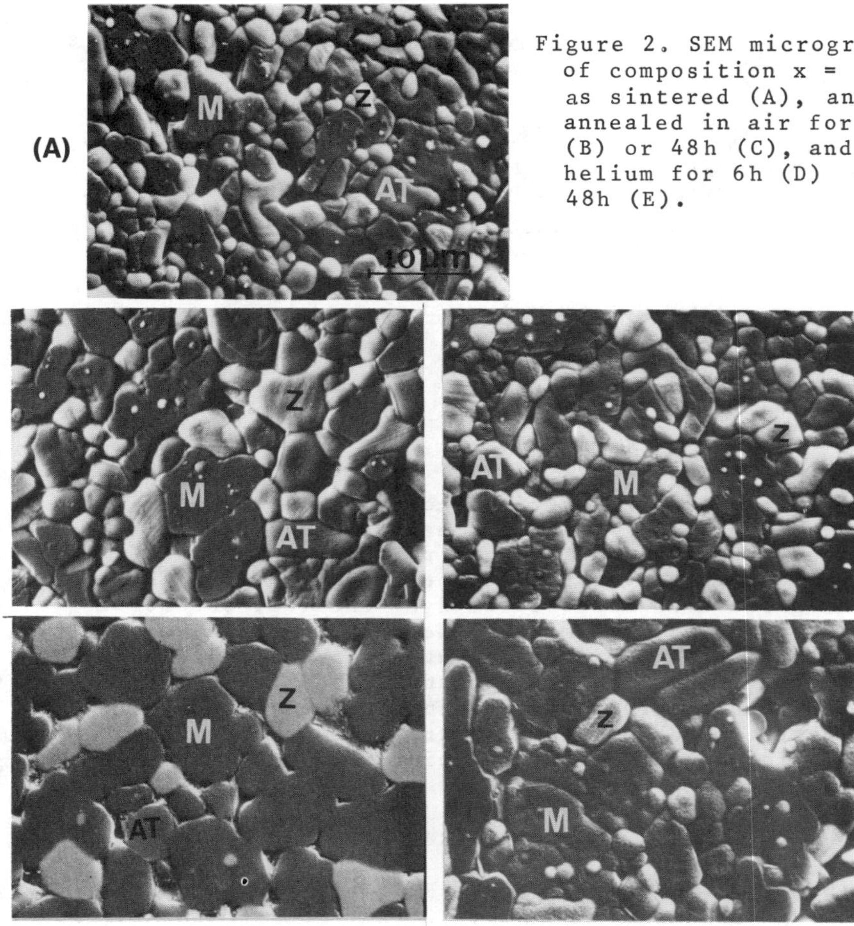

Figure 2. SEM micrographs of composition x = 1.0 as sintered (A), and annealed in air for 6h (B) or 48h (C), and in helium for 6h (D) or 48h (E).

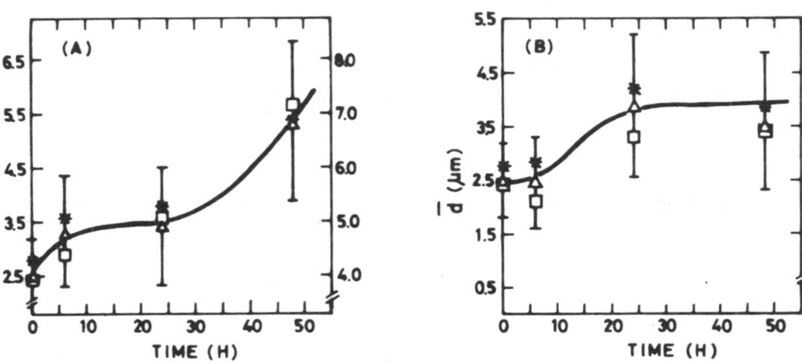

Figure 3. Grain size evolution in composition x = 1.0 in air (A) and in helium (B). * AT; □ A_3S_2; ▽ m-Z.

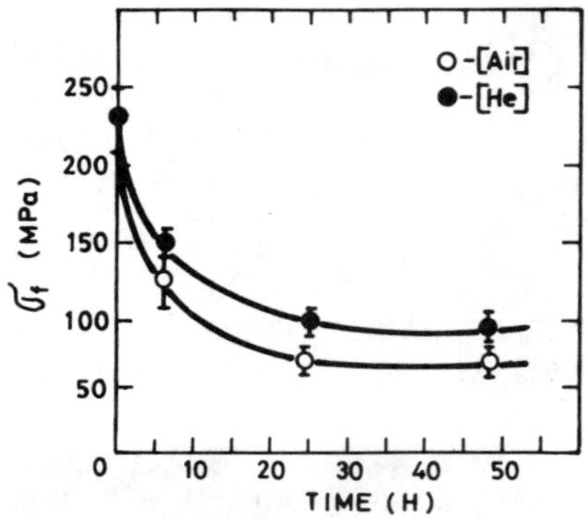

Figure 4. Bending strength for composition x = 1.0.

CONCLUSIONS

Observed degradation of mechanical properties may be related to pore coalescence and particle coarsening. Improvement in toughness for the first annealing periods seems to be correlated with a concomitant decrease in porosity.

Ripening behaviour could be traced to microchemical changes at grain boundaries induced by chemical potential gradients mainly of impurity elements. The driving force should be the concentration of ionic oxygen at grain surfaces due to different oxygen fugacities in the annealing atmospheres. Such effect becomes more apparent as titanium content increases.

Furthermore, growth anisotropy inherent mainly to mullite and aluminium titanate would reinforce both ripening and pore coalescence.

REFERENCES

1. Kibbel, B. and Heuer, A.H., Exaggerated grain growth in ZrO_2 - toughness Al_2O_3. J. Amer. Ceram. Soc., 1986, 69, 231-236.

2. Melo, M.F. and Moya, J.S., Ageing effect on microstructural and mechanical properties of mullite/ZrO_2/TiO_2 composites, J. Mater. Sci., in press.

3. Melo, M.F. and Figueiredo, M.O., Behaviour of titanium in mullite/zirconia composites. Mater. Sci. & Eng., 1989, 109A, 61-68.

4. Pena, P. and de Aza S., Study in the system ZrO_2-Al_2O_3-SiO_2--TiO_2. In Sci. Ceram. 12, ed. P. Vincencini, Ceramurgia S.R..L. Faenza, Italia, 1983, pp 201-208.

5. Garvie, R.C. and Nicholson, P.S., Phase analysis in zirconia systems. J. Amer. Ceram. Soc., 1972, 55, 303-305.

6. Miranzo, P. and Moya, J.S., Elastic-plastic identation ceramics: fracture toughness determination method. Ceram. Int., 1984, 10, 147-152.

HIGH TEMPERATURE UNIAXIAL ALTERNATING FATIGUE TESTING OF ENGINEERING CERAMICS

D. BOLSCH AND J. BRESSERS
JOINT RESEARCH CENTER OF THE EUROPEAN COMMUNITIES
INSTITUTE FOR ADVANCED MATERIALS
1755ZG PETTEN, THE NETHERLANDS

ABSTRACT

A testmethod is described, which allows fatigue testing of engineering ceramics under uniaxial alternating load up to a temperature of 1600°C and up to a frequency of 120 Hz in air. A flat, easy to grip sample geometry is selected. Special care is given to achieve a homogeneous temperature and stress distribution, and a low bending component. Some results of constant stress amplitude HCF–tests are presented for a monolithic HPSN .

INTRODUCTION

For future applications of Engineering Ceramics such as in gas turbine blades or turbo charger rotors the cyclic fatigue behaviour of the material at the service temperatures must be known. From the point of view of design engineering uniaxial tensile type data are preferred over bend data. To investigate the fatigue behaviour a method of testing is developed with the aims of:

- Determination whether a specific fatigue effect exists in ceramics
- Generating of fatigue data
- Recommendation for future standardization

MATERIALS

A Hot Pressed Silicon Nitride (HPSN) from Ceradyne Inc. was chosen for the fatigue test specimens. This material contains 8 wt.% Y_2O_3 and 2 wt.% Al_2O_3 as sintering additives. The material was pressed into rectangular plates of 200 mm x 200 mm x 12 mm. Out of this plate flat specimens with dimensions of 160 mm x 20 mm x 6 mm (Gauge section 30 mm x 8 mm x 6 mm) were cut and longitudinally ground with a 400 grid diamond wheel.

Figure 1. **Fatigue testing installation.**

METHODS

STRESS DISTRIBUTION

Alignment of the loading train is one of the most critical points in uniaxial fatigue testing of brittle materials. In our method the sample is gripped in a pair of hydraulic water cooled grips. In order to achieve a homogeneous stress distribution over its cross—section each sample is equipped with 8 strain gauges. The alignment is checked and adjusted if necessary . Bending and precision of alignment are calculated by means of the following formulas:

$$B = 100 * \frac{\varepsilon_b}{\varepsilon_0}$$

$$P = \tan\alpha = \frac{\varepsilon_b * l_0}{r} \quad \text{with } r = \frac{a}{2} \text{ or } \frac{b}{2}$$

B	= Bending [%]
P	= Precision of alignment
ε_b	= Bending strain
ε_0	= Uniaxial strain
l_0	= Strain gauge length [mm]
a	= Width [mm]
b	= Depth [mm]

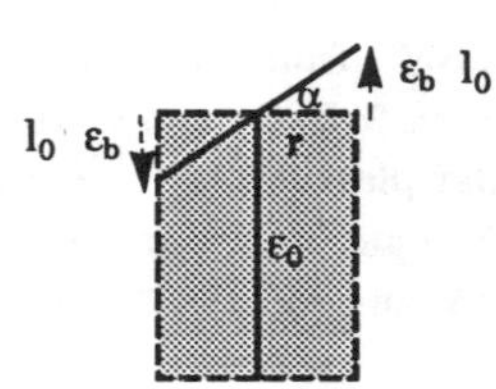

The advantage of using Precision of alignment as an indicator of the quality of the alignment is obvious from the results of 150 alignment tests (Figure 2 and 3) at different stress levels . One number describes the homogeneity of the stress distribution in the sample independent from the stress level. This allows to perform the alignment adjustment at a small stress and avoids preloading effects at the test sample.

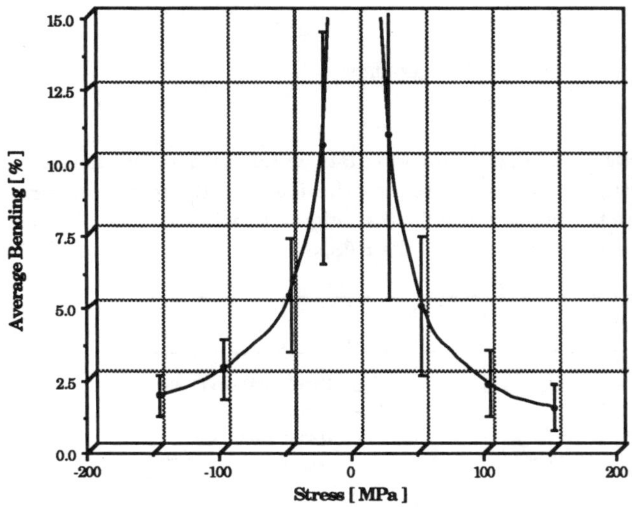

Figure 2. Bending statistics 150 of alignment tests.

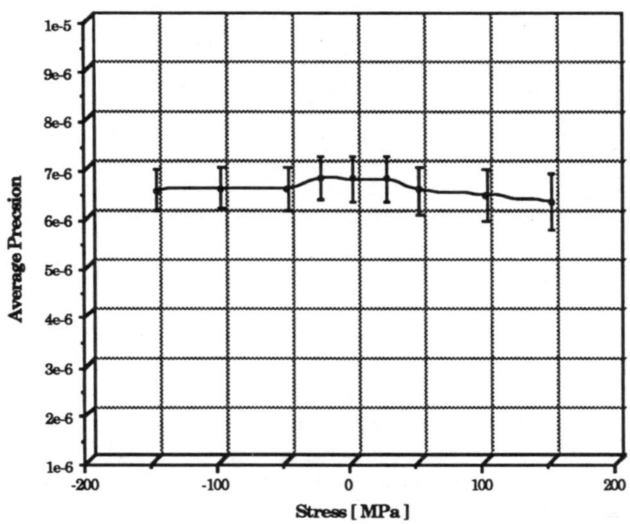

Figure 3. Precision of Alignment statistics of 150 alignment tests.

Temperature Distribution

A 12 kW induction heating system is used with a split furnace and a ceramic susceptor element. The split furnace of own design is mounted following the alignment procedure without releasing the grips. The furnace allows max. temperatures of 1600°C in air with a temperature gradient of less than 0.6% at 1400°C over ± 10 mm. The temperature gradient measurements and the furnace calibration were made on a HPSN sample with thermocouples type B inserted in 5 holes at distances of 5 mm over the gauge length.

Results

Tensile Tests

As a basis for the selection of the stress limits in fatigue testing a set of uniaxial tensile tests were conducted to investigate the stress—strain behaviour and the initial strength. Based on the results of these tests the temperature for the fatigue tests is set at 1200°C because of the still linear elastic stress—strain behaviour of the HPSN.

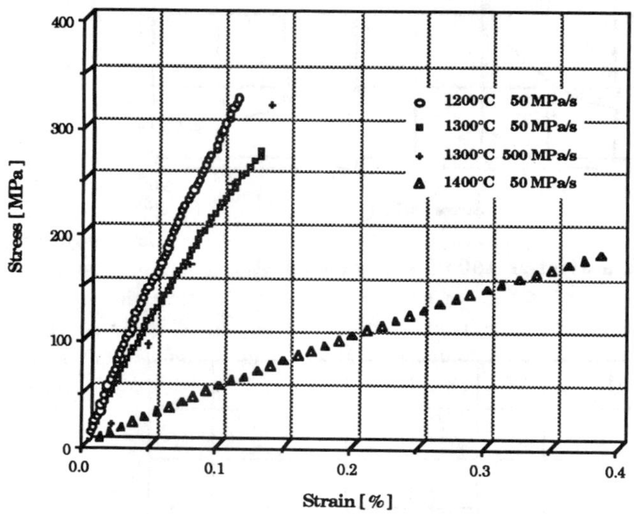

Figure 4. Uniaxial high temperature tension stress—strain behaviour of HPSN.

Fatigue Testing

On the fatigue testing facility High Cycle Fatigue (HCF) tests are run with a sinusoidal stress function, a stress amplitude ratio R of -1 at frequencies of 10 Hz and 100 Hz at a temperature of 1200°C in air. Stress and strain are continuously monitored, digitized and stored via a real time data acquisition system. The Strain measurements are performed with a modified high temperature extensometer with extension rods made of HPSN, a stiffer spring and an optimized weight for the 10 Hz tests. The 100 Hz tests will be monitored with a Laser optical extensometer. Figure 5 presents some loops of a 10 Hz, 1200°C HCF test. No degradation of the HPSN is obvious in the compression part of the cycle, but an increase in strain in the tension part of the cycle is observed .

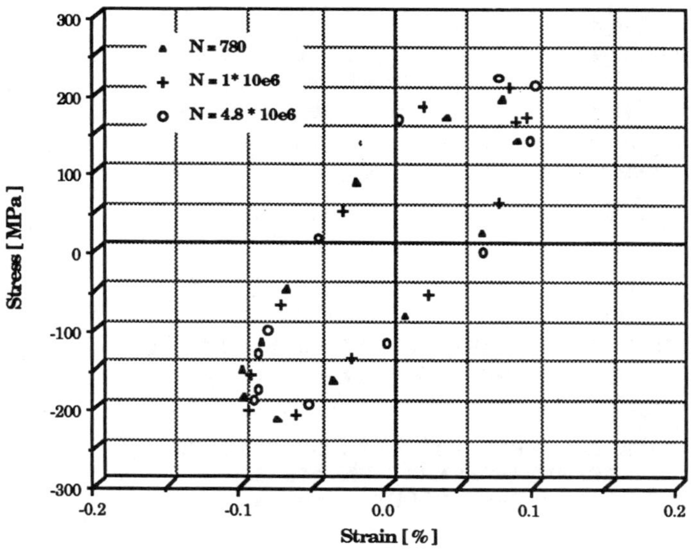

Figure 5. HCF stress—strain loops of HPSN at 1200°C.

CONCLUSIONS

The proposed method of testing allows an easy to use and economic generation of uniaxial fatigue data at temperatures up to 1600°C. In average a precision of alignment of $6 * 10^{-6}$ and a homogeneous temperature gradient are achieved. The use of Precision of Alignment P as descriptor of the quality of the alignment of the load train and the sample is prefered over percentage bending B. Up to now two constant stress range fatigue tests were conducted at 1200°C in air on a monolithic HPSN, the samples survived 10^{7} cycles with loads of ± 100 MPa and ± 180 MPa at a test frequency of 10 Hz.

ACKNOWLEDGEMENT

The results are part of a ongoing Ph. D. work in the frame of the Advanced Materials Program of the European Communities. D. Bolsch likes to express his thanks to the Commission of the European Communities for the grant and to all members of the Petten staff for their support.

FRACTURE OF SINTERED GLASS AS A FUNCTION OF POROSITY

Luis CORONEL, Frédéric OSTERSTOCK
LERMAT - ISMRa, UA n°1317
14032 CAEN CEDEX, France

ABSTRACT

Sintered glass has been investigated as a function of porosity for fracture mechanical purposes. Only the influence of the morphology and phenomenological aspects have been looked for. The fracture mechanical parameters, Kic and Gic, exhibit apparently contradictory variations as porosity increases. After having put down necessary and sufficient conditions for modelling purposes, it is proposed for the design of structural ceramics parts to take into account the conditions of use i;e; either constant load or fixed grips.

INTRODUCTION

In the family of brittle materials glass holds a special place. It was used by Griffith to test his modell and is still considered as a modell material for fracture mechanical purposes. On the other hand the influence of porosity on rupture and fracture mechanical parameters is not well understood in the case of polycristalline ceramics. Modells have already been proposed (1)(2)(3). They attempt to fit experimental data (2)(4)(5) obtained in different ways. Furthermore the variation of internal stresses of the second order and impurities at the grain boundaries is difficult to take into account. They however have an important influence on the micromechanics of crack propagation.
These drawbacks do not exist in sintered glass wich can thus be used to investigate basic principles for further theoriticall developpements. The results will be discussed in view of current modells and basic definitions.

EXPERIMENTALS

Glass microspheres (Blastoline from Vestglass, FRG) have been sintered to various densities under argon in order to obtain specimens ~ 3x7x35 mm^3 for mechanical and fracture mechanical purposes. The specimens were sized by smooth polishing. Mechanical testing was done in three point bending with a span of 28 mm using a Schenk-Trebel 100RMC testing machine. The fracture mechanical specimens were furnished with a notch of relative length a/w $\simeq$ 0.5 and loaded at a crosshead speed such that maximum load was attained within 10 seconds. The fracture mechanical parameters, K_{IC} and G_{IC} as well as the rupture stresses and the Young's modulus have been calculated using the classical formulaes (6) (7) (8).

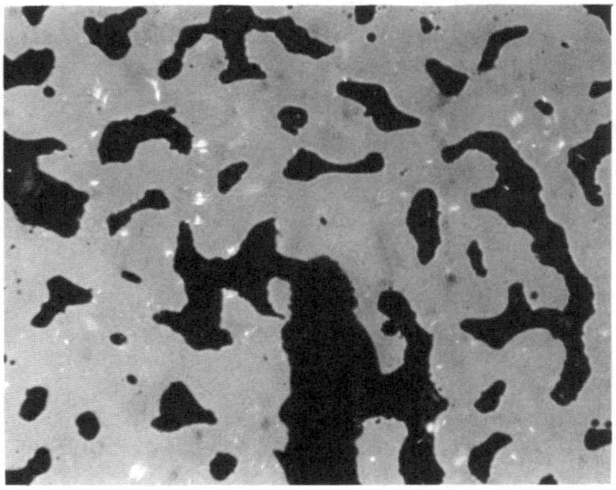

Figure 1. Starting notch in a toughness sample of intermediate porosity.

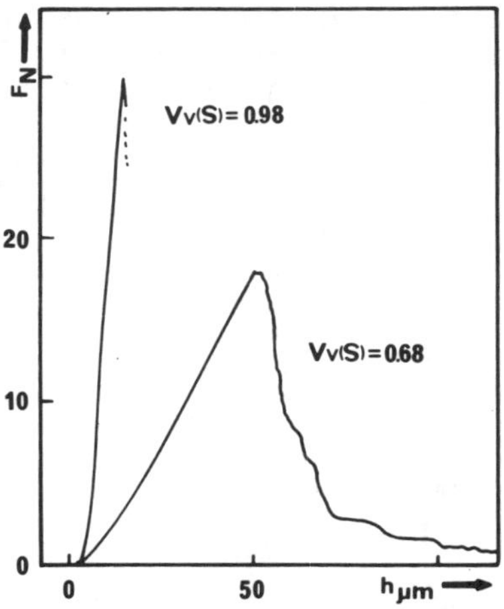

Figure 2. Load-displacement records for to notched samples of extreme porosities.

RESULTS

A notch, introduced with a diamond fitted copper blade - 50μm in thickness - is shown in figure 1 for a sample of intermediate porosity (~20%). The shape and size did not change over the whole range of porosity. Figure 2 shows two load-displacement curves for notched specimens of extreme porosity content. K_{IC} was calculated from the maximum load in all cases and G_{IC} was obtained using Irwin's relationship. The Young's modulus of each sample was measured before notching.
The Young's modulus the rupture stress. decrease continuously as porosity increases towards the porosity of the initial powder before sintering. This behavior is usually observed for sintered materials (9).

As can be seen in figure 3, K_{IC} also decreases as porosity increases. On the contrary, G_{IC}, (figure 4) passes through a maximum; this has not yet been predicted by any model. However the observation of the areas under the load-displacement curves confirms that trend.

DISCUSSION

R.W. Rice et al. derived exponential laws for the variation of G_{IC} with porosity (1)(2). Their work was based on the assumption of F.P. Knudsen (10), i.e. the crack follows the shortest path in the solid phase. This may be admitted because pores are believed to attract a crack (11)(12). How ever it should be outlined that $\underline{G_{IC}}$ is an energy rate which defines the instability conditions of a crack and not a quantity which may be multiplied by a relative area of solid cracked surface. This can be seen on the analytical transcription of the : "critical strain energy release rate":

$$G_{IC} = \left(\frac{Pr^2}{2B}\right)\left(\frac{\partial C}{\partial a}\Big|_{ac}\right)$$

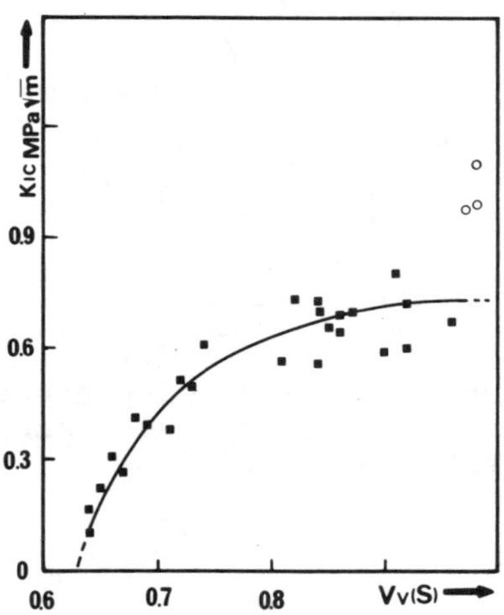

Figure 3. Variation of K_{IC} with porosity.

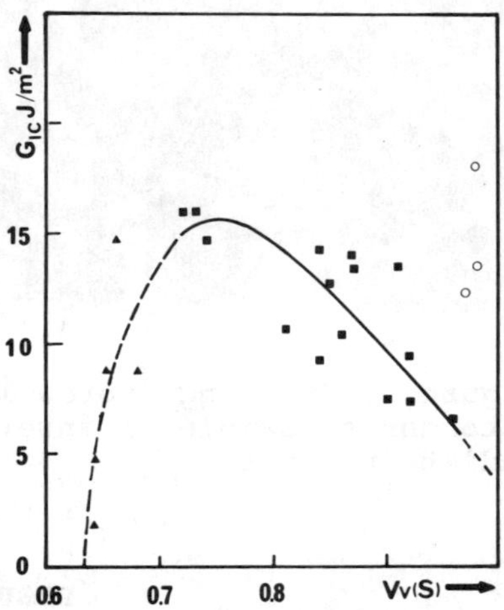

Figure 4. Variation of G_{IC} with porosity.

where Pr is the maximum load in the case of brittle fracture and C is the compliance of the sample containing a notch of length a_c.
From that transcription the influence of porosity may be only partially derived. The variation of $\partial C/\partial a|_{ac}$ with porosity may be obtained, but not that of Pr which is an experimental measurement and is directly linked to K_{IC}. One thus comes to a deadlock.

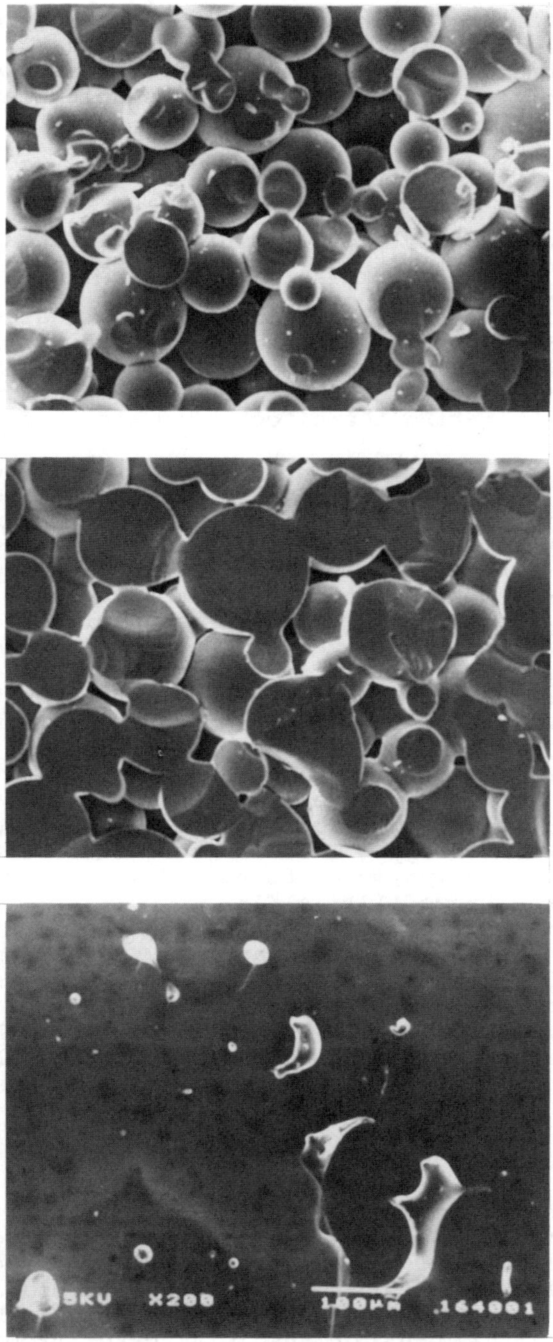

a) $V_V(S) = 0.65$

b) $V_V(S) = 0.80$

c) $V_V(S) = 0.97$

Figure 5a, b, c. Fracture surfaces at different porosities. Various micromechanisms of crack propagration are put in evidence.

The use of G_{IC} as a quantity defines the "work of fracture" concept. It may be made only in very specific cases. If a crack of length, a, and unit thickness propagates over a given increment Δa, the work of fracture, refered to the unit area, is given by :

$$\gamma wof = \frac{1}{\Delta a} \int_{a}^{a+\Delta a} G_c(\Delta a)\,da$$

If one uses G_c as a quantity similarly as γwof, $G_c(\Delta a)$ should be independent on crack extension, i.e. no R-Curve should exist. Then the above integration yields $\gamma wof = G_c$.
For the case where the influence of porosity is investigated, it should in addition be verified whether G_c in the solid phase remains the same as porosity increases.
Thus necessary and sufficient conditions for the use of Gc similary to γwof for investigating the effect of porosity have been derived.
That full dense glass exhibits no R-Curve behavior at room temperature is actually well accepted. However as can be seen on the fractographs of figures 7, a, b, c, the micromechanisms of crack propagation change drastically as porosity increases. At low porosities, the crack front is pinned by the isolated pores - see the trails - and the reinforcement may be described by the modell of F. Lange (7)(12). Crack deflection through the spheres occurs at intermediate porosities which also causes a strengthening (locally mixed modes). Rupture of the necks takes place only in the extreme range of porosity where G_{IC} decreases towards 0. The constancy of G_c in the solid phase as porosity increases is thus not fullfilled.
K_{IC} and G_{IC} are both fracture mechanical parameters but with different meanings. K_{IC} is linked to a load bearing capacity and should be used for constant load conditions. G_{IC} says how a materials relaxes strain energy. This is best adapted to imposed deformation (fixed grips) conditions and well illustrated by thermal shock resitance (13)(14)(15).
In other words, both define a criterion for the onset of crack propagation, but should be investigated separatly as a function of porosity. Even more, modells may be checked by the use of the Irwin's relation which introduces the influence of porosity on Young's modulus. If, with that relation, the variation of the one parameter describes that the other, the modell may be well founded.

CONCLUSION

On the basis of experimental results phenemenological aspects of the variation of fracture mechanical parameters with porosity have been discussed. Necessary and sufficient conditions for modellisation have also been proposed. The complete change of micromechanisms of rupture when porosity varies should be considered as well as their inflence on the local crack propagation criteria in the solid phase. This can be made only if the porosity range is divided in distinct areas depending on their fabrication process and on their microstructure.

REFERENCES

1 - R.W. RICE and S.W. FREIMAN, 6th. Int. Materials Symp., Univ. of California, Berkeley, Aug. 1976.

2 - R.W. RICE, K.R.Mc KINNEY, C.C.M. WU, S.W. FREIMAN and W.J.Mc. DONOUGH, J. Mat. Science, 1985, 20, p. 1392.

3 - K.K. PHANI, S.K. NIYOGI, A.D. DE, J. Mat. Science, 1988, 7, p. 1253.

4 - A.G. EVANS and G. TAPPIN, Bull. British Ceram. Soc., 1972, 20, p. 275.

5 - R.F. PABST, in "Fracture Mechanics of Ceramics", Vol. 2, (Plenum Press, New York, 1974), p. 555.

6 - L. CORONEL, Thesis, University of Caen, Frebruary 1989.

7 - F. OSTERSTOCK, "Festigkeitsseminar des MPI-Stuttgart", April 1989, to be published in Ceram. Forum Int....

8 - L. CORONEL, J.P. JERNOT, F. OSTERSTOCK, submitted to J. Mat. Science.

9 - J.P. JERNOT, Thèse de Docteur d'Etat, University of Caen, 1982.

10 - F.P. KNUDSEN, J. Am. Ceram. Soc., 1959, 42, p. 376.

11 - C.T. FORWOOD, A.J. FORTY, Phil. Mag., 1965, 11, 1067.

12 - F.F. LANGE, Phil. Mag., 1970, 22, 983.

13 - W.D. KINGERY, "Introduction to ceramics", John Wiley, N.Y., 1960.

14 - D.P.H. HASSELMAN, J. am. Ceram. Soc., 1969, 52, 426 & 600.

15 - R.D. SMITH, H.U. ANDERSON, R.E. MOORE, Ceram Bull., 1976, 55(11), p. 979

POST-HIPPING OF SILICON NITRIDE-BASED MATERIALS

A. BELLOSI, V. BIASINI, S. GUICCIARDI
Research Institute for Ceramics Technology
via Granarolo 64, 48018 Faenza, ITALY

ABSTRACT

Starting from four commercial powders pre-sintered Si_3N_4-based materials have been hipped without canning. A comparison of microstructural characteristics and room temperature mechanical properties, before and after hipping, indicates that this treatment is not always positive for the final performances.

INTRODUCTION

Post-hipping treatments on pre-sintered Si_3N_4-based materials could be a usefull method to enhance mechanical properties, but some open questions still exist on the influence of microstructural characteristics of the pre-sintered materials and the influence of type and amount of secondary phases on the mechanical properties of hipped materials (1-3). In this paper some preliminary results are presented on: density, microstructure, room temperature (RT) mechanical properties for different materials before and after hipping.

EXPERIMENTAL

Four commercial Si_3N_4 powders (Table 1) have been used to prepare pre-sintered samples. All the powders were mixed with 3 wt% Al_2O_3+8 wt% Y_2O_3 (composition A) and powders 1 and 4 with 1 wt% MgO+8 wt% Y_2O_3 (composition B); pressureless sintering (4,5) runs have been carried out in flowing N_2 atmosphere at 1800 °C and 2 hours holding time. The pre-sintered materials were post-treated by hipping (performed at National Forge-Belgium), without canning, in nitrogen, at a temperature of 1750°C and a pressure of 200 MPa for 1 hour.
Materials have been characterized before and after hipping by

TABLE 1
Chemical and physical characteristics of the Si_3N_4 powders.

sample	S.S.A m^2/g	equiv. spherical diameter μm	agglom size μm	α-Si_3N_4 %	chemical composition % O	Ca	Fe	Al	Na	K	Si	C	Cl
1 *	18.8	0.10	0.75	93	1.98	0.008	0.008	0.048				0.16	
2 *	15.0	0.13	1.1	93	1.40	0.03	0.04	0.06				0.1	
3 *	5.3	0.35	4.4	78	1.50	0.3	0.5	0.5	0.12	0.033	2	0.2	
4 §	9.5	0.20	0.9	83	0.7	0.001	0.002	0.002	0.001	0.001		0.04	0.12

* produced by Si nitridation; § produced by silicon diimide decomposition

TABLE 2
Density and mechanical properties of pressureless sintered and post-hipped Si_3N_4-based materials.

Mat.	Green density (%)	Sintered density (%)	Average grain size (μm)	σ (MPa)	K ($MPam^{1/2}$)	H (GPa)
Composition A°						
1+	61.8	96.4	0.90	703± 36	6.3	12.3±1.3
1*	/	98.8	1.18	563± 94	9.4	13.7±0.9
2+	57.3	91.0	1.08	439± 68	6.2	10.2±0.5
2*	/	93.4	1.22	554± 54	6.8	8.3±0.6
3+	50.6	93.0	0.75	374± 49	6.5	12.7±1.2
3*	/	95.5	1.07	353± 73	6.6	9.3±0.8
4+	49.9	97.8	0.58	661± 72	7.1	16.7±0.2
4*	/	99.6	0.90	534±128	7.2	15.4±0.8
Composition B°°						
1+		87.9	0.78	445±45	8.1	13.1±2.2
1*		89.4	1.09	518±75	7.6	10.2±1.0
4+		98.3	0.60	641±39	9.6	17.9±1.9
4*		99.8	0.88	773±45	9.8	17.8±0.5

°A: Si_3N_4+3wt%Al_2O_3+8wt%Y_2O_3; °°B: Si_3N_4+1wt%MgO+8wt%Y_2O_3;
+ presintered materials; * post-hipped materials.

density measurements (Archimede's principle), x-ray diffraction, scanning electron microscopy and microanalysis on polished, etched and fracture surfaces. Three points flexural strength (σ) has been measured on samples 3mmx3mmx30mm on a span of 26mm, with a crosshead speed of 0.5 mm/min. The tensile surface of the bars has been machined and polished with 1 µm diamond paste, and the edges chamferred. The critical stress intensity factor (K_{IC}) has been evaluated by indentation technique (6). The Vickers microhardness (HV) has been measured with a load of 500 g, loading rate< 0.3 mm/sec and indentation time of 10 seconds.

RESULTS AND DISCUSSION

Table 2 summarizes the data of density, grain size and RT mechanical properties (σ, K_{IC},HV).

For all the materials, also when an amount of open porosity is present, i. e. density<95%, an increase in density is observed after hipping , the increase being some about 2% nearly independent on the starting value. In no case was the theoretical density reached, even with the hipping treatment, because the "bridge effect" of elongated β-grains in the pre-sintered material (1).

The densities are very strongly dependent on the starting powder and/or composition. The best values have been obtained with powder 4 in both the compositions. Powder 1 exhibits good sinterability in the composition A but not in the composition B, presumably owing to its high purity. After the pressureless sintering only β-Si_3N_4 was detected. The crystalline grain boundary phases at this stage consist mainly of Y-silicates or orthosilicates and of Y-nitrogen silicates; after post-hipping no presence of crystalline intergranular phase has been observed.

Grain morphology stands for a liquid-phase sintering mechanism with directional growth of β-Si_3N_4 to form an interconnected network. The differences in grain size and morphology can be related to different liquid-phase viscosities during sintering, to the chemical composition of the starting powder and to type and amount of additives (4,5).

The finest grains, Table 2, occur with powder 4; the coarsest ones with powders 2 and 3, with enhanced effects of directional growth and interlocking of β-grains. The less uniform texture characterizes the material derived from powder 3, due to the agglomeration of this powder.

Although the arrangement of grains during post-hipping is not changed considerably, generally a decrease of the aspect ratio of β-Si_3N_4 and grain coarsening are observed.

During hipping, further densification is accompained by geometrical changes such as porosity reduction, an example of wich is shown in figs.1a,b for material 4, localised plastic deformation at contact points of grains and squeezing of liquid phase between two grains or from a triple point into pore sites (7). This pore-filling is controlled by the viscosity and the amount of liquid phase and porosity. In

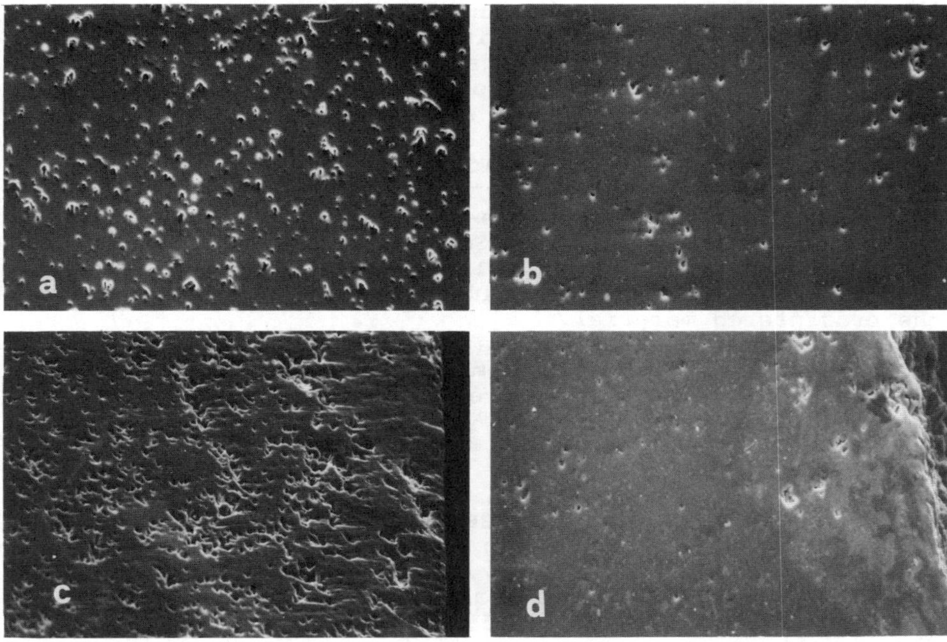

Figure 1. Bulk porosity after pre-sintering (a) and after hipping (b); material from powder 4, composition A. Cross section after pre-sintering (c) and after hipping (d) showing segregation of liquid phase close to the surface; material from powder 2, composition A. Magnifications 300x.

porous bodies pore-filling is very evident at the first surface layer of the material, figs.1c,d, material 2. For dense samples the intergranular phase is already more concentrated at the surface layer after the pre-sintering but after the post-hipping the same phase has disappeared. This effect, not always detected, should be strictly related to the properties of the liquid phase, expecially its refractoriness (1).
From the mechanical point of view, data reported in Table 2 don't indicate an univocal trend.
In spite of augmented density, hardness, inside the experimental errors, is unchanged, if not degraded, in most cases; K_{IC} improves in all the materials of system A but not so in the system B; strength seems to be relatively independent on composition, density and process.
Changes in hardness and toughness are in this way strictly related to changes in amount and crystallinity of the intergranular phase. The behaviour of the strength is instead controlled by the complex defect-stress at fracture relationships, i. e. the nature of the defect, its geometry and its position in the stress field. When failure origins of pre-sintered and post-hipped materials have been identified they resulted to be, in both cases, typical processing defects

(agglomerations and voids), or defects originated from powder impurities. In this case hipping has proved to be ineffective to eliminate such imperfections.

CONCLUSIONS

Post-hipping treatments on pre-sintered silicon nitride result in slight density increase. Squeezing out liquid phase from grain boundary causes pore filling, but theoretical densities cannot be achieved for a "bridging effect" of the β-grains in the presintered material.
Improved mechanical properties have not been observed. Better properties by post-hipping demand the use of high purity and fine grained powders, taylored Si_3N_4-additives compositions and optimized forming process.

REFERENCES

1. Ziegler, G. and Wotting, G., Post-treatment of pre-sintered silicon nitride by hot isostatic pressing. Int. J. High Tech. Ceram., 1985, 1, 31-58.

2. Larker, H., Hot Isostatic pressing of shaped silicon nitride parts. In High-pressure Science and Technology, vol. 2, ed. K. D. Timmerhaus and M. S. Barber, Plenum Pub. Corp., New York, 1981, 1979, 651-654.

3. Yamada, T., Shimada, M. and Koizumi, M., Fabrication of Si_3N_4 by hot isostatic pressing, Am. Ceram. Socc. Bull., 1981, 11, 1225-1228.

4. Bellosi, A., Galassi, C., and Dalle Fabbriche, D., Sintering characteristics of Si_3N_4 powders. High temp. high press., 1988, 20, 335-343.

5. Bellosi, A., Biasini, V. and Vincenzini, P., Influence of powder characteristic on some processing steps of silicon nitride ceramics. In Sintering '87, Elsevier Appl. Sci., 1988, 968-975.

6. Evans, A. G. and Charles, A., Fracture toughness determination by indentation. J. Am. Ceram. Soc., 1976, 59, 371-372.

7. Kwon, O. H. and Messing, G. L., Macropore filling during hot isostatic pressing of liquid phase sintered ceramics. In Sintering '85, ed. Kuczynski, G. C., Uskokovic, D. P., Palmour III, H. and Ristic, M. M., Plenum Pub. Corp., New York, 1985, 165-171.

THE EFFECT OF THE GREEN MICROSTRUCTURE ON THE MECHANICAL PROPERTIES OF DENSE ALUMINA

L.A. CORREIA, P.P.A.C. PEX and H.J. VERINGA
Netherlands Energy Research Foundation, ECN
P.O. Box 1, 1755 ZG PETTEN, the Netherlands

ABSTRACT

In ceramic materials intrinsic flaws as well as processing flaws introduced during compaction of the powder, are often not completely eliminated during densification. In order to study the influence of the green microstructure on the mechanical properties of the final ceramic product, compacts are made by slip casting using submicron alumina powder, A16SG. Suspensions with several degrees of deflocculation and a high solid content are used. These compacts are densified at the appropriate temperature in air and rectangular bars are machined for mechanical testing. Flexural strength is measured using a four point bending test, while the fracture toughness is measured using chevron-notched specimens. The different degrees of deflocculation and sintering temperatures cause different specific densities of the ceramics. It is shown that there is a tendency for the characteristic Weibull strength to reach a stable level above a certain specific density, whereas the fracture toughness can be considered as a constant.

INTRODUCTION

The mechanical properties of ceramics depends very sensitively on microstructural defects of the dense material. From Griffith's Theory it is known that a brittle material exhibits a characteristic strength σ_0 depending on the flaw size c, and where the fracture toughness K_{Ic} is considered as a material parameter:

$$\sigma_0 \sim \frac{K_{Ic}}{\sqrt{c}} \tag{1}$$

Ideally, a ceramic only has intrinsic flaws of the magnitude of grain-size dimensions. However, in processing dense ceramic materials, spontaneous agglomeration of the powder particles introduces a wide variation in pore size. According to Weibull statistics the largest pores act as weakest links in a brittle material. So, the largest pore size will be reflected by the characteristic Weibull strength.

Colloidal processing shows to facilitate deagglomeration of the powder particles. The effect of agglomeration on the development of the microstructure of ceramics, formed by slip casting is discussed in a preceding paper [1]. Here the influence of the green microstructure on the mechanical properties of the dense ceramic will be discussed. For this purpose suspensions of alumina powder, A16SG (Alcoa), in the as received condition, with several degrees of deflocculation are processed into compacts by slip casting.

EXPERIMENTAL PROCEDURES

Materials
The materials are made by sintering compacts which are produced by slip casting suspensions containing 30 vol% Alcoa A16SG powder in the as received condition. Four suspensions are used, each with a different amount of nitric acid, as shown in table 1.

TABLE 1

Suspensionnumber.	I	II	III	IV
mmol HNO_3/gram powder	0,145	0,100	0,075	0,039

The compacts were sintered for 1 and 2 hours at temperatures of 1500°C and 1600°C. In this way alumina plates of 60 x 60 x 5 mm were obtained.

Bending tests
In order to measure the mechanical properties of the alumina, 8-10 rectangular bars with dimensions 4 x 4 x 50 mm were ground out of one plate. The final finish of the bars was established using a grinding wheel containing a D126 characteristic diamond grain size. The bars were chamfered 0.1 mm in order to avoid artificial influences on the strength [2].
The four point bending strengths were measured using a jig, which was specially designed to minimize the influence of misalignment of the load train and the non-orthogonality of the bars. The support rolls of the jig were at a distance of 40 mm and the loading rolls at a distance of 20 mm. From the flexural strengths of the bars the characteristic strength of the two-parameter Weibull statistics was calculated using the "maximum likelihood" analysis.

Fracture toughness tests
The fracture toughness was measured using chevron notched bars. The middle bar from each plate was not chamfered and was used for fracture toughness testing. With a 50 μm diamond saw a chevron notch with an angle of 60° was cut into the bar.
The fracture toughness test were performed with a computer controlled Instron 1362 testing machine on which a very stiff jig was mounted. The support and loading roll distances were similar to the bending tests. The test were performed with an actuator speed of 1 μm/s. From the load vs. displacement curve, which was recorded by the computer, the validity of the test could be checked, i.e. stable crack growth during the test should be visible [3].

RESULTS AND DISCUSSION

The characteristic Weibull strength is plotted versus the specific density in Fig. 1. It can be seen that material I, which had the highest amount of nitric acid in suspension, has a very low strength at a low density. However, the strength shows a very pronounced improvement at higher densities and tends to reach a stable level. Material II has this tendency in a much stronger way, whereas its level of stabilization is the lowest of all materials. Material III has no definite stabilization level, but the strength data are situated within the scattering of the strength data of material I. The strength of material IV at low density is high when compared to the data of the other materials at low density. With increasing density the strength of material IV is increasing to a stabilization level which is the highest of all materials. In general it seems that each material will reach a characteristic stabilization level above a specific density of 3.83 g/cm³. Further microstructural analysis has to take the scattering out of the data. Pores originating from agglomerates are expected to be the origin of fracture rather than sinter cracks or machining damage of the bars.
The various levels of stabilization of the strength which are recognized above a specific density of 3.83 g/cm³ are not encountered in the fracture toughness values of the materials. In Fig. 2. the fracture toughness is plotted versus the specific density and it shows that the K_{Ic}-values of all materials give a slight scattering around 4.2 MPa$\sqrt{m}$. Thus the fracture toughness is not depending on the specific density and is not influenced by the amount of nitric acid in suspension. It should be noted that all K_{Ic}-values are checked very carefully for validation [3]. For this reason there are less fracture toughness data than strength data.
Following these observations the high characteristic strength at low density of material IV should be due to a distribution of very fine but very many pores when equation 1 is considered. This is confirmed in Fig. 3 where optical micrographs show the appearance of the surfaces of material II and IV, both sintered for 1 hour at 1500°C. Material II has fewer but larger pores which cause a low strength.

CONCLUSIONS

From the observations the following conclusions can be drawn:

- The characteristic strength of colloidal processed dense alumina reaches a stabilization level above a specific density of 3.83 g/cm³. The different stabilization levels caused by different acid concentrations in the suspension give an average characteristic strength of 420 MPa with a scatter of 20%.

- The fracture toughness is not depending on the specific density and is not influenced by the acid concentration in the suspension. The fracture toughness value can be estimated on 4.2 MPa$\sqrt{m}$.

- Microstructural evidence for the mechanical behaviour has been found.

ACKNOWLEDGEMENT

Financial support from the National Program on Technical Ceramics IOP-TK is gratefully acknowledged.

REFERENCES

1. Correia, L.A. and Goris, M.J.A.A., The effect of the green microstructure on sintering of alumina. This volume.

2. Barrata, F.I., Requirements for flexure testing of brittle materials. 1982, AMMRC TR 82-20.

3. Munz, D., Effect of specimen type on the measured values of fracture toughness of brittle ceramics. In Fracture Mechanics of Ceramics vol. 6, ed. R.C. Bradt, A.G. Evans, D.P.H. Hasselman and F.F. Lange, Plenum Press, New York, 1983, pp. 1-26.

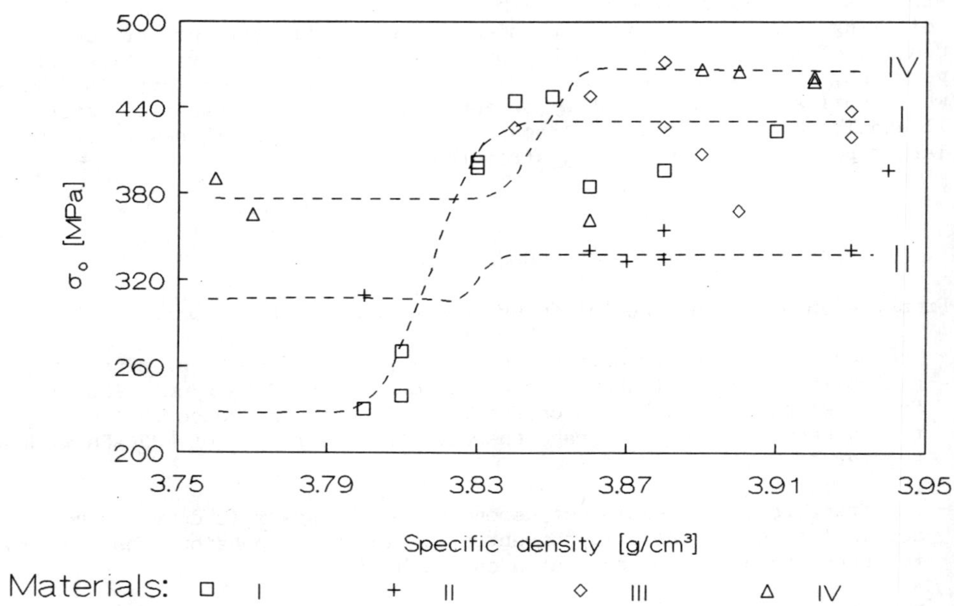

Figure 1. The characteristic Weibull strength σ_0 versus the specific density for all the materials.

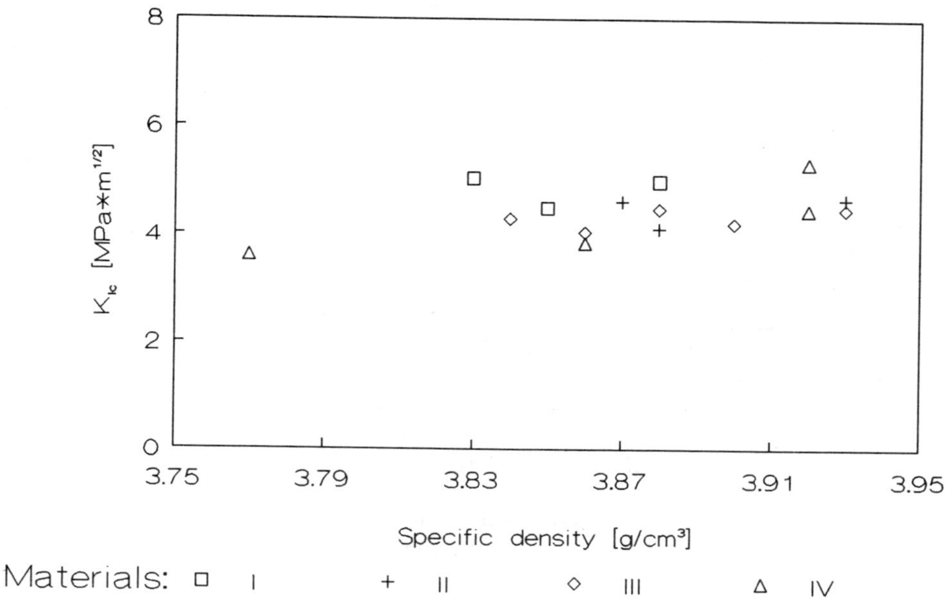

Figure 2. The fracture toughness versus the specific density.

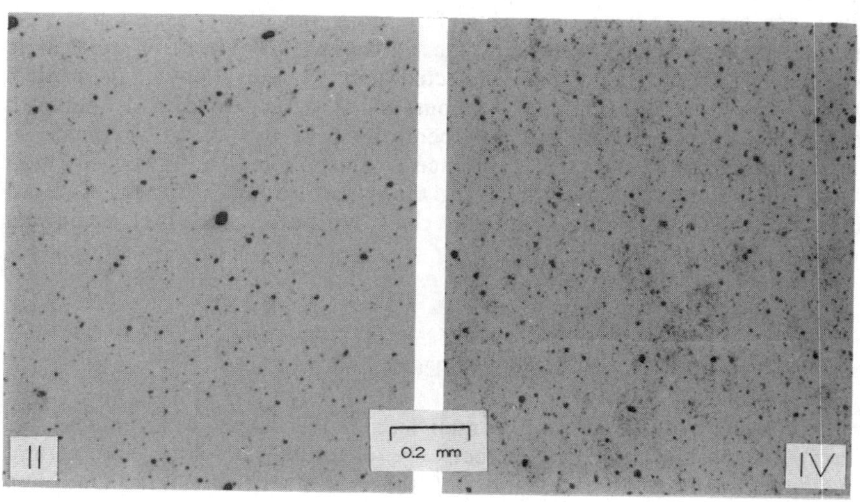

Figure 3. Optical micrographs showing the surface of material II and IV, both sintered for 1 hour at 1500°C.

RELATIONSHIPS BETWEEN GREEN AND FIRED STRENGTH OF Al_2O_3 WITH CONTROLLED DEFECTS

BILL BERGMAN, KRISTIN BREDER and MATS PETERSSON
Department of Physical Metallurgy and Ceramics
The Royal Institute of Technology
S-100 44 Stockholm, Sweden

ABSTRACT

Controlled defects in the form of 20μm polymer spheres and powder agglomerates were added to alumina. The evolution of these defects and their effect on the strength distribution were studied using the diametral compression test. The mean strength and the Weibull modulus are analysed and discussed in relation to density and fractographic information. Material with added agglomerates was shown to fail from the flaws associated with these and the strength scaled well with the measured flaw sizes. Material with added polymer particles failed from connected pore systems. No single critical defect was observed in the material without added defects and it is believed that arrays of small pores were strength controlling in this case. The material containing agglomerates and the reference material had a lower Weibull modulus in the sintered state than in the green state. In the material containing polymer particles (pores) the Weibull modulus remained unchanged after firing.

INTRODUCTION

In order to achieve reliable, strong ceramics it is necessary to eliminate the defects that exist in the material. Defects are differing in source and nature, and the complete control or elimination of them is a difficult task. One step towards achieving this goal would be to be able to relate the strength and defect distribution in the green state to that in the fired state. That is, it is important to know how certain defects develop during the sintering [1,2,3,4].

EXPERIMENTAL PROCEDURE

Alumina was chosen for this study because of its well known properties. One batch (ASR) was used in its as-received condition. To the second batch (POLY) was added 10% polymer particles , with a median particle size of 20μm and to the third batch (AGG) was added 28% preagglomerated alumina powder . The preagglomerated powder, of a size <0.5mm, was obtained by heating to 1300°C for two hours. All three materials were treated in the same way in order to avoid any unwanted effects from different processing. Hence, the processing parameters were not optimized for each material. The powders were uniaxially pressed into pellets, 12mm, in diameter and 7mm in height using a pressure of 25MPa. Sintering was done for 2h at 1425°C and 1525°C at a heating rate of approximately 12°C/min.

The density and porosity of the sintered samples were measured using mercury porosimetry. The specimens were strength tested in diametral compression using a universal testing machine at a crosshead speed of 0.1cm/min. Strength was calculated according to [5]:

$$\sigma = \frac{2\ P}{\pi\ t\ D} \qquad (1)$$

where P is the load, t the thickness and D the diameter of the sample. The fracture strength was analyzed according to the Weibull distribution [6,7] and fractography by stereo microscopy and SEM was performed. For a detailed description of material preparation, see ref. [8].

RESULTS AND DISCUSSION

The results from the porosimetry measurements are summarized in Table 1. Table 2 gives the average strength and the Weibull moduli. Figures 1, 2 and 3 are the corresponding Weibull plots for the green state and the two sintering stages.

The strength in the green state is as expected very low. However, the different series have different green strengths with the agglomerated material having the highest. The Weibull moduli are moderately low and from the plots in Fig. 1 it is reasonable to assume unimodal distributions. Fractography of the green samples showed no special features on the as-received material, hence, it is difficult to identify the strength limiting defect in this case. In the agglomerated samples the agglomerates were easily identifiable, see Fig. 4, and these were large and unevenly distributed in the material. The samples with polymer particles had these evenly distributed throughout the material and the fracture surface consisted of ridges and interconnecting cracks between the polymer particles.

After firing for 2h at 1425°C the samples were only partially sintered. This can be seen from the low density and high porosity given in Table1. Also seen in Table 1. are the total pore area and the median pore diameter. From these numbers it is clear that there is different pore structures in the samples with polymer particles than in the as-received and agglomerated samples. There is an order of magnitude larger pores in the POLY-samples than in the others. Notice, however, that the measured pore size is smaller than the size of

TABLE 1

Summary of porosimetry data.

Sintering Temperature	ASR				AGG				POLY			
	ρ	P	A	D	ρ	P	A	D	ρ	P	A	D
1425°C	3.63	13.6	1.18	0.11	3.30	20.8	1.52	0.12	3.04	18.2	0.58	1.04
1525°C	3.72	4.5	0.51	0.10	3.72	4.3	0.30	0.14	3.45	15.3	0.28	1.07

ρ is density, g/cm^3, P is porosity, %, A is pore surface area, m^2/g, D is median diameter,μm.

TABLE 2

Summary of mean strength, $\bar{\sigma}$, and Weibull modulus, m.

Condition	ASR		AGG		POLY	
	$\bar{\sigma}$ [MPa]	m	$\bar{\sigma}$ [MPa]	m	$\bar{\sigma}$ [MPa]	m
Green state	0.080 (0.023)	6.1 (0.3)	0.107 (0.021)	5.4 (0.4)	0.062 (0.016)	4.4 (0.5)
1425°C	65.4 (30.4)	2.1 (0.1)	47.6 (17.7)	2.6 (0.1)	34.4 (12.0)	4.3 (0.5)
1525°C	76.0 (21.6)	3.8 (0.2)	63.8 (25.9)	2.3 (0.2)	43.8 (13.8)	3.6 (10.3)

* Numbers in parenthesis are one standard deviation.

the polymer particles which were originally added. Further, the total pore surface area is smaller in the POLY-batch, showing the existence of fewer but larger pores. The strengths of the partially sintered samples are shown in Fig. 2. All strengths are low and the Weibull moduli are even lower than in the green state, reflecting a larger spread in strength. The distribution of the AGG and POLY samples are unimodal, while the ASR set may have a bimodal distribution, see below.

Sintering for 2h at 1525°C results in denser samples and lower porosity, see Table 1. There is now a clear difference between the POLY samples and the rest. The strength levels, shown in Table 2 and Fig. 3, have not improved significantly. The Weibull moduli are also very similar to those of 1425°C.

The POLY-batch is the only set with constant Weibull modulus from the green to the sintered state. The fractography supports the assumption that the same fracture initiation process is active in all states, see Fig. 5. All the large

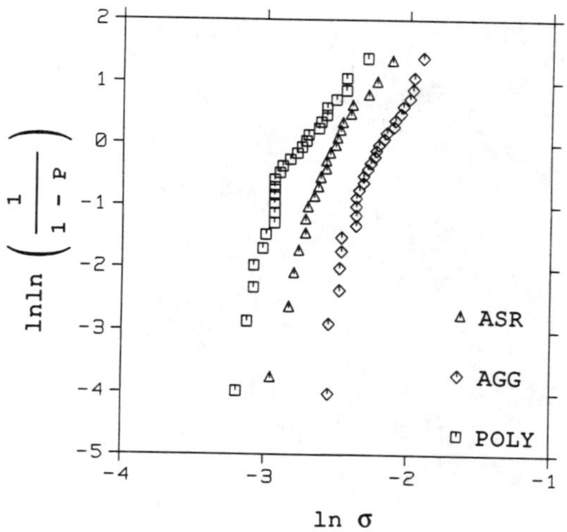

Figure 1. Weibull plot of the strength results of the green samples.

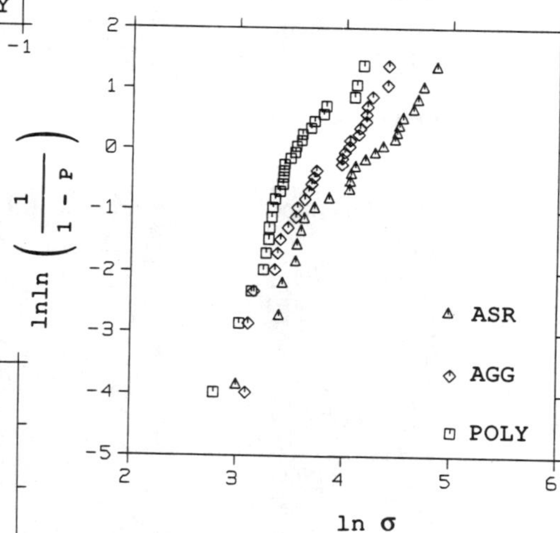

Figure 2. Weibull plot of the strength results after firing at 1425°C.

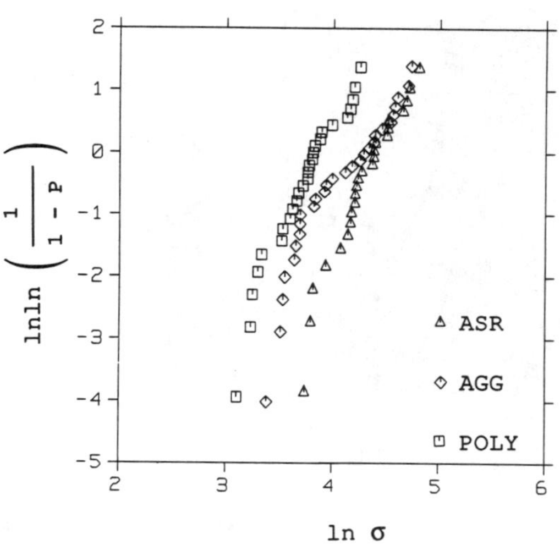

Figure 3. Weibull plot of the strength results after firing at 1525°C.

pores with interconnecting cracks are clearly shown, and the measured fracture stress is the stress needed to link these rather than to propagate a single crack from one large flaw [4]. Hence, the low strength and the constant Weibull modulus are well accounted for.

The batch with agglomerates has low strength and low Weibull modulus. This is consistent with the many large defects unevenly distributed throughout the material. The Weibull plot for 1425°C suggests one failure mode and the size of the agglomerates will account for the measured strength. The plot from 1525°C however, may suggest a bimodal distribution. It is possible that

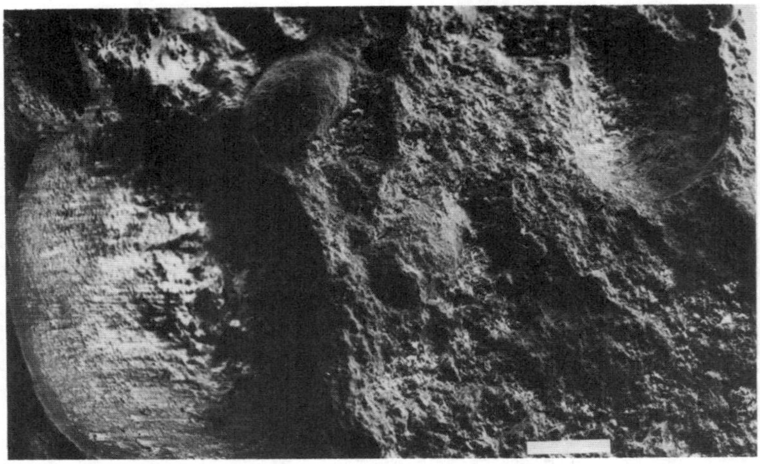

Figure 4. Fracture surface of material with agglomerates, green state. Bar is 100μm.

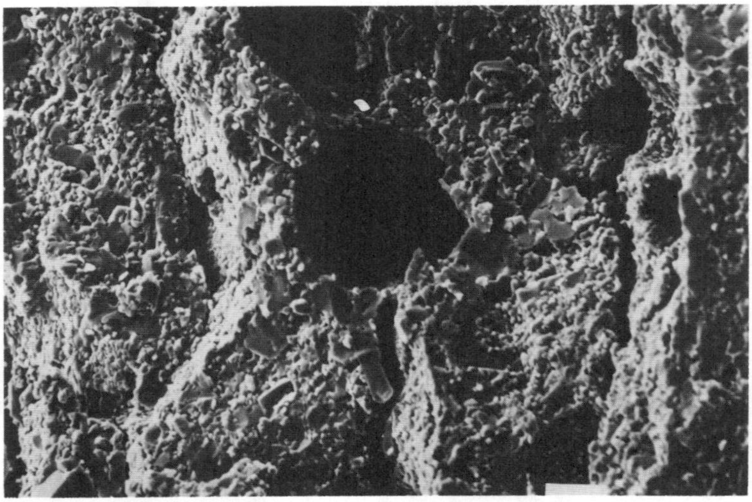

Figure 5. Fracture surface of material with polymer particles, sintered at 1525°C. Bar is 10μm.

the linking of pores and failure from one single large defect are competing mechanisms. Fractography did not resolve this, even though large defects were found.

Generally, fractography on these diametral compression samples turned out to be very difficult because of a complete shattering of the high strength samples [9]. The problem in performing the fractography is most evident in the ASR batch. The strength levels of these are not significantly different from the agglomerated samples, but no single large defect were observed as fracture initiating. It is therefore believed that the low fracture strengths are due to the high porosity, i.e. the fracture stress is the stress needed to link the pores. A bimodal distribution may be suggested for ASR at 1425°C, and it is possible that there is a competing mechanism of a crack propagating from one single pore or defect.

CONCLUSIONS

By introducing a well defined defect population like the polymer particles the same fracture mode was observed in the green state as in various sintering stages. For the as-received material and the material with added agglomerates, the variability in the strength of the sintered samples were larger than of the green samples. This shows that sintering is a critical step as differential sintering opens up voids and cracks. For the sintered as-received and agglomerated material, linking of pores is an important fracture mechanism. The development of added defects was well monitored by measuring the fracture strength and evaluating the Weibull modulus, and further combine this with fractographic information.

REFERENCES

1. B.D. Mosser, J.S. Reed and J.R. Varner, Relationships between green and fired strength distributions of dry pressed alumina compacts, Paper #209-B-88, Presented at the 90th Annual Conference of the American Ceramic Society, Cincinnati, OH, May, 1988.

2. J. Heinrich and H. Hausner, Microstructure and mechanical properties of reaction bonded silicon nitride, in Proceeding of the 4th CIMTEC, edited by P. Vincenzini, Saint Vincent, Italy, 1979, 780-792.

3. J. Heinrich and D. Munz, Strength of reaction-bonded silicon nitride with artificial pores, American Ceramic Society Bulletin, 1980, **59**, 1221-1222.

4. J.E. Ritter Jr and R.W. Davidge, Strength and its variability in ceramics with particular reference to alumina, Journal of the American Ceramic Society, 1984, **67**, 432-437.

5. R. Berenbaum and I. Brodie, Measurement of the tensile strength of brittle materials, British Journal of Applied Physics 1959, **10**, 281-287.

6. W.Weibull, A statistical theory of the strength of materials, Ingenjörsvetenskapsakademiens handlingar, 1939, **151**, 1.

7. B. Bergman, On the estimation of the Weibull modulus, Journal of Materials Science Letters, 1984, **3**, 689-692.

8. M. Petersson, B. Bergman and K. Breder, Development and changes of controlled defects during processing and their effect on strength, 1989, submitted to Journal of the American Ceramic Society.

9. A. Rudnick, A.R. Hunter and F.C. Holden, An analysis of the diametral-compression test, Mater.Res.Stand. 1963, **3**, 283-289.

STUDY OF MACROSCOPIC THERMAL STRESSES IN $BaTiO_3$ BASED PTC THERMISTORS

C. DEWITTE, J.P. MICHENAUD and F.DELANNAY
Dept des Sciences des Matériaux et des Procédés
Université Catholique de Louvain
Place Sainte Barbe, 2, B-1348 Louvain-la-Neuve (Belgium)

ABSTRACT

When PTC thermistors are subjected to a high inrush power, some of them fail by fracturing in two parts along a plane parallel to the electrodes. This failure mode is due to high thermal stresses resulting from the transient temperature gradients that form in the sample during self-heating. We have calculated the thermomechanical stresses in PTC thermistors subjected to a high inrush power taking into account their electrical and physical properties.

INTRODUCTION

PTC(R) refers to the Positive Temperature Coefficient of Resistivity exhibited by certain semiconducting ceramics, and particularly by donor-doped barium titanate, in the vicinity of the ferroelectric Curie temperature [1]. When such PTC thermistors are subjected to a high inrush power (up to 30 to 60 W/mm^3), some of them fail by fracturing in two parts along a plane parallel to the electrodes.We call this mode of failure "rupture by delamination". It is due to the formation of transient temperature gradients in the sample during the self-heating and is intrinsically similar to what is commonly called a "thermal shock". We have undertaken a comprehensive research program aiming at a better understanding of the mechanisms of this thermal shock rupture of PTC ceramics, sintered in the disk geometry.

This mode of rupture by delamination can be reproduced under controlled conditions in an electrical cycling test [2]. The observation of the rupture surfaces, illustrated in figure 1a, indicates that failure starts by nucleation of a crack either inside the thermistor or on its lateral surface, at a point located in a plane nearly equidistant from both contacts surfaces. Waves observed on the rupture surface suggest that the crack propagates step by step during each successive cycle in a direction parallel to the contacts until the rupture is completed. Some samples present also flaws on the cylindrical surfaces without complete rupture. In order to disclose the mechanism of rupture, it appeared necessary to apprehend the temperature distribution and the corresponding stress field distribution for different sets of electrical parameters.

The present paper concerns the calculation of the temperature and macroscopic stress distributions in PTC thermistors subjected to a high inrush power. Our model takes into account the electrical and physical properties of those thermistors, in particular, the thermal expansion behaviour which exhibits a volume contraction during the ferroelectric-paraelectric transition [3]. We also study the influence of electrical inhomogeneities on the temperature and stress distributions.

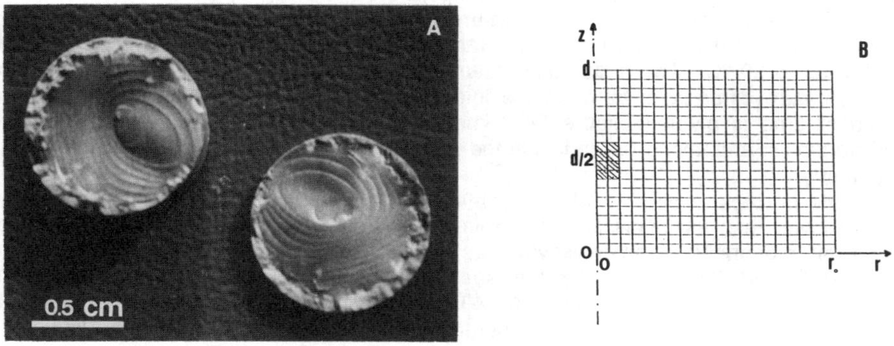

Figure 1. (a) Rupture surfaces of a delaminated PTC thermistor; (b) Axisymmetric grid used for the temperature and stress distributions calculation.

METHODS

Temperature Distributions

Temperature distribution calculations are based on the partial differential equation

$$k \nabla^2 T = - Q + \delta C \partial T / \partial t \qquad (1)$$

subjected to the boundary condition that the heat flux across the boundary surfaces is proportional to the difference between the surface temperature and the known temperature To of the surrounding medium:

$$(To - T_{surface})\, h = - k \partial T / \partial n. \qquad (2)$$

In the equations (1) and (2), k is the thermal conductivity, δ the density, C the specific heat, n the outward drawn normal to the surface and h the heat transfer coefficient at the surfaces. The source term Q represents the Joule heat and has been calculated using a parallel/serie electrical model. A finite difference method was carried out in a two dimensional model with rotational symmetry (figure 1b). The computation makes use of temperature independent thermal conductivity and density, of a non linear heat capacity. We also use a temperature dependent resistivity function which approximates the resistivity-temperature characteristic of a PTC thermistor.

Thermal Stress Distributions

We map the temperature values to the axisymmetric grid depicted in figure 1b and obtain the stresses using a finite element computation method based on linear thermoelasticity. In the present problem, one must take into account that some material parameters, i.e. the Young's modulus E and the thermal expansion coefficient α, may themselves be functions of the temperature. We use a non-linear expansion coefficient including the volume contraction during the transition and, in a first approximation, a temperature independent Young's modulus (E = 100 MPa).

RESULTS

Temperature Distributions

An example of temperature distribution in an electrically homogeneous PTC disk is presented in figures 2a and b (full lines). After the voltage is switched on, the temperature rises and reaches the Curie temperature (Tc=120 °C) after one second. At this time, there are small radial temperature differences (< 1 °C) but large axial ones (~10 °C). The latter build up particularly rapidly when Tc is exceeded. They can reach values of up to 30 °C. The radial temperature differences remain small. The evolution of the temperature differences between the interior and the surfaces of the specimen as a function of time is given in figure 2c. The maximum temperature differences, at r=0 along the z-axis, and, along the radius in the mid plane z=d/2, are defined by ΔT_z and ΔT_r, respectively.

In the practice, a ceramic always contains certain inhomogeneities, e.g. a resistivity higher or lower than the average within a limited volume. In order to modelize the effect of such inhomogeneities, the resistivity was modified in a cylinder centered around the point (0,d/2) and represented by the shaded area in figure 1b. The temperature distribution and evaluation of ΔT_z and ΔT_r in the case of an inhomogeneity with a resistivity lowered by a factor 10, is presented on figures 2a, b and c (dashed lines). A cold layer develops in the central region of the disk. Both ΔT_z and ΔT_r are amplified.

Thermal Stress Distributions

For an electrically homogeneous PTC disk, the magnitude of the three stress components Szz and Srr = Sθθ remain of the same order of magnitude. Here, we present only results concerning the axial stress component Szz as it is this stress component which appears responsible of the rupture by delamination illustrated in figure 1a. As an example, figure 3 presents the isostress lines Szz after 1.15 s. At this time, tensile stresses are observed both in the bulk and at the cylindrical surface.

In order to locate the maximum axial stress Szz, we plot, in figure 4a, Szz along the radius at mid plane (r,d/2) for different times. The amplitude of the stress is related to the temperature gradients. Its sign depends on the sign of the thermal expansion coefficient which exhibits a negative value in the transition region. The bulk of the sample is first subjected to compressive stresses, the maximum tensile stress being at the surface. In the vicinity of Tc, the bulk changes from a compressive stress state to a low tensile one and the surface then becomes in compression. Above Tc, compressive stresses are restored in the bulk, the maximum tensile stress being again located at the surface. Figure 4c (full lines) presents the evolution as a function of time of the maximum tensile stress Szz in the mid plane. This maximum is always located at the surface, except for a while around 1s when the surface is under compression.

In the case of a local lower resistivity, the evolution of Szz (fig. 4b) is similar except around the point (0,d/2) where the inhomogeneity is located. This volume is first subjected to a high tensile stress state (15 MPa). When its temperature reaches Tc, it changes to a compressive one. Above Tc, it returns to a high tensile stress state but whose the magnitude is lower than the tensile stress at the surface. In figure 4c, the maximum stress before the transition (~1s) is located in the bulk whereas the values after 1.2 s correspond to a maximum stress at the cylindrical surface. They are the same as in the homogeneous case because they are only affected by the external cooling.

DISCUSSION

Temperature Distributions

For an electrically homogeneous PTC disk, the temperature differences between the interior and the surfaces depend on the geometry and on the surface cooling conditions. Large differences are obtained when a resistivity inhomogeneity is introduced. This can be

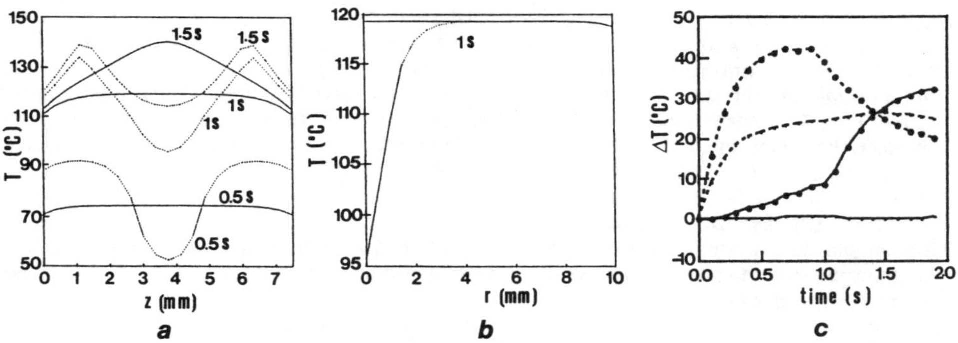

Figure 2.Temperature distribution in a homogeneous (full lines) and inhomogeneous (dashed lines) PTC thermistor, (a) along the z axis at r = 0; (b) along the radius at the mid-plane ; (c) ΔT_Z (-●-) and ΔT_r.

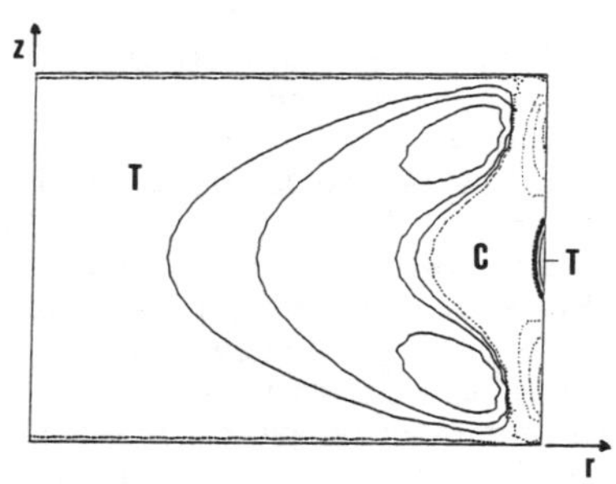

Figure 3. Pattern of isostress lines Szz after 1.15 s. in a homogeneous PTC disk.

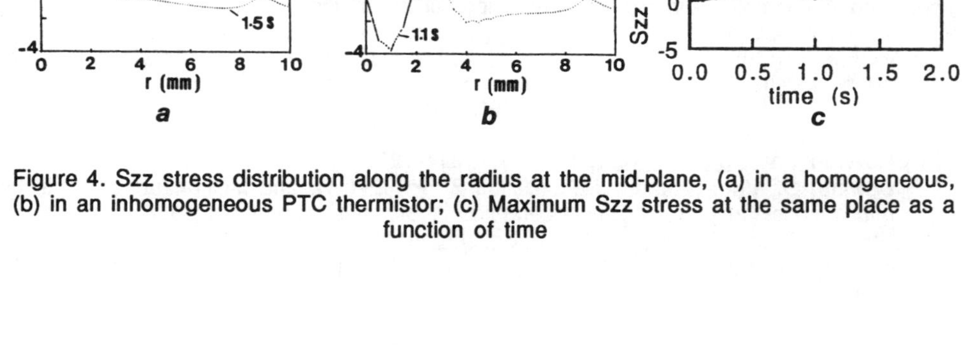

Figure 4. Szz stress distribution along the radius at the mid-plane, (a) in a homogeneous, (b) in an inhomogeneous PTC thermistor; (c) Maximum Szz stress at the same place as a function of time

explained as follows. The local lower resistivity induces a slightly increased local power consumption in the adjacent region, and, hence a temperature increase. As a result of the PTC effect, this brings about an increase of the locally generated Joule heat. The temperature differences gradually increase, then decrease until the thermistor stabilises above Tc. The thermistor is then in a high resistivity state and the inhomogeneity of resistivity becomes masked. The internal conduction of heat and the external cooling level out the temperature at an elevated value (140 °C).

Thermal Stress Distributions

The tensile stresses resulting from the temperature gradients may lead to the rupture of the thermistor if their level exceed the stress allowing propagation of the critical defect present in the ceramic.

In the case of an electrically homogeneous PTC disk, tensile stresses appear both in the bulk and at the cylindrical surface. The tensile stresses in the bulk are due to the anomalous contraction corresponding to the phase transition in $BaTiO_3$ and are quite low. Their magnitude will be a function of the negative shape of the expansion coefficient which is very sensitive to the chemical composition. The tensile stresses at the cylindrical surface are much higher. Their magnitude depends on the convective heat tranfer coefficient. The nature of the electrodes can particularly influences it. In the case of an electrically inhomogeneous PTC, very high tensile stresses build up around the inhomogeneity, especially before Tc is reached.

Our calculations also allow us to understand the influence of the electrical properties of the PTC thermistors on the temperature distribution and finally on their sensitivity to failure by delamination. The results of our calculations are also consistent with the observed mode of rupture where crack origins are found both in the interior and on the cylindrical surface. However, considering a KIc value of the order of 1 MPa√m [4], rupture under a stress of 10 to 15 MPa corresponding to the maximum stresses in figure 4c would involve the presence of a critical defect size larger than 1 mm. This could account for the propagation of a macroscopic crack during each cycling but not for its nucleation in an undamaged PTC disk. In order to justify the presence of stresses high enough for the nucleation of a crack, we should assume that PTC thermistors can have simultaneously different kind of inhomogeneities, e.g. lower of higher local resistivity, variation of the Curie Temperature, non-conductive phases, ... which can give rise to more important temperature gradients and higher thermal stresses. It is also possible that subcritical crack propagation occur around large pores during cycling under high voltage. Work is in progress to assess these hypotheses.

ACKNOWLEDGEMENTS

We would like to ackowledge the use of the finite element computer program of the Applied Mechanics Department (MEMA) from our university. We also thak the MBLE company for providing the samples and the IRSIA for supporting this work.

REFERENCES

[1] Heywang, W., J.Mater.Sci., 1971, **6**, 1214-1226.

[2] Dewitte, C., Keustermans, J.-P., Delannay, F., Elst, R. and Michenaud, J.-P., to be published.in the proc. of Electroceramics II, Brussels, september 1988.

[3] Shirane, G. and Takeda, A., J.Phys.Soc.Japan, 1952, **7**, 1-4.

[4] de With, G., and Parren, J.E.D., in Science of Ceramics 12, 1984, 537-542.

OXIDATION AND REDUCTION REACTIONS/MECHANICAL STRENGTH RELATIONSHIPS IN Mn-Zn FERRITES.

PASCAL PERRIAT*, MARC ABOUAF**
* Thomson-LCC, BP 18 - F21201 BEAUNE CEDEX
** ENSMP, Centre des Matériaux, BP 87 - 91003 EVRY CEDEX

ABSTRACT

The paper examines the influence of oxidation/reduction reactions upon the mechanical properties of Mn-Zn ferrites during sintering. During the rise in temperature, the reactions with oxygen, which are inhomogeneous inside the ferrite component imply large deformations. Shrinkage and reactions are characterized by dilatometric measurements and TGA. They are correlated, first to the correspondant fracture test (measured by the diametral compression test), then to the final mechanical strength (analysed by Weibull statistics) and to the magnetic properties.

INTRODUCTION

It is well known that the control of the partial pressure in oxygen is very important for the magnetic properties (grain growth during the sintering soak [1], control of the Fe2+ amount during cooling [2]). During the rise in temperature, oxidation and reduction reactions are the driving forces of sintering. During cooling the precipitation of hematite which has a higher density leads to cracks.

The correlations between oxidation reactions and densification are presented. Then the followings are examined:

- the apparition of cracks in the cores during debinding : the exothermicity of binder removal leads to inhomogeneous reactions and deformations inside the material
- the influence of low temperature reactions upon the final mechanical strength : deformations at low temperatures induce stresses which remain during the whole process.

EXPERIMENTAL PROCEDURE

Three Mn-Zn ferrite powders OX, INT and RED (Fe2O3 :71.5 wt% ; MnO : 19.2 wt% ; ZnO : 9.3 wt%) were prepared with different degrees of oxidation and specific areas. The powders preparation processes and their characteristics are resumed in table 1.

	OX.	INT.	RED.
Conditions for preparation	900° C 2 hours under air slow cooling	1100°C 2 hours under air slow cooling	1200°C 2 hours under nitrogen quenching
Oxidation degree $[Mn^{3+}] - [Fe^{2+}]$	1.65 %	1.3 %	-0.35%
% Fe_2O_3	28.6 %	11.2 %	0.6 %
Initial BET (m2/g)	1.25	0.1	0.1
Pounding time to reach			
• BET = 1.25 m2/g	0	15 min.	10 min.
• BET = 4.25 m2/g	5 h 20 min	4 h 30 min	3 h 45 min
Binder content	1.5 %	1.5 %	1.5 %

Table 1 : Studied powders.

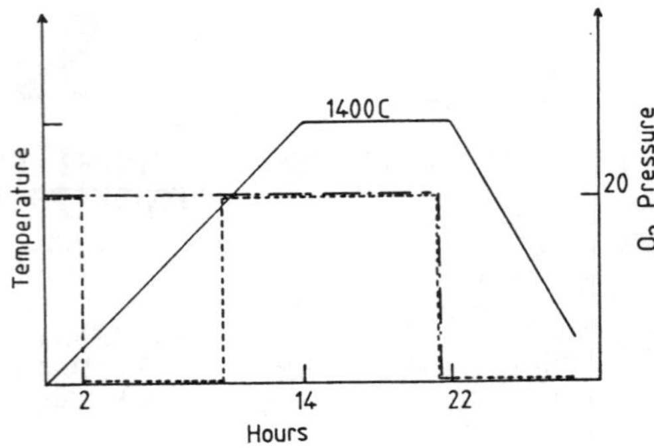

Fig 1 : Sintering cycles.

1- The study of the correlations between oxidation/ reduction reactions was made by the classical methods of TGA and dilatometry. For dilatometry a compressive stress of 0.01 MPa was applied to the material.

2- The study of the mechanical strength during the binder removal stage was made by the diametral compression test performed on discs which had been subjected to various binder removal cycles stopped at different temperatures. The compression speed was 0.5 mm/min.

3- The study of the final mechanical strength was made using Weibull statistics. The three point bending test was performed on bars with a compression speed of 0.4 mm/min. The bars were obtained from the powders OX., INT. and RED. which were subjected to the two sintering cycles of figure 1.

RESULTS AND DISCUSSION

1- Reactions with oxygen as the driving forces of sintering (fig 2).

The reactions with oxygen which imply a flow of matter lead to sintering at very low temperatures. With the more reduced powder (BET=4.25 m²/g), the first oxidation corresponds to a shrinkage of about 1% and the following reduction is accompanied by a very high densification (about 2% per 40°C). The oxidation of Mn2+ with precipitation of hematite between 530 and 650°C is not correlated to any shrinkage.

Fracture stress is closely linked to shrinkage. After debinding, the mechanical properties are improved by the oxidation reaction. However reactions which are too violent (especially the first reduction reaction) lead to deformations, residual stresses and lower the mechanical cohesion. This is shown by the decrease of fracture stress of the reduced powder at 550°C.

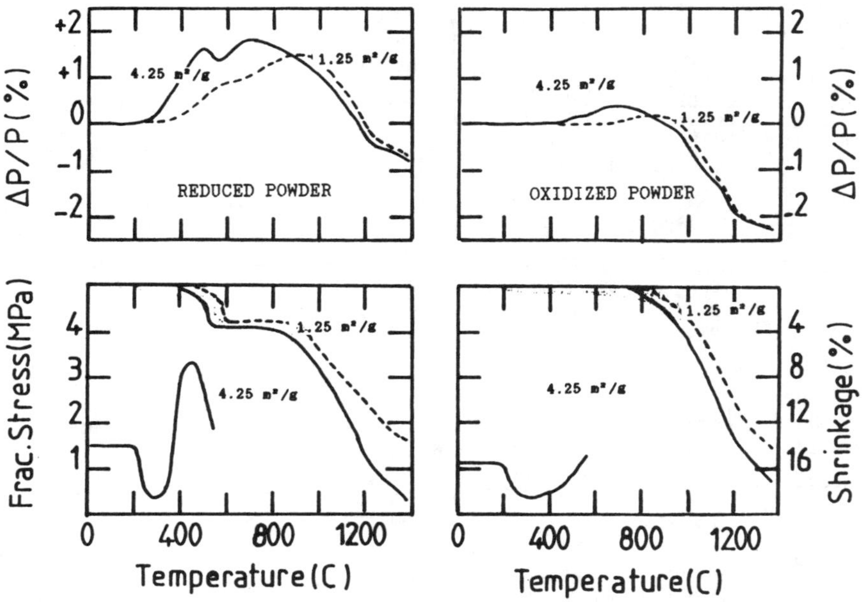

Fig 2 : Correlations between TGA, dilatometry (powders without PVA) and fracture stress (with PVA).

2- Debinding.

Cracks occur during debinding on some samples before 300°C (fig 3). A possible explanation would be the pressure developed in the material by the gases produced by the combustion of PVA. The evaluation of the pressure using the Darcy law (fig3) leads to a value of 0.03 MPa which is less than the fracture stress of 0.3 MPa.

In fact these cracks result from the reoxidation of the more reduced powders. During debinding a temperature rise of almost 100°C is observed at 300°C inside the discs. Oxidation is then possible for powders INT and RED but only at the surface of the discs : inside oxygen has been consumed for binder removal. This difference of shrinkage leads to large deformations and cracks.

3- Influence of low temperature reactions upon fracture stress (fig4).

Low temperature reactions lower the fracture stress. For temperature rise under air, fracture stress is greater for the more oxidized powder and the lower BET. For temperature rise under nitrogen, fracture stress is generally greater than for under air. This is because there is neither possibility for oxidation, nor for the first reduction of Mn^{4+}. In this case the mechanical properties are improved by a low initial degree of oxidation with exception of powder RED. with BET=4.25 m²/g. This can be explained by inhomogeneous oxidation occuring during debinding at about 250°C, when oxygen partial pressure

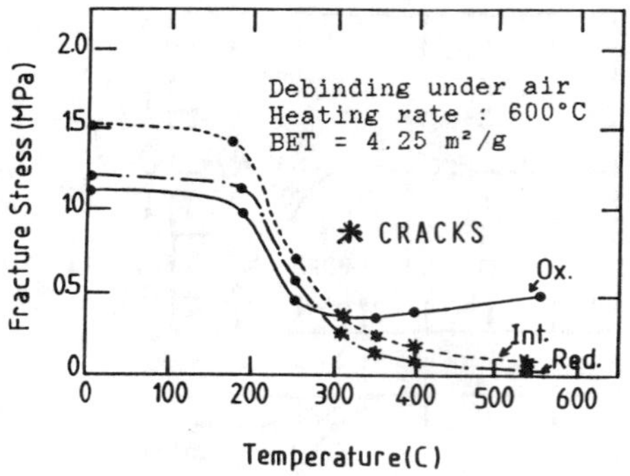

(a)

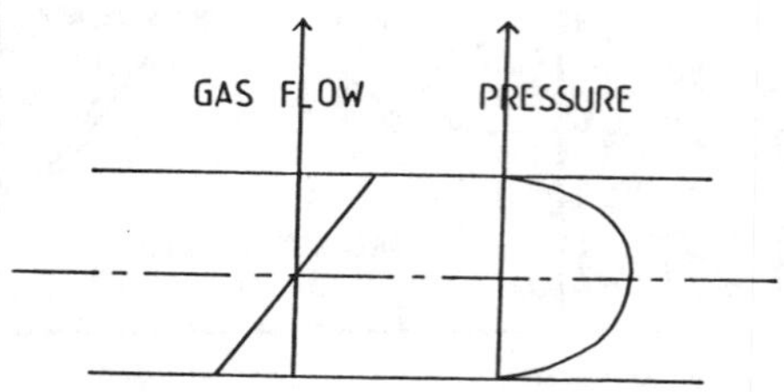

(b)

Fig 3 : Fracture stress during debinding (a) and cross section profile of gas flow and pressure in a disc (b).

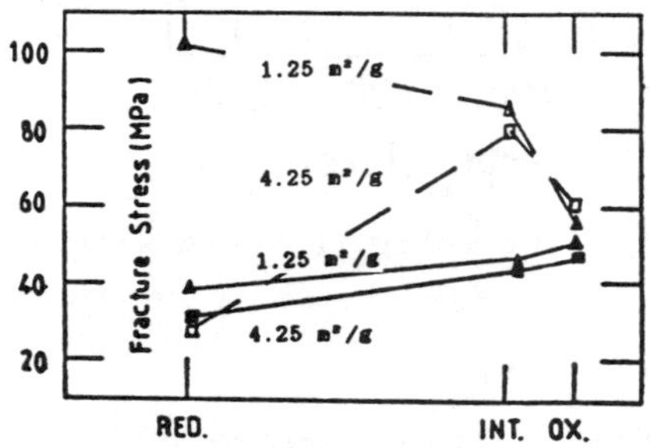

(a)

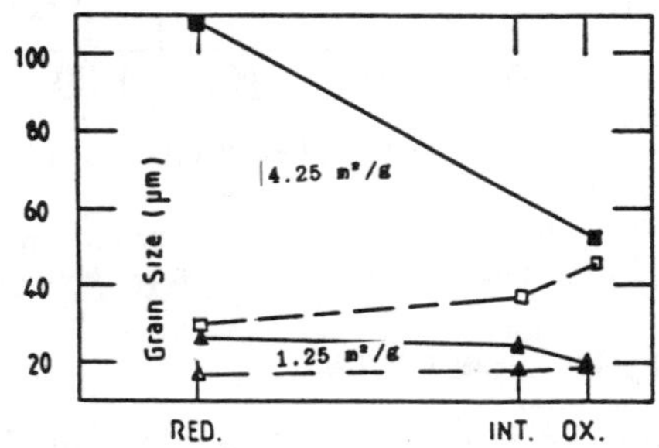

(b)

Fig 4 : Evolution of fracture stress (a) and grain size (b) for different temperature rise —— under air — — under nitrogen

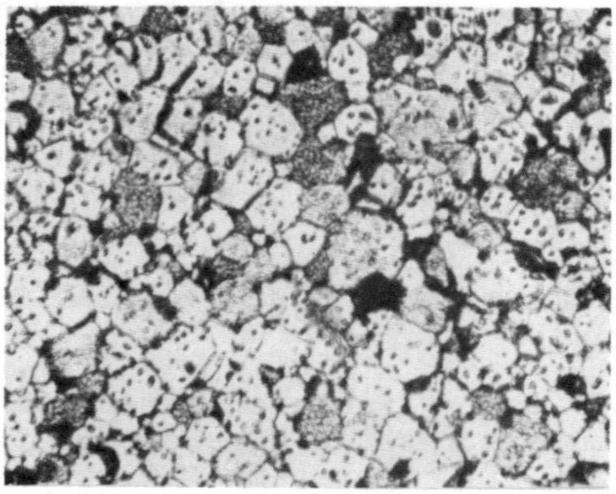

(a)

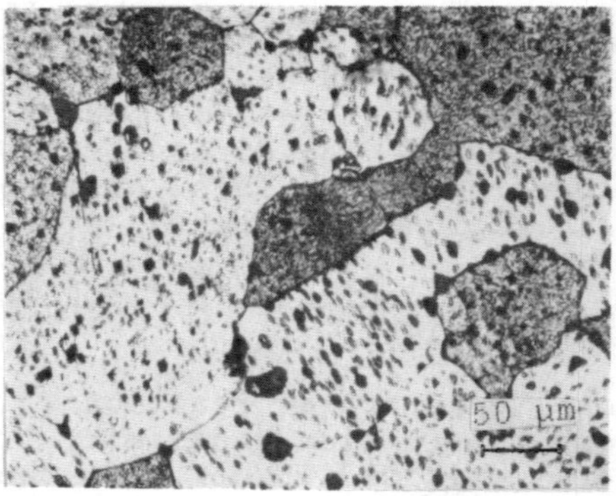

(b)

Photos 1 : Microstructure for powder RED (BET = 4.25 m²/g) for temperature rise (a) under nitrogen (b) under air.

is still important.

Concerning microstructure analysis, low temperature reactions enhance grain growth by dissipating important deformation energy (fig 4 and photo 1). For powder RED. with BET=4.25m²/g the final grain diameter is 30 µm for the temperature rise under nitrogen (when there is no reaction) and reaches 110 µm under air (when reactions are maximal).

For temperature rise under air, permeability is lower when the initial degree of oxidation decreases, although grain size increases (fig 5). This can be explained by important residual stresses which increase the effective coefficient of anisotropy.

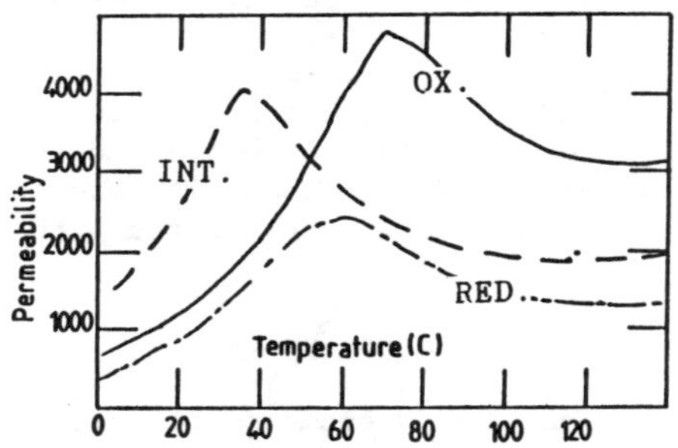

Fig 5 : Evolution of permeability for a temperature rise under air (BET = 4.25m²/g)

CONCLUSION

Diffusion phenomena of low temperature (heat diffusion, gas diffusion in porous media) lead to inhomogeneous reactions inside ferrite cores, which are responsible for large deformations. The influence of these deformations upon the apparition of cracks during the binder removal stage and the final mechanical properties have been shown.

ACKNOWLEDGEMENTS

The authors would like to thank B.Bonnet and J.Lima for their technical assistance.

REFERENCES

1. RÖss,E. and Hanke,I., Z.angew.Physik,1970,pp225-234
2. Morineau,R.,IEEE Transactions on Magnetics,vol. Mag-11,n° 5,September 1975

EXPERIMENTAL INFLUENCES ON THE R-CURVE BEHAVIOUR OF ALUMINA

K.K.O. Bär, G. Kleist, H. Nickel, R. Spelthann
Institut für Reaktorwerkstoffe, KFA Jülich GmbH,
Postfach 19 13, D-5170 Jülich

Abstract

A close inspection of published experimental data on R-curve behaviour of Al_2O_3 shows that measured R-curves might be influenced by experimental parameters and the applied evaluation method. The material dependent reasons for enhanced crack resistance are related to the microstructure, the second phases and to residual stresses. It was therefore felt necessary to perform special fracture mechanical experiments to obtain really controlled crack growth in four-point bend specimens, which were annealed and protected against moisture. R-curves are presented for different load displacement rates including stress relaxations. The R-curves were evaluated with different calculation methods.

Introduction

Crack resistance of ceramics in dependence of crack extension (R-curve behaviour) is often measured by 3-point bending in laboratory environment at a constant load displacement rate. Since in many cases /1, 2, 3/ crack length measurements are not performed simultaneously, the crack length increments are calculated by means of the compliance method which makes use of the established elastic compliance curve for the special material. The experiments often include effects from environmental influences on the subcritical crack growth, or varying crack growth velocities, and of residual stresses. It was felt necessary, therefore, in controlled crack growth experiments with one alumina grade of high purity and mainly intercrystalline microfracture behaviour, to try to seperate, as far as possible, experimental influences on the R-curve from the causes inherent in the material. Specially controlled crack growth experiments were executed and evaluated with different evaluation methods taking into account all the available experimental information.

Experimental Performance

The investigated material was alumina AF 99.7 (Demarquest) with mainly intercrystalline fracture behaviour. Some property data is mentioned in another presented paper /4/. Bend specimens of dimensions $5 \times 10 \times 105$ mm^3 where machined with high precision, notched to relative notch lengths of about $a_o/_W = 0.4$, and polished. They were heat treated in flowing dry nitrogen at 1100°C for 2 hours with controlled heating and cooling rates of 30K/h. Thereafter gold scales with a thickness of about 30 nm were sputtered upon the side faces for better optical contrast and for surface protection. The specimens were immersed thereafter into silicon oil (H_2O < 80 ppm) and stored in a dessicator until they were mechanically tested. Provision was made that the notch root and the side faces kept their oil films throughout the test procedure.

4-point bending at controlled deformation rates, with span widths of 45 and 90 mm, was applied to the specimens in a servohydraulic testing machine (overall stiffness: 13 KN/mm). Special equipment including a travelling immersion microscope of high resolution and a video system, allowed a precise measurement of the crack length a (t) better than 20 μm.

The bending experiments were performed

- at a constant displacement rate of $\dot{u}_1 = 3 \ \mu m/min$
- at a displacement rate $u_2 = k \cdot t^{-1/2} < \dot{u}_1$ ($k = 0.53 \ mm \cdot s^{-1/2}$)
- at a constant displacement rate of $\dot{u}_1$ to about the point of a crack initiation with intermediate stress relaxations at different displacement levels after crack initiation.

Time dependent measurement data are available for load P, displacement u, and crack-length a in addition to the load-displacement diagrammes.

Evaluation Methods

The evaluation of crack resistance R was performed in different ways:

- by use of the K_R-method from measured values of crack length a, load P(a) and Young's modulus (5)
- by use of the compliance method
  - a) with experimental values of P, displacement u and with a, derived from the theoretical complicance curve (2)
  - b) with experimental values of P(a), u (a) and a only, after having established the experimental compliance curve (3)
  - c) with only experimental values of P (a) and a and with reference to the theoretical compliance curve (4)

- by the more general evaluation according to /5/ which makes allowance for displacement offsets from non-linear effects, if the specimen had been unloaded. Indeed they were not, but the hypothetical elastic unloading-reloading steps are assumed to be controlled by the theoretical compliance curve with experimental values of P (a) and a. (1)

Results

The crack growth experiments with annealed Al_2O_3-specimens (AF 99.7) under the same inert conditions in 4-point-bending allow the evaluation of crack elongation Δ a vs. time. (The crack propagation for $\dot{u}_1$ = 3 um/min (Fig. 1a) 6 specimens) occurs in single steps which may be as large as several hundred micrometers, whereas the $\dot{u}_2$-controlled experiments (Fig. 1a, 3 specimens) show a more continuos crack growth with single steps up to 100 um, the average crack propagation velocity being about one third of that of the $\dot{u}_1$-experiment. This allows a more convenient measurement of crack growth in the $\dot{u}_2$-experiment , since the displacement rate decreases with crack propagation and with decreasing specimen load. Fig. 1b shows the crack propagation Δ a vs-time for a $\dot{u}_1$-experiment with intermediate relaxation steps. During the relaxation steps the crack

- Since the experimental compliance curve for 4-point bending exceeds the theoretical elastic compliance curve, the conventional compliance method with calculated crack length values seems to be in some doubt.
- Three-point bending tests resulted in appreciably lower maximum R-values (R_{max} = 85 N/m after Δ a = 3,0 mm) than in 4-point-bending (conventional compliance method). This result might imply that the R-curve behaviour is dependent on the test geometry.
- Different evaluation methods result in different R-curves. Some of the inconsistencies may be due to the approximations made in the fitting procedures for the measurement data, since R-values are dependent on the derivative of the compliance curve. However, the evaluation for different test specimens are in good agreement. The differences, especially between the inelastic evaluation (1), the elastic compliance methods (2), (3), (4), and the elastic K_R-method (5) should be further discussed in terms of the applicability of testing and evaluation method.

References

/1/ R. Knehans, Fortschrittsberichte der VDI-Zeitschriften, Reihe 18: Bruchvorgänge und Schadensanalysen, Düsseldorf, 1984

/2/ F.W. Kleinlein, Dissertation Universität Erlangen-Nürnberg, 1980

/3/ H. Hübner, W. Illek, Proc. 7. Sitzung des Arbeitskreises Bruchvorgänge, Deutscher Verband für Materialprüfung, 8.-10.10.1975, Aachen

/4/ E. Babilon, K.K.O. Bär, G. Kleist, H. Nickel, another paper in this proceedings

/5/ A.G. Atkins and Y.W. Mai, "Elastic and plastic fracture", J. Wiley and Sous (eds), New York, 1985

/6/ F. Deuerler, Fortschrittsberichte der VDI-Zeitschriften, Reihe 18: Mechanik/Bruchmechanik, Nr. 38, VDI-Verlag, Düsseldorf 1987

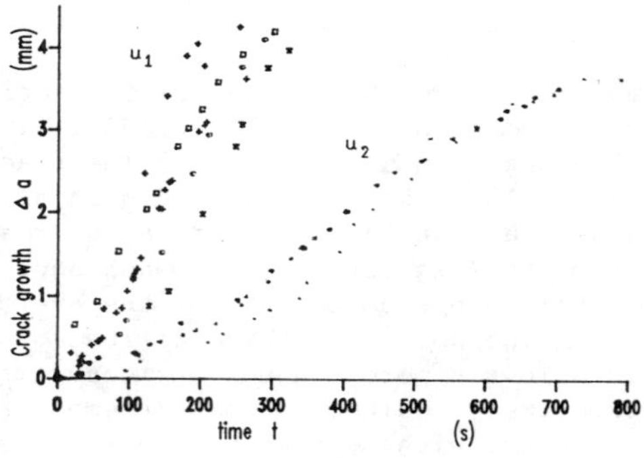

Fig. 1a: Crack growth Δ a versus time for constant load displacement rate u_1 and load displacement rate $u2 = k \cdot t^{-1/2}$

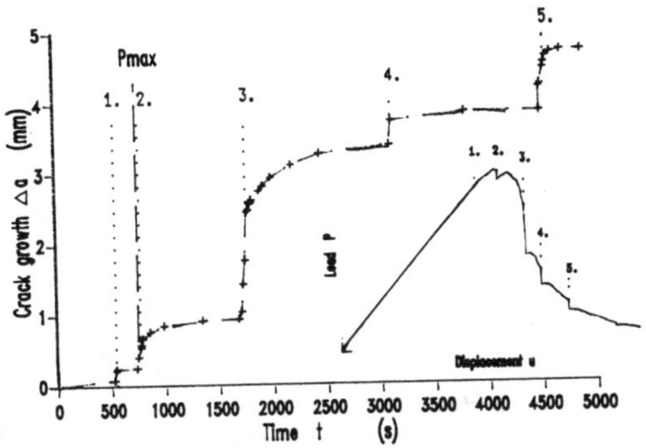

Fig. 1b: Crack growth Δa versus time for constant load displacement rate u_1 and intermediate relaxations

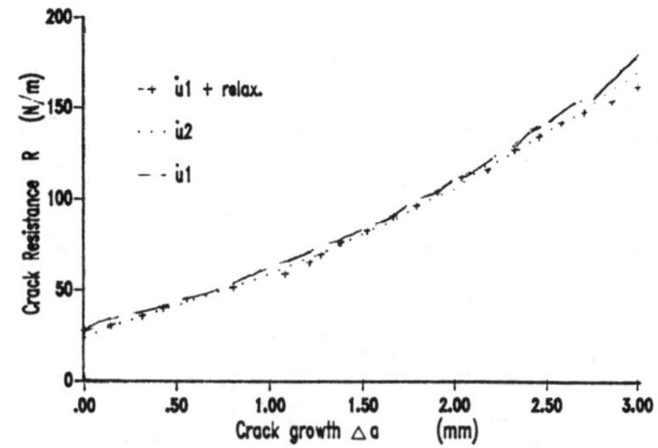

Fig. 2: R-curve behavior calculated by conventional compliance method for the three different performed crack growth experiments

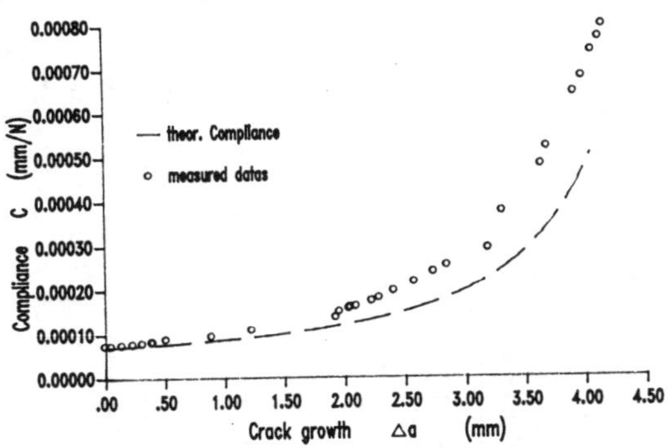

Fig. 3: Compliance versus crack length in 4-pt bending

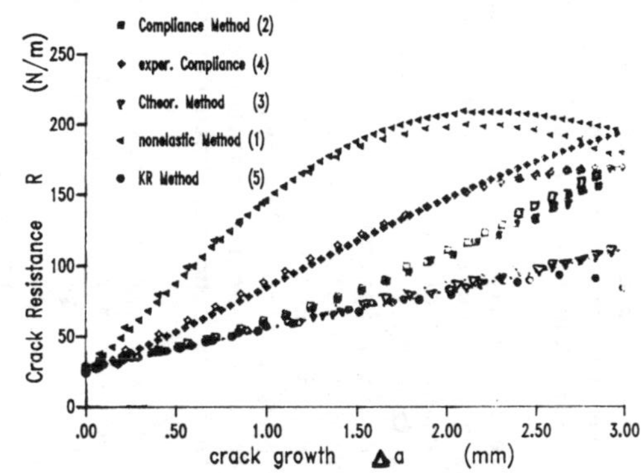

Fig. 4: R-curve behavior evaluated by different methods

growth velocity decreases continuously whereas during the periods with constant displacement rate the crack velocity is comparatively high. The first larger relaxation beginning at about 800 sec is related to the P-u-diagramme immediately behind the load maximum.

R-curve evaluations with crack lengths evaluated from the theoretical compliance curve are presented in Fig. 2 for all three kinds of displacement control. The results are very similar, the R-curves are rising from R_o = 25 N/m to about 170 N/m (with relaxations) and about 200 N/m ($\dot{u}_1$-, $\dot{u}_2$-control) for equal crack extensions of Δ a = 3,0 mm. During periods of relaxation, the equivalent R-curve intervals tend to slow down in accordance with a decreasing stress relaxation rate and crack propagation velocity. Thus, while equilibrium conditions during relaxation are being approached, the material exhibits reduced crack resistance as compared with constant displacement rate conditions.

In Fig. 3 the experimental compliance curve (upper curve) for our annealed specimens in inert condition is plotted together with the theoretical compliance curve for 4-point bending, with a_o = 4 mm. The compliance is calculated as C(a) = u(a)/P(a). Experimental compliance curves for 3-point bending are reported to lie below and right of the theoretical curve /6/. Thus, Alumina AF 99.7 shows a comparatively pliable behaviour in four-point bending with a generally steeper slope in dC/da as anticipated.

Fig. 4 contains R-curves for two specimens, with $\dot{u}_2$-control, evaluated according to the different methods.

The K_R-Method (5) furnishes the lowest R-curve with a maximum value at 100 N/m. The three different compliance methods(2), (3), (4) give higher R-values. The highest values are obtained by use of the experimental compliance curve from measured values of P, u, and a; followed by the conventional compliance-R-values and the R-curve which makes additional use of the measured crack length. The most general evaluation method which allows irreversible displacement effects and which takes fully into account all the experimental measurement values of P, u and a, results in a steeper increase of the R-curve (1) over a crack length of only 1,5 to 2,0 mm, followed by a plateau value at about 200 N/m. Attention is drawn to the fact that the individual R-curves for the two specimens nearly or completely coincide.

Conclusions

- Crack progagation velocities are dependent on the imposed displacement rate in bending tests.
- Crack propagation during periods of stress relaxation tends to furnish lower R-values than in the case if the constant displacement rate before relaxation had been retained. This apparently reflects the tendency towards decreased fracture resistance of the material in a state of equilibrium between external and internal constraints. Further investigations seem to be necessary.

Investigation of Load Induced Microcracks in Alumina with R-Curve Behaviour

E. Babilon, K.K.O. Bär, G. Kleist, H. Nickel
Institut für Reaktorwerkstoffe, KFA Jülich GmbH
Postfach 1913, D 5170 Jülich

Explanations for R-curve behaviour of ceramics refer to energy dissipation effects at the crack tip and in the wake regions. This presentation gives results of small angle X-ray scattering (SAXS) experiments on DCB-specimens with evidence that stress induced mikrocracks build up a microcrack zone. The lateral size of the cracked zone increases with decreasing crack propagation velocity. A preferred orientation of the microcracks was detected. Acoustic emission analysis on DCB-specimens, while being loaded without macrocrack formation, and following SAXS investigations indicate the generation of microcracks at the notch root. In situ loading of DCB-specimens with alternative SEM or SAXS observations gives some further insight into the nucleation and growth of microcrack regions.

INTRODUCTION

Some ceramic materials, e.g. Al_2O_3, exhibit increasing crack resistance in controlled crack propagation experiments. This is known as R-curve behaviour and several models are discussed in the literature. Load induced changes in the microstructure at the crack tip and the wake regions are postulated, which may be characterized by changes in local residual stresses and by the generation of microcracked zones (1-4). In other models, mechanical interactions across the crack flanks are assumed, which enhance the resistance of specimens to crack propagation (5,6). In a research programme sponsored by the 'Deutsche Forschungsgemeinschaft' (DFG), several German institutes are collaborating in the investigation of microfracture processes in alumina to clarify the mechanisms causing the R-curve behaviour.
In this paper small angle X-ray scattering experiments have been used to show that load induced microcracks exist in regions near to a macrocrack in alumina. Further attempts were directed towards the measurement of the crack sizes, the crack densities and the orientation of microracks. Some conclusions are drawn with respect to proposed models.

EXPERIMENTAL METHODS

Small angle X-ray scattering is a well known method for detecting local inhomogeneities such as segregations, pores, inclusions and microcracks in the submicron range (7). The measurement effect is based on local differences of the electron density arising from these 'particles' with respect to the matrix, preferably with sharp transitions. Since all these inhomogeneities, if present in the material, give a non separable contribution to the scattered X-ray intensity, load induced scattering centres in the microstructure can only be determined by comparing the scattered intensities of the loaded sample with an unloaded reference sample. The transformation of the scattering intensities from reciprocal to real space leads to a relative frequency distribution of the 'diameters' of scat-

tering particles. Since segregations and phase transformations in the investigated alumina materials during mechanical testing can be excluded, the load induced additional scattering particles must be interpreted as microcracks.
The SAXS experiments were carried out using a Mo-K_α radiation (λ = 0.71 Å) and a Kratky camera, which gives a line focus of dimensions 3 x 0.008 mm^2. Because of the high absorption in alumina, only specimens with a thickness of about 1 mm were used in these tests. For the scattering particles, only that dimension which is perpendicular to the line focus of the incident beam can be resolved. Presuming that the lengths of microcracks are of the order of the grain size, not the length, but preferably the opening of the microcracks is measured.
Results from the investigations of 4-point bend specimens have already been reported (8). In this paper only the results obtained from DCB-specimens of dimensions 25 x 60 x 1 mm^3 are presented. For the in-situ mechanical loading of DCB-specimens inside the SAXS equipment a loading rig was used allowing controlled crack propagation in DCB-specimens between SAXS measurements. Acoustic emission analysis in combination with SXAS experiments with DCB-specimens were performed to show evidence of microcrack generation in DCB-specimen before forming a macrocrack.

THE MATERIAL

In the research programme on microfracture processes all partners made their tests with specimens from the same two Al_2O_3-grades: B40 (Feldmühle AG) and AF997 (Demarquest). Information on these materials can be taken from the following table.

	B40		AF997	
Purity	98,8	%	98,5	%
Density	3,79	g/cm^3	3,8	g/cm^3
Mean Grain Size	5 - 15	µm	10	µm
Bending Strength	180-250	MPa	300	MPa
Young's Modulus	357	GPa	365	GPa
Crack Resistance R_o *	20	N/m	20	N/m

* Courtesy R. Steinbrech

RESULTS

Extension of Microcrack Regions

In continuation of former work, the influence of the crack propagation velocity on the lateral extension of a microcrack zone on both sides of the macrocrack was investigated. Specimens with a controlled mean crack velocity of about 0.5 mm/min and other specimens having experienced spontaneous crack propagation over a length of 10 - 20 mm, were taken for SAXS measurements. From the frequency distribution curves, measured for different distances from the macrocrack border, the distribution curves pertaining to the inherent scattering centres of the unloaded sample were subtracted (Fig. 1). In the resulting curves an increase in frequency of scattering particles around 50 nm extension, representing the microcracks as explained above, can clearly be seen. A plot of the peak values of these curves vs. the distance of the measurement site from the macrocrack border (Fig. 2) shows the influence of

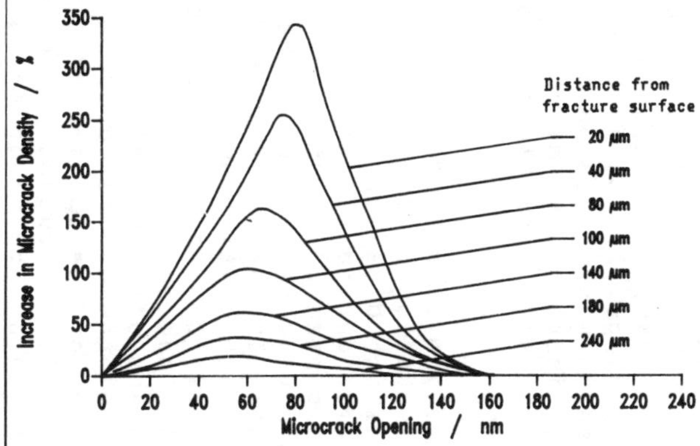

Fig. 1 Load induced microcrack density in B40-DCB-specimen with slow crack growth

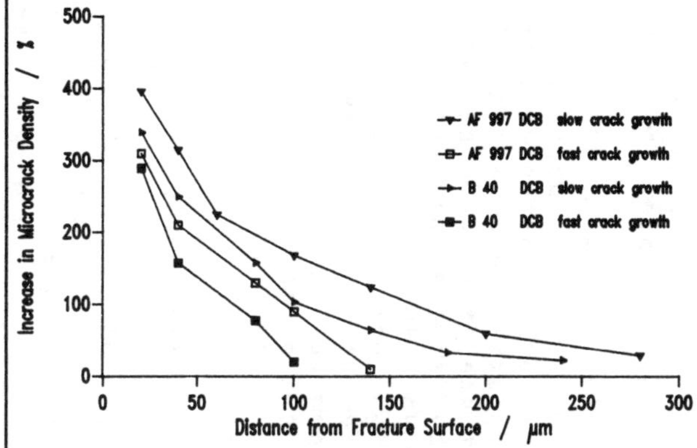

Fig. 2 Peak values of the frequency distribution curves of load induced microcracks

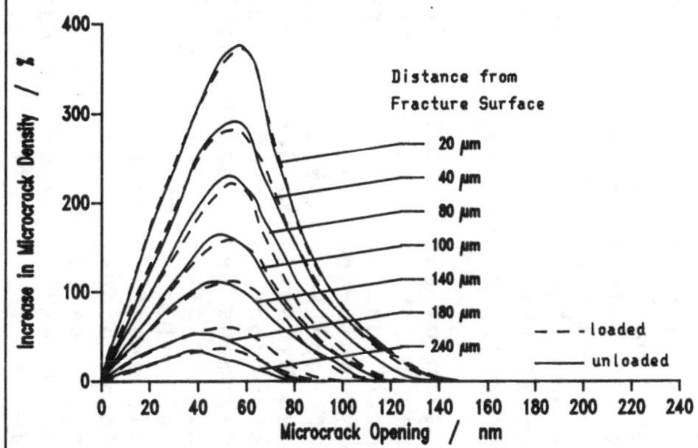

Fig. 3 Frequency distribution curves of micro-cracks in a DCB-specimen with and without load

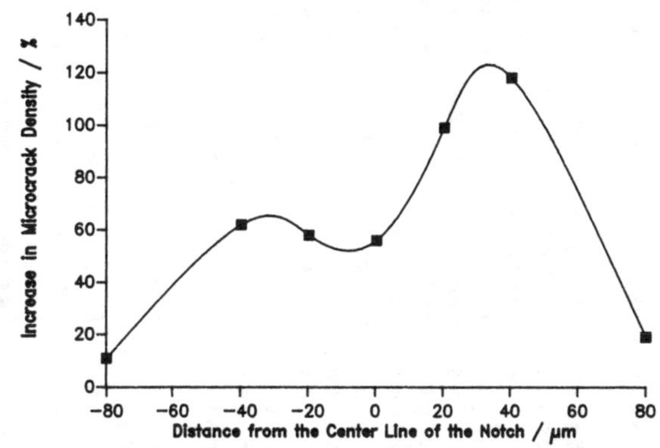

Fig. 4 Microcrack density at the notch root due to loading before macrocrack initiation

crack velocity on the load induced microcrack density and on the lateral extension of the microcrack region in DCB-specimens for both Al_2O_3-materials. In addition, for equal crack velocities constant lateral extensions of microcrack zones on both sides of the macrocrack along the whole crack path were found.

Orientation of Microcracks

A random distribution in orientation of elongated particles leads to a superposition of their individual scattering pictures thus resulting in an isotropic scattering behaviour of the tested specimen volume. The existance of a preferred orientation of particles can be detected by using a point focus camera in only one scattering experiment. The line focus camera, as used in our experiments for high local resolution, requires several measurements with different angles between the focus line and the direction of the macrocrack in the DCB-specimens. It was found that the microcracks on both sides of a macrocrack were orientated with angular deviations up to 40° with respect to the macrocrack direction.

Change of the Microcrack Opening of Reloadad Specimens

In order to obtain information about the opening behaviour of microcracks in reloaded DCB-specimens, a macrocrack with a length of 20 mm was first induced in a DCB-specimen of AF997 at a velocity of 0.5 mm/min. Then with the unloaded specimen SAXS measurements were executed at distances of 7 mm and 15 mm behind the crack tip. After that the specimen was reloaded to a level of about 80% of the preceding maximum load. In this condition, the microcrack zones were measured again at the same locations as before. These measurements show (Fig. 3) that for the position 7 mm behind the crack tip, the reloading leads to a 10 to 15 % increase of microcrack openings. At the position 15 mm behind the crack tip, no changes in microcrack opening were found. Further, reloading did not increase the microcrack density at the crack flanks which can be seen from the constant peak heights of the distribution curves.

Generation of Microcracks Before Formation of a Macrocrack

In order to obtain evidence of the generation of microcracks in the notch root region before the formation of a macrocrack, acoustic emission analysis was performed during loading tests with DCB-specimens (9). All samples had been previously investigated by SAXS and SEM in order to have a reference of the microstructure before the loading tests. In these tests, several specimens were loaded until macrocrack initiation was observed. For other specimens, the maximum load was confined to about 80% of the mean crack initiation load and frequent acoustic events were registered. By means of adequately positioned acoustic probes the origin of the events could be traced to the notch root. Cyclic loading of the specimens showed the existence of the Kaiser effect. Subsequent to these experiments the specimens were reexamined by SEM in order to detect load induced changes on the surface. In addition, dye penetrant tests showed that no macrocrack was indeed present or at least detectable, at the notch root of these specimens. Only those DCB-specimens without any SEM detectable change in the surface appearance were tested again in the SAXS equipment for the change in scattering behaviour. They showed a clear increase of scattered intensity in the notch root region compared with the virgin sample (Fig. 4). This is interpreted as a load induced microcrack density occurring before the initiation of a macrocrack.

CONCLUSIONS

* Identical crack propagation conditions lead to similar microcrack densities and lateral extent of the microcrack zones near to a macrocrack for any distance along the macrocrack, so that the increasing crack resistance over a crack length of 10 mm and more in DCB-specimens (10) cannot yet be attributed to the detectable microcracks.
* However, recent results obtained from bend-specimens (11) show a plateau value of crack resistance after a crack path of about 1,0 to 1,5 mm. SAXS investigations over this limited range will be performed subsequently despite difficulties in local resolution.
* Reloading of a specimen does not change the opening of microcracks more than 5 mm behind the crack tip if they are very close to the fracture surface. This means that mechanical interaction of the crack flanks in this region of a DCB-specimen is either absent or has no effect on the microcrack opening, although the macrocrack flanks are torn apart. However, microcrack opening is definitely observed further away from the crack path at a position 5 mm behind the crack tip, apparently due to local stress changes.
* The generation of microcracks in the notch root region before the initiation of a macrocrack shows that in this material (AF997) microcracking occurs at a load level lower than necessary for macrocrack initiation. This evidence from SAXS measurements is supported by acoustic analysis. Further SAXS experiments are planned to shed light on the growth kinetics of microcrack zones around the tip of a macrocrack.

REFERENCES

1. A.G. Evans
   Journ. Am. Cer. Soc., Vol. 67, (1983), pp 327-335
2. Fu Yen   Diss. University of Cal., Berkeley, (1983)
3. F.E. Buresch
   Soc. of Ceramics, Vol. 7, (1973), pp 381-398
4. F.E. Buresch
   Ber. d. dt. keram. Gesellsch., Vol. 54, (1977), pp 425-429
5. R. Steinbrech, R. Knehans, W. Schaarwächter
   Journ. of Mat. Sci. Vol. 18, (1983), p 265
6. R. Knehans
   Forschungsbericht VDI, Reihe 18, (1984), Nr. 16
7. O. Glatter, O. Krattky   Academic Press Inc., London, 1982
8. E. Babilon, G. Kleist, F.E. Buresch, H. Nickel
   Science of Ceramics 14, (1987) pp 665-669
9. Ch. Sklarczyk
   Arbeitsber. des Forschungsvorh. "Mikrobruchvorgänge"(1988)
10. F. Deuerler
    Fortschr. Ber. VDI, Reihe 18, Nr. 38, (1987)
11. K.K.O.Bär, G.Kleist, H. Nickel
    Paper presented at this conference

INFLUENCE OF MAGNESIA ON MICROFRACTURE AND R-CURVE BEHAVIOR OF ALUMINA

G. Mundry, Lehrstuhl f. Werkstoffwissenschaften, Universität Dortmund;
R. W. Steinbrech, Institut f. Reaktorwerkstoffe, KFA-Jülich, F.R.G.

ABSTRACT

Aluminas, sintered with various additions of MgO (0.02 - 2 wt%), were studied in SENB-fracture tests under conditions of quasi static slow crack growth. With increasing MgO-content the mode of microfracture changed sharply from trans- to intergranular and then gradually went back to partially transgranular. As R-curve behavior, the increase of crack resistance with crack extension, was most pronounced in case of purely intergranular fracture, an optimum of crack impediment occured (0.04 wt% MgO). In general, the increase in crack resistance could be correlated with the roughness of the crack surface. The results are discussed in terms of wake controlled crack tip shielding due to crack surface interaction.

INTRODUCTION

In order to reduce the brittleness and to improve the reliability of modern structural ceramics, many efforts in material development focus on utilizing the R-curve effect. Ceramics which exhibit this increase in crack resistance (R) with crack extension (Δa) are, to a certain extent, flaw tolerant and thus provide additional safety for practical applications. Alumina, among the ceramics with R-curve behavior, has been of major scientific interest in the past [1,2,3]. From various experimental crack extension studies a general R-curve shape could be deduced, which plateaued out after a certain initial increase. However, the actual shape of an R-curve strongly depends on microstructural features. The increase in crack resistance is most pronounced for coarse grained material and diminishes (flat R-curve) for fine grained material [4]. This grain size dependence only holds for Al_2O_3 with intergranular microfracture. In the case of transgranular crack growth, the R-curve effect is much smaller. Although the mechanisms which control the mode of microfracture are not yet fully understood, crack extension studies indicate the importance of chemical composition, e.g. pure alumina (>99.7 wt%) preferently fractures intergranulary whereas aluminas with small amounts of glassy phase favour transgranular fracture [5].

As MgO is the key additive in stabilizing the grain size of alumina, its influence on R-curve behavior was examined in greater detail. It is the scope of the present work to extend the body of results gained for the grain size, strength and toughness dependence of MgO [6] on crack extension and crack resistance behavior. In addition, changes in grain size and microfracture were observed. Furthermore, the study tries to answer the question if an optimum MgO-content with respect to R-curve effect and thus "flaw-tolerance" exists.

EXPERIMENTAL DETAILS

Alumina (ALCOA; CT 8000 SG) with an initial MgO-content of 0.02 wt% was dry mixed with different amounts of magnesia (MERCK, pa-grade). The final MgO-content of the batches mixed was 0.02, 0.03, 0.04, 0.06, 0.08, 0.1, 0.12, 0.2, 0.5, 1 and 2 wt%. The powders were isostatically pressed and sintered in air at 1700°C for 12h. The sintered bodies were machined into bend bars (65 by 7 by 5 mm), polished on one side surface, thermally etched and notched. The notch depth a_n (normalized to sample height w=7mm) was $a_n/w=0.6$ and the notch width was 100µm.

The SENB samples were tested in 3PB under conditions of quasi static crack growth using a univeral testing machine (INSTRON, 1195) with a constant crosshead speed (5µm/min). Load, displacement and crack length were measured simultaneously. In situ crack growth observation was achieved with a travelling microscope, and therefrom the crack resistance was determined with a compliance method. All samples were mechanically tested at room temperature in water.

Standard microscopic techniques were used to determine the grain size distribution with the grain size referred to grain area: $D_A = 1/A * \Sigma (A_i * D_i)$ with A: total area, A_i: area of a grain, D_i: diameter of a grain.

RESULTS

The variation of MgO-content had a significant influence on D_A and gave rise to changes in the mode of microstructure and the

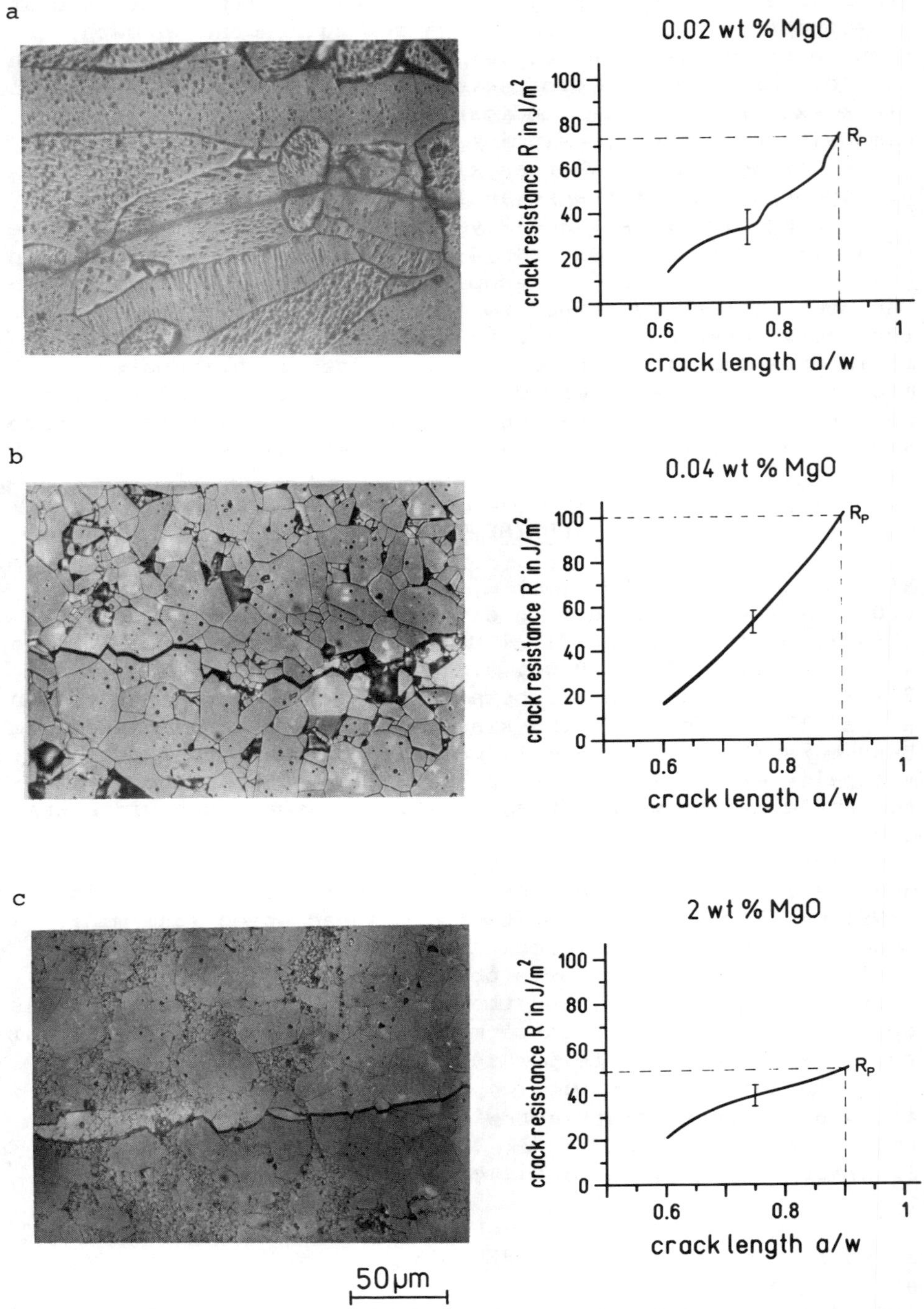

Figure 1. Microstructure, crack path and R-curve for aluminas with different MgO content.

slope of the R-curve. Three regimes could be distinguished (Fig. 1).

At low MgO-content (0.02 wt%, Fig. 1a) the microstructure is characterized by huge elongated grains ($D_A \cong 80\mu m$), typical for discontinous grain growth in absence of stabilizing MgO [6]. The crack propagates transgranulary, generating a relatively smooth microscopic fracture surface. However, due to large scale crack deflection, some macroscopic tortuousity occurs. Typically, the crack grows in large steps and these steps are reproduced by the R-curve which gains resistance at each step.

At 0.04 wt% MgO (Fig. 1b) a relatively homogeneous microstructure is prevalent ($D_A \cong 25\mu m$). The pronounced intergranular fracture (IF≅85%) generates rough crack surfaces on both microstructural and macroscopic levels. The R-curve exhibits a steeper slope and, at a crack length a/w=0.9, the highest crack resistance of all MgO-Al_2O_3 batches is measured ($R_p = R_{a/w=0.9} = 100 J/m^2$).

Further increase of MgO-content (2 wt%, Fig. 1c) reduces the average grain size ($D_A \cong 13\mu m$) and the homogeneity deteriorates. Patches of small grains alternate with agglomerates of larger grains. Although fracture is still predominantly intergranular (IF≅83%), the crack surfaces now look much smoother and the slope of the R-curve is much shallower.

In considering all MgO-Al_2O_3 batches processed, the parameters D_A, IF and R_p are plotted as a function of MgO-content in Fig. 2. Maximum resistance and percentage of intergranular fracture follow a maximum curve, whereas the grain size is continously decreasing with increasing MgO-content. The R_p- and IF-curve are only slightly shifted with respect to their maximum which corresponds fairly well with the solubility limit of MgO in Al_2O_3 at about 0.04 wt% [7]. Before the maximum, R_p is affected stronger by IF and beyond the maximum, R_p seems to follow the decrease of D_A.

DISCUSSION

The previous results do not define a unique correlation between any 2 of the 3 curves shown in Fig. 2. However, under the assumption that microfracture depends on residual stresses and that R-curve behavior is wake controlled by crack surface interaction, the interdependence of the three curves seems qualitatively plausible.

In pure alumina, residual stresses build up due to the anisotropy of thermal expansion [8]. A combination of these stresses with the crack tip stress field usually favours the intergranular crack propagation. But there is a trade-off with grain size. With increasing grain size the probability of extended crack deflection and grain circumnavigation decreases

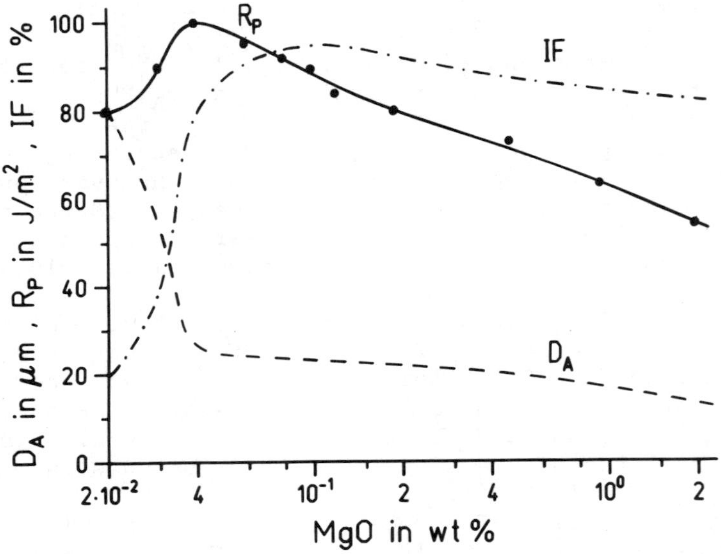

Figure 2. Influence of MgO content on grain size D_A, percentage of intergranular fracture IF and crack resistance $R_p = R_{a/w=0.9}$

because in this case transgranular fracture requires less energy. With increasing MgO-content the solubility limit in the alumina lattice is passed and spinel forms as second phase [6]. If the spinel reduces part of the residual stresses, a decrease in the amount of intergranular fracture is very likely.

Both mode of microfracture and grain size determine the topography of the crack surface. The crack surface roughness is highest in the case of maximum grain size at which intergranular fracture is still predominant. This crack surface condition correlates with the maximum in the R_p-curve, as indicated in Fig. 2 by considering both D_A- and IF-behavior.

Such a correlation can be rationalized if crack surface roughness causes crack bridging effects which shield the crack tip, as proposed in recent R-curve models [9,10,11]. It is assumed that an interaction zone, e.g. interlocking grains [11], builds up behind the crack tip. The crack flanks have to be displaced against the occuring bridging forces. The separation of the bridging element furthest away from the crack tip determines the size of the interaction zone.

Thus, crack opening displacement and crack surface roughness influence the R-curve behavior. A coarser topography of the crack surface bridges larger distances between the crack flanks and therefore causes a steeper increase of the crack resistance. Accordingly, large grain size and intergranular microfracture yield high crack resistances, which agrees with the experimental observations.

In summary, the results demonstrate that for alumina "flaw tolerance" can be enhanced by improvement of the crack surface roughness, i.e. by optimization of grain size and mode of microfracture.

REFERENCES

1. R.W. Steinbrech, R. Knehans and W. Schaarwächter, "Increase of Crack Resistance During Slow Crack Growth in Al_2O_3 Bend Specimens", J. Mat. Sci., 18, 265-270 (1983)
2. P. Swanson, C.J. Fairbanks, B.R. Lawn, Y.W. Mai and B.J. Hockey, "Crack-Interface Grain Bridging as a Fracture Resistance Mechanism in Ceramics: I, Experimental Study on Alumina", J. Am. Ceram. Soc., 70, 279-289 (1987)
3. M. Sakai and R.C. Bradt, "The Crack Growth Resistance of Non-Phase-Transforming Ceramics", Nippon Seramikkusu Kyokai Gakujutsu Ronbunshi, 96 [8] 801-9 (1988)
4. R. Knehans and R.W. Steinbrech, "Effect of Grain Size on Crack Resistance Curves of Al_2O_3 Bend Specimen", Science of Ceramics 12, 613-619 (1983)
5. F. Deuerler, "Bruchverhalten von polykristallinem Aluminiumoxid unter dem Einfluß von Gefüge, Testgeometrie und Umgebungsbedingungen", Fortschr.-Ber. VDI Reihe 18 Nr. 38, VDI-Verlag, Düsseldorf, p.48 (1987)
6. P. Stingl and H. Hausner, "Microstructure and mechanical properties in the system Al_2O_3-MgO", Ber. Dt. Keram. Ges., 62, 364-376 (1985)
7. K.S. Roy and R.L. Coble, "Solubilities of Magnesia, Titania and Magnesiumtitanate in Al_2O_3", J. Am. Ceram. Soc., 51, 1-6 (1968)
8. R.W. Rice, S.W. Freiman and P.F. Becher, "Grain-Size Dependence of Fracture Energy in Ceramics: I, Experiment", J. Am. Ceram. Soc., 64, 345-350 (1981)
9. Y.W. Mai and B.R. Lawn, "Crack-Interface Grain Bridging as a Fracture Resistance Mechanism in Ceramics: II, A Model", J. Am. Ceram. Soc., 70, 289-294 (1987)
10. B.S. Majumdar, A.R. Rosenfield and W.H. Duckworth, "Analysis of R-Curve Behavior of Non-Phase-Transforming Ceramics", Engng. Fracture Mechanics 31 [4] 683-701 (1988)
11. R.W. Steinbrech, A. Reichl and W. Schaarwächter, "R-Curve Behavior of Long Cracks in Alumina", submitted to J. Am. Ceram. Soc.

MECHANICAL PROPERTIES OF HOT-ISOSTATIC-PRESSED TITANIUM NITRIDE

M. DESMAISON-BRUT, L. THEMELIN
Laboratoire de Céramiques Nouvelles, CNRS UA 320,
Université de Limoges, FRANCE

F. VALIN, M. BONCOEUR
Commissariat à l'Energie Atomique, CEN/Saclay, FRANCE

ABSTRACT

Hot isostatic pressing has been successfully applied for the consolidation of TiN powder which does not contain additives. Highly dense material was obtained at 1600°C and 180 MPa using a suitable encapsulation technique. Correlative relations between the mechanical properties and the porosity of the nitride were established.

INTRODUCTION

Densification of TiN powder has already been achieved with cobalt or nickel additives. More recently, conventional sintering [1], hot pressing [2], high pressure hot pressing [3] and hot isostatic pressing [4] have been successfully applied to produce dense and even nearly net shape materials.

The aim of this work was to study the influence of applied pressure on the densification of a coarse TiN powder and to correlate the properties with the microstructure and porosity of the TiN body obtained after different H.I.P. treatments.

MATERIALS AND METHODS

Commercial-grade TiN powder (H.C. STARCK, Berlin) was used as the starting material. The average particle size was 1-6 µm. A small percentage of the grain size is < 1 µm (5%) and a significant amount consists of large grains > 10 µm (8%). A few titanium balls were observed (diameter = 60-180 µm) by SEM. The lattice parameter of TiN was 4.2468 Å. The main characteristics of the starting powder and the experimental procedure were presented in a previous paper [5].

Hot isostatic compression tests were conducted with an A.C.B. Alsthom Atlantique press at 1600°C under argon. The pressure was applied during 1 hour and varied from 50 MPa to 180 MPa. The shrinkage of the specimen (cylinder of 35 mm in diameter, 45 mm high) is about 13%.

RESULTS AND DISCUSSION

Influence of pressure parameters on densification

A treatment at 1600°C and 180 MPa for one hour permits a maximum density (99.3%) to be achieved. However a density of 97% is observed at 50 MPa. The average grain size is of the order of 4.2 to 4.8 µm for all tested values of the applied pressure.

Microhardness

Vickers microhardness values increase as a function of pressure (Fig. 1).

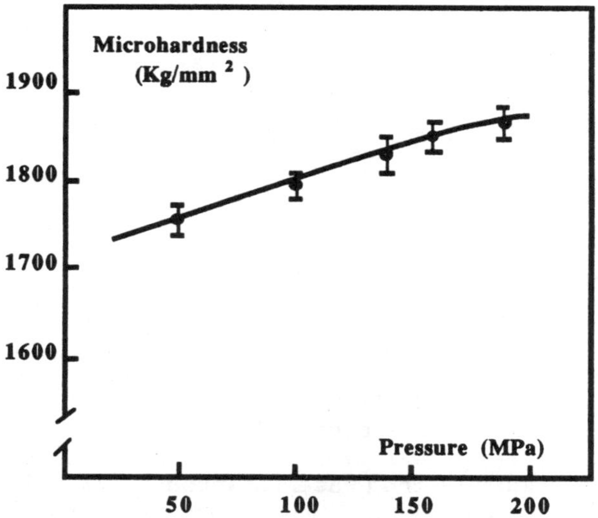

Fig. 1. Relation between microhardness and pressure.

Mechanical strength and toughness

Room Temperature M.O.R. data were obtained from three point bend tests.

The maximum value obtained is 550 MPa with a standard deviation of 50 and a Weibull slope of 11 (Fig. 2). The M.O.R. value starts to drop significantly at 50 MPa (σ_f = 360 MPa , m = 6.5). Observation of the fracture surface by scanning electron microscopy permits fracture sources to be identified : in a few cases a surface flaw could be associated with machining damage but the origin of failure was mainly localised in regions where large pores or titanium inclusions intersected the surface. The fracture is intergranular in the small and medium size regions (2 to 7 µm) and transgranular in the large grain zones (> 8 µm).

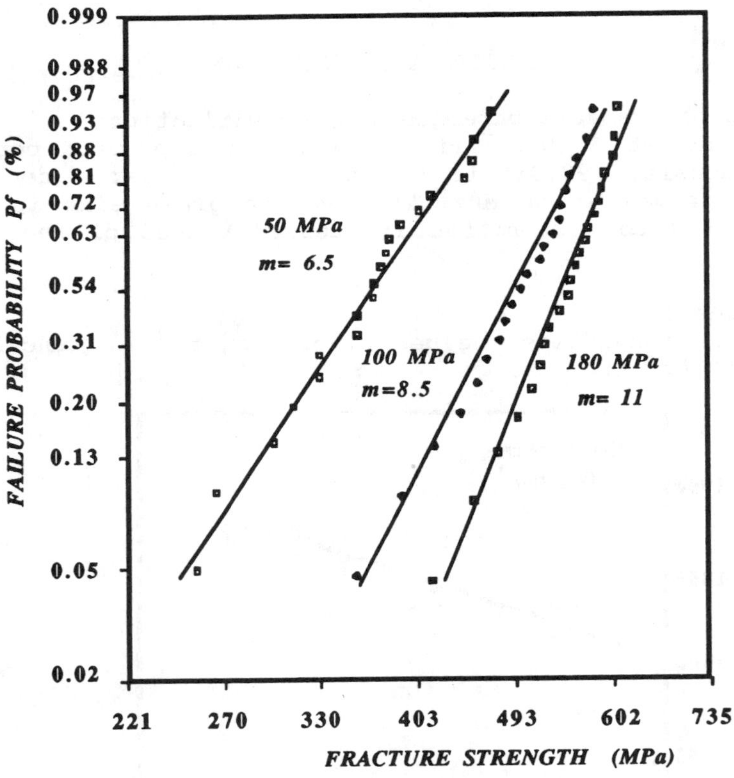

Fig. 2. Weibull plots of Modulus of rupture strengths against failure probability. Tested at room temperature.

The Single Edge Notched Beam Method (S.E.N.B.) used to measure K1C is a technique by which narrow notches are fractured by three point bending. The fracture toughness value obtained : 5 MPa $\sqrt{m}$ is independent on the porosity (0<P<3%).

The theoretical strength of a ceramic material depends also on factors such as Young's modulus E and the surface energy γ. The measurements of the elastic constants have been done by the vibrating discs technique [6]. The knowledge of those parameters leads to a direct calculation of the effective surface energy γ.

Results are given in Table I. The γ_1 value obtained is in the range of commonly observed ones [7] 10-50 J/m^2.

By knowing the M.O.R. and fracture toughness values, the largest defect size may be calculated : a_c = 25 µm [8] . This value is closed to the largest grain size and is very different from the maximum pore size which is less than 1 µm. Titanium inclusions are strongly bonded into the TiN body and do not initiate the rupture except when they intersect the surface.

Thermal shock resistance

The data were obtained by measuring the three-point bending strength of materials after quenching them into water at 20°C from high temperature. At about 205-210°C the crack suffers a sudden extension with an associated large decrease in strength of the material (Fig. 3).

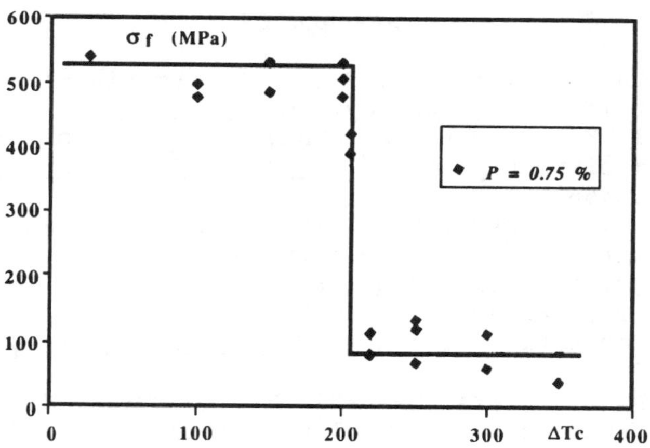

Fig. 3. Strength as a function of quenching temperature difference for dense TiN.

Two parameters of the thermal shock damage have been analyzed (Table I) : the thermal stress transfer R (high Biot-number ß>>1) and the theoretical crack propagation resistance parameter R"" [9]. A value of $9.10^{-6}K^{-1}$ was used for the coefficient of thermal expansion (Table I).

TABLE I

Material	E(GPa)	ν	$K_{1}C$ (MPa√m)	R(K)	R""(μm)	T_C(K)	γ J/m2
TiN HIP 180 MPa	465	0.222	5	102	50	210	25

Discussion and conclusion

At 1600°C and with one hour dwell time, a wide range of applied pressure (50 to 180 MPa) does not lead to a large difference in densification : (theoretical density 97 to 99.25 %). Except for the Modulus of rupture and microhardness values all mechanical strength parameters are nearly unaffected by the HIP treatment. In fact, the grain size has been found to be independent of the applied pressure such that the H.I.P. effect on strength is caused by the flaw size reduction only (essentially pores). Titanium inclusions are chemical inhomogeneities but they are very well bonded with the titanium nitride grains.

REFERENCES

1. KUZENKOVA, M.A., KISLYI, P.S., "Vaccum sintering of titanium nitride", Poroshkovaya Metallurgiya 98, 2, 1971, 125.
2. RAPOPORT, E., BRODHAG, C., THEVENOT, F., "Hot pressing of titanium nitride powders", Revue de Chimie Minérale, 22, 4, 1985, 456.
3. YAMADA, T., SHIMADA, M., KOIZUMI, M.,"Fabrication and characterization of titanium nitride by high pressure hot pressing", Am. Ceram. Soc. Bull., 59, 6,1980, 611.
4. YAMADA, T., SHIMADA, M., KOIZUMI, M., "Fabrication of TiN by Hot Isostatic Pressing", Yogyo Kyokai Shi, 89, 11, 1981, 621.
5. THEMELIN, L., DESMAISON-BRUT, M., BONCOEUR, M., VALIN, F., "Microstructure, mechanical properties and oxidation behaviour of hot isostatic pressed titanium nitride", L'Industrie Céramique, 828, 6, 1988, 427.
6. GLANDUS, J.C., BOCH, P., "Non destructive testing of silicon oxynitride thermal shock sensitivity", Energy and Ceramics, P. VINCENZINI Ed. Elsevier, Amsterdam 1980, 661.
7. DAVIDGE, R.W., Mechanical Behaviour of Ceramics, Cambridge University Press, 1980.
8. ORANGE, G., "Etude des propriétés mécaniques de matériaux céramiques : mise au point d'un dispositif de déformation haute température", Thèse, University de Lyon, 1980.
9. HASSELMAN, D.P.H., "Thermal stress resistance parameters for brittle ceramics, a compendium", Am. Ceram. Soc. Bull. 49, 12, 1970, 1033.

EFFECT OF SiC-WHISKER CHARACTERISTICS ON INTERFACE AND MECHANICAL PROPERTIES OF SILICON NITRIDE MATRIX COMPOSITES

W. Braue, A. Hölscher, B. Saruhan and G. Ziegler
Deutsche Forschungsanstalt für Luft- und Raumfahrt (DLR)
Institut für Werkstoff-Forschung
D-5000 Köln 90, FRG

ABSTRACT

Despite the variability of microstructural features on a nm-scale, SiC(w) bulk impurities in SiC/Si_3N_4 composites are of minor influence on the mechanical properties at room temperature. Fracture toughness data were all improved 30 % irrespective of the whisker grade. Differences in SiC(w) morphology and size affect processing and uniformity of the final composite microstructure which account primarily for the fracture strength variations observed. The issue of high-resolution interface analysis of SiC(w)/Si_3N_4 boundaries is discussed.

INTRODUCTION

It is generally believed, that the nature of the whisker/matrix interface and the SiC raw material characteristics account for the property variations reported in the literature. Because of their effect on toughening mechanisms a fundamental understanding of interfacial structures in the SiC(w)/Si_3N_4 system is of particular interest.
In this context the impact of different commercial SiC(w) grades on both microstructural features and mechanical properties was studied for a constant Si_3N_4 baseline material. The following outline gives a comprehensive description of results discussed elsewhere in more detail [1].

MATERIALS AND METHODS

The Si_3N_4 baseline material was prepared from Toyo Soda TS10 α-Si_3N_4 powder (O 1.5 wt%, C 0.07 wt%, Cl 0.03 wt%, Fe 0.01 wt%) The sintering additive composition was 5 wt% Y_2O_3 + 1.1 wt% Al_2O_3. Complete densification of 20 vol.% SiC(w)/Si_3N_4 composites was achieved by presintering of the green compacts at 1500°C/0.1 MPa Ar and subsequent HIPing at 1780°C/190 MPa Ar. Standard four-point bending tests were performed at room temperature. Fracture toughness data were evaluated from the

Vickers hardness indentation technique. Analytical electron microscopy was performed in a Philips EM 430 TEM/STEM.

TABLE 1 Characterization of as-received SiC(w)

Whisker Grade	Impurities LE [wt%]	MET [wt%]	Length [μm]	Diameter [μm]	Aspect Ratio
AMERICAN MATRIX (AM)	1.7	-	100	2.00	50
NIKKEI (N)	5.0	-	80	0.40	200
TOKAI (TC)	0.9	0.15	50	0.65	77
HUBER (H)	1.1	-	150	0.90	167
TATEHO (T)	2.9	0.30	45	0.45	100

(LE: O, N, (Ca), this study; MET: metal imp., suppliers data)

RESULTS AND DISCUSSION

VLS-grown whiskers from different sources exhibit substantial variations in aspect-ratio and chemical purity (Table 1). Most impurities, in particular transition metals, are related to the specific design of the reaction chamber and proprietary agents added to increase whisker yield. A thin surface layer enriched in light elements (e.g. excess carbon, nitrogen, oxygen) is a unique feature of all as-received SiC(w). Some grades as (T) and (N) contain high amounts of calcium which may be detrimental to high temperature properties of the composite.
Due to the high density of planar defects perpendicular to the growth axis, the structure of β-SiC(w) is best described as a random mixture of short period SiC polytypes (see also Fig. 1d). Besides different surface morphologies TEM characterization of as-received SiC(w) reveals characteristic structural heterogeneities, e.g. like secondary phase inclusions (AM) and low-density core regions (T).
Bulk impurities are often incorporated by large whiskers, e.g. for (T) (Fig. 1a), (AM) and (H) grades. They form crystalline particles with a typical elongated grain shape which obviously are associated with SiC(w) stacking faults. Moreover, impurities may segregate to form individual grains which often are not connected to SiC(w) (Fig. 1b).
In several composites reinforced with very fine whiskers like (N) a significant fraction of SiC(w) was not associated with the grain boundary network, but bound into the Si_3N_4 materials grains (Fig. 1c).
No interfacial reactions or corrosive attack of the glassy phase on SiC(w) surfaces were observed for the composites investigated. Because of microfacets of alternating {111} planes the stepped surface structure is a characteristic feature of all VLS grown β-Sic(w) (Fig. 1d). The whisker grades investigated, however, exhibit large variations in their macroscopic surface morphology (e.g. strong serrated (AM) or smooth (TC) surfaces), which are already evident in the as-re-

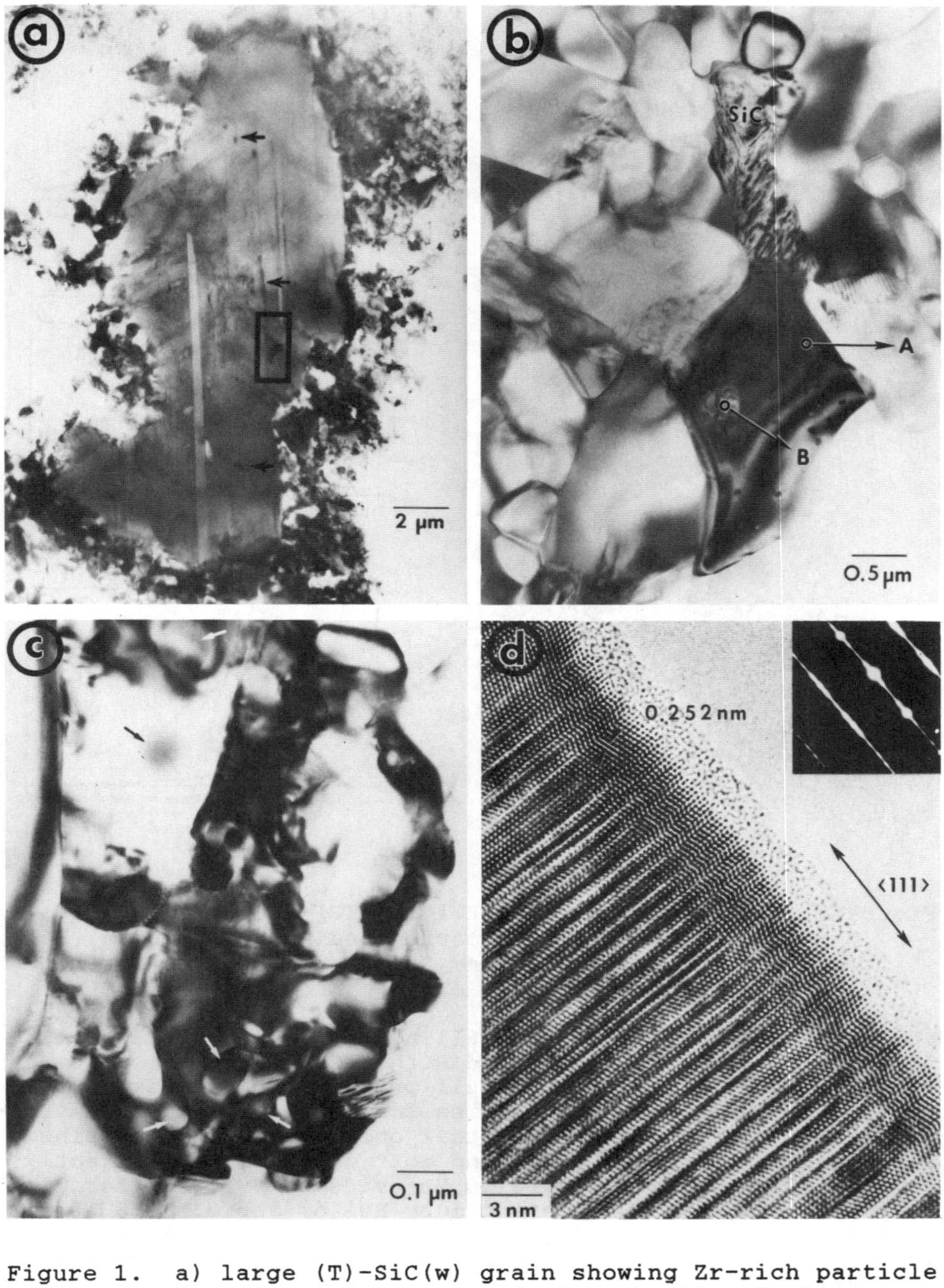

Figure 1. a) large (T)-SiC(w) grain showing Zr-rich particle (boxed area) associated with stacking faults; b) Fe-Si-rich grain (pos. A) with W-rich inclusion (pos.B) adjacent to (N)-SiC(w),; c) Small SiC(w) (see arrows) intragranular to Si_3N_4 matrix, (N); d) HREM image (400 KV) of (TC)-SiC(w) in [110] projection, from [2].

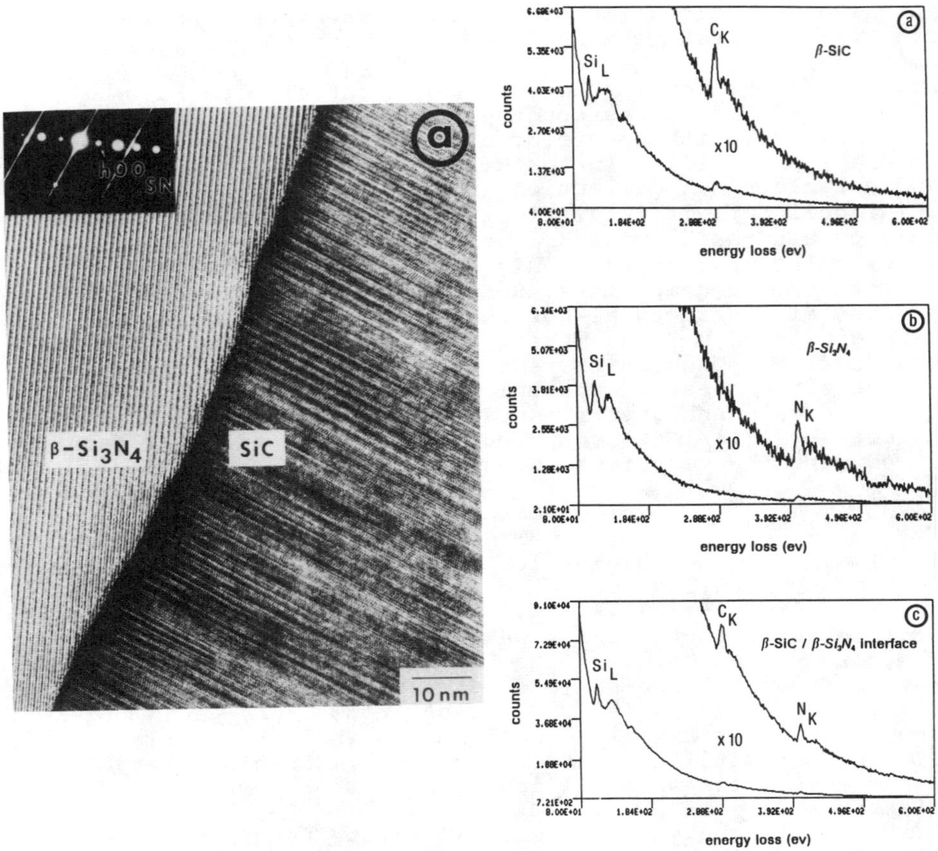

Figure 2. a) HREM image (400 KV) of (TC)-SiC(w)/Si_3N_4 interface, [2]; b) corresponding ELS spectra collected with a 5 nm FEG TEM probe from interfacial constituents and the boundary, [2].

ceived condition. SiC(w)/crystalline matrix interfaces from a Si_3N_4 base composite reinforced with (TC)-SiC(w) [2] were examined by HREM (Fig. 2a) and small probe microanalysis. A careful inspection of such boundaries far away from amorphous triple grain junctions concluded that only a minority contained a continuous amorphous phase and most whiskers were directly bounded to the matrix crystals. No evidence evidence for light element segregation was detected by EDS or serial EELS at 5 nm spatial resolution (Fig. 2b). Recently the continuous nature of thin glassy films at all SiC(w)/Si_3N_4 boundaries was emphasized [3].

Because of improved spatial resolution the combined effort of HREM and EELS in parallel detection (PEELS) seems to be the optimum instrumental approach for complete characterization of such interfaces. Recent work on oxygen segregation to thin SiC/SiC interfaces [4] with a detection limit of 5 at% and a

typical acquisition time of 1 sec per spectrum emphasizes the potential of PEELS for high-resolution interface analysis in composites.
Compared to the monolithic baseline material with K_{IC} = 6.8 MPa · $m^{1/2}$ fracture toughness of the composites was improved by 30 % with no effect of the SiC(w) grades. Although the crack propagation in the different materials revealed considerable crack deflection and branching with very little SiC(w) pull-out, it is difficult to correlate composite response on a nm-scale with K_{IC} values.
SiC(w) bulk impurity show only minor effect on RT fracture strength of the composites. Besides machining defects, whisker-free microstructural heterogeneities and exaggerated grain growth of β-Si_3N_4 were identified as the major failure-related flaws. Thus, differences in SiC(w) morphology and size affect processing and uniformity of the final microstructures. Indeed, a higher flexural strength was obtained with the coarse (AM)-SiC(w) compared to composite material reinforced with the very fine (N)-SiC(w) grade.

CONCLUSIONS

SiC(w) are non-stoichiometric, often polyphase components which add a major impurity source to the composite system. A significant fraction of small SiC(w) is bound into the matrix and may not interact with the crack wake. All SiC(w) surfaces are rough on atomic scale, however, the whisker grades investigated exhibit different large-scale surface morphologies. HREM and serial ELS at 5 nm spatial resolution from a (TC)-SiC(w)/Si_3N_4 material did not reveal a continuous amorphous interlayer at all SiC(w)/crystalline matrix boundaries. Fracture toughness of the composites were all improved 30 % irrespective of the whisker grade.
Flexural strength variations at RT relate to differences in SiC(w) morphology and size which affect processing and uniformity of final microstructure.

REFERENCES

[1] Braue, W., Hölscher, A., Saruhan, B., Ziegler, G. SiC(w)/Si_3N_4 Microstructures: III. Effect of SiC-Whisker Characteristics on the Interface and Mechanical Properties of Silicon Nitride Matrix Composites. Submitted to J. Mat. Sci., 1989

[2] Braue, W., Carpenter, R.W., Smith, D.J. HREM Interface Studies in SiC-Whisker Reinforced Al_2O_3 and Si_3N_4 Ceramics Proc. 46th Annual Meeting of the Electron Microscopy Society of America, (G. Baily, ed.), San Fransisco Press, 1988, 743

[3] Campbell, G.H., Rühle, M., Dalgleish, B.J., Evans, A.G. Whisker Toughening: A Comparison Between Al_2O_3 and Si_3N_4 Toughened with SiC, Submitted to J. Am. Ceram. Soc., 1989

[4] Weiss, J.K., Carpenter, R.W., Braue, W., Higgs, A.A. Scanning Probe Parallel EELS Analysis of Interfaces in Ceramics and Ceramic Composites Submitted to 47th Annual Meeting of the Electron Microscopy Society of America, San Antonio, TX, USA, August 6-11, 1989.

THE STRESS DEPENDENCE OF THE CREEP BEHAVIOR OF SILICON CARBIDE WHISKER REINFORCED ALUMINA

K. Y. DONALDSON, A. VENKATESWARAN, D. P. H. HASSELMAN
Department of Materials Engineering
Virginia Polytechnic Institute and State University
Blacksburg, Virginia 24061, USA
and
J. F. RHODES
Advanced Composite Materials Corporation
Greer, South Carolina 29651, USA

ABSTRACT

Creep tests of SiC-whisker reinforced alumina at 1500°C yielded creep strain vs. time curves exhibiting typical primary, secondary and tertiary creep. The initial creep rate, which is proportional to the matrix creep rate, exhibited a stress exponent of 1.59, typical for single-phase polycrystalline alumina, while the apparent stress exponent for secondary (steady-state) creep was 2.88. The presence of the whiskers appeared to suppress cavitation or other damage, thereby eliminating any contribution from elastic creep by crack growth or crack-enhanced creep to creep deformation.

Analysis of the creep behavior of a short elastic fiber reinforced matrix based on the theory of Kelly and Street indicated that stress dependent sliding at the SiC-alumina interface and stress-dependent partial whisker fracture, resulting in a decrease in average aspect ratio, could be mechanisms responsible for the higher apparent stress exponent in the secondary regime.

INTRODUCTION

Silicon carbide whisker-reinforced alumina ($SiC_w - A\ell_2 0_3$) matrix composites exhibit greatly improved stress-strain behavior (in terms of a marked decrease in brittleness), increased fracture toughness and improved wear and thermal shock resistance when compared to unreinforced alumina. The reinforcement of alumina with silicon carbide whiskers also leads to a marked increase in creep resistance [1-4]. As indicated by changes in the stress exponent this increase is more pronounced at the lower rather than the higher stress levels. Decreases in creep rate on addition of the whisker phase possibly could be due to a change in the dominant creep mechanism of the matrix phase or to a higher stress dependence for creep deformation of the whiskers. However, as the SiC whiskers are expected to behave elastically at temperatures at which alumina exhibits significant creep deformations this latter mechanism is not expected to make a significant contribution. Improvements in creep resistance and associated changes in stress dependence can also result from matrix-whisker interactions, which form the primary focus of this study. A direct comparison of the creep behavior of single-phase and SiC_w - reinforced alumina should be approached with caution, as the presence of the whiskers modifies the microstructure of the matrix phase. An analysis [5] of the creep behavior of fiber-reinforced composites indicates that the initial creep rate of a matrix reinforced with elastic fibers is proportional to the creep rate of the matrix. Therefore, by determining the initial and steady-state creep rate of a composite, a direct comparison of the stress dependence of the creep behavior of the matrix phase and the composite can be made.

EXPERIMENT AND ANALYSIS

The composite material tested consisted of mixtures of alumina powder with 20 wt. % SiC whiskers hotpressed in the laboratory of one of the authors (J. F. R.) at appropriate temperatures and pressures. Average matrix grain size was less than 1 μm. The average whisker diameter was 0.66 μm, with length ranging from 5 to 10 μm. Creep samples were in the shape of 6 x 6 x 50 mm retangular bars.

Creep testing was conducted in 4-point bending at 1500°C in Argon. Experimental details were presented in an earlier paper [6]. The slope of the creep curve resulted in values for the creep rate as a function of time. Extrapolation of the creep rate to zero time resulted in a value for the initial creep rate, at the instant of load imposition, and is representative of the creep deformation of the matrix. Similarly, the creep rate determined for the steady-state regime corresponds to the creep rate of the composite.

A complete solution was obtained for the steady-state creep rate of a short elastic fiber reinforced composite accompanied by sliding at the matrix-fiber interface, based on the original work of Kelly and Street [7]. The mathematical details were presented elsewhere [6].

RESULTS, DISCUSSION AND CONCLUSIONS

Figure 1 shows the stress dependence of the initial and steady-state creep rate. The stress exponent of 1.59 for the initial creep rate agrees well with the expected value for single-phase alumina. The much higher stress exponent of 2.88 for the steady-state creep rate suggests that single-phase and SiC whisker-reinforced alumina are subject to different dominant mechanisms of creep.

Young's modulus of elasticity measured following creep deformation did not differ significantly from the value for the as-received specimen. This indicates that the whiskers suppress cavitation and crack formation, thereby suppressing contributions to creep deformation from elastic creep by crack growth and crack-enhanced creep [8-10].

Figures 2a and 2b show the calculated values for the average stress in the matrix relative to the applied stress as a function of sliding factor for three values of the matrix phase creep exponent, m, and for aspect ratios of 6 and 40, respectively. These results show that at the lower values of the sliding factor, stress in the matrix lies well below the applied stress, σ_c, thereby leading to a major increase in creep resistance. In contrast, as the sliding factor approaches unity, the whiskers are free to slide and the applied stress is transferred to the matrix, so that the stress in the matrix can actually exceed the applied stress. In this case, the presence of the whiskers will lead to a decrease in creep resistance.

Comparison of figures 2a and 2b shows that at any value of sliding factor, the matrix stress increases with decreasing whisker aspect ratio. For this reason, at any value of stress and sliding factor, decreases in aspect ratio are expected to lead to increases in creep rate. The whiskers are expected to exhibit a distribution of strength values. With increasing stress, a proportionally larger fraction of the whiskers is expected to undergo fracture, thereby decreasing the mean value of the aspect ratio. In terms of the results shown in figures 2a and 2b, this would also lead to an increase in stress exponent.

In summary, the present experimental data confirm literature data which show that the improvement in creep resistance of an alumina matrix due to reinforcement with SiC whiskers is more pronounced at the lower than at the higher stress levels. The analytical results suggest that these observations could be due to stress-dependent sliding at the whisker-matrix interface and/or to a decrease in average whisker aspect ratio due to an increasingly large fraction of the whiskers undergoing fracture with increasing stress.

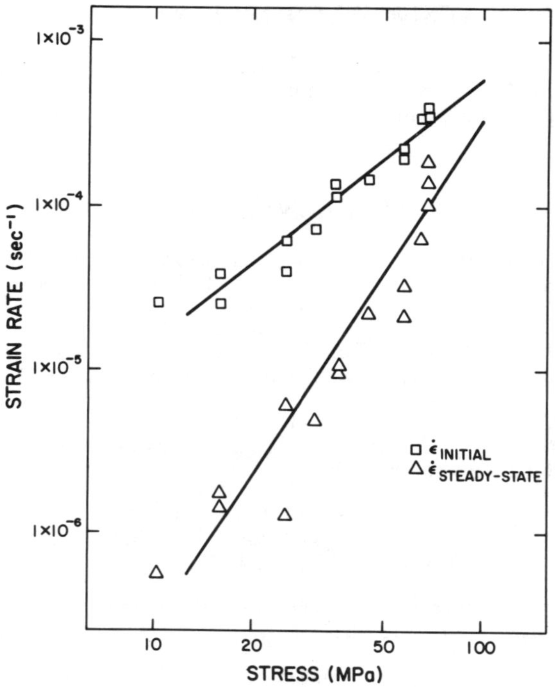

Figure 1. Stress dependence of initial and steady-state creep rate of SiC-whisker reinforced alumina matrix composite at 1500°C.

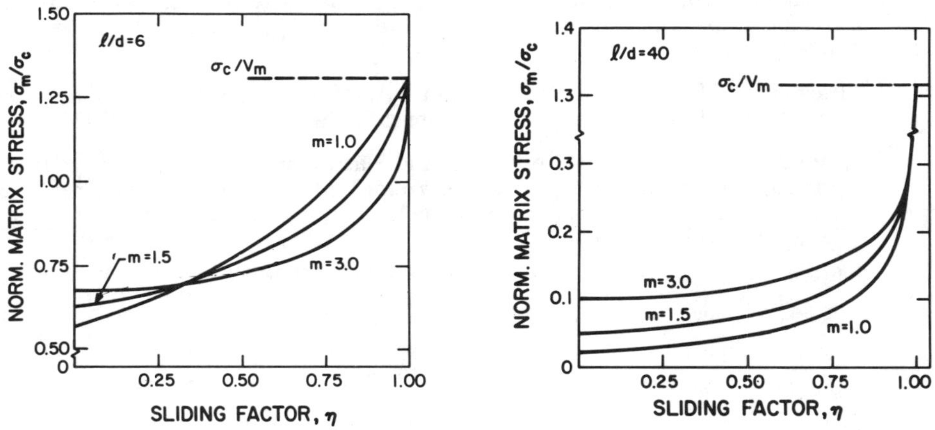

a.　　　　　　b.

Figure 2. Mean matrix stress relative to applied stress as a function of sliding factor for whisker aspect ratios of a: 6 and b: 40.

ACKNOWLEDGEMENT

This study was supported by the Army Research Office under Contract Number: DAAL03-88-K-0073. The authors are indepted to the American Ceramic Society for permission to use Figs. 1 and 2 from Ref. 6.

REFERENCES

1. Chokshi, A. H. and Porter, J. R., Creep Deformation of an Alumina Matrix Composite Reinforced with Silicon Carbide Whiskers. J. Amer. Ceram. Soc., 1985, 6, C144-45.

2. J. R. Porter, F. F. Lange, A. H. Chokshi, Processing and Creep Performance of SiC-Whisker-Reinforced $A\ell_2 0_3$. Am. Ceram. Soc. Bull., 1987, 66, 343-47.

3. Xia, K. and Langdon, T. G, The Mechanical Properties at High Temperatures of SiC Whisker-Reinforced Alumina. In High Temperature/High Performance Composites, Materials Research Society (in press).

4. Porter, J. R., Dispersion Processing of Creep Resistant Whisker-Reinforced Ceramic-Matrix Composites. In Whisker-and-Fiber-Toughened Ceramics, ASM International, Metals Park, Ohio, 1988, pp. 147-52.

5. McLean, M., Creep Deformation of Metal-Matrix Composites. Composites Science and Technology, 1985, 23, 37-52.

6. Donaldson, K. Y., Venkateswaren, A., Hasselman, D. P. H. and Rhodes, J. F., Speculation on the Creep Behavior of Silicon Carbide Whisker Reinforced Alumina. In Proceeding of 13th Annual Conference on Composites and Advanced Ceramics, American Ceramic Society, Westerville, Ohio (in press).

7. Kelly, A. and Street, K. N., Creep of Discontinuous Fibre Composites II, Theory for the Steady-State. Proc. Roy. Soc., London, A., 1972, 328, 283-93.

8. Venkateswaran, A. and Hasselman, D. P. H., Elastic Creep of Stressed Solids Due to Time-Dependent Changes in Elastic Properties. J. Mater. Sci., 1981, 16, 1627-32.

9. Hasselman, D. P. H. and Venkateswaran, A., Role of Cracks in the Creep Deformation of Brittle Polycrystalline Ceramics. J. Mater. Sci., 1983, 18, 161-72.

10. Venkateswaran, A., Donaldson, K. Y. and Hasselman, D. P. H., Role of Intergranular Damage-Induced Decrease in Young's Modulus in the Non-Linear Deformation and Fracture of an Alumina at Elevated Temperatures. J. Amer. Ceram. Soc., 1988, 7, 565-76.

PLASTIC DEFORMATION OF $Al_2O_3/ZrO_2/SiC$ CERAMICS

R. DUCLOS*, J. CRAMPON* and B. CALES+
*Université de Lille 1, LA 234, Bat C6,
59655 Villeneuve d'Ascq Cedex, France.
+C.T. Desmarquest, 2 av. A. Einstein, 78190 Trappes, France.

ABSTRACT

A SiC whisker reinforced alumina-zirconia ceramic has been deformed between 1250 and 1450°C at constant stress ranging from 16 to 300MPa. A diffusional non newtonian viscous creep was observed with an activation energy of 850kJ/mol and a stress exponent depending on the stress. This is due to the existence of a temperature dependent threshold stress related to the difficulty for boundaries to act as perfect sources or sinks for vacancies.

INTRODUCTION

Whisker reinforced ceramics are now actively developed with the object of obtaining ceramics with a high mechanical reliability. A strong improvement in the fracture toughness of a single phase material can be indeed obtained by incorporating high strength whiskers, that improvement resulting mainly from crack deflection and whisker bridging and/or pullout processes[1]. If these mechanisms are particularly efficacious during fracture of the composite, the whisker reinforcement can be also a potential solution in order to increase the creep resistance of the matrix. It becomes therefore important for high temperature applications to study the high temperature creep performances of these composites.

Moreover, little discussion has appeared in the literature on the plastic properties of these reinforced materials[2,3] and it is of interest under these conditions to study by which processes the whisker reinforcement can modify the high temperature mechanical behaviour of the matrix.

To this end, the mechanical properties of a SiC whisker reinforced Al_2O_3-ZrO_2 composite have been studied during compressive creep tests performed at high temperature. Deformation was limited by interfacial processes and a threshold stress, below which no deformation virtually occured, was observed.

EXPERIMENTAL PROCEDURE

An alumina-zirconia ceramic reinforced with SiC whiskers was obtained by hot pressing. The composite was densified to 4.01 g/cm3 corresponding about to the theoretical density. The flexural strength measured at room temperature was 900MPa. The weight composition was 20% zirconia and 20% SiC whiskers. The role of zirconia was primarily to avoid an excessive grain growth of the alumina phase during sintering and also to reinforce the composite by the transformation toughning mechanism.

The initial microstructure observed by TEM is shown in Fig.1. The average grain size of the alumina and zirconia phases was about 1 µm and 0.5 µm respectively. These grain sizes allow to obtain a superplastic behaviour of the matrix in the experimental temperature range. SiC whiskers were approximately 1 µm in diameter and up to 10 µm long.

From disks, creep samples of size 3.2mmx3mmx7.5mm were cut with the compression axis perpendicular to the HP direction; whiskers were thus oriented on planes parallel to the compression axis. Creep experiments were performed in air between 1250 and 1450°C at constant stress varying from 16 to 300MPa according to experimental temperature.

After deformation, the microstructure evolution was studied by TEM at 200kV on thin foils obtained by ionic thinning.

RESULTS AND DISCUSSION

Creep tests were performed up to strains ranging from 20 to 30%. All the creep curves exhibited well defined steady state conditions beyond a few percent strains; the creep rate became then nearly strain independent. For tests performed in the same temperature and stress conditions the steady state creep rate was reproduced within a factor 2. The creep rate-stress dependence is given in Fig.2 as a plot of the creep rate $\dot{\varepsilon}$ vs the applied stress σ in logarithmic scales. One can seen that the stress exponent n in the relation $\dot{\varepsilon} + \sigma^n$ is strain rate or stress dependent. The creep rate was rapidly decreasing when stress was lowered and became negligible below a threshold stress defined as the asymptotic value of the stress on the $\ln\sigma$-$\ln\dot{\varepsilon}$ curves. The values of the threshold stress are equal to 60, 42, 35, 22 and 14MPa at 1250, 1300, 1350, 1400 and 1450°C respectively. If now at a given temperature, the threshold stress σo is substracted from the applied stress a linear relation between $\ln\sigma e$ and ln. is obtained, $\sigma e=\sigma-\sigma o$ being the effective stress (Fig.3). An average value of 1.4±0.2 has been determined for the effective stress exponent.

The creep activation energy Q has been determined by temperature changes performed during tests at constant applied stress. The stress was chosen high enough so that the effective stress was nearly the same at the lower and upper temperatures of the changes. An activation energy of 850±50 kJ/mol has been thus obtained.

The TEM study has revealed that the main modification of the composite structure concerned the cavity formation. Cavities were observed for the most severe stress conditions and one of the consequence was to lower the composite density of a few percent, 2 to 3 in the extreme cases. These cavities never produced the sample fracture. They were generally located between the SiC whiskers and the two other phases. Their shape, wide and short, proves that they grew, preferentially in a parallel direction with the compression axis, by diffusional processes (Fig.4).

The other point concerns the chemical stability of the composite bulk. After deformation tests in air samples were covered with a thin grey layer of mullite, the thickness of which was about 30 to 40 µm, due to surface oxidation phenomena. It has been verified that the sample bulk was oxidation free and that no new cristallographic phase was observed. This means that the above results concern a material of same composition than the original composite.

The above values (stress exponent and activation energy) and the TEM observations suggest that deformation, due to grain boundary sliding, is diffusion controlled. The high activation energy is different from those measured during deformation of fine grained alumina (420 to 490 kJ/mol)[4], zirconia (570 kJ/mol)[5] or from that of the alumina-zirconia matrix (600 to 700 kJ/mol)[6]. This high value must account for the whisker reinforcement. Indeed, the activation energy for creep is similar to that for carbon or silicon diffusion through the lattice, respectively equal to 791 and 789 kJ/mol[7,8].

However the fact that a threshold stress exists can indicate that grain boundaries do not act as perfect sources or sinks for vacancies. The creation or annihilation of vacancies at grain boundaries can then become rate controlling. In this case the activation energy for creep is related to creation/annihilation processes.

On the other hand, if a threshold stress must be simply exceeded in order that diffusional creep occurs, the origin of that threshold stress must be now discussed. Only a few models exist accounting for such a phenomenon:

1) the presence of hard particles at grain boundaries which impede the motion of boundary dislocations[9] is to exclude in this study for the simple reason that TEM observations has not revealed such particles at boundaries.

2) the fluctuation in grain boundary dislocation length[9] during creep, resulting in a threshold stress equal to $\sigma o = Gb/2d$, where G is the shear modulus, d the grain size and b the Burgers'vector of boundary dislocations estimated generally to one third of the Burgers'vector of lattice dislocations.

3) the necessity of maintaining the boundary dislocation density by means of climb sources[10]. The size of the source is limited by that of the grain inducing a threshold stress of Gb/d, twice the previous one.

The above points 2) and 3) give values of the threshold stress of about 10MPa; this value is weaker than those measured in the present study, but the main disagreement resides in the temperature dependence of the threshold stress which decreases faster than does the shear modulus G. More complex processes must be therefore considered in order to explain the origin of the threshold stress.

CONCLUSION

The present study has shown that a diffusional non newtonian creep was observed during the high temperature deformation of a SiC whisker reinforced ceramic. This was due to the existence of a temperature dependent threshold stress and was related to the difficulty for boundaries to act as perfect sources or sinks for vacancies.

ACKNOWLEDGEMENTS

The authors wish to thank the french Research and Technology Ministry for the financial support of this work (Contract 87 A 0050).

REFERENCES

1. Homeny, J., Vaugh, W.L. and Ferber, M.K., Am. Ceram. Soc. Bull., 1987, **67**, 333-338.
2. Porter, J.R., Lange, F.F. and Chokshi, A.H., Am. Ceram. Soc. Bull., 1987, **66**, 343-347.
3. Backhaus-Ricoult, M., Castaing, J. and Routbort, J.L., Revue Phys. Appl., 1988, **23**, 239-249.
4. Cannon, R.M., Rhodes, W.H. and Heuer, A.H., J. Am. Ceram. Soc., 1980, **63**, 46-53.
5. Duclos, R., Crampon, J. and Amana, B., Acta Metall., 1989, **37**, 877-883.
6. Martinez, R., Crampon, J. and Duclos, R., to be published.
7. Hong, J.D. and Davis, R.F., J. Am. Ceram. Soc., 1980, **63**, 546-552.
8. Hong, J.D., Davis, R.F. and Newbury, D.E., J. Mater. Sci., 1981, **16**, 2485-2494.
9. Artz, E., Ashby, M.F. and Verrall, R.A., Acta Metall., 1983, **31**, 1977-1989.
10. Burton, B., Mat. Sci. Eng., 1972, **10**, 9-14.

Figure 1. Typical microstructure of hot-pressed specimens. The zirconia phase is the dark one. Scale bar = 1 μm.

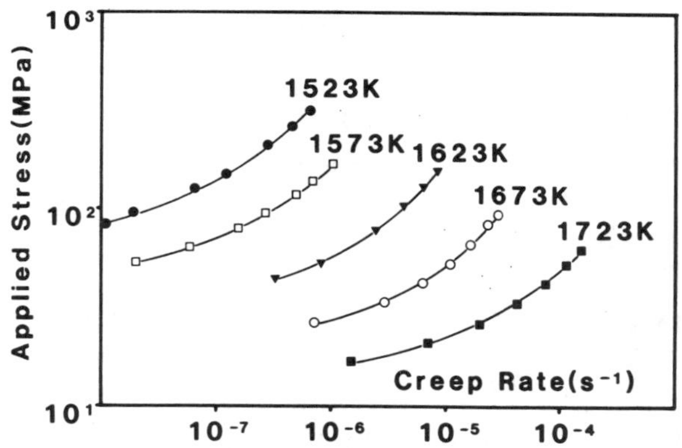

Figure 2. Log applied stress - log steady state creep rate curves.

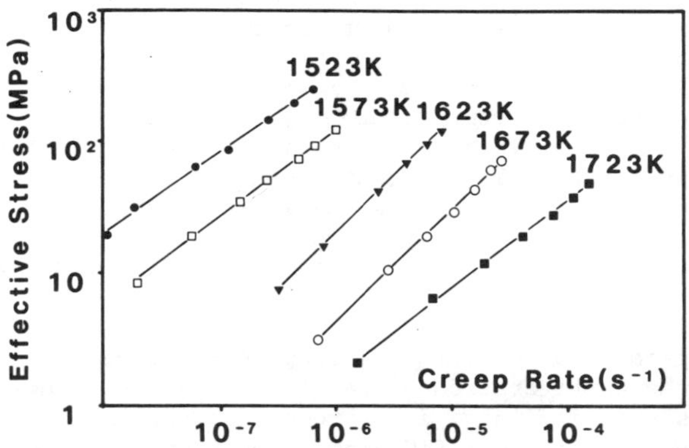

Figure 3. Log effective stress - log steady state creep rate curves.

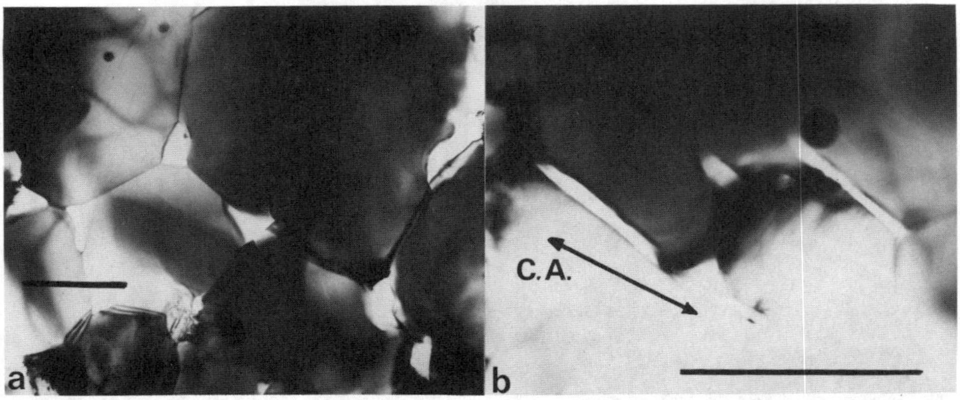

Figure 4. Microstructure of a specimen deformed at 1250°C. Final strain 7%. Applied stress 250 MPa. a) foil perpendicular to the C.A. b) foil parallel with the C.A. Scale bar = 1 μm.

EFFECT OF TEMPERATURE ON TRIBOLOGICAL PROPERTIES OF Al_2O_3 AND SiC CERAMICS

Philippe BOCH, Francis PLATON, Georges KAPELSKI
Ecole Nationale Supérieure de Céramique Industrielle
47 à 73 Avenue ALBERT THOMAS, 87065 LIMOGES CEDEX, FRANCE

(Extended abstract)

In tribological systems, ceramic materials offer the advantages of high hardness, good high-temperature resistance, and low chemical reactivity. But their brittleness is the main concern, and can result in cracking of the wear track. The present work was devoted to the study of one of the "velocity accommodation mechanisms" (VAM) [1] : the formation of small rolls in the "third body". The rheological properties of such rolls play a prominent role on the tribological behaviour of ceramic-to-ceramic couples.

The tribological tests were carried out using a laboratory-made tribometer with the configuration of a fixed ball sliding on a rotating disc. Two couples were studied : a heterogeneous one (Al_2O_3 ball/SiC disc) and a homogeneous one (SiC ball/SiC disc). The temperature could be varied from 20 to 1000°C. The atmosphere was controlled. The usual conditions were a loading force of 4 N, a sliding distance of 100 m, and a sliding velocity of 0.1 m/s.

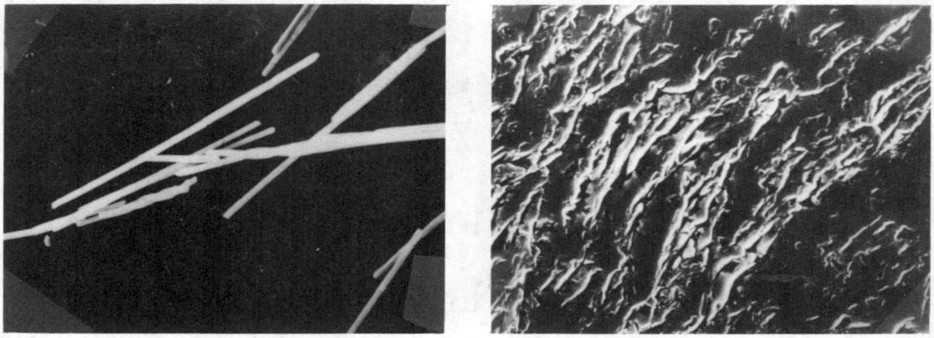

(a) 10 μm (b)

Figure 1 : (a) tribological rolls at 500°C (Al_2O_3 ball/SiC disc) and cracking of the wear track on the SiC disc at 300°C (b).

The coefficient of friction (f) keeps rather a constant value from room temperature to 400°C. It is ≈ 0.65 for the Al_2O_3/SiC couple and ≈ 0.45 for the SiC/SiC couple. Beyond 400°C, f decreases rapidly, down to 0.4 for Al_2O_3/SiC and 0.16 for SiC/SiC. This drop is due to a change in the morphology of the third body at the sliding interface. From room temperature to 400°C, the debris layer is constituted of equiaxed aggregates of various sizes. Beyond 400°C, the debris organize to form tribological rolls, which arrange themselves perpendicularly to the sliding movement of the ball (Figure 1a).

Below 400°C, the aggregated debris do not protect the sliding surfaces against damage. The coefficient of friction is high, which leads to high stresses inside the first bodies, therefore helps to develop cracks in the wear track (Figure 1b). Beyond 400°C, the rolls act to form ball-bearings, which decreases the coefficient of friction, hence prevents the formation of cracks. Rolls are not stable outside the temperature range where they were formed : in the case of tests started at 500°C to develop rolls and then continued at room temperature, the rolls were destroyed, and the coefficient of friction increased again (from 0.45 to 0.60). Rolls develop in a similar manner in the Al_2O_3/SiC couple and in the SiC/SiC one. As far as the phase composition is concerned, EDAX analyses demonstrated that silicon is fully oxidized into silica inside the roll agglomerates, whereas it is partly oxidized into SiO_2 and partly combined into the initial SiC compound inside the non-roll agglomerates.

In conclusion, this work shows that the third-body approach is applicable to Al_2O_3/SiC and SiC/SiC tribological couples. The main velocity accommodation mechanism is the formation of rolls. Rolls act as ball-bearings, which reduces the coefficient of friction, hence prevents the development of cracks in the first bodies. Rolls are only observed in special conditions of temperature, loading force, and sliding distance. A study is currently going on to determine how to widen the domain of formation and how to improve the stability of these beneficial tribological rolls.

[1] Berthier Y., Godet M., Brendle M., "Velocity accommodation in friction", ASME/STLE Tribology Conference, Baltimore (U.S.A.) Oct. 16-19, 1988.

The present work was conducted in the frame of a EURAM project involving a producer (Céramiques et Composites, F) and three laboratories (Surface Lab. at the Univ. of Surrey, UK, Mécaniques des Contacts Lab. at INSA-Lyon, F, and Ceramics Lab. at ENSCI-Limoges, F).

TOUGHENING MECHANISMS IN HEAVY-DUTY CERAMICS

WOLFGANG H. MÜLLER
TU-Berlin, Hermann-Föttinger-Institut
Straße des 17. Juni 135, 1000 Berlin 12, Germany

ABSTRACT

The paper presents a simple quantitative model for the description of crack shielding and debonding in whisker or fiber-reinforced ceramics: The stress-intensity-factors, the stresses and the displacements of a crack in front of or terminating at a fiber are calculated for 4 different matrices.

INTRODUCTION

The experimental work (1-4) of Becher, Claussen, Rühle et al has shown how the fracture toughness of ceramic materials can be increased, even at very high temperatures: The idea is to reinforce the ceramic by adding Zirconia particles, SiC- whiskers or fibres and/or Al_2O_3-platelets.

The reinforcement is based upon the (combined) effect of several micromechanisms:

1.) The tetragonal -> monoclinic phase transition of the ZrO_2-particles ("transformation toughening");
2.) Crack deflection, crack shielding, crack bridging by inclusions, fibres and whiskers;
3.) Pull-out and debonding of fibres and whiskers.

Several attempts have been made to describe these mechanisms mathematically: The stress-induced transformation toughening was analyzed extensively by Claussen, Evans et al (4,5) using the concept of transformation zones. Müller presented an alternative model: He calculated the stress-intensity-factors and thus the increase in toughness of a Griffith-crack in the vicinity of transformed ZrO_2-particles. To that end he made use of Isida's Laurent series expansion method (6) and of Erdogan's singular integral equation technique (7).

Toughening by means of crack bridging, the pull-out and the debonding of fibres have been subject of several theoretical investigations by Becher, Budiansky, Evans et al (1,8).

Finally Li and Bradt (9) have calculated the stresses around an inclusion (for platelet to whisker geometries) in a composite applying an Eshelby approach. Their results indicate how the elastic mismatch as well as the different thermal expansion of the components may affect the toughening.

Nevertheless, for a profound understanding of crack deflection and crack shielding it is not enough to determine the stresses in an uncracked matrix! Rather it is indispensable to solve the elastic problem of a crack approching and eventually entering an inclusion. The objective of the present paper is to find such solutions.

THE MODEL

Consider the following model for a composite consisting of a ceramic matrix and a fiber (Fig.1): A straight crack runs into and terminates perpendicularly at the plane boundary between two bonded materials.

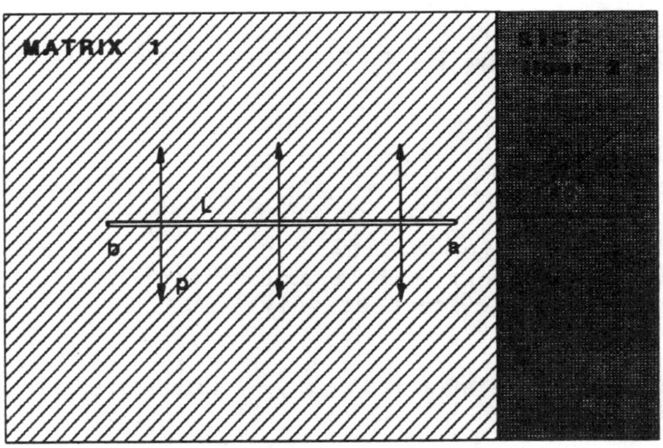

Figure 1: Crack in a ceramic matrix approaching a fiber

ANALYSIS

The Physical Basis

Erdogan et al (10-11) have shown how to tackle such problems. The basic principle is to simulate the crack by an unknown continuous array of edge dislocations. The distribution of the dislocations is determined by the fact that the flanks L of the crack must either be free of forces or as in our case are subject to a constant pressure p.

Hence the normal and tangential stresses at every point of L, which may be calculated according to the principle of superposition by an integral over all stress contributions from the dislocations, have to be counterbalanced by the external loads in the medium, i.e. the pressure along the crack flanks.

Mathematically speaking this consideration leads to singular integral equations of the Cauchy-type. These equations can be solved numerically and allow finally the calculation of all quantities of interest viz. the displacements and stresses around the crack as well as the corresponding SIF's.

The Integral Equation

A detailed derivation of the required integral equation is given in (10). It therefore suffices to summerize the results: The unknown distribution of the Burger vectors $f(r_o)dr_o$ at a point r_o (cp. Fig.1) of the crack's flank can be obtained from the following integral equation:

$$\frac{2\mu_1}{\pi(1+\kappa_1)} \int_a^b \frac{f(r_o)}{r_o - r}\, dr_o + \frac{1}{\pi} \int_a^b H(r,r_o) f(r_o) dr_o = -p \quad , \quad a<r<b \qquad (1)$$

Herein $H(r,r_o)$ stands for a nonsingular integral kernel:

$$H(r,r_o) = \frac{\mu_1}{(1+\kappa_1)} \frac{1}{(1+m\kappa_1)(m+\kappa_2)} \left\{ \frac{1}{r_o + r} [(1+m\kappa_1)(m+\kappa_2) - m(1+\kappa_1)(1+m\kappa_1) - \right. \qquad (2)$$

$$\left. -3(1-m)(m+\kappa_2)] + 12(1-m)(m+\kappa_2) \frac{r}{(r_o + r)^2} - 8(1-m)(m+\kappa_2) \frac{r^2}{(r_o + r)^3} \right\}$$

μ_1 is the shear modulus of the matrix and m, κ_1 and κ_2 are combinations of the shear moduli and Poisson's constant of the matrix and the SiC-fiber respectively:

$$m = \frac{\mu_2}{\mu_1} \;,\; \kappa_i = 3-4\nu_i \text{ (plane strain)}, \; \kappa_i = \frac{3-\nu_i}{1+\nu_i} \text{ (plane stress)}, \; i=1,2 \qquad (3)$$

In order to ensure a unique solution of this equation the continuity equation for the displacement has to be fulfilled:

$$\int_a^b f(r_o) dr_o = 0 \qquad (4)$$

Eqs. (1-4) must be treated numerically as outlined in (11).

Stress-Intensity-Factors, Displacements and Stresses

After the integral equation has been solved the stress intensity factors can be calculated as shown in eq. (5). The third relation clearly indicates that if the crack terminates at the interface the stress-singularity at the a-tip will be no longer of the square-root-type:

$$K_I(b) = -\frac{2\mu_1}{1+\kappa_1}\lim_{r\to b}\sqrt{2\pi(b-r)}\, f(r) = p\sqrt{\pi a_o}\, Y(b)\ ,\ a_o = \frac{b-a}{2},\ a\geq 0$$

$$K_I(a) = \frac{2\mu_1}{1+\kappa_1}\lim_{r\to a}\sqrt{2\pi(r-a)}\, f(r) = p\sqrt{\pi a_o}\, Y(a)\ ,\ c = \frac{b+a}{2},\ a>0 \qquad (5)$$

$$K_I(a) = \mu^*\lim_{r\to 0}\sqrt{2\pi}\, r^{\omega} f(r),\ \mu^* = \mu_1 m\frac{(3-2\omega)(1+m\kappa_1)-(1-2\omega)(m+\kappa_2)}{(m+\kappa_2)(1+m\kappa_1)\sin\pi(1-\omega)},\qquad a=0$$

Rather the power of the singularity is given by an irrational number ω , which can be obtained from a solution of the following characteristic equation:

$$2\alpha\cos\pi(1-\omega) - \beta(1-\omega)^2 - \gamma = 0,\ \alpha = (m+\kappa_2)(1+m\kappa_1)$$
$$\beta = -4(m+\kappa_2)(1-m),\ \gamma = (1-m)(m+\kappa_2) + (1+m\kappa_1)(m+\kappa_2) - m(1+\kappa_1)(1+m\kappa_1) \qquad (6)$$

Finally the crack-surface-displacements $u_\vartheta(r)$ and the important stress components in the cleavage ($\vartheta=0$) and in the debonding plane ($\vartheta = \pi/2$) are given by integrals of the following kind:

$$u_\vartheta(r) = \frac{1}{2}\int_a^r f(r_o)dr_o\ ,\ t_{ij}(r) = \int_a^b t_{ij}(r,r_o,\vartheta) f(r_o)dr_o \qquad (7)$$

where $t_{ij}(r,r_o,\vartheta)$ stands for the following integrands:

$$t^2_{\vartheta\vartheta}(r,r_o,0) = -\bar{\mu}\left[-(1+m\kappa_1)\frac{(r+3r_o)}{(r+r_o)^2} - (m+\kappa_2)\frac{r-r_o}{(r+r_o)^2}\right],\ \bar{\mu} = \frac{\mu_2 f}{\pi(1+m\kappa_1)(m+\kappa_2)}$$

$$t^2_{rr}(r,r_o,0) = -\bar{\mu}\left[-(1+m\kappa_1)\frac{(3r+r_o)}{(r+r_o)^2} + (m+\kappa_2)\frac{r-r_o}{(r+r_o)^2}\right],$$

$$t^2_{\vartheta\vartheta}(r,r_o,\tfrac{\pi}{2}) = -\bar{\mu}\left[-(1+m\kappa_1)\frac{r_o}{r^2+r_o^2} + (m+\kappa_2)r_o\frac{(3r^2-r_o^2)}{(r^2+r_o^2)^2}\right],$$

$$t^2_{r\vartheta}(r,r_o,\tfrac{\pi}{2}) = \bar{\mu}\left[(1+m\kappa_2)\frac{r}{r^2+r_o^2} + (m+\kappa_2)r\frac{(r^2-3r_o^2)}{(r^2+r_o^2)^2}\right],$$

$$t^2_{rr}(r,r_o,\tfrac{\pi}{2}) = -\bar{\mu}\left[-3(1+m\kappa_1)\frac{r_o}{r^2+r_o^2} + (m+\kappa_2)r_o\frac{(r_o^2-3r^2)}{(r^2+r_o^2)^2}\right], \qquad (8)$$

$$t^1_{rr}(r,r_o,\tfrac{\pi}{2}) = -\bar{\mu}\frac{1}{m(1+\kappa_1)}\left[-(1+m\kappa_1)(m+\kappa_2)r_o\frac{(3r_o^2+7r^2)}{(r^2+r_o^2)^2} + \right.$$
$$\left. + m(1+\kappa_1)(1+m\kappa_1)\frac{r_o}{r^2+r_o^2} + 3(1-m)(m+\kappa_2)r_o\frac{(r_o^2-3r^2)}{(r^2+r_o^2)^2}\right]$$

As before (7) must be solved numerically e.g. by means of the procedure in (11).

RESULTS

Material Constants

In the following the integral equation (1) is solved for 4 different types of matrices (Cordierite, Mullite, Si_3N_4, Al_2O_3) containing an SiC-fiber or whisker as shown in Fig.1. To that end it is necessary to know the elastic constants of all these materials (9,12). They are summarized in Table 1.

Furthermore Table 1 contains the values ω of the power of the stress-singularity in the case when the crack terminates at the matrix-SiC-interface. These values follow directly from equation (6). Note that all matrix materials but Alumina show a clear tendency towards a lower stress concentration ($\omega < 1/2$).

Table 1
Elastic constants of matrix and fiber materials

Material	Shear Modulus (GPa)	Poisson's Ratio	Stress Singularity
Cordierite	54	0.3	0.4172
Mullite	87	0.27	0.4501
Si_3N_4	126	0.26	0.4838
Al_2O_3	163	0.23	0.5040
SiC	175	0.17	------

Numerical results

Fig. 2 shows the resulting stress-intensity factors at both crack tips. In the case of the Cordierite and Mullite matrices crack shielding is distinctly visible: The correction function Y(a) decreases rapidly as the crack advances towards the interface accounting for a strong increase in toughness.

Table 2 presents the stresses (for plane strain) in the neighborhood of a crack tip terminating at the interface. One observes that debonding ($\vartheta = \pi/2$) can take place as a result of normal as well as shear stresses. (In fact the line for the SiC contains the stresses that occur in the case of a homogeneous matrix. These values may serve as an orientation.)

TABLE 2
Stresses in the neighborhood of a crack terminating at the interface (all stresses in units of p, $\delta = 10^{-2} a_0$)

Matrix	$t^2_{\vartheta\vartheta}(\delta,0)$	$t^2_{rr}(\delta,0)$	$t^2_{\vartheta\vartheta}(\delta,\frac{\pi}{2})$	$t^2_{r\vartheta}(\delta,\frac{\pi}{2})$	$t^1_{rr}(\delta,\frac{\pi}{2})$	$t^2_{rr}(\delta,\frac{\pi}{2})$
Cordierite	6.537	6.541	2.311	2.673	3.563	7.503
Mullite	6.357	6.398	2.015	2.639	4.536	7.120
Si_3N_4	6.111	6.113	1.678	2.700	5.666	6.663
Al_2O_3	6.002	5.957	1.484	2.677	6.525	6.362
SiC	6.124	6.124	1.557	2.519	6.518	6.518

The SIF's corresponding to the same situation can be found in Table 3. They are closely connected with the powers ω of the stress-tip-singularity. In order to get some idea of the corresponding increase in toughness one should apply the local stress criterion of (11) to these data.

Finally Fig. 3 shows the crack surface displacement for all materials. As expected the curves are slightly asymmetrical with respect to the center of the crack.

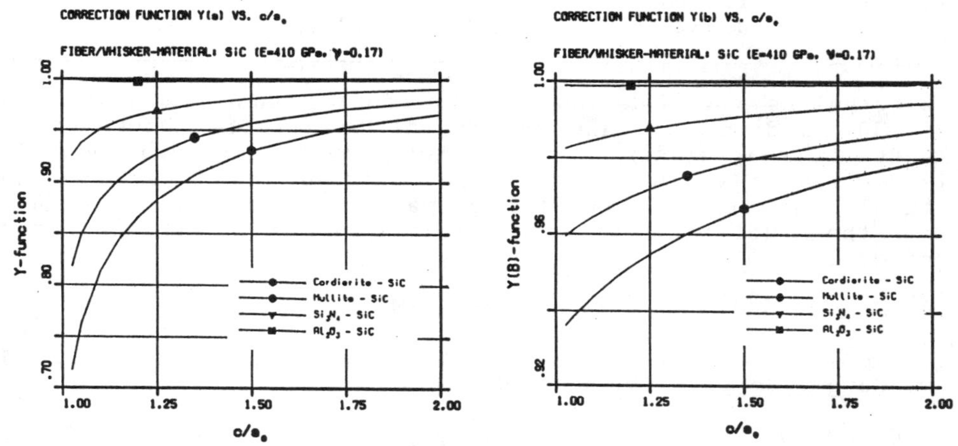

Figure 2. Stress intensity factors at both crack tips

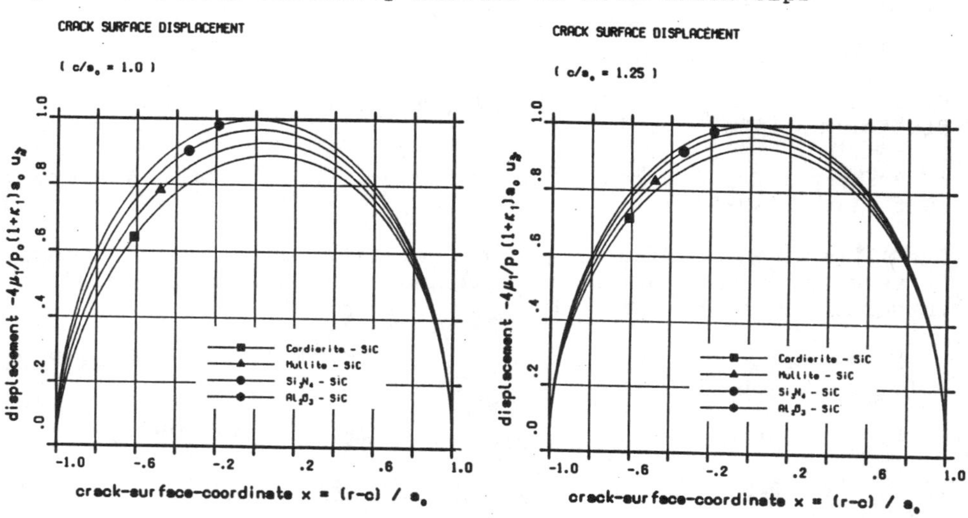

Figure 3. Crack surface displacements

CONCLUSION AND OUTLOOK

By means of the presented model it is possible to understand two basic toughening mechanisms in ceramic compounds quantitatively: crack shielding and the debonding of fibers during crack propagation.

TABLE 3
Stress-intensity-factors of a crack terminating at the interface

Matrix	Cordierite	Mullite	Si_3N_4	Al_2O_3
Y(a=0)	1.6149	1.3246	1.0715	0.9542
Y(b)	0.9327	0.9570	0.9815	0.9990

Nevertheless the model has still several shortcomings: First of all it does not take account of the finite thickness and length of the whisker or fiber. Secondly the integral equation is no longer valid if the crack crosses the interface. And thirdly: The crack must lie perpendicular to the interface. Thus the model in it's present form is not applicable to crack deflection.

REFERENCES

1. Becher, P.F., Hsueh, C.H., Angelini, P., Tiegs, T.N., J. Am. Ceram. Soc., 1988, **71**, 1050-1061

2. Claussen, N. and Petzow, G., Journal de Physique, 1986, **47**, C1 693-703

3. Claussen, N., Weisskopf, K.L. and Rühle, M., J. Am. Ceram. Soc., 1986, **69**, 288-292

4. Claussen, N., Z. Werkstofftech., 1982, **13**, 1982

5. Evans, A.G.,Proc. Sc. of Zirconia II, ed. Claussen et al, Stuttgart, 1984, pp. 193-212

6. Müller, W.H., Proc. ECF6, ed. van Elst et al, Amsterdam, 1986, pp. 2129-2145

7. Müller, W.H., The exact calculation of stress intensity factors in transformation toughenedd ceramics by means of integral equations, Int. J. Fract., in print

8. Budiansky, B., Amazigo, J.C., Evans, A.G., J. Mech. Phys. Sol., 1988, **36**, 167-187

9. Li, Z., Bradt, R.C., J. Am. Ceram. Soc., 1989, **72**, 70-77

10. Cook, T.S., Erdogan, F., Int. J. Engng. Sci., 1972, **10**, 677-697

11. Erdogan, F., Gupta, G.D., Cook, T.S., Methods of analysis and solutions of crack problems, ed. Sih, Noordhoff Leyden, 1973, pp. 368-425

12. Steinmann, D.,Deutsches Industrieforum für Technologie, Frankfurt, 1989

SUBCRITICAL GROWTH OF AS-INDENTED PYRAMID AND KNOOP CRACKS IN SODA-LIME GLASS

MITSUO YODA
College of Engineering
Nihon University
Koriyama, 963, Japan

ABSTRACT

Subcritical crack growth data on soda-lime glass subjected to sustained bend stress in water were obtained using the small pyramid and Knoop indentation cracks. To compare the growth of large cracks, the compact type (CT) specimens were also used. The stress intensity facter K_I-crack velocity V curves for the as-indented cracks show that there is some effect which increases crack growth at the K_I value less than that for the CT specimen. In addition, the slope of the V-K_I curves is smaller than that for the CT specimens. However, the annealed indentation crack shows the same trend of crack growth as that for the CT specimens. Residual stress effect can be used to explain this anomalous growth behavior of the as-indented pyramid and Knoop cracks.

INTRODUCTION

Ceramics and glass are susceptible to subcritical crack growth under sustained load in certain environments. In this case, the crack growth behavior can be described adequately by the crack velocity and stress intensity factor. The double torsion (DT) and compact type (CT) specimens have been commonly used to determine fracture toughness and subcritical crack growth. However, fracture and crack growth in such materials usually occur at the origin of cracks or flaws much smaller than those used in DT and CT specimens.

For the purpose of evaluating fracture toughness and subcritical growth of small cracks, artificial semi-elliptical surface cracks have been recently used (1-4). The cracks are introduced by the Vickers microhardness indentation and they closely resemble the natural contact damage that glass and ceramics experience during surface finishing and service. There are some problems associated with the use of these indentation cracks. The indentation cracks produce residual stress and lateral cracks occur besides the surface cracks. The indentation cracks show an anomalous subcritical growth behavior due to the reasons described above. In this paper, subcritical crack growth data on soda-lime glass were obtained using the pyramid and Knoop indentation cracks under sustained load in water. The growth characteristics were compared with those for CT specimens.

Experimental Procedure

The plate material is soda-lime glass and its thickness h is 2.75mm. Initial surface indentation cracks of length c_0 were introduced at the center of the specimens by the Vickers microhardness pyramid and Knoop indenter. The indentation load F were 4.9, 9.8N for the pyramid, and 9.8N for the Knoop. Figure 1 shows the pyramid and Knoop indentation cracks and four-point bend test apparatus. The crack length c_0 ranged from 60 to 110 μm. A fine shallow notch was machined to avoid fracture from intrinsic flaws. Moreover, the stiffened plates of the same glass were attached by adhesive bonding to prevent fracture at the contact point of the knife-edge (N). The specimen (T) was placed so that the crack was on the tensile side and was subjected to bend stress σ in water. Surface radial crack growth c was measured by a low-power microscope at each interval of time by unloading the specimens.

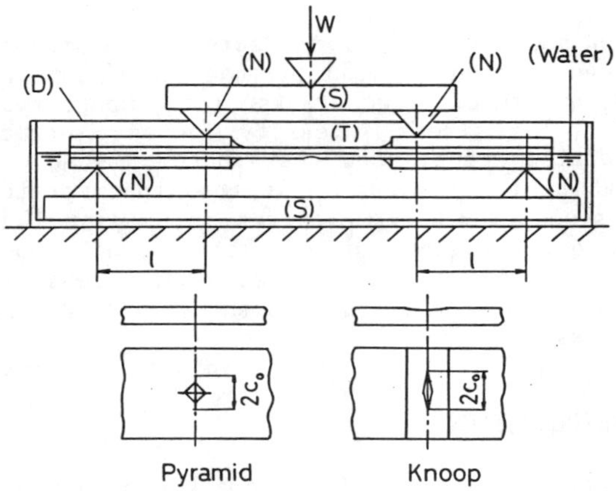

Fig.1. Pyramid and Knoop indentation cracks and four-point bend test apparatus.

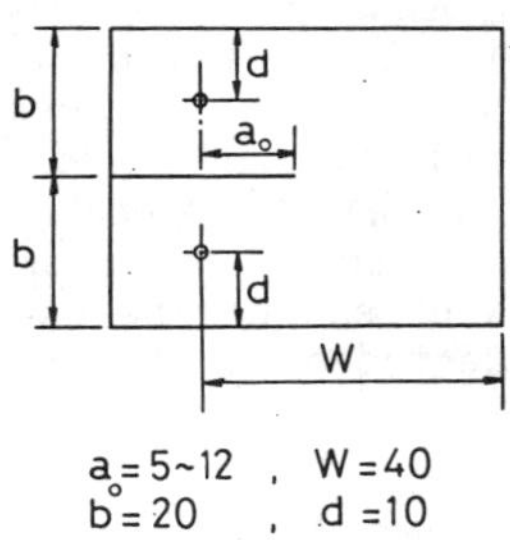

Fig.2. CT specimen geometry.

The CT specimen geometry is shown in Fig.2. Initial cracks were introduced by the thermal stress and their length, a_0 ranged from 5 to 12mm. Both tests were carried out on the as-received specimens and those annealed at 600°C after the crack introduction.

RESULTS AND DISCUSSION

Figure 3 shows the variation of subcritical surface crack growth c with time t for the Knoop indentation cracks. At the initial stage, the crack growth is large and the crack tends to grow somewhat discretely. When unloading is repeated for the crack length inspection, the resulting principal stress will change its direction and the fracture surface becomes undulated. Thus, arrest lines can be seen on the fracture surface,

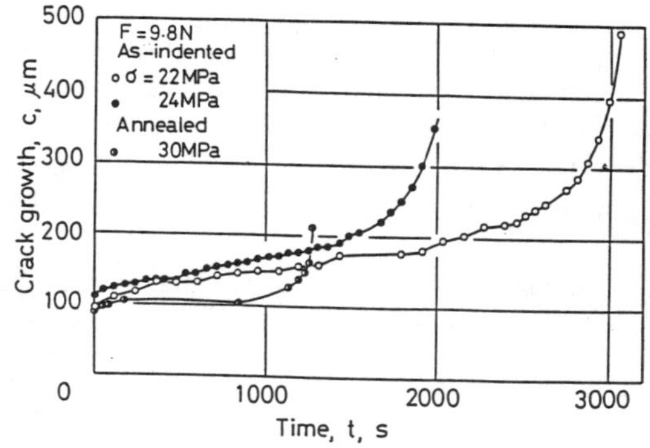

Fig.3. Subcritical crack growth vs. time for the Knoop indentation cracks.

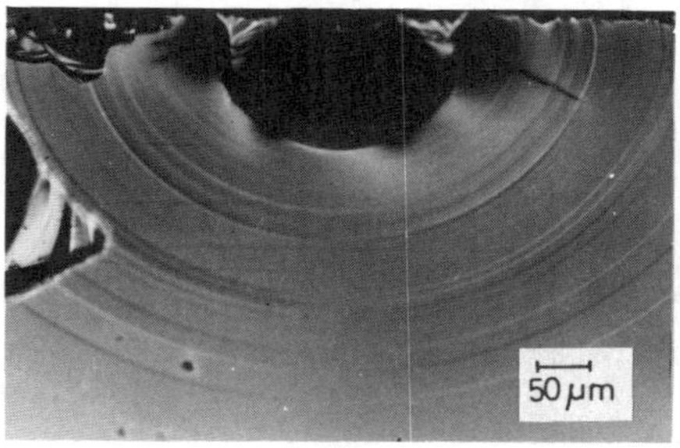

Fig.4. Fracture surface for the Knoop indentation crack.

as shown in Fig.4. Such arrest lines represent the position of the crack front during its growth. In the Knoop indentation, the initial semi-circular crack grows gradually into a semi-elliptical shape. For the pyramid indentation crack, the crack extends in the radial direction at the initial stage because the lateral crack parallel to the surface obstructs the downward extension. Then it begins to grow under the lateral crack and finally develops into a semi-elliptical shape. Both semi-elliptical cracks tend to grow more in the radial direction than in the downward direction because of the stress gradients of bend stress.

Typical crack growth data obtained for the CT specimens are shown in Fig.5, where the logarithm of the crack velocity da/dt is plotted as a function of the applied stress intensity factor K_I. The stress intensity factor K_I for the CT specimen is calculated by (5)

$$K_I = \frac{2P(2W+a)}{h(W-a)^{3/2}} \cdot F_I \tag{1}$$

where P is the applied load, h the thickness of the plate and F_I the correction factor. The position and slope of the da/dt-K_I curves can be placed into one category. The da/dt-K_I curves can be approximately represented by a straight line and the slope n of the curves is 16.

Surface crack velocity dc/dt-K_I curves were obtained for the pyramid and Knoop indentation cracks, as shown Figs 6 and 7, respectively. Since the maximum stress intensity factor for a semi-elliptical crack occurs at the intersection of the minor axis with the crack, the stress intensity factor K_I can be calculated by (6)

$$K_I = M\sigma\sqrt{\pi l}/\Phi \tag{2}$$

where l is the crack depth, σ the bend stress, Φ the complete elliptic integral of the second kind and M the correction factor. In calculating the K_I values, the average ratio l/c was taken to be 0.8. The dc/dt-K_I curves for the as-indented pyramid cracks are divided into two regions, as shown in Fig.6. At the initial stage, dc/dt is high, and decreases and finally increases with K_I, independent of c_o and σ. The dc/dt-K_I curves for the as-indented Knoop cracks show the same trend as that for the as-indented pyramid cracks. The slope n of the dc/dt-K_I curves for the as-indented pyramid and Knoop cracks ranges from 10 to 13, which is less than that of the curves for the CT specimens. However, the dc/dt-K_I curves for the annealed Knoop indentation crack shows the same trend as those for the CT specimens and the value of the slope n is 16. For the as-indented cracks, the residual stress will act in concert with subsequently applied tensile loading. Accordingly, the stress intensity factor associated with the residual stress is incorporated and this stress intensity factor K_{Ir} is given by (7)

$$K_{Ir} = X_r F / c^{3/2} \tag{3}$$

where F is the indentation load and Xr the constant. Thus, the effective stress intensity factor K_{Ieff} can be expressed in terms of the surface crack length c as

$$K_{Ieff} = 1.12 M\sigma\sqrt{c} + X_r F / c^{3/2} \tag{4}$$

Since the K_{Ieff} value has a minimum, the value of Xr can be given experimentally. If the crack velocity is controlled by the stress intensity factor, the minimum crack velocity corresponds to the minimum stress intensity factor obtained by differentiating eqn (4). The crack velocity dc/dt is plotted against the effective stress intensity factor K_{Ieff} for the same as-indented pyramid and Knoop cracks as in Figs 6 and 7, as shown in Fig 8. The position and the slope of the dc/dt-K_{Ieff} curves for the as-indented cracks are almost the same as those for the CT specimens, except that the data on the high crack velocity cannot be obtained.

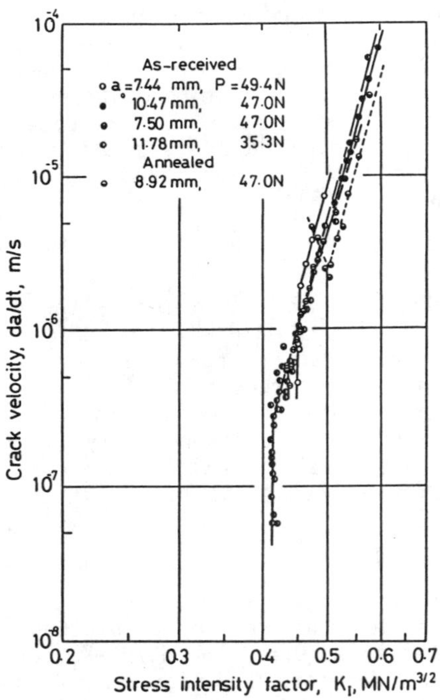

Fig.5. Crack velocity da/dt-stress intensity factor K_I curves for CT specimens.

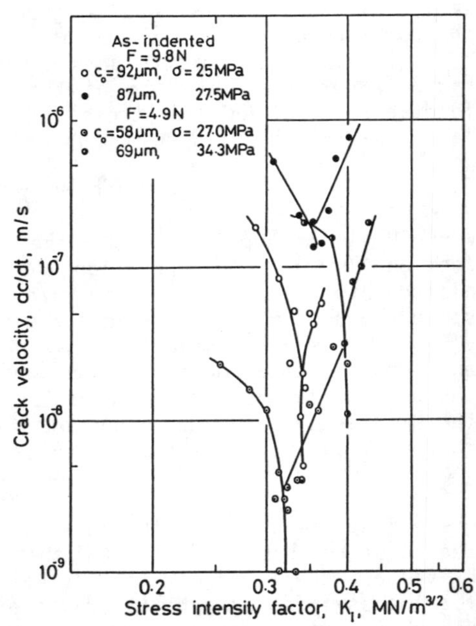

Fig.6. Crack velocity dc/dt-stress intensity factor K_I curves for the as-indented pyramid cracks.

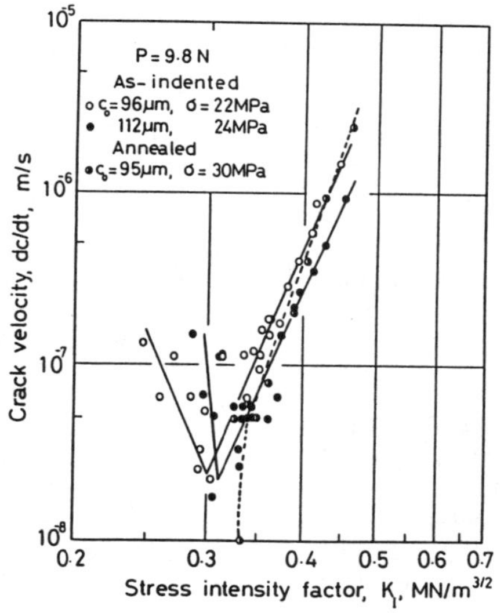

Fig.7. Crack velocity dc/dt-stress intensity factor K_I curves for the Knoop indentation cracks.

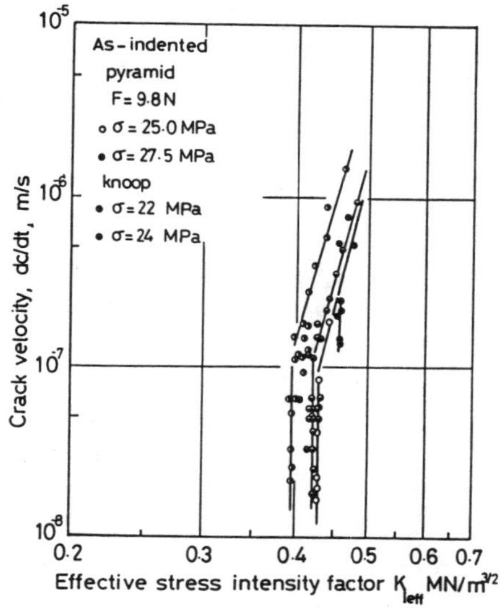

Fig.8. Crack velocity dc/dt-effective stress intensity factor K_{Ieff} curves for the as-indented cracks.

CONCLUSIONS

The subcritical crack growth data on soda-lime glass were obtained using the small pyramid and Knoop indentation cracks. The experimental results were compared with those for the conventional CT specimens with long cracks. The crack velocity dc/dt-stress intensity factor K_I curves for the as-indented pyramid and Knoop cracks can be divided into two regions. The crack velocity is initially high, decreases with K_I reaching a minimum and thereafter increases with K_I. The slope of the curves is smaller than that for the CT specimens. However, the annealed indentation crack shows the same trend as that for the CT specimens. It is shown that the residual stress effect can be used to explain the anomalous growth of the as-indented cracks.

REFERENCES

1. Lawn, B.R., and Swain, M.V., J.Mater.Sci., Vol. 10, 1975, pp. 113-122.
2. Evans, A.G., and Charles, E.A., J.Am.Ceram.Soc., Vol. 59, No. 7-8, 1976, pp. 371-372.
3. Yoda, M., and Yoshikawa, Y., J.Am.Ceram.Soc., Vol. 70, No. 11, 1987, pp. C-301-302.
4. Yoda, M., Engng Fracture Mech., Vol. 29, No. 2, 1988, pp. 189-196.
5. Tada, H., Paris, P., and Irwin, G., The Stress Analysis of Cracks Handbook, Del Research Corporation, 1973, p. 2.29.
6. Shah, R.C., and Kobayashi, A.S., ASTM STP 513, 1972, pp. 3-21.
7. Lawn, B.R., Evans, A.G., and Marshall, B., J.Am.Ceram.Soc., Vol. 63, No. 9-10. 1980, pp. 574-581.

EFFECT OF PRE– AND POST–DENSIFICATION HEAT TREATMENT ON MICROSTRUCTURE DEVELOPMENT AND STRENGTH OF HPSN

HEINZ HÜBNER, GABRIELA WROBLEWSKA
Arbeitsbereich Werkstoffphysik
Technische Universität Hamburg–Harburg
P.O.Box 901403, D–2100 Hamburg 90

ABSTRACT

In order to optimize the microstructure of HPSN, the temperature–time cycle during densification was varied using three different temperature routes, i.e. (1) "normal" hot–pressing at 1850°C and 30 MPa during 1 hour, (2) heat treatment at 1690°C before hot–pressing and (3) post–densification thermal treatment at 1300°C performed "in situ". Using route 2, a more homogeneous material was obtained than by normal hot–pressing. The grain size distribution was considerably smaller and the strength was somewhat higher, demonstrating the effectiveness of the $\alpha \rightarrow \beta$ phase transformation prior to densification. Route 3 resulted in a material of exactly the same mean grain size and distribution as was obtained by normal hot–pressing. However, additional crystalline phases appeared in the microstructure which were supposed to form from glass phase residues. Additionally, the distinct strength increase observed was taken as a further evidence of the occurrence of in–situ crystallization of the intragranular amorphous phase.

INTRODUCTION

HPSN–ceramics are considered as candidate materials for engineering structural applications. Many studies have been performed with the aim to optimize the microstructural parameters with respect to improved mechanical performance. For example, investigations carried out by Ziegler et al. [1], Knoch and Ziegler [2] and Himsolt et al. [3] have shown that both fracture strength and fracture toughness of HPSN increase with growing content of the β phase. Moreover, as has been shown by the investigations of Wötting et al. [4], the flexural strength of HPSN materials is dependent on the morphology of the β crystallites. Materials with elongated β grains have better mechanical properties than materials with globular ones. Elongated Si_3N_4 grains form an interlaced type of microstructure which leads to an improvement of the mechanical behaviour. The formation of a globular grain structure from elongated β grains can be avoided by applying a suitable and short hot–pressing process.

As to the high–temperature regime, mechanical properties are strongly dependent on the nature of the grain boundary phases. Materials which exhibit crystalline second phases, e.g. HPSN with Y_2O_3 and Al_2O_3 additions, show improved mechanical properties at temperatures above 1000°C as compared to materials with amorphous grain boundary phases, e.g. HPSN with MgO additions [5]. The optimum type of microstructure for high–temperature applications should consist of elongated β crystallites, completely crystallized grain boundary phases, and a minimum number of pores. The purpose of the present study was to optimize the hot–pressing parameters in order to obtain Si_3N_4 materials of the microstructure described above.

MATERIALS AND METHODS

Hot–pressing experiments were performed using the silicon nitride powder LC 12 (H.C.Starck Berlin) which had an α–Si_3N_4 content of 93 vol.% and a surface area of 15,7 m^2/g. The powder was mixed with varying additions of Y_2O_3(3,5,7 and 9 wt.%) in ethanol using agate balls and polyethylene containers. Disks were hot–pressed in graphite dies at a temperature of 1850°C under a pressure of 30 MPa for 1h. To investigate the $\alpha \rightarrow \beta$ phase transformation additional hot–pressing tests were performed at 1390, 1485, 1590, and 1690°C under a pressure of 30 MPa for 1h. The transformation of the β fraction was examinated using quantitative X–ray analysis [6]. The density of the samples was measured by the immersion technique. The microstructure was studied in a Cam Scan electron microscope. The grain size distribution was determined by counting about 500 grains. The strength was measured in 4–point bending (outer span 30 mm, inner span 10 mm, sample dimensions 3.5 x 3.0 x 32.0 mm); five samples were tested for each data point.

RESULTS AND DISCUSSION

During hot–pressing of Si_3N_4 powders, a series of processes take place simultaneously, such as (1) the formation of a liquid phase, (2) the densification of the powder compact, (3) the $\alpha \rightarrow \beta$ phase transformation, and, eventually, (4) the crystallization of the amorphous phase. The processes 2, 3 and 4 were studied in detail in the present paper. For that, different densification routes were employed which are shown in Fig. 1. Route 1 is the densification process normally used in the fabrication of HPSN. Route 2 is characterized by a pre–densification heat treatment the aim of which was to complete the $\alpha \rightarrow \beta$ transformation prior to compaction. The process of route 3 consists of route 1 plus a post–densification heat treatment at 1300°C which was performed "in–situ", however without pressure, in order to promote the crystallization of the glassy grain–boundary phase.

Hot–pressing experiments along route 1 were performed with samples containing different amounts of the Y_2O_3 additive. The densification of these samples was shown in Fig. 2. It demonstrates the well known fact that the density increases with increasing amount of the additive. However, an Y_2O_3 content of 3 wt.% is insufficient to achieve full density of the compact, even at the highest hot–pressing temperature. All further experiments were carried out with powder mixtures containing 7 wt.% of Y_2O_3.

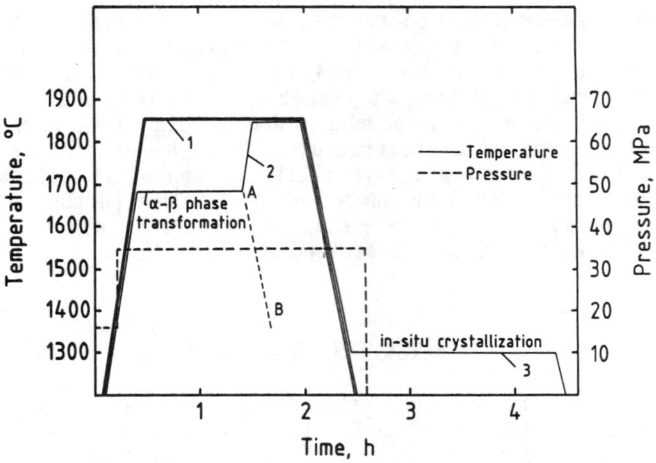

Figure 1. Temperature and pressure–profiles during hot–pressing process.

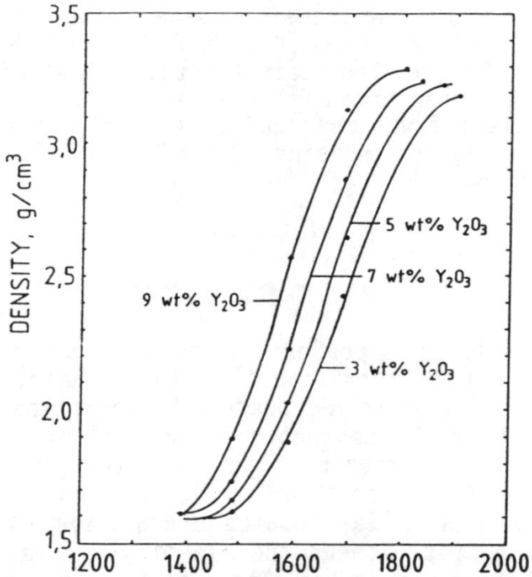

Figure 2. Density of HPSN material vs. hot–pressing temperature

To study the amount of the $\alpha \to \beta$ phase transformation caused by the pre–densification heat treatment according to route 2, specimens heat–treated at various temperatures were cooled down along the line AB of Fig. 1 and studied by X–ray diffraction. Figure 3 shows diffraction results of samples exposed to four different temperatures. As can be seen from the figure, the $\alpha \to \beta$ transformation proceeds with increasing temperature and is completed at 1690°C. Quantitatively, the following amounts of the β phase have been measured: 1390°C/8 vol.%; 1485°C/11 vol.%; 1590°C/42 vol.%; 1690°C/100 vol.%.

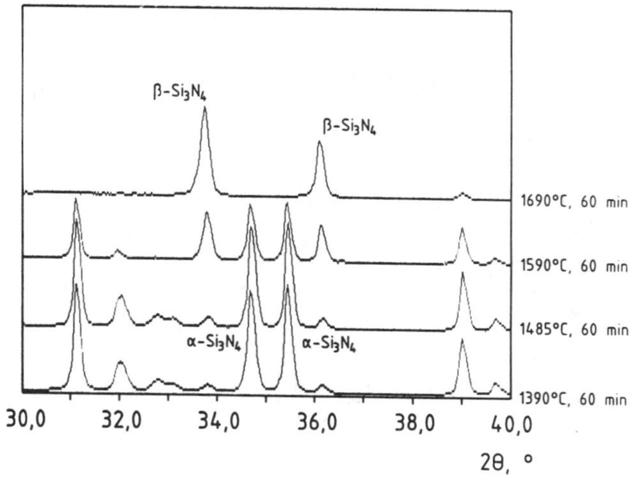

Figure 3. X—ray diffraction of HPSN+Y_2O_3 after various annealing temperatures prior to densification.

The $\alpha\rightarrow\beta$ transformation is generally attributed to the presence of a liquid phase. The results listed above are comparable with literature data for the system Si_3N_4—SiO_2—Y_2O_3, where starting temperatures for the formation of the liquid phase of about 1500°C have been reported [7,8]. Regarding the system Si_3N_4—Y_2O_3 only, the maximum formation temperature of the liquid phase has been observed to occur at 1650°C [8]. Thus the observed temperature of 1690°C which was necessary to complete the $\alpha\rightarrow\beta$ transformation in our experiments seems to be in reasonable agreement with data from the literature [8].

The crystallization behaviour of the amorphous phase was studied by in—situ heat treatments according to route 3 of Fig. 1. The annealing times were 1h, 3h, 6h and 10h at 1300°C. X—ray diffraction tests gave evidence of the formation of the phases $Y_2Si_2O_7$ and $Y_{20}N_4Si_{12}O_{48}$ in specimens heat—treated for 1 hour or longer. By increasing the annealing time, the composition of the samples was changed only insignificantly.

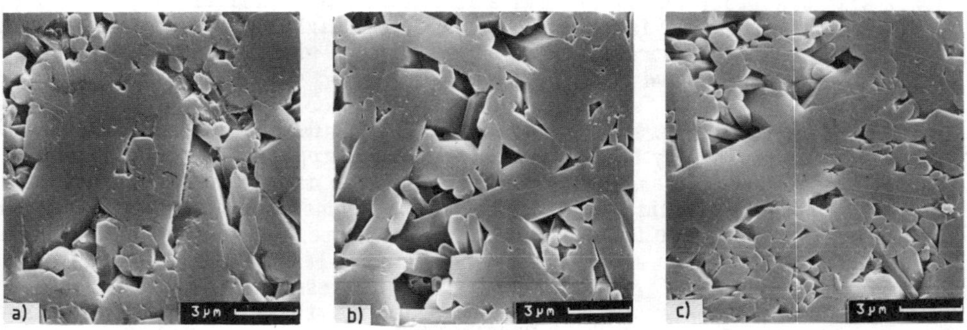

Figure 4. SEM micrographs of polished and etched surfaces of the three HPSN materials fabricated along a) temperature route 1 b) temperature route 2 c) temperature route 3

Table 1

Properties of HPSN materials with 7 wt% Y_2O_3

Temperature route	Density [g/cm³]	Phase composition	d_{50} [μm]	σ	Flexural strength [MPa]
1	3.23	β–Si_3N_4	1.3	0.60	725
2	3.25	β–Si_3N_4	1.2	0.48	750
3a	3.24	β–Si_3N_4, Y_1,Y_2	1.3	0.62	810
3b	3.25	β–Si_3N_4, Y_1,Y_2	—	—	800
3c	3.25	β–Si_3N_4, Y_1,Y_2	—	—	780
3d	3.23	β–Si_3N_4, Y_1,Y_2	—	—	760

$Y_1 = Y_2Si_2O_7$, $Y_2 = Y_{20}N_4Si_{12}O_{48}$

Figure 4 shows microstructures of the samples obtained by the three different fabrication routes 1–3. The microstructure of the material hot–pressed along route 1 is characterized by small globular grains and large elongated grains (Fig. 4a). The process route 2 resulted in a more uniform microstructure consisting of elongted β grains (Fig. 4b), whereas route 3 is indicative of some growth of the elongated β grains (Fig. 4c).

Table 1 is a compilation of microstructural parameters and strength values of the three materials. It contains the crystalline phases found in material 3, as well as the results of the quantitative evaluation of the grain size. Lognormal distributions were found for the three different microstructures of Fig. 4, with d_{50} the grain size at the maximum of the distribution curve and $\sigma = d_{84}/d_{50}$ the width of the distribution. The table shows that the width of the grain size distribution of material 2 is considerably smaller than that of the other two materials. Thiis fact may be due to the higher nucleation rate of the β phase at the smaller transformation temperature of only 1690°C, compared to 1850°C of the routes 1 and 3, respectively.

The room temperature strength values of Table 1 demonstrate that a strength increase was obtained by the two "unconventional" routes 2 and 3 as compared to normal hot–pressing along route 1. This increase is more pronounced for the process of post–densification heat treatment than for that of the pre–densification phase transformation.

CONCLUSIONS

1. By employing a pre–densification heat treatment (route 2), the $\alpha \rightarrow \beta$ phase transformation of silicon nitride can be completed prior to compaction.

The HPSN material obtained by this fabrication route is characterized by a narrow size distribution of elongated β grains and by some increase in strength.

2. A post–densification heat treatment performed "in–situ" (route 3) causes several crystalline phases to form from the intragranular amorphous phase. The grain size distribution remains essentially unchanged, whereas a distinct increase in strength is observed.

3. Optimum hot–pressing conditions are to be expected by combining pre–transformation and in–situ crystallization, i.e. by employing routes 2 and 3 together.

ACKNOWLEDGEMENT

This work was supported by Stiftung Volkswagenwerk

REFERENCES

1. Ziegler, G., Heinrich, J. and Wötting, G., Relationship between processing, microstructure and properties of dense and reaction–bonded silicon nitride. J.Mat.Sci., 1987, **21**, 3041–87.

2. Knoch, H. and Ziegler, G., Einfluß von Pulverzusammensetzung auf Umwandlungskinetik, Gefüge und mechanische Eigenschaften von heißgepreßtem Siliciumnitrid. Ber. Dt.Keram.Ges., 1978, **60**, 242–45.

3. Himsolt, G., Knoch, H., and Hübner, H., Mechanical properties of hot–pressed silicon nitride with different grain structures. J.Am.Ceram.Soc., 1979, **62**, 29–32.

4. Wötting, G., Kanka, B., and Ziegler, G., Microstructural development, microstructural characterization and relation to mechanical properties of dense silicon nitride. In Non–oxide technical and engineering ceramics, ed. S. Hampshire, Elsevier Applied Science Publishers, London, 1983, pp. 83–94

5. Knickerbrocker, S., Zangvil, A., and Brown, S.D., High–temperature mechanical properties and microstructures for hot–pressed silicon nitrides with amorphous and crystalline intergranular phases. J.Am.Ceram.Soc., 1985, **68**, C–99–101.

6. Knoch, H. and Gazza, G.E., On the α to β–phase transformation and grain growth during hot–pressing of Si_3N_4 containing MgO, Ceramurgia International, 1980, **6**, 51–56.

7. Gauckler, L.J., Hohnke, H., and Tien, T.Y., The system Si_3N_4–SiO_2–Y_2O_3, J.Am.Ceram.Soc., 1980, **63**, 35–37.

8. Wills, R.R., Holmquist, S., Wimmer, J.M., and Cunningham, J.A., Phase relationships in the system Si_3N_4–Y_2O_3–SiO_2, J.Mat.Sci., 1976, **11**, 1305–9.

CREEP BEHAVIOUR OF Si_3N_4 WITH TiN PARTICLES

J.CRAMPON*,R.DUCLOS* and P.VIVIER+
*Université de Lille 1,La 234 ,Bat C6,
59655 Villeneuve d'Ascq Cedex, France.
+C.T.Desmarquest , 2 av .A.Einstein,78190 Trappes, France.

ABSTRACT

The compression creep behaviour of Silicon Nitride sintered with the aid of Y_2O_3 and Al_2O_3. and containing TiN particles was studied between 1260 and 1340°C at stress ranging from 100 to 300 MPa. The volume fraction Φ of TiN particles was varied from 0 to about 40 vol % and two particle sizes :1µm and 2.5µm were studied.The dominant creep mechanism of the matrix was viscous creep ($n \approx 1$) up to 1340°C and 200 MPa. The effect of the TiN addition on the creep behaviour was marked by a decrease of the creep strength with increa-sing volume fraction and decreasing particle size of TiN. In the same way the steady state creep rate increased as the ratio Φ/d.

INTRODUCTION

Additives containing Si_3N_4 has led to increasing attention being devoted to it because it is recognized as a prime candidate for certain structural applications. The primary method of producing fully dense Si_3N_4 ceramics is conventional hot-pressing (HPSN),but this method don't allow to obtain complex shapes. Fully dense Si_3N_4 can now be fabricated via pressureless sintering of ultra-fine powders using suitable oxide additions (SSN). Since it was expected that nitride additives can prevent the formation of glassy grain- boundary phases, causing the degradation of mechanical properties at elevated temperature, AlN,YN and TiN have been added in isostatic hot-pressed silicon nitride [1]. Indeed, the addition of AlN and YN was effective for densifying the Si_3N_4 but in fact, due to the presence of a small amount of oxygen in the starting powder, it was believed that densification was promoted by liquid phase sintering mechanism as with oxide additions. TiN additives were not so effective for densification, but nevertheless the result was encouraging. Since TiN additives are conducting particles, their incorporation in SSN could now be envisaged to allow the fabrication of dense intricate components via electro-erosion method.

The thermal expansion mismatch between TiN particles and Si_3N_4 matrix will produce a compression stress in the matrix during cooling after the composite is sintered at high temperature. The alteration of Si_3N_4 through TiN dispersoid additions may then offer a potential for improvement of the composite's strength at room temperature but the effects at elevated temperature may be adverse. The determination of the high temperature deformation behaviour of these composites is then a necessary stage before their use in engineering applications.

A limited number of creep studies have been performed on particles or high strength whiskers containing Si_3N_4. In the case of SiC particles, early studies suggested that SiC additions result in improved creep resistance [2-3], but in contrast more recent work has indicated that the presence of a dispersion of SiC particles could detrimentally affect the creep behaviour of HPSN [4].

The present work was then undertaken to consider the influence of dispersion of TiN particles on the creep strength of pressureless sintered Si_3N_4

EXPERIMENTAL PROCEDURE

The Y_2O_3/Al_2O_3-doped Si_3N_4 composites with TiN additives were supplied by the C.T.Desmarquest.Lab(KERSIT 601). Billets were prepared from commercial silicon nitride powder to which high purity Y_2O_3 and Al_2O_3 and the desired amount (0,30,40 wt%) of TiN particles(1μm and 2.5μm in diameter) were added. Pressureless-sintering following cold-pressing was then performed.

Samples were observed by T.E.M throughout this study. Thin foils for T.E.M observations were taken from crept and from only heated samples..

Specimens ($3x3x7mm^3$) were used for compressional creep experiments performed in air between 1260 and1340°C,using constant load machine. Stresses ranging from 100 to 300 MPa were applied to the sample by Si_3N_4 rods and SiC discs to prevent from indentation.

RESULTS AND DISCUSSION

The compression creep properties of typical compositions of the composites are presented in Fig 1a. All the materials showed normal transient and secondary creep curves. At the lowest stresses and temperatures the deformation remain in the quasy steady-state for all the compositions, but a final tertiary period with an acceleration of the creep strain was only observed at the highest temperatures and stresses.

In all cases,the dependence of the secondary creep rate,$\dot{\epsilon}_s$,on stress,σ,could be described by the equation : $\dot{\epsilon}_s=A\sigma^n$.

The stress exponent,n, was determined by making stress changes during secondary creep and was found to be of the order of 1 for stress-jumps 100-150-200 MPa, while it increased up to about 1.8 for stress jumps 200-250-300 MPa.

The influence of TiN additions on the secondary creep rates of the composites was then studied at 200MPa,the limit stress for which the secondary creep exhibited nearly viscous creep ($\dot{\epsilon}_s=A\sigma^n$; $n<1.5$).

It was established that a dispersion of TiN particles could detrimentally affect the creep behaviour of SSN. Additions of TiN of the finest particle diameter caused the highest

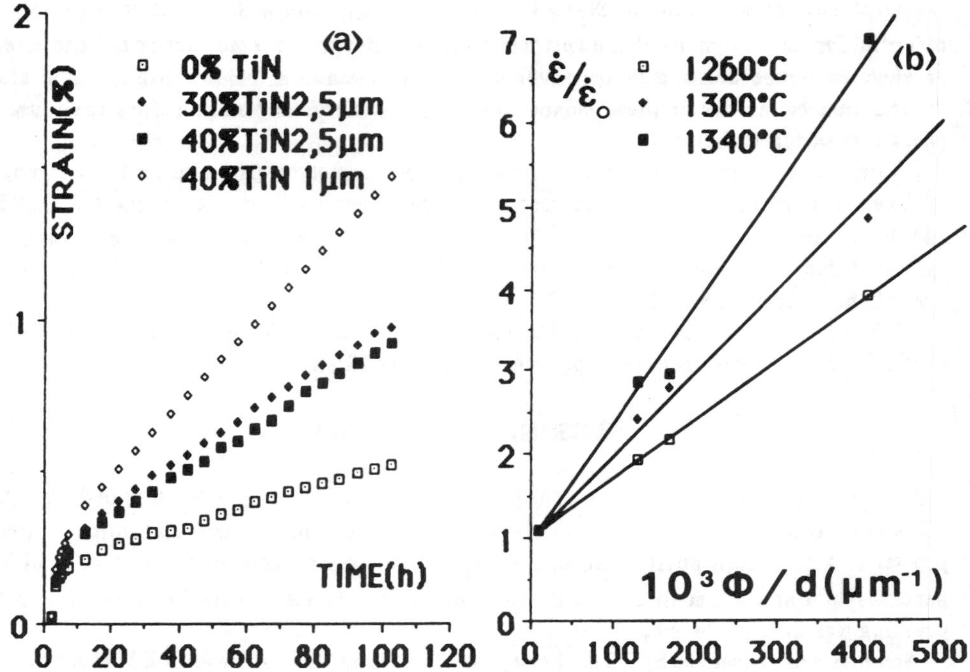

Fig1.Creep curves at 200MPa and 1260°C(a) and $\dot{\varepsilon}/\dot{\varepsilon}_0$ versus Φ/d (b)

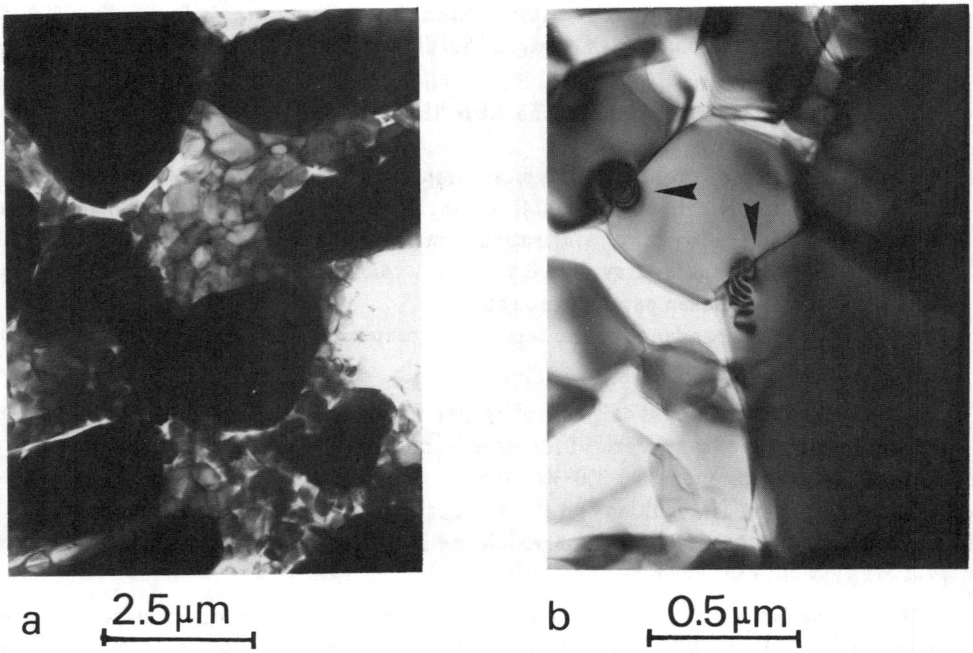

Fig 2. TEM micrographs of a sample containing 40% TiN-2.5 µm deformed at 1300°C.

increase in creep rate and the shortest creep strain at the onset of the tertiary creep. The effect of the amount of nitride added particles was also to increase the creep rate and to decrease the creep strength by increasing volume fraction of nitride.

The results for all combinations of mean particle size and volume fraction can be correlated by plotting the observed secondary creep rate as a function of the ratio of the volume fraction (ϕ) to the particle size (d). Then over the tested range, the creep rate appears to follow an empirical law of the form: $\dot{\varepsilon}_s = \dot{\varepsilon}_{so}(1+\phi\Delta/d)$ where $\dot{\varepsilon}_{so}$ was the creep rate of the matrix (Fig1b).

It must be recognized that the effect of the TiN additions on the creep rate was dependent upon the temperature, the maximum increase in creep rate observed being about 7 at 1340°C. Yet, the effect of addition was rather marked on the creep ductility,the strain at the onset of the tertiary creep being about half of the value obtained for pure SSN.

In the transmission electron microscope the starting material generally appears perfectly dense and in the case of TiN addition the particles are homogeneously distributed. The microstructure of the matrix was rather inhomogeneous varying from about 250 nm to 1µm in grain size. In most of the triple point junctions an intergranular amorphous phase could be detected. Generally the starting material was dislocation free. Addition of TiN particles does not change the general morphology of the sample. The particles are perfectly embedded in the matrix and interfacial amorphous phase could be detected in the TiN/Si_3N_4 boundaries.

From the mechanical view-point, a common microstructural feature was present in all load-cooled samples after deformation:numerous strain whorls where located only along grain-boundaries of the Si_3N_4 matrix and they where manifestations of viscous grain-boundary sliding accommodated by elastic strain.

Samples which were deformed in the tertiary regime showed particle matrix interfaces separated by large voids. In the extrem case,extended microcracks appear and they lie along matrix particle interfaces parallel to the compression axis(Fig2a). Before the rupture,these cavities propagate along the Si_3N_4 grain-boundaries. In this later case numerous viscoelastic whorls were associated with dislocations activity due to the high elastic local stress field at such grain-boundaries which were not yet separated(Fig2b).

The effect of TiN additions on the deformation characteristics of SSN can be considered on the basis that the creep rate of the marix is determined primarly by solution-diffusion-precipitation accommodated grain-boundary sliding. By incorporating the TiN particles the interface boundary sliding cannot be longer accommodated by such material transport to preserve the integrity of the material since cavities in the deformed samples were observed to extend firstly into the interface boundaries.

Under compression creep conditions, cavities form preferentially on boundaries parallel to the compression axis ,i.e on boundaries across which tensile stresses were developed. Due to the thermal expansion mismatch between TiN particles and Si_3N_4 matrix the particle matrix interfaces were in tension after sintering and cooling, and they were then the primary sites of cavity nucleation and propagation.

In these conditions the steady state creep rate of the composite material, under an applied stress σ_0 , can be regarded as the sum of two components :

(i) $\dot{\varepsilon}_{so}=B\sigma_0$ being related to the viscous creep accommodation of the matrix [5].

(ii) $\dot{e}_c = C\sigma_o^n$, ($n \geq 2$) being related to cavitational creep accommodation [6] of the particles.

The ease of formation of extended cavities along the boundaries of TiN particles was shown in Fig (2a). The incorporation of largest volume fraction and finest particle sizes would intoduce TiN/Si_3N_4 boudary facets along which numerous cavities can develop affecting both the creep rate and the creep ductility. The observed dependence of the creep rate on the ratio (ϕ/d) (Fig 1b) can then be accounted for in terms of this quantity providing a measure of the area fraction S of nitride additions along which cavitational creep occurs.

The area fraction S is related to the ratiio (ϕ/d) by: $S = \phi\delta/d$ with $\delta = [\phi/d + (1-\phi)/d_{SN}]^{-1}$ and where d_{SN} is the Si_3N_4 grain size.

In the composite the resulting creep rate e_s can then be roughly written as the sum :

$$\dot{e}_s = (1-S)\dot{e}_{so} + S\dot{e}_c$$

$$\dot{e}_s = \dot{e}_{so}[1 + S(C\sigma_o^{n-1}/B - 1)]$$

The proposed deformation process is in agreement with all our microscopy observations. It described the steady state creep rate of TiN/Si_3N_4 composites with a relatively complex dependence on the ratio (ϕ/d) ,but the trend is an increase of the crep rate with the ratio (ϕ/d) as observed.

CONCLUSION

As in the case of the incorporation of SiC particles into samples of HPSN [4] the addition of TiN particles in SSN did not result in improved creep properties .Indeed TiN particles resulted in slightly increased creep rates and significantly decreased creep ductilities.

In the matrix the creep rate appeared to be predominantly determined by diffusionally accommodated grain boundary sliding,but in the composite material cavitational creep became more important.specially at the TiN/SSN interfaces rather than in the surrounding material.

ACKNOWLEDGEMENTS

The authors wish to thank the French Research and Tecnology Ministry for the financial support of this work(Contract 86 D 0219).

REFERENCES

1. Uchida,N., Koizumi,M. and Shimada,M., J.Am.Ceram.Soc.,1985, 68, **2**, C 38-40.
2. Parr,N.L., Martin,G.F. and May,E.R.W., in Special Ceramics, Vol 1, Brit. Ceram. Res.Assoc, Stoke-en-Trent,1960, p 102 .
3. Parr,N.L. and Martin,G.F.,in Special Ceramics, Vol 1, Brit.Ceram.Res.Assoc, Stoke-en-Trent, 1960, p 76 .
4. Birch,J.M. and Wilshire,B.,J.Mat.Sci. ,1978,**13**,2627-2636.
5. Rakotoharisoa,N.S., Ing.Doct.Thesis.,U.S.T.L.F.A.,Lille,November 1988.
6. Evans.A.G. and Rana.A., J.Mat.Sci., 1980, **28**, 129-14

CREEP CAVITY FORMATION IN PURE AND VITREOUS–BONDED ALUMINA

JOACHIM STARK, HEINZ HÜBNER
Arbeitsbereich Werkstoffphysik,
Technische Universität Hamburg–Harburg
P.O.Box 901403, D–2100 Hamburg 90, FRG

ABSTRACT

The effect of stress and strain on creep cavity formation was studied in two different types of alumina, a vitreous bonded material and an essentially pure material, by measuring the density changes induced by creep deformation in bending. For both materials it was found that the creep porosity increased linearly with creep strain. Thus, a creep cavitation sensitivity ω (relative density change per unit strain) could be defined which differed markedly for the two aluminas at same stress levels. The ω value of the vitreous bonded material was about 20 times that of the pure material, demonstrating the proneness of the glass phase to creep damage formation. Pore size measurements obtained by small–angle neutron scattering and by electron microscopic observations showed that the creep cavitation process in pure alumina was dominated by the growth of pores, whereas in vitreous bonded alumina it was controlled by the continuous nucleation of new pores.

INTRODUCTION

Nucleation and growth of creep cavities are the early stages in the failure sequence of creep damage evolution in structural ceramics. A series of models have been presented in the literature to describe the mechanisms of creep cavity formation both in single phase ceramics having "pure", clean grain boundaries [1,2] and in liquid phase sintered ceramics containing a continuous amorphous grain boundary phase [3,4,5].

This paper reports on the results of a study [6] which aimed to establish the influence of an intragranular glass phase on the kinetics of creep damage formation. For that, the effect of creep strain, stress and time on the formation of creep pores in a pure and a vitreous–bonded alumina was studied.

MATERIALS AND METHODS

The vitreous bonded alumina was a commercial material (V38, Feldmühle AG, Plochingen, FRG) containing about 8 vol.% of a silicate phase. The mean grain size was 5 µm and the porosity less than 1 %. The pure alumina was made of a commercial alumina powder containing 0,1 % MgO. (CT 8000 SG, Alcoa Chemie GmbH, Ludwigshafen, FRG) by cold pressing and sintering in air. The mean grain size was 3,3 µm and the porosity 1,8 %. Neither in TEM studies nor in SEM observations an amorphous phase was found in this material.

Creep experiments were carried out under four-point bending in a constant-load creep machine in air. Three techniques were used to detect the creep-induced cavity formation, i.e. density measurements, small-angle neutron scattering (SANS) and transmission electron microscopy. The samples used for the SANS measurements were deformed in compression.

The relative density change induced by the creep deformation, $\Delta\rho/\rho$, was obtained from the expression $\Delta\rho/\rho = (\rho_c - \rho_o)/\rho_o$, where ρ_c is the density of the material deformed by creep and ρ_o is the density of the undeformed material. Both ρ_c and ρ_o were measured on the same bend specimen by cutting it into three sections, i.e. the section between the inner span (which gave ρ_c) and the two remaining outer sections (which gave ρ_o). Thus, the value of $\Delta\rho/\rho$ measured in this way was independent of the density variations occurring from sample to sample and also of those induced by the thermal treatment only [6].

RESULTS AND DISCUSSION

Fig. 1 shows relative density changes obtained for the vitreous-bonded material at 1170°C and at various stress levels as a function of creep strain. The creep porosity increases linearly with strain. Obviously, there is no threshold strain necessary for the beginning of creep pore formation. According to Fig. 1, increasing stress leads to increasing pore formation. This is demonstrated in Fig. 2 which is a cross-cut of Fig. 1 at strains of 0.1, 0.2 and

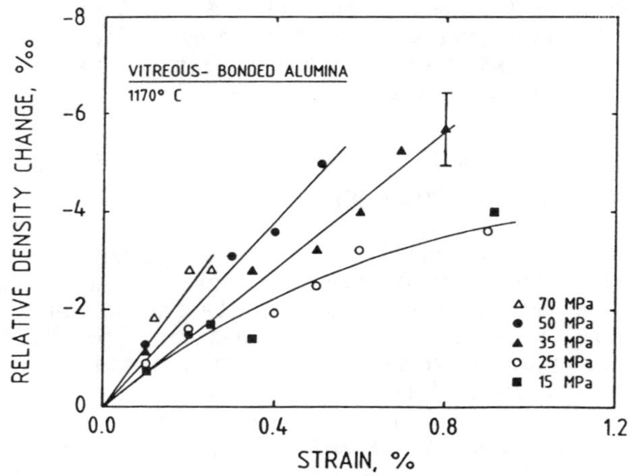

Figure 1: Relative density change versus strain in vitreous-bonded alumina

0.4 %, respectively. There is a linear dependence of the relative density change on the stress, as indicated by the slope of the straight lines of Fig. 2.

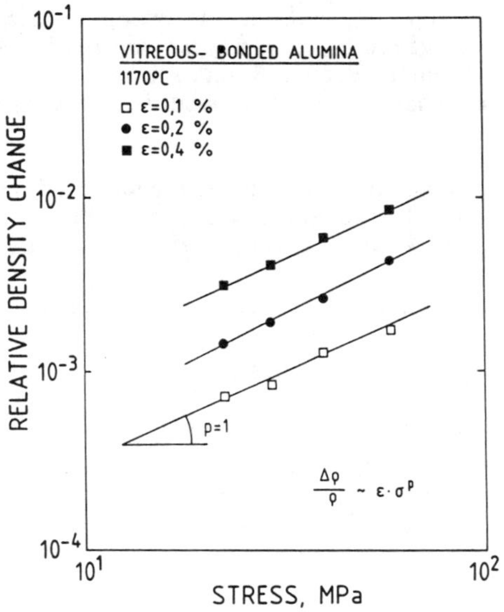

Figure 2: Relative density change versus stress in vitreous–bonded alumina

Density changes obtained for pure alumina at 1350°C are shown in Fig. 3. The temperature of 1350°C was chosen in order to obtain, at same stress levels, a creep rate of the same order of magnitude as that of the vitreous–bonded material at 1170°C. Again, a linear variation of the creep porosity with strain

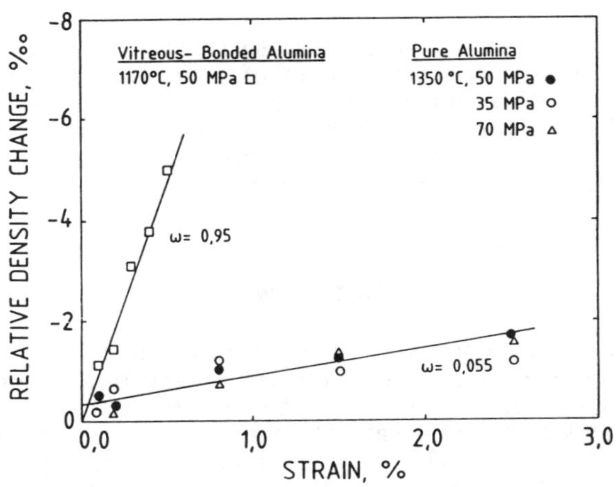

Figure 3: Comparison of creep cavitation sensitivity of pure and vitreous bonded–alumina

was found. However, no effect of stress on the pore volume could be detected in this case. Figure 3 also contains the density variation of the vitreous–bonded material at a stress of 50 MPa for comparison. The slope of the straight lines of Fig. 3 is a measure of the proneness of the material to creep cavity formation. Hence, this slope was called the creep cavitation sensitivity of the material, ω, which is given by $\omega = \Delta P/\Delta \epsilon$ where P is the creep porosity formed due to a deformation ϵ. Figure 3 shows that ω of the vitreous–bonded alumina is about 20 times that of the pure material at same values of stress and creep rate.

To get information about the size and number of the creep pores SANS experiments were carried out on crept samples of vitreous bonded alumina. The results are plotted in Fig. 4. Up to a strain of 0.9 % the mean pore radius

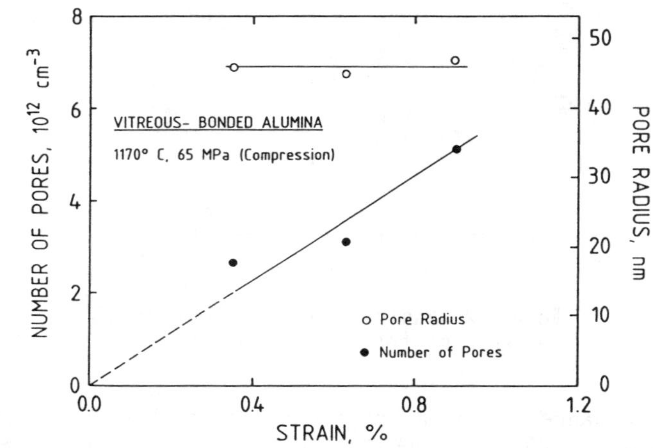

Figure 4: Mean pore radius and number of pores obtained by SANS for vitreous–bonded alumina

remained constant whereas a linear increase of the cavity number was found. This finding, together with the results of pore size measurements by TEM, suggests that the creep porosity of the vitreous–bonded material increases by the nucleation of new pores rather than by the growth of existing pores. In pure alumina, on the other hand, the growth of pre–existing triple–point cavities seems to be the controlling mechanism of creep damage evolution.

CONCLUSIONS

A linear increase of creep porosity with strain was found in pure and vitreous bonded alumina. In both materials no minimum strain is necessary for the formation of creep cavities. In the glass–bonded ceramic a linear increase of cavity volume with stress was found. At same levels of stress and creep rate, the creep cavitation sensitivity of the vitreous–bonded ceramic exceeds that of the pure alumina by a factor of 20, thus demonstrating the deleterious effect of the amorphous grain–boundary phase on the mechanical performance under creep conditions. SANS experiments and microscopic observations indicate that the increase of creep porosity with strain is caused by the nucleation of new pores in vitreous bonded alumina and by the growth of preexisting pores in pure alumina.

ACKNOWLEDGEMENTS

Thanks are due to GKSS for performing the SANS experiments. Financial support of the Deutsche Forschungsgemeinschaft is gratefully acknowledged.

REFERENCES

1. Evans, A.G. and Rana, A., High temperature failure mechanisms in ceramics. Acta Met., 1980, **28**, 129–141.

2. Page, R.A., Lankford, J., Spooner, S., Small–angle neutron scattering study of creep cavity nucleation and growth in sintered alumina. J.Mater.Sci., 1984, **19** (10) 3360–3374.

3. Marion, J.E., Evans, A.G., Drory, M.D., Clarke, D.R., High temperature failure initiation in liquid phase sintered materials. Acta Met., 1983, **31** (10) 1445–1457.

4. Clarke, D.R., High–temperature deformation of a polycrystalline alumina containing an intergranular glass phase. J.Mater.Sci., 1985, **20** (4) 1321–1332.

5. Page, R.A., Lankford, J., Chan, K.S., Hardman–Rhyne, K., Spooner, S., Creep cavitation in liquid–phase–sintered alumina. J.Am.Ceram.Soc., 1987, **70** (3), 137–145.

6. Stark, J., Deformation behaviour and creep pore formation in pure and vitreous–bonded alumina (in German). Ph.D. Thesis, Technische Universität Hamburg–Harburg, September 1988.

CYCLIC FATIGUE OF SILICON NITRIDE

A.-P. NIKKILÄ, T.A. MÄNTYLÄ
Tampere University of Technology
Institute of Materials Science
P.O. Box 527, 33101 Tampere, Finland

ABSTRACT

Cyclic fatigue properties of silicon nitride were studied. To avoid the difficulties of fatigue test of brittle ceramics in pull-push test, a special 4-point bending jig was constructed. The test were made at room temperature. Effects of different loading types were studied using three different fatigue test modes: 1) sinusoidal R= -1 (tension - compression), 2) sinusoidal R= 0 (tension) and 3) positive half sinusoidal R= 0 (tension); negative part of the loading cycle is cut off. Theoretical crack propagation differences of three fatigue modes were calculated and compared to measured values. Results will be presented ans discussed.

INTRODUCTION

So far the data of fatigue for advanced ceramic materials has been scarce. More information is also needed of the mechanisms by which different fatigue loading modes affect the fatigue behaviour. The slow crack propagation during loading causes the fatigue behaviour in ceramics. The fatigue behaviour can be tested by static, dynamic and cyclic loading. Each loading type gives different results. Also different kind of stresses or their combinations effect on fatigue. The role of compression stresses during loading cycle of fatigue is also poorly understood. The development of commercial advanced ceramics has resulted more homogeneous materials, which makes fatigue testing more reasonable since the effects are not so easily masked by the large scatter in mechanical properties of earlier engineering ceramics. In this work we studied the effects of loading modes to the fatigue behaviour of silicon nitrides and to the life prediction parameters, which can be obtained from these test.

EXPERIMENTAL PROCEDURES

Three different commercial silicon nitride were used in this study. They are denoted in this presentation by A, B and C. A and B were sintered silicon nitrides and C was hot-pressed. The materials were obtained as unfinished plates (5 · 100· 100mm). The specimens for mechanical testing were prepared from these plates by cutting, grinding and polishing. The specimens in strength and fatigue tests were rectangular bars and their size was 3·4·40mm.

Strength of each material was measured by four-point bending. The loading span was 10 mm and the support span 30 mm. Crosshead speed was 0.5 mm/min. Strength measurements were done at room temperature. The number of specimens for each material was 15.

RESULTS AND DISCUSSION

The distribution of measured strength values was guite narrow for material A and C. Material B had higher scatter in strength. Low scatter in strength values was desirable to find out fatigue phenomena in these materials.

Material C (hot-pressed) had the highest bend strength and it had also the best resistance against fatigue. Material B had the lowest Weibull modulus in bend tests. It had also in fatigue tests the highest scatter in measured fatigue strength values. Material A had higher bend strength than material B, but its resistance against fatigue loading was lower than the resistance of material B.

The fatigue resistance of these materials can be estimated by calculating the subcritical crack extension parameter n. The higher the n value is, the better is the fatigue resistance. This parameter is the exponent of stress intensity, K_I, in the crack growth rate equation:

$$da/dt= A \cdot K_I^n, \qquad (1)$$

where n = subcritical crack extension parameter
K_I= stress intensity
A = constant

By using n parameter the relation between fatigue strength and the number of fatigue cycles can be written to the following form:

$$\sigma^n \cdot N= \text{constant}, \qquad (2)$$

where σ = fatigue strength
N= number of fatigue cycles

The values for n parameter can be determined from experimental results presented in log-log-plot . Following n parameters can be obtained for the test materials: material A n=31, material B n=41, material C n=43. Fatigue resistance can be increased by decreasing the amount of sintering additives. By choosing suitable sintering additives it is possible to increase to fatigue resistance of silicon nitride.

Fatigue tests were interrupted after 10^6-10^7 cycles. In Fig. 1 there are two specimens, marked with filled circle and arrow, which didn't fracture during fatigue tests of 444 N/mm^2 / 4265000 cycles and 455 N/mm^2 / 2104500 cycles. The bend strength of these specimens was measured after fatigue test. The strength values obtained were same within measurement accuracy as the bend strength of the specimens before fatigue. This indicate that at this stress level the growth rate of flaws in these materials has been very slow. Our results indicate that at fatigue stress level lower than 2/3 of the average bend strength the growth of flaws is negligible and long fatigue lifes can be expected.

The effects of different loading modes on fatigue behaviour of material A is compared in Fig. 1. The highest fatigue strength values were obtained by using loading mode 3, positive cut sinusoidal. The lowest values were obtained by cyclic tension compression mode. These results clearly show that compressive stresses during fatigue also decrease the fatigue life. This means, that crack propagation can also happen during compression stresses. This is in contradiction to the opinions presented in literature, which claim that compression stresses have no effect on fatigue behaviour.

Theoretically it can be calculated that in positive cut sinusoidal fatigue mode the fracture time should be 1.4 times higher than in positive sinusoidal mode. Our experimental results are in agreement with this.

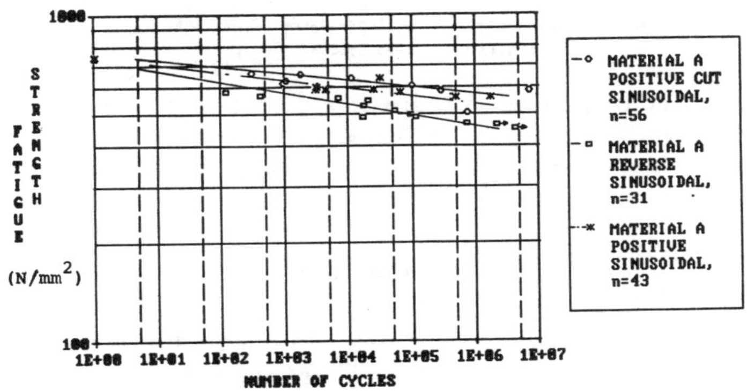

Figure 1. Effect of different fatigue modes. Presented in log-log-plot.

The scattering of fatigue lives were very small during fatigue test. Fracture origins in these silicon nitrides were normally spherical pores or cavities. If we combine the Griffith equation with equation number 1, we get the relation between crack size and crack propagation rate. According this the crack propagation is very stronly depended on crack size. When parameter n is 30, then crack propagation rate is equal to crack size raise to the power 15. If previously mentioned is true for silicon nitride materials the scattering of the measuring points would be very large. In figure 2 there are show the measuring points and calculated strength distributions at certain fatigue life level with and without crack size effect on crack propagation rate.

According to figure 2 the crack sizes have little effect on crack propagation rate in silicon nitrides. This is due to spherical fracture origins in tested silicon nitrides.

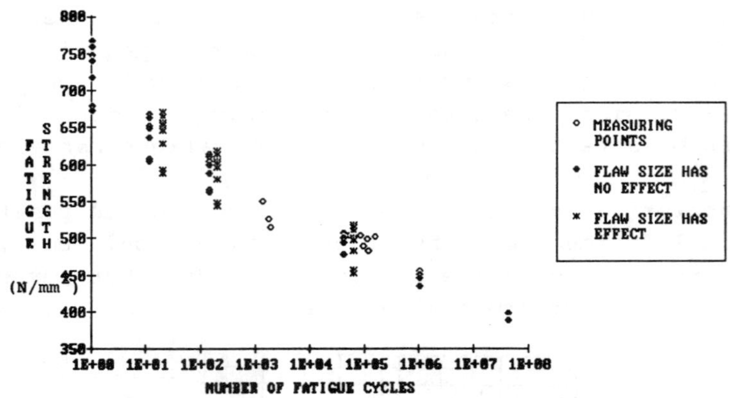

Figure 2. Comparison of measuring points to calculated points with effect of flaw size on crack propagation rate and without.

CONCLUSIONS

The fatigue resistance of the studied hot-pressed silicon nitride was higher than the resistance of studied sintered silicon nitrides due to lower amount of glassy phases at the grain boundaries. Also by choosing right sintering additives the fatigue resistance can be improvered.

If fatigue stress level is lower than 2/3 of the average bend strength, the crack growth in materials is negligible and very long fatigue lifes can be expected. The values obtained for subcritical crack extension parameter n from cyclic tension compression tests were between 31 and 43 for the materials studied. The n values obtained from other fatigue loading modes for silicon nitrides weré higher and are too optimistic, if they are used to predict fatigue behaviour under cyclic tension compression fatigue.

The theoretical calculations of difference between fatigue lifes for positive loading modes give very reliable results according to practical measurements.

Crack propagation rate in silicon nitrides doesn't depend remarkably on flaw size. The fracture strength distribution decreased during fatigue.

INVESTIGATION OF THE THERMAL FATIGUE BEHAVIOUR OF HPSN,SIC AND GLASS

K. Keller, D. Munz
Institut für Keramik im Maschinenbau
Universität Karlsruhe
Postfach 6980, 75 Karlsruhe 1, F.R.G
T.Fett
Institut für Material und Festkörperforschung IV
Kernforschungszentrum Karlsruhe
Postfach 3640, 75 Karlsruhe 1, F.R.G

ABSTRACT

A test procedure allowing the thermal fatigue behaviour of SiC, HPSN, and glass to be investigated in different quenching media is described. For HPSN and SiC the thermal fatigue damage was determined indirectly by measurement of the remaining bending strength. The glass specimens were pre-cracked with a Knoop indenter, and the crack growth was measured directly on the fracture surface. To predict the remaining strength, the cyclic crack extension was calculated in the following steps: analytical temperature distribution, transient stress distribution, calculation of the time-dependent stress intensity factor applying the method of weight function, crack-growth evaluation from the subcritical crack-growth parameters, which have been determined in dynamic bending tests as well as in lifetime tests.

INTRODUCTION

The application of ceramic materials at high temperatures requires knowlewdge of the material behaviour under real conditions. Ceramic components are often subjected to thermal cyclic loading. Due to temperature gradients, which cause thermal stresses, crack growth can occur, which leads to a decrease of the remaining strength. To allow lifetime predictions to be made under these conditions it is necessary to know the temperature- , stress distribution and time-dependent K-values during one cycle.

At high temperatures oxidation often occurs. The surface may be damaged by this oxidation. This leads also to a decrease of the bending strength. Lifetime predictions are then very complicated.

Experimental results of the thermal fatigue behaviour of HPSN, SiC and glass in different quenching media will be represented in this paper. The results will be compared with theoretical crack-growth calculations.

MATERIALS

In this study three materials were investigated.

- Material I: sintered α-silicon carbide (SSIC), boron doped
- Material II: hot-pressed silicon nitride (HPSN), containing 5.5 weight-% Y_2O_3
- Material III: borosilicate glass

The investigation was performed with bending bars 3.5x4.5x45mm (HPSN,SiC) and 4x5x50mm (glass) in size. Additionally, the glass specimens were Knoop-damaged.

For crack-growth calculations it is necessary to know the subcritical crack-growth behaviour of the materials. Often, the subcritical crack-growth rate v can be expressed by a power law.

$$v = \frac{da}{dt} = AK^n \tag{1}$$

A and n are the subcritical crack-growth parameters. The crack-growth parameters of HPSN and SiC had been determined in dynamic bending tests. The n-values for HPSN were 30 (1200°C) and 37 (1100°C). For SiC n-values of 24 (1350°C) and 35 (1200°C) were found. The subcritical crack-growth of glass was evaluated from lifetime measurements [1].

THERMAL FATIGUE EXPERIMENT

Two test devices for high and low temperature were available. In the first the thermal fatigue behaviour of HPSN and SiC was investigated. In the second device, the glass specimens were tested in water.

Test procedure

In a high-temperature furnace a series of eight specimens (HPSN,SiC) were heated up to 1250°C. After 20 minutes, a time span chosen to guarantee a homogeneous temperature distribution in the specimens, the samples were transferred into the quenching medium. The quenching media investigated were compressed air, a fluidized bed and a water-air jet.

After a cooling time of 10-60 s (dependent on the quenching medium), the specimens were retransferred into the furnace and one cycle was finished. After n cycles the room-temperature bending strengths of the samples were measured.

The glass specimens were heated in hot water (96°C) and quenched in cold water (4°C). After n-cycles the samples were broken in a 4-point bending-test device. Due to the Knoop-indentation, the crack growth could be measured on the fracture surface.

Results

SiC and HPSN: SiC showed no decrease of the bending strength in any quenching medium used.

After cooling in the water-air jet a reduction of the bending strength of HPSN could be measured (figure 1).

The question arose, whether the reason of this effect was subcritical crack-growth or if oxidation influenced this result.

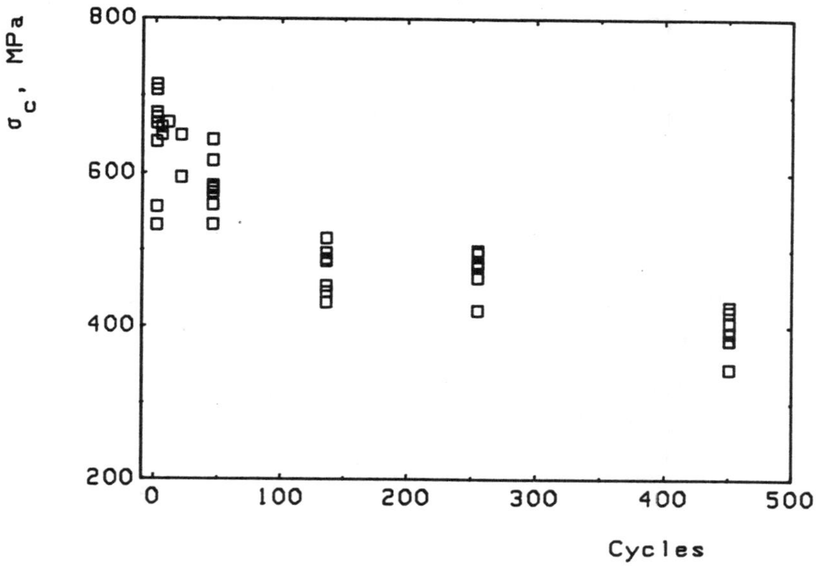

Figure 1. Bending strength of HPSN after quenching in the water-air jet

Therefore,a pure oxidation test with HPSN specimens in a water-vapour atmosphere at 1250°C was carried out. After 13 hours the bending strength at room-temperature was measured. It was ascertained that there was a reduction of the bending strength of nearly 200 MPa.

After the high temperature tests the fracture surfaces of the cycled and the oxidized specimens were examined. Pores and a melted layer on the surface were detected. The evaluation of the cycled samples yielded that the quantity and the size of the pores were increasing with increasing number of cycles. An element analysis of all fracture surfaces showed that yttrium-silicates and silicon-oxides had been formed.

From these results it can be concluded that the reason of the decrease of the bending strength was oxidation.

Glass: In figure 2 the crack-growth versus the number of cycles is plotted for two specimens. It can be recognized that the cracks grow more in width (c) than in depth (a).

THEORETICAL INVESTIGATIONS

To calculate the amount of crack-growth, the temperature- and stress distributions and the stress-intensity factor K for a thermal cycle have to be known. In [2] two analytical solutions were derived for the temperature and stress calculations.

Based on [3], two solutions for calculating local and weighted averaged stress-intensity factors were applied. With these solutions it is possible to calculate the K-factor

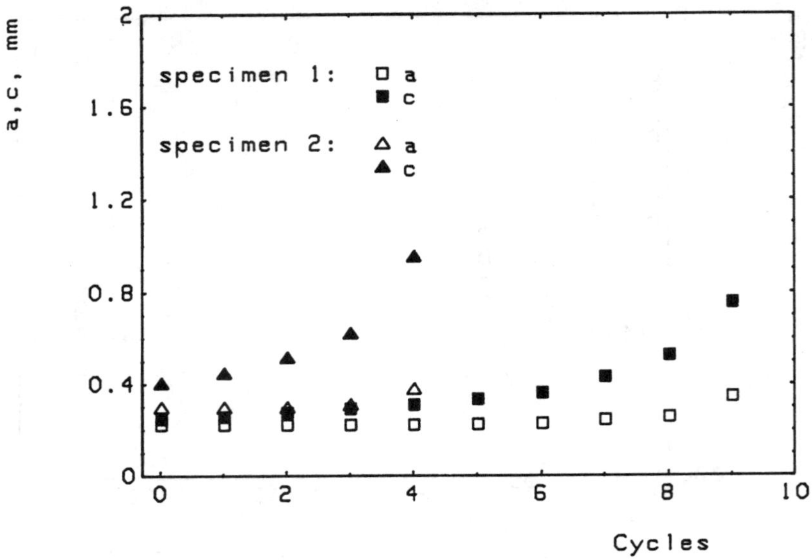

Figure 2. Crack-growth in width and depth for two glass specimens

$$K = \sigma \sqrt{a}\ Y \tag{2}$$

at the surface and at the deepest point of a semi-elliptical surface crack with arbitrary gradients. σ is a characteristic stress, a is the crack depth and Y is the geometric factor.

Crack-growth calculations

Integration of equation (1) over one cycle yields the crack-growth in width (c) and depth (a). After n cycles the remaining bending strength can be calculated from

$$\sigma_{Bn} = \frac{K_{Ic}}{\sqrt{a_n}\ Y} \tag{3}$$

with the fracture toughness K_{Ic} and the geometric factor Y from Newman-Raju [4] for bending.

Results

SiC and HPSN: The calculated crack-growth for SiC and HPSN was $< 10^{-10}$ mm/cycle. One reason for this were the low thermal stresses in compressed air and in the fluidized bed. Though the stresses in the water-air jet were somewhat higher, also here no crack growth worth mentioning is possible. The second reason is the effect of the decreasing subcritical crack growth with decreasing temperature.

Glass: In figure 3 the crack propagation is plotted; t is the thickness of the specimen. The comparison of the calculated with the experimental data shows a good agreement.

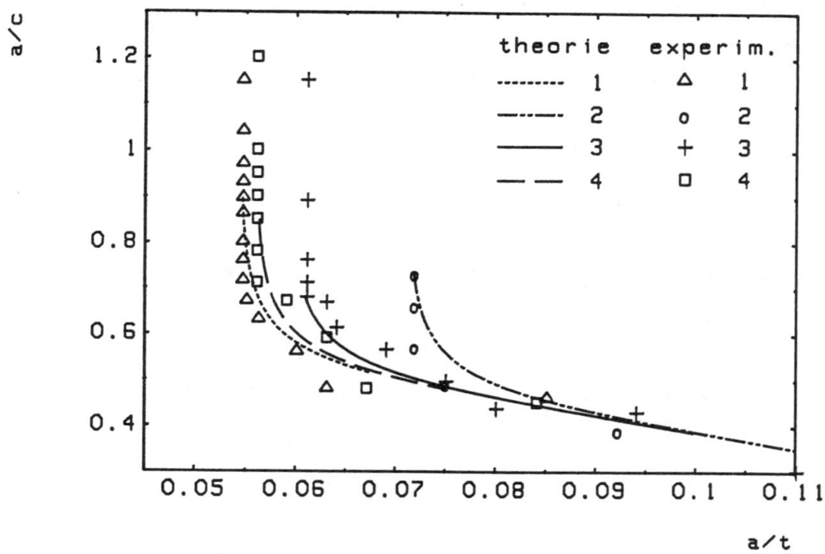

Figure 3. Crack-propagation in the glass specimens

CONCLUSIONS

- SiC showed no decrease of the bending strength in any quenching medium used.
- The decrease of the bending strength of HPSN ,after quenching in the water-air jet, was a pure oxidation effect.
- A calculation of the decrease of the bending strength is only possible if oxidation effects do not influence the strength and if the material shows subcritical crack growth even at lower temperatures.
- For the glass specimens, the comparison of the calculated crack propagation with the experimental values shows a good agreement.

REFERENCES

1. Fett, T., Munz, D. and Keller, K., Determination of subcritical crack growth on glass in water from lifetime measurements on Knoop-cracked specimens. J. Mater. Sci., 1988, 16, 798-803.

2. Keller, K., Theoretische und experimentelle Untersuchungen zur Thermoermüdung keramischer Werkstoffe. Dissertation 1989, Universität Karlsruhe.

3. Fett. T, The crack opening displacement field of semi-elliptical surface cracks in tension for weight-function applications, Int. J. of Fracture, 1988, 36 , 55-69.

4. Newman, J.C., Raju, I.S., Analysis of surface cracks in finite plates under tension or bending loads. NASA Technical Paper 1578, Dec. 1979

CREEP OF Y_2O_3 FULLY-STABILIZED ZrO_2 SINGLE CRYSTALS

J. MARTINEZ-FERNANDEZ, M. JIMENEZ-MELENDO, A. DOMINGUEZ-RODRIGUEZ

Departamento de Física de la Materia Condensada
Facultad de Física. Aptdo. 1065. 41080 Sevilla (SPAIN)

and

A.H. HEUER

Departament of Materials Science Engineering
Case Western Reserve University. Cleveland, Ohio 44106 (USA)

ABSTRACT

Fully stabilized cubic ZrO_2 single crystals containing 9.4 mol % of Y_2O_3 and oriented for single slip on (001)|110| have been crept in compression under nominal stresses (σ) between 50 and 160 MPa, at temperatures (T) between 1300 and 1550 °C, and at two oxygen partial pressures (Po_2), 0.21 and 10^{-6} atm. The creep parameters and the dislocation substructure change with the temperature suggesting a change in the mechanism controlling the deformation.

INTRODUCTION

Although the mechanical behavior at low temperatures of ZrO_2-based ceramics have received much attention (1-4) because of transformation thoughning little attention has been given to high temperature plasticity. The slip systems activated during deformation at high temperature for CaO (5) and Y_2O_3 (6,7) -stabilized cubic ZrO_2 have been determined and compared with other compounds with the fluorite structure (8).

Some work has been devoted to the creep of ZrO_2 stabilized with diferents oxides (9-12). In all cases, the stress exponent was close to 1 and these data were interpreted as diffusional creep controlled by cation diffusion. However, the activation energy was widely scattered; between 3.2-3.9 eV (9) for Sc_2O_3 and Y_2O_3-stabilized ZrO_2, 4.1 eV (10) for CaO-stabilized ZrO_2, and 5.6 eV (11) and 5.7 eV (12) for Y_2O_3-stabilized ZrO_2.

The growth of fully-stabilized ZrO_2 single crystals of high quality has allowed us to use these crystals to study the intrinsic high temperature mechanical behavior, in the absence of grain boundaries and other processing defects present in sintered polycrystals. This paper deals with fully-stabilized cubic ZrO_2 single crystals containing 9.4 mol % Y_2O_3, crept at temperatures between 1300 and 1550 °C.

EXPERIMENTAL PROCEDURE

Single crystals, optically transparent and grown by skull melting, were used in this study. Compression specimens, 2.5 by 2.5 by 6 mm, were prepared using techniques reported elsewhere (6). The orientation chosen had a loading axis parallel to <112> (the other two faces are {110} and {111}) which provided a Schmid factor of 0.47 for the primary slip system {100} <110>. All compression tests were performed in a high temperature creep machine described elsewhere (13), in the temperature range 1300 to 1550 °C, under nominal stresses between 50 and 160 MPa and at two oxygen partial pressures, 0.21 and 10^{-6} atm. Pads cut from the same crystals being deformed, with a lower Schmid factor, were used during deformation to avoid both indentation of the Al_2O_3 compression rods and fracture of the samples due to thermal effects.

The elongation versus time curves were transformed to strain rate ($\dot{\varepsilon}$) versus strain (ε) curves (figure 1).

Transmission electron microscopy foils (3 mm disks) were cut, usually parallel to the glide plane, although foils parallel to other planes, {111} and {100}, were also prepared. They were polished with diamond paste, "dimpled" on one side to 40-50 μm thickness, ion-thinned to electron transparency and coated with a thin carbon film to avoid charging during TEM observation. The thin foils were examined in a Hitachi H800-2 transmission electron microscope operating at 200 kV, utilizing conventional electron microscopy techniques.

RESULTS AND DISCUSSION

A typical ln $\dot{\varepsilon}$ - ε curve is shown in figure 1. All the curves show a sigmoidal shape, which can be correlated with the upper and lower yield points exhibited by these samples when deformed at constant strain rate (6). The steady state is reached after few percent deformation (≃ 3 %).

The creep law for steady state creep can be written (14):

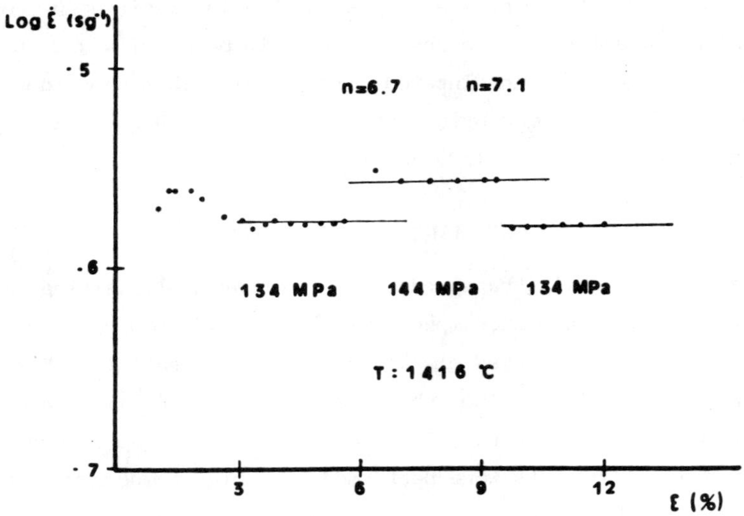

Fig. 1. Typical strain rate $\dot{\varepsilon}$ versus strain ε for constant load compression. The curve shows determination of n of the creep equation.

$$\dot{\varepsilon} = A\ \sigma^{n}\ (Po_2)^{m}\ \exp\ (-\ Q/kT)$$

Changes of σ (fig. 1), Po_2 or T, keeping the other variables constant, were performed in order to study the strain rate sensitivity.

The stress exponent n decreased from 7 to 4.5 when the temperature increased. With such n values, it is difficult to predict the mechanisms controlling plasticity, except for n = 1, because it is always possible to find an "ad hoc" model for any n value (15). At the same time, the activation energy for creep also decreases from 7.3 to 6.2 eV with increasing temperature. The transmission electron microscopy observations show a change in the dislocation substructure. At 1300 °C, we observe many long curved dislocations belonging to the (001) primary slip plane. The stereo pair shown in fig. 2 indicates many segments of dislocations on secondary slip planes, $(1\bar{1}1)$ and $(\bar{1}11)$. This is a good evidence that substantial cross-slip occurred during deformation.

When the temperature is raised, the dislocation structure changes and the stereo pair shown in fig. 3, corresponding to a sample deformed at 1500 °C, indicates that the dislocations do not belonging to the primary slip planes, but are mainly perpendicular to it, with Burgers vectors of

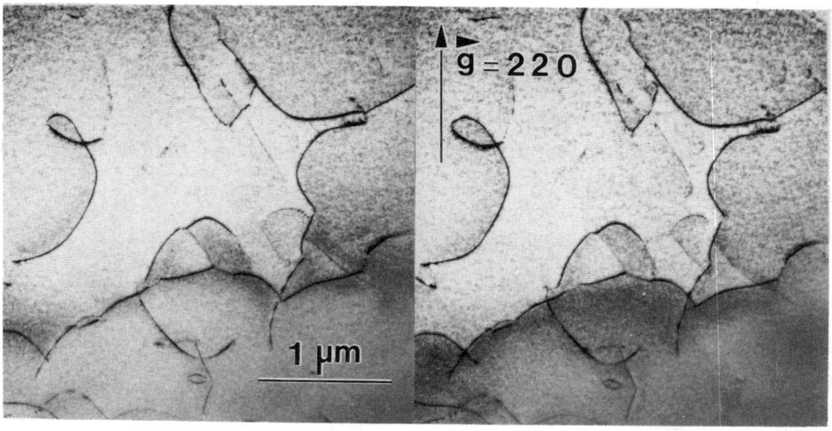

Fig. 2. Dislocation substructure in 9.4 mol % Y_2O_3-stabilized ZrO_2 sample deformed at 1300 °C, shown as stereo pair using **b** = 220. Foil plane is close to the (001) primary slip plane.

the type $1/2|0\bar{1}1|$ and $1/2|\bar{1}01|$. These segments are lying in (100) and (001) planes into which they must have climbed.

The creep parameters and dislocations substructure suggest that a change in the mechanism controlling plasticity occurred in this temperature range.

The $n = 4.5$ and $Q = 6.2 \pm 0.3$ eV for $T > 1450$ °C suggest that a recovery creep mechanism starts to take place. An activation energy of 5.6 eV (11) and 5.7 eV (12), similar to our data, has been found for Y_2O_3-

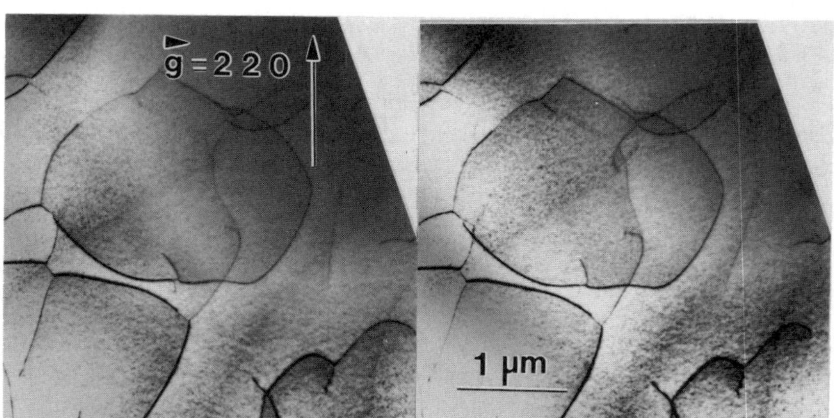

Fig. 3. Dislocation substructure in sample deformed at 1500 °C. Same conditions as fig. 2.

stabilized ZrO_2 deformed by a diffusional creep mechanism. The activation energy for cation difusivity, obtained by prismatic loop annealing, is 5.0 ± 1.0 eV (16), again close to our data. Finally, our data shown that the creep rate is independent of P_{O_2}; the same result was found in ref. (12), suggesting that probably $V_{Zr}^{4'}$ is the minority defect in Y_2O_3-fully stabilized ZrO_2.

Acknowledgments. This research was supported by the U.S. - Spanish Joint Commite for Scientific and Technological Cooperation under grant CCB8504-029.

REFERENCES

1. Advances in Ceramics vol. 3. Science and Technology of ZrO_2. Ed. by A. H. Heuer and L.W. Hobbs. Amer. Cer. Soc., Columbus OH, 1981.
2. Advances in Ceramics vol. 12. Science and Technology of ZrO_2 II. Ed. by N. Claussen, M. Ruhle and A. Heuer. Amer. Cer. Soc., Columbus OH, 1984.
3. Advances in Ceramics vol. 24. Science and Technology of ZrO_2 III. Ed. by S. Somiya, N. Yamamoto and H. Hanagida. Amer. Cer. Soc., Westerville OH, 1988.
4. J. Amer. Cer. Soc., 1986, **67**, n° 3 and 7. Special issue.
5. Mecartney, M.L., Donlon, W.T. and Heuer, A.H. J. Mat. Sci., 1980, **15**, 1063.
6. Domínguez-Rodríguez, A., Lagerlof, K.P.D. and Heuer, A.H. J. Amer. Cer. Soc., 1986, **69**, 281.
7. Domínguez-Rodríguez, A. and Heuer, A.H. Crys. Latt. Def. and Amorph. Mat., 1987, **16**, 117.
8. Keller, R.J., Mitchell, T.E. and Heuer, A.H. Acta Metall., 1988, **36**, 1073.
9. Evans, P.E. J. Amer. Cer. Soc., 1970, **53**, 365.
10. St-Jacques, R.G. and Angers, R.J. J. Amer. Cer. Soc., 1972, **55**, 571.
11. Seltzer, M.S. and Talky, P.K. J. Amer. Cer. Soc., 1972, **55**, 124.
12. Dimos, D. and Kohlstedt, D.L. J. Amer. Cer. Soc., 1987, **70**, 531.
13. Gervais, H., Pellisier, B. and Castaing, J. Rev. Int. Htes. Temp. Ref., 1978, **15**, 43.
14. Bretheau, T., Castaing, J., Rabier, J. and Veyssiere, P. Adv. Phys., 1979, **28**, 835.
15. Walser, B. Scripta Metall., 1982, **16**, 213.
16. Cheong, D.S. Ph. D. dissertation, Case Western Reserve University, 1989.

FLOW BEHAVIORS AT HIGH TEMPERATURE OF YTTRIA DOPED ZIRCONIA POLYCRYSTALS

M. NAUER and C. CARRY
Laboratoire de céramique, EPFL
34, ch. de Bellerive, CH-1007 Lausanne

ABSTRACT

Samples with different grain sizes (0.3 to 1.5 μm) have been elaborated from two batches of commercial yttria doped (3 % mole) zirconia powders which differ only by their residual impurity contents. These materials are deformed in tension and in compression between 1250 °C and 1450 °C in creep or in traction conditions. For the same grain size strain rates can differ by an order of magnitude from one batch to the other and flow stresses at 1450 °C are twice higher for the material with the lowest impurity content. The apparent stress exponent n ($\dot{\varepsilon} \propto \sigma^n$) decreases from 3 to 1.6 when the grain sizes are changed from 0.3 to 1.5 μm in the purest material. Such unusual behavior for a superplastic material is discussed in terms of volume fraction morphology and distribution of grain boundary glassy phases.

INTRODUCTION

In recent years large tensile and compressive strains have been reached on fine grained ceramic materials [1-4]. The macroscopic and microscopic behaviors of such ceramics during hot deformation can be characterized as superplastic according to the metallurgical approach [5]. Now yttria doped tetragonal zirconia polycristals (YTZP) with very fine grain sizes (0.3 μm) can easily be prepared from commercial powders. This finest grain size for a ceramic material appears to be a crucial advantage for high ductility. But the stress exponent n in the phenomenological relation $\dot{\varepsilon} \propto \sigma^n$ must be low ($n \leq 2$) to ensure the stability of the deformation and for 3 % mole Y_2O_3 TZP materials rather different n values ($1 < n < 3$) have been reported [1-4]. In this work we compare the high temperature flow behaviors of several YTZP ceramics which differ only by their residual impurity contents or their grain sizes. Deformation tests are performed in uniaxial tension or compression and in creep (constant stress) or traction (constant elongation rate) conditions. We specifically discuss the likely deformation micromechanisms according to the influence of various material parameters (impurity contents, crystalline and glassy phases and grain sizes).

EXPERIMENTAL

Materials were elaborated by cold isostatic pressing (200 MPa) and air sintered commercial powders (3 % mole Y_2O_3 from TOYO SODA, Japan) from two batches differing by their impurity contents (Table 1). The informations relevant to the eight dense materials that have been investigated are summarized in Table 2, including powder batch reference. Annealing treatment to get larger grain sizes were conducted after sintering in the same conditions (air furnace). Grain sizes were evaluated as $d = 1.38 \sqrt{\tilde{s}}$ from SEM micrographs of diamond polished thermally etched cuts ($\tilde{s}$ is the average grain section area). The amounts of cubic phase in the studied materials were measured by X ray diffraction [6]. The shape of diamond machined compressive and tensile specimens, the testing configuration and the creep conditions have been described elsewhere for alumina materials [7]. On the same machine some tests were performed in traction conditions (various constant elongation rates corresponding to different initial strain rates) and true stress-true strain curves were plotted assuming no local necking during the deformation.

TABLE 1
Chemical analysis (weight %) of powder batches used in this work

		Y_2O_3	Al_2O_3	SiO_2	Fe_2O_3	Na_2O	TiO_2
Batch 1	S.	5.15	0.065	0.002	0.003	0.007	-
	X.F.	5.20	0.093	-	0.013	0.005	0.05
Batch 2	S.	5.19	0.005	0.006	0.010	0.008	-
	X.F.	5.20	0.010	-	0.017	0.008	0.07

S. = supplier's analysis X.F. = X ray fluorescence analysis

TABLE 2
Sintering and annealing conditions and characteristics of materials

	Sintering (°C) temperature and time (h)	Annealing (°C) temperature and time (h)	Densities (gr/cm^3)	Grain Size (µm)	Cubic volume fraction %
Batch 1	1400 - 2 h	-	6.03	0.33	< 2 %
	1400 - 4 h	-	5.98	0.37	< 5 %
	1400 - 20 h	-	5.96	0.51	~ 8 %
Batch 2	1400 - 2 h	-	6.04	0.30	< 2 %
	1450 - 2 h	-	6.07	0.40	< 2 %
	1450 - 2 h	1500 - 15 h	6.07	0.76	15 %
	1450 - 2 h	1500 - 68 h	6.03	1.37	15 %
	1450 - 2 h	1500 - 63 h *	6.07	1.46	15 %

* without cooling after sintering

RESULTS AND DISCUSSION

In traction conditions three tests and one test were run at 1450 °C on samples from batch 2 (grain size 0.40 µm) and batch 1 (grain size 0.33 µm) respectively. The results are presented in Figure 1. While an elongation to rupture of 148 % was reached for the batch 1 material (0.9 true strain) at a temperature higher than the sintering one, the batch 2 flow stresses are much higher (x 2 for 2.810^{-4}/s initial strain rate) and its rupture strains seem limited at 0.56 (75% elongation). The batch 2 stress exponent n, calculated from the maximum true stresses during these tensile tests, is about 3.3. If we compare the present results with published works on nominally identical materials, the batch 1 flow stress is quite the same as Wakai's one [2] and the batch 2 behavior is very close to Nieh's YTZP ceramic one [3] (flow stresses and stress exponent).

In creep conditions (constant stress) typical curves (strain rates-true strains) at 1350 °C are shown in Figure 2 for batch 1 and batch 2 ceramics. First the strain rates are not significantly different in tension and in compression for both materials. Batch 1 strain rates are one order of magnitude higher than for batch 2 materials and tensile rupture strains are much higher for batch 1 (0.7) than for batch 2 (0.47) as at 1450 °C in traction conditions. Apparent stress exponents n were measured by stress changes or calculated from tests under different stresses and both methods give similar results. At 1450 °C for batch 2 the apparent stress exponent from compression tests (Figure 3a) clearly decreases (2.8 → 1.7) for increasing initial grain size (0.4 µm → 1.37 µm). At 1350 °C (Figure 3b) the same observation can also be made (n from 2.6 to 1.6 for the similar grain size increase), but for batch 1 materials, stress exponents are significantly lower and a tendency of decrease for increasing grain size is also observed. The temperature dependence of creep strain rate was

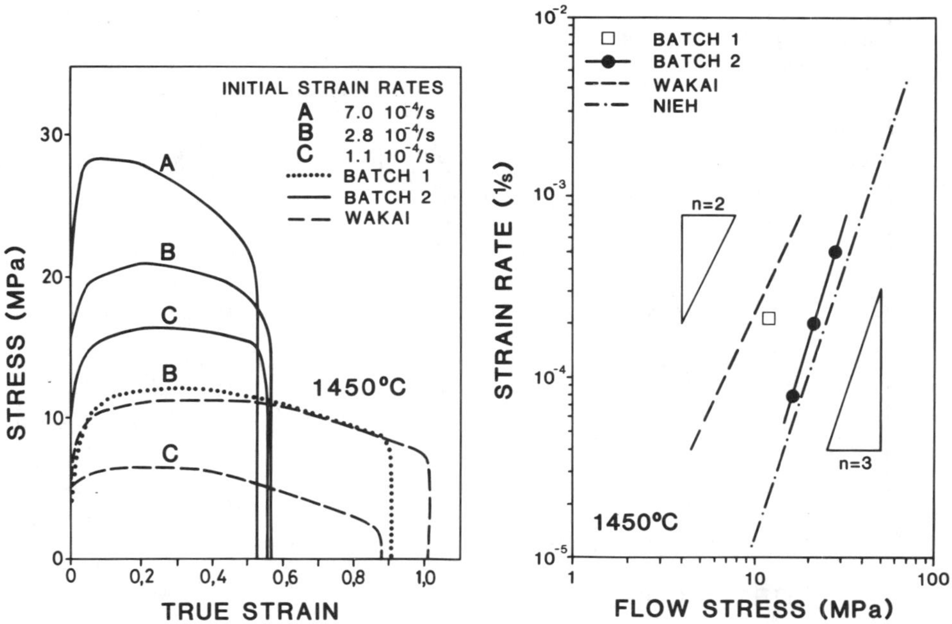

True stress-true strain curves   Strain rates versus flow stress

Figure 1. Flow behaviors of YTZP in traction conditions at 1450 °C: grain size 0.3 - 0.4 µm.

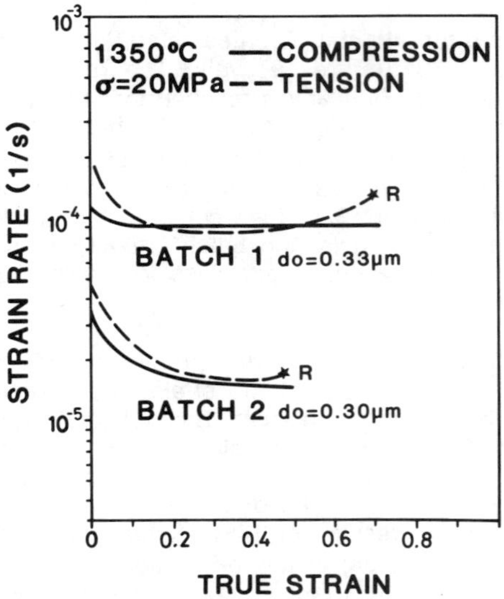

Figure 2. Strain rates under constant stress at 1350 °C.

obtained from tests at different temperatures between 1250 °C and 1450 °C (Figure 4). The apparent activation energy so estimated is about 580 KJ/mole which value is in good agreement with those reported by other authors [2-4]. The influence of initial grain sized creep strain rate $\dot{\varepsilon}$ was characterized by the apparent grain size exponent p in the phenomenological relationship $\dot{\varepsilon} \propto 1/d^p$. For batch 2 materials at 1450 °C and 1350 °C under 20 MPa, the apparent grain size exponent is about 2 which is in good agreement with other works [8].

It appears from these results that the flow behaviors of fine grained YTZP materials strongly depend on impurity contents and grain sizes. On the one hand, larger elongations to rupture and lower flow stresses are observed for materials with comparatively a high impurity level (batch 1, Table 1) while on the other hand stress exponents decrease with increasing grain sizes (Figure 5) which is rather unusual in

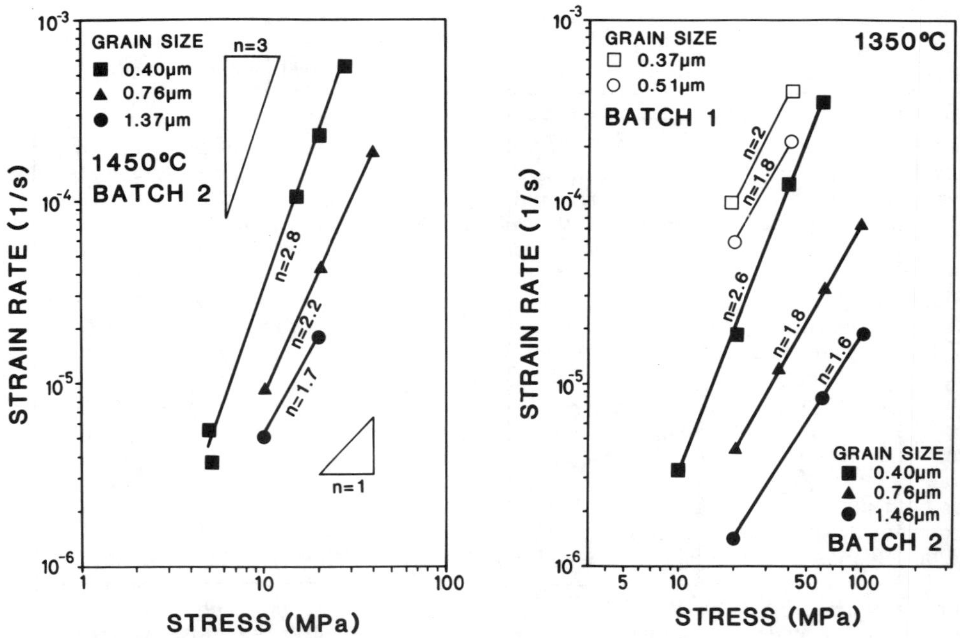

a) 1450 °C

b) 1350 °C

Figure 3. Compression creep strain rates versus stress curves showing a decrease of stress exponents with increasing grain sizes.

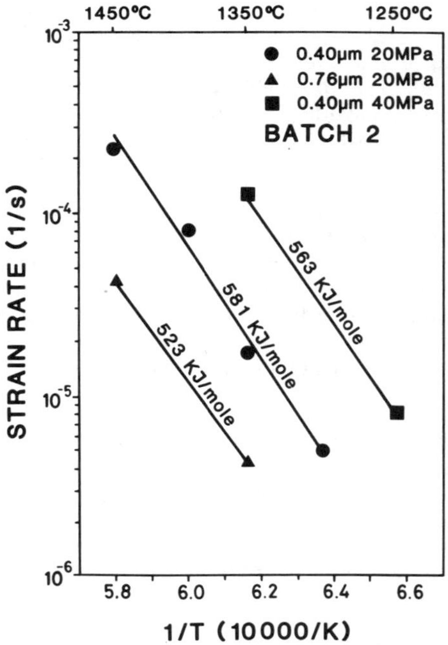

Figure 4. Apparent activation energies for batch 2 materials (compression tests).

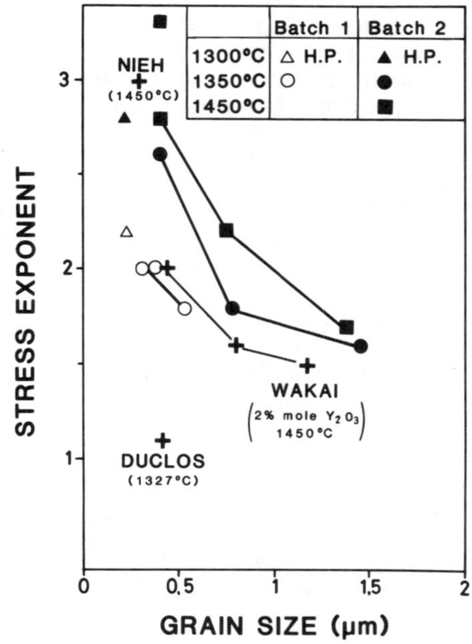

Figure 5. Stress exponents versus grain size for different YTZP materials.

superplastic metallic materials. In ceramic materials many combinations of impurities can lead to the formation of low temperature melting phases and for YTZP materials it has been reported that a stable thickness of well wetting films at grain boundaries is about 2 nm and that the glassy phase in excess is concentrated in pockets at multiple grain boundary junctions [9]. As qualitative transmission electronic microscopical observations have evidenced such thin glassy films in both materials and some grain boundaries devoided of any glass [10] differences in macroscopic behaviors could be explained by simple considerations on the quantity, repartition shape and morphology of the glassy-liquid phase. Comparing the chemical analysis (Table 1) of the two materials, one can say that the quantity of glassy phase should be at least twice as large for the batch 1 than for the batch 2 material. Assuming a constant volume of liquid phase for a material elaborated with one powder batch and an uniform thickness of typically one nanometer for grain boundary phase in 0.33 µm grain sized batch 1 ceramic, the film of glass in 0.3 µm batch 2 material should be thinner than 0.45 nm or non uniformly distributed with grain boundaries devoid of any liquid phase. For the 0.76 µm batch 2 material, the liquid phase can be more uniformly distributed with a thickness close to those of 0.33 µm batch 1 ceramics and if creep behavior is controlled by a grain boundary sliding mechanism with liquid phase, the stress exponent could be the same for both materials as experimentally observed. It is rather difficult to further develop the argument by comparing the strain rate values, because the composition of the liquid phase certainly varies from one batch to the other and so its melting temperature and viscosity.

For a 0.5 µm grain sized YTZ material, Duclos and al. [4] reported a n value close to 1 (Figure 5), but this very low stress exponent can be explained by a larger volume fraction of glassy phase which is evidenced in their TEM micrographs by the large number of triple grain junctions decorated by a glass pocket. Such a decrease of stress exponents with grain size is also observed for a 4 % mole Y_2O_3 material and was mentioned by Wakai [11] for a 2 % mole Y_2O_3 TZP [Figure 5] meaning that the cubic phase volume fraction of these materials does not directly influence the decrease of n with grain size. Some differences in stress exponents have also been observed for hot pressed materials elaborated from the same powder batches (Figure 5). For the highest values of n measured on finest grain sized materials, it can be proposed that a transgranular mechanism (dislocation creep) significantly contributes to the overall deformation in parallel to the classical grain boundary sliding which might not be so easy when an important fraction of grain boundaries is devoid of liquid phase. Elongated grains [10] parallel and perpendicular to the stress in respectively tensile and compressive specimen and the absence of cavities in fine grained compressed samples as observed in alumina [7] support a transgranular deformation mechanism which could have a classical higher stress exponent (n = 3 or 4). The grain size exponent 2 might be an apparent value resulting from two deformation mechanisms acting in parallel, one more or less insensitive to the grain size (dislocations) and the other more grain size depending (grain boundary diffusion). Highest elongations to rupture (> 100 %) seem to have always been obtained at a temperature higher than the sintering one and the sluggish grain growth phenomena [12] could be the decisive mechanism which contributes to the redistribution of the grain boundary liquid phase and reduces the cavitation development.

CONCLUDING REMARKS

For YTZP materials, finest grain size and highest purity which lead to high stress exponents appear to be not a crucial advantage for high ductility and large elongation to rupture. A "pure" YTZP ceramic devoid of any glassy phase might not be superplastic at all in a temperature range ($< T_{sintering}$) where the grain growth remains more than sluggish.

Acknowledgements

This work has been supported by the Swiss Federal Office for Education and Science as a part of the European COST 503 programme.

REFERENCES

1. Carry, C. and Mocellin, A., Ceramics International **13** (1987) 89-98.
2. Wakai, F., Sakaguchi, S. and Matsuno, Y., Advanced Ceramic Materials **1** (1986) 259-263.
3. Nieh, T.G., McNally, C.M. and Wadsworth, J., Scripta Metall. **22** (1988) 1297-1300.
4. Duclos, R., Crampon, J. and Amana, B., Acta Metall. **37** (1989) 877-883.
5. Carry, C. and Mocellin, A. In Superplasticity, ed. B. Baudelet and M. Suéry, C.N.R.S., Paris, 1985, pp. 16.1-16.19.
6. Patterson, A. and Stevens, R., J. Mater. Research **1** (1986) 295-299.
7. Gruffel, P., Carry, C. and Mocellin, A., Effect of Testing Conditions on Superplastic Creep of Alumina Doped With Ti and Y. In Science of Ceramics 14, ed. D. Taylor, The Institute of Ceramics, UK, 1988, pp. 587-592.
8. Wakai, F., Sakaguchi, S. and Kato, H., Yogyo-Kyokai-Shi **94** (1986) 721-725.
9. Mecartney, M.L., J. Amer. Ceram. Soc. **70** (1987) 54-58.
10. Nauer, M., Stoto, T. and Carry, C., to be published.
11. Wakai, F. and Nagono, T., J. Mater. Sci. Letters **7** (1988) 607-609.
12. Lange, F.F., Marshall, D.B. and Porter, J.R. In Ultrastructure Processing of Advanced Ceramics, ed. J.D. Mackencie and D.R. Ulrich, Wiley, 1988, pp. 519-531.

THE ROLE OF THE INTERGRANULAR GLASSY PHASE IN THE SUPERPLASTIC DEFORMATION OF Y-TZP ZIRCONIA

THOMAS HERMANSSON, HÅKAN SWAN and GORDON DUNLOP,
Department of Physics,
Chalmers University of Technology,
S-412 96 Gothenburg, Sweden

ABSTRACT

Y-TZP zirconia materials with different intergranular glassy phases were superplastically deformed in both tension and compression at 1350°C. Stress exponents and activation energies were determined as a function of compositional additives. The flow stress and creep activation energy was found to depend on the chemical composition of the intergranular glassy film in such a way that the rate of superplastic flow in Y-TZP is believed to be determined by the properties of the intergranular phase.

INTRODUCTION

Superplastic deformation of zirconia-based ceramics provides a potential technique for the forging of these outstanding room temperature materials into near net shapes of complex design [1]. The superplastic deformation of zirconia has little effect on the initial microstructure if limited to less than 100% nominal strain at temperatures higher than 1400°C [2]. The major strain providing mechanism is grain boundary sliding (GBS), which is believed to be promoted by a thin film (1-2 nm) of an intergranular glassy phase that is present in these materials.

The superplastic flow of Y-TZP zirconia has many of the characteristics of the superplastic flow of metals (e.g. small grain size, high strain rate sensitivity and an inverse square grain size dependence)[1,2]. However, an important microstructural difference between ceramics and metals is that the ceramics generally have a thin film of glassy phase coating the grain boundaries and deformation of the grains by dislocations generally requires high stresses. It is tempting to consider that the intergranular glassy phase must be important for the extensive grain boundary sliding that occurs during superplastic flow of fine grained Y-TZP ceramics [2]. Therefore, this paper investigates the influence of chemical composition and volume fraction of the intergranular glassy phase on the superplastic flow behaviour of a fine grained Y-TZP material.

EXPERIMENTAL

Y-TZP zirconia specimens for tensile as well as compressive tests were fabricated from starting materials that came from four different powder batches based on TZ-3Y powder (Toyo Soda Manufacturing Co. Ltd) and mixed together with different glass forming oxides. The as-sintered specimens had a relative density of 98-99 % and an average grain size of about 0.25μm. The starting powder compositions of the four different Y-TZP materials were as follows:

3Y-TZP-a: apart from 5.25 wt% Y_2O_3 in solid solution, this material also contained impurities such as 0.092 wt% Al_2O_3, 0.011 wt% SiO_2, 0.005 wt% Fe_2O_3 and 0.004 wt%Na_2O from the TZ-3Y starting powder.

3Y-TZP-b: the same starting composition as 3Y-TZP-a but with an addition of about 0.5 wt% SiO_2 due to attrition wear during ball milling.

2.5Si-3Y-TZP: contained apart from the content of 3Y-TZP-b an extra addition of 2.5 wt% SiO_2.

2.4Al-2.4Si-3Y-TZP: contained apart from the content of 3Y-TZP-b an addition of 2.4 wt% Al_2O_3 and 2.4 wt% SiO_2.

Tensile specimens fabricated from the 3Y-TZP-a and the 2.5Si-3Y-TZP material were superplastically deformed at initial strain rates of 10^{-6} to 10^{-4} s^{-1} at 1250-1450°C. Compression tests of all four materials were carried out in a pneumatic creep machine at initial stresses of 10 to 40MPa at 1250-1450°C

RESULTS

Starting microstructures

The microstructures of the as-sintered samples varied according to the milling treatment and the different oxide additions (see Fig.1). The 3Y-TZP-a specimens contained equiaxed grains with sharp triple junctions and straight grain boundary facets, while the other materials had somewhat rounded grain corners with glass pockets at the triple junctions. In all cases the intergranular glassy film along the grain facets had a thickness of 1-2 nm. The following volume fraction of glassy phase were estimated: 3Y-TZP-a: 1-2% ; 2.5Si-3Y-TZP: 5-7% ; and 2.4Al-2.4Si-3Y-TZP: 9-11%.

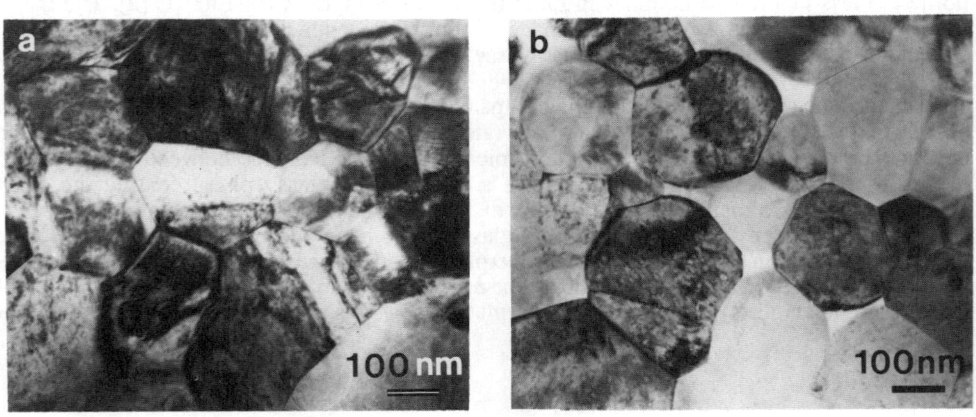

Figure 1. Bright field transmission electron microscopy micrographs showing the microstructures of (a) 3Y-TZP-a and (b) 2.5Si-3Y-TZP.

High temperature flow behaviour
Stress versus strain rate relationships are shown in Fig.2. The 3Y-TZP-a material had a higher flow stress both in tension and in compression compared to the doped materials, but the slopes of the curves did not change significantly. It is quite remarkable that the 2.4Al-2.4Si-3Y-TZP material, which had the highest volume fraction of glass showed a higher flow stress than 3Y-TZP-b and 2.5Si-3Y-TZP. The general equation for steady state creep is usually expressed as ;

$$\dot{\varepsilon} = A\,(1/d^p)\,\sigma^n \exp(-Q/RT) \quad (1)$$

where $\dot{\varepsilon}$ is the strain rate, A is a material constant, σ is the flow stress ,n is the stress exponent, d is the grain size, p is the grain size exponent, Q the creep activation energy and RT has its usual meaning.

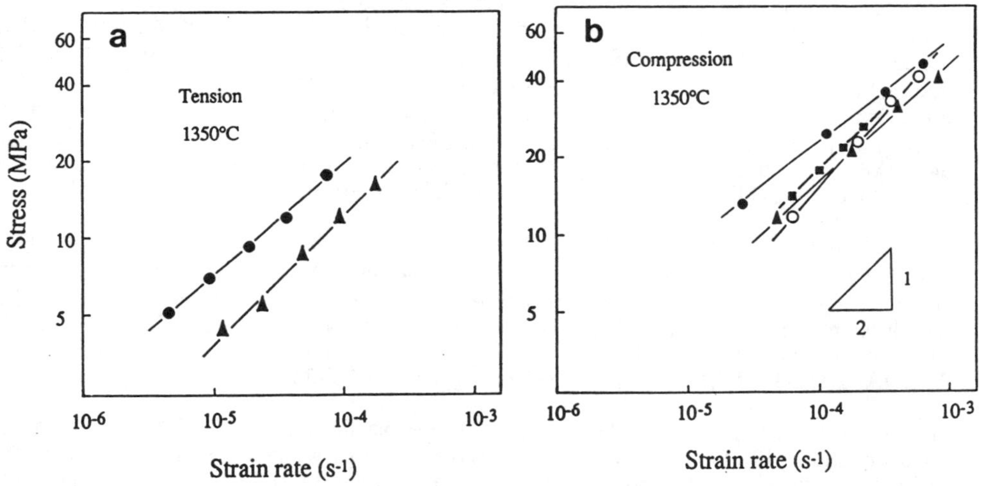

Figure 2. Log stress vs log strain rate curves for the materials: (●) 3Y-TZP-a; (O) 3Y-TZP-b; (▲) 2.5Si-3Y-TZP and (■) 2.4Al-2.4Si-3Y-TZP in tension Fig. 2a and in compression Fig. 2b.

The stress exponent n varied between 1.9 and 2.4 for the different materials. The creep activation energy was determined from compression tests in which the load was kept constant while the temperature was varied. Values of Q for the different materials are shown in TABLE 1, where it can be seen that when silica was added to the 3Y-TZP-a material the creep activation energy decreased. The 2.4Al-2.4Si-3Y-TZP material had creep activation energy which was similar to 3Y-TZP-a

TABLE 1.
Experimental creep activation energies, Q (kJ/mol), for the superplastically deformed zirconia materials.

	3Y-TZP-a	3Y-TZP-b	2.5Si-3Y-TZP	2.4Al-2.4Si-3Y-TZP
Compression	600 ± 50	380 ± 50	360 ± 75	610 ± 50

DISCUSSION

The most significant affect of the various glass forming additions that were made to the 3Y-TZP-a material was that they caused a decrease in the flow stress and altered the activation energy for superplastic flow. Similar effects have been noted previously by Cuillier and Carry [3] in a comparison between experiments on different batches of Y-TZP materials. The largest measured difference in flow stress due to the glass forming oxide additions occurred between specimens of 3Y-TZP-a and the two materials that were doped with silica. It seems that the volume fraction of the glassy phase was less important for the flow stress than was its chemistry. Even though 2.4Al-2.4Si-3Y-TZP probably contained more than double the volume fraction of glass as compared to 3Y-TZP-b, it crept slightly slower.

The glassy phases in the present materials are expected to have compositions which essentially lie within the SiO_2-Al_2O_3-Y_2O_3 ternary system. The solubility of ZrO_2 in the glassy phase is expected to be low and therefore will only have a limited effect on the properties of the glass. Also, because ZrO_2 composed the vast bulk of the materials, the amount of ZrO_2 in the glassy phase would have been almost the same in all four materials. Studies of the SiO_2-Al_2O_3-Y_2O_3 system [4,5] have shown that the lowest eutectic temperature (1335°C) in this system occurs for SiO_2-rich compositions. Thus additions of SiO_2, (which probably dilute the Y_2O_3 concentration in the glassy film) would be expected to result in glassy phases with lower melting temperatures and lower viscosities than 3Y-TZP-a. This is consistent with the lower flow stresses and creep activation energies (TABLE 1) of these two materials as compared to the original 3Y-TZP-a.

An addition of Al_2O_3, as in 2.4Al-2.4Si-3Y-TZP, could be expected to take the composition of the glassy phase away from the SiO_2-rich end of the SiO_2-Al_2O_3-Y_2O_3 ternary system into compatibility triangles where the eutectic temperatures are higher (1450°C and 1550°C)[4]. Thus the glassy phase in this material should be more viscous than in 2.5Si-3Y-TZP or 3Y-TZP-b. This is consistent with the slightly slower creep rates and significantly higher activation energy for 2.4Al-2.4Si-3Y-TZP as compared to 3Y-TZP-b and 2.5Si-3Y-TZP.

Previous work has shown that ~83% of the total superplastic strain in 3Y-TZP-a is due to grain boundary sliding [2]. Grain boundary sliding is the means by which individual grains can move relative to each other and rearrange themselves in the polycrystal thus providing large overall strains. The rate controlling mechansim for superplastic flow can either be grain boundary sliding itself or the mechanism that is responsible for the change of grain shape that must take place in order to accommodate the concentrated shear at the grain boundaries and maintain contiguity between the grains.

The measured activation energies for superplastic flow of the present materials are in the same range as that for cation interdiffusion in cubic zirconia (Q = 423 kJ/mol)[6] and are also in the same range as that for viscous flow of fused silica glasses in the temperature range 1250 - 1450°C (Q = 600 ± 25 kJ/mol)[7]. It is unlikely that the activation energy for lattice diffusion could be influenced as strongly by glass forming additions as were the present creep activation energies and therefore it seems reasonable to associate the measured values with the glass phase, or at least the interface between the ZrO_2 grains and the glass.

CONCLUSIONS

1. Small additions of SiO_2 and/or Al_2O_3 to a Y-TZP material increased the volume of intergranular glass located at multigrain junctions but had little affect on the thickness (1-2 nm) of the glassy film located along grain facets.

2. The flow stress and activation energy for superplastic flow of Y-TZP zirconia are highly sensitive to the composition of the intergranular glassy phase.

3. The superplastic flow properties of Y-TZP zirconia are relatively insensitive to the volume fraction of intergranular glass that is mainly present.

4. The superplastic flow of Y-TZP zirconia is controlled by the properties of the intergranular glass phase.

ACKNOWLEDGEMENT

Financial support from the Swedish Board for Technical Development's Technical Research Council is gratefully acknowledged.

REFERENCES

1. Wakai F., Sakaguchi S. and Matsuno Y., Superplasticity of Yttria-Stabilized Tetragonal ZrO_2 Polycrystals, Adv. Cer. Mat., 1986, **1**, 259-63.

2. Hermansson T., Lagerlöf K.P.D. and Dunlop G.L., Superplastic Deformation of Y-TZP Zirconia, Proc. Int. Conf. on Superplasticity and Superplastic Forming, ed. Hamilton C.H. (Blaine Washington State USA : TMS/AIME 1988), to be published.

3. Carry C., High Ductilities, Superplastic Behaviour and Associated Mechanisms in Fine Grained Ceramics, Proc. Symp. Superplasticity, Int. Meeting on Advanced Ceramics (Mat. Research Soc.: Tokyo Japan 1988) to be published.

4. O'Meara C.,Dunlop G.L. and Pompe R., Phase relationships in the system SiO_2-Al_2O_3-Y_2O_3, High Tech. Ceramics 6th CIMTEC, ed. P. Vincenzini (Elsevier; Amsterdam 1987), pp 265-270.

5. Bonder I.A. and Galakov F.Ya., Izv. Akad. Nauk. SSSR. Ser. Khim,. 1963, **7**, 1325.

6. Oishi Y., Ando K. and Sakka Y., Lattice and Grain Boundary Diffusion Coefficients of Cations in Stabilized Zirconia, Advances in ceramics Vol. 7, eds. M.F. Yan and A.H. Heuer (The American Ceramic Soc.: Columbus Ohio 1983), pp 208-219.

7. Hetherington G, Jack K.H. and Kennedy J.C., Phys. Chem. Glasses, 1964, **5**, 130.

PLASTIC DEFORMATION OF STABILIZED ZrO_2 SINGLE CRYSTALS BELOW 1000°C

P. TERACHER, H. GAREM and J. RABIER
Laboratoire de Métallurgie Physique, URA 131 CNRS
Faculté des Sciences, 86022 POITIERS Cedex, FRANCE

ABSTRACT

Fully stabilized cubic zirconia (ZrO_2 + 9.4% mol Y_2O_3, ZrO_2 + 12.6% mol Y_2O_3, ZrO_2 + 14.9% mol CaO) single crystals were deformed in the temperature range 250°C - 550°C at constant strain rate $\dot{\epsilon} = 2.10^{-4}\ s^{-1}$ in a Griggs-type apparatus. The compression axis [112] was chosen to favour the (001) [110] glide system. Slip trace analysis confirms the activation of this system ; furthermore cross-slip is evidenced. TEM observations show that the deformation substructures are mainly built with glide loops elongated in the screw direction. Numerous dipoles resulting from jog dragging by screw dislocations confirm the occurence of cross-slip at the macroscopic level.

INTRODUCTION

Stabilized cubic ZrO_2 single crystals with the fluorite structure can be plastically deformed at high temperatures in compression [1] [2] [3] (T > 1350°C). In this temperature range glide systems have been found to be {001}<110> or {111}<110> by slip trace analysis and Transmission Electron Microscopy (T.E.M.). Due to the brittleness of these materials, mechanical properties at low temperatures were studied mainly by microhardness testing [4]. From hardness anisotropy measurements, it has been postulated a {001}<110> or {111}<110> glide system. Whilst no direct evidence for other operating slip system was found, activation energy change which was found at around 400°C suggested different mechanisms of deformation at lower temperature [4].

In order to understand this plastic behaviour at low temperatures, we have studied the plastic deformation of cubic zirconia using deformation under confining pressure. This technique allows to deform plastically brittle solids in a temperature range where it is usually impossible to get macroscopic plasticity. As a consequence, glide systems can be directly investigated. Furthermore TEM observations of the deformation substructure is also possible in large areas of the deformed samples. In this paper preliminary results are reported on plasticity of cubic zirconia at temperatures below 1000°C, at the macroscopic and microscopic levels.

MATERIALS AND METHODS

Cubic ZrO_2 single crystal stabilized with CaO and Y_2O_3 were used in this study : ZrO_2 +

9.4% mol Y_2O_3, ZrO_2 + 12.6% mol Y_2O_3, ZrO_2 + 14.9% mol CaO. The samples were cut with a diamond saw in the shape of parallelepipeds of 3x3x8 mm^3 and mechanically polished, finishing with a diamond paste 3 µm-grade. The longitudinal axis was taken as [112]. This orientation activates the (001)[110] single slip at high temperatures.

Plastic deformation tests were achieved in a Griggs-type apparatus [5] set up in an Instron frame which allows to deform brittle solids. In order to suppress the nucleation and propagation of cracks, an hydrostatic pressure is super imposed to the applied stress. Samples were deformed at a constant strain rate of $\dot{\epsilon} = 2.10^{-4}\ s^{-1}$ under a confining pressure of 0.8 GPa.

From these deformed specimens, disks 3 mm in diameter were cut parallel to the (001) plane and mechanically polished down to about 60 µm. Electron beam transparency was obtained by ion thinning at liquid nitrogen temperature. Thin foils were observed in a JEOL 200 CX electron microscope operating at 200 kV using a goniometer stage allowing ± 45° tilt in two orthogonal directions.

RESULTS

Mechanical tests

Using this technique cubic zirconia can be deformed in the temperature range 250°C-550°C. Results of mechanical tests are summarized in figure 1. The flow stresses have been plotted as a function of temperature for the three sets of crystals. These curves exhibit at about 400°C a flow stress anomaly which is characterized by an increase in the mechanical properties in the three compositions studied.

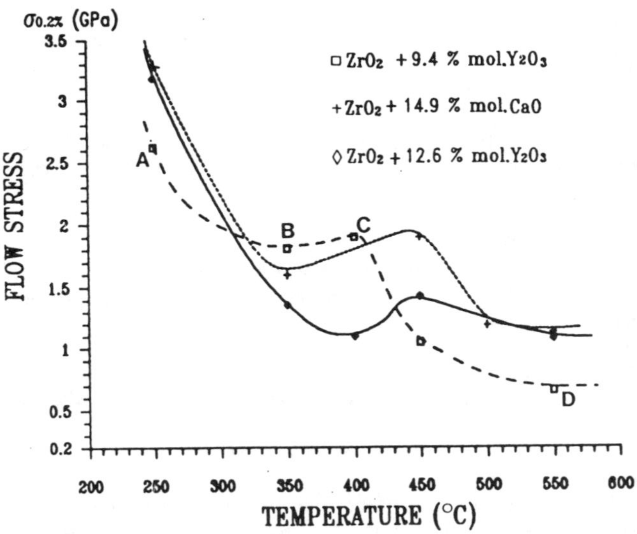

Figure 1. Flow stresses as a function of temperature.

Optical observations

Optical observations of the lateral surface of a deformed sample are shown in figure 2. Slip lines are consistent with a plastic deformation proceeding by glide on the (001) plane. On the (11$\bar{1}$) surface glide lines are wavy. This can be explained by dislocation cross slip.

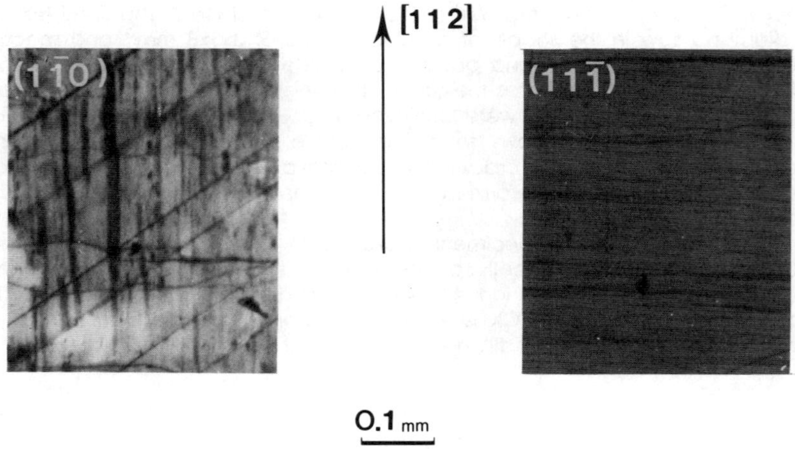

Figure 2. Optical micrographs of the (1$\bar{1}$0) and (11$\bar{1}$) surfaces.

T.E.M. Observations

T.E.M. observations show that plastic flow is related solely to dislocation activity. Observations of deformation substructures were performed at the edge of glide bands since the large dislocation density inside the glide bands prevented to get good contrasts for studying the dislocation fine structures. In what follows, observations performed on ZrO_2 + 9.4 % mol Y_2O_3 in the (001) glide plane are reported, as a function of the deformation temperature.

- T = 250°C (A on figure 1) :

The deformation substructure is characterized by long screw dislocations. These screw dislocations are pinned and bow out between pinning points. Dislocation dipoles are left behind by dragging and have mainly a screw character. (Figure 3a).

- T = 350°C (B on figure 1) :

The screw orientation is still favoured in the deformation substructure with numerous pinning points. Dislocation dipoles are shorter compared to figure 3a and have a mixed or screw character. (Figure 3b)

- T = 400°C (C on figure 1) :

The substructure is nearly the same as that found at 350°C. However some large dipolar loops can be seen. (Figure 3c).

- T = 550°C (D on figure 1) :

The glide loops have larger edge components although the screw character prevails in the substructure. This indicates a change in the relative dislocation velocities : screw dislocation are faster than at lower temperatures. (Figure 3d).

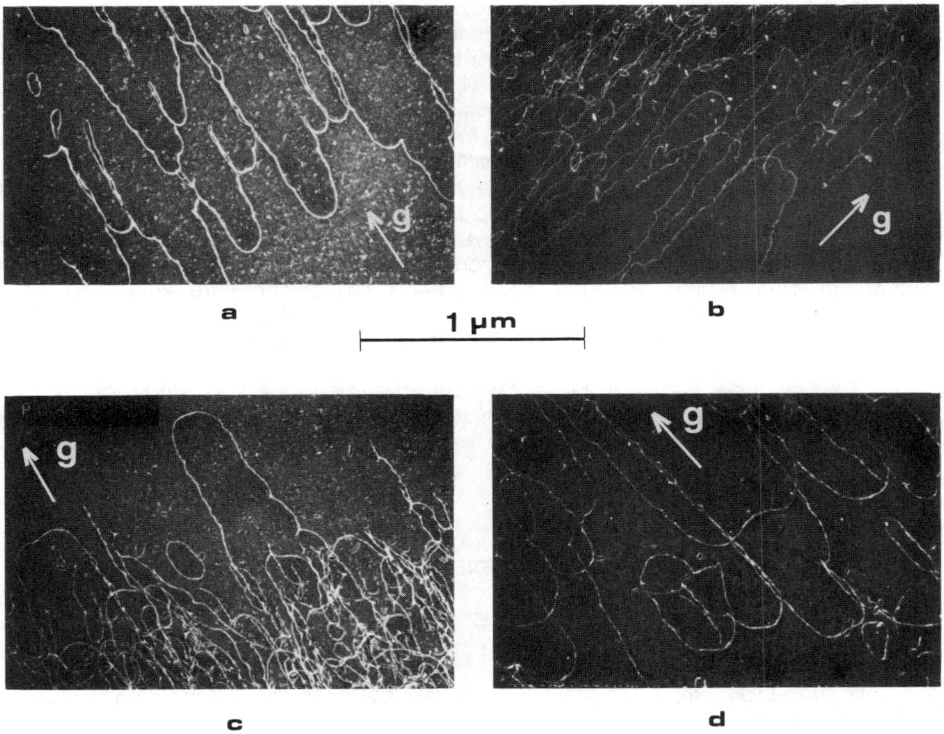

Figure 3 - a. Deformation Temperature (D.T.) 250°C, Weak Beam Dark Field (W.B.D.F).
g = 220, 3.9 g excited, foil plane (001).
b. D.T. 350°C, W.B.D.F., g = 220, 5.1 g excited, foil plane (001).
c. D.T. 400°C, W.B.D.F., g = 220, 3 g excited, foil plane (001).
d. D.T. 550°C, W.B.D.F., g = 220, 3.1g excited, foil plane (001).

All these dislocation substructures are built up with long screw dislocations on which numerous dipoles can be seen. They result likely from jog dragging on screw dislocations. This confirms the cross slip activity at the microscopic level. The same type of substructure have been found in the other types of samples.

DISCUSSION

In the low temperature range investigated, the three types of crystals exhibit a yield stress anomaly. The optical observations as well as the TEM ones confirm that the same glide system as that found at high temperature [1], [2] [3], i.e. (001)<110> is activated. Cross slip has been evidenced at the macroscopic and microscopic levels. At the TEM scale the plastic deformation of cubic zirconia below 550°C is characterized by an heterogenous deformation which is a feature of low temperature, high stress deformation. Screw dislocations appear to be the slowest ones in all the temperature range investigated since long screw dislocation segments prevail in the deformation substructure. Cross slip is required in the formation of dislocation dipoles which originate from local perturbation on screw segments.

Flow stress anomaly, i.e. an increase of the flow stress with temperature, has been reported in different types of materiels : super alloys, ionic crystals... In super alloys hardening effects when temperature increases can be explained by a decrease in screw dislocation mobility due to cross slip of parts of the screw segment in an easy glide plane. This effect is related to an intrinsic property of the dislocation cores [6]. In ionic crystals, flow stress anomaly was found to result from impurity effects [7] : impurities precipitating on dislocations affect their mobilities. Edge dislocations are usually involved in these interactions due to the hydrostatic component of the stress tensor around an edge dislocation. Our observations show that screw dislocations are likely to be involved in hardening process, since numerous pinning points are found along their lengths. Those pinning points can be due to local cross slip resulting from dislocation core effects. However point defects associations are known to occur between aliovalent impurities [8] needed to stabilize the cubic phase of zirconia (Y_2O_3 or CaO). These point defects clusters can promote such cross slip events.

To conclude between these two possible mechanims a study of the fine structure of dislocation jogs nucleated on screw dislocations as well as the dislocation segment located in the cross slip plane is required at the TEM level. This study is in progress.

REFERENCES

1. Mecartney, M.L., Donlon, W.T., Heuer, A.H., Plastic deformation in CaO-stabilized $Zr0_2$ (CSZ). J. Mat. Sci. Letters, 1986, **15**, 1063-65.

2. Dominguez-Rodriguez, A., Lagerlöf, K.P.D. , Heuer, A.H., Plastic deformation and solid-solution hardening of Y_2O_3 stabilized $Zr0_2$. J. Am. Ceram. Soc., 1986, **69**, 281-84.

3. Dominguez-Rodriguez, A., Heuer, A.H., Plastic deformation of Y_2O_3 stabilized ZrO_2 (YSZ) single crystals. Cryst. Latt. Def. and Amorph. Mat., 1987, **16**, 117-123.

4. Hannink, R.H.J., Swain, M.V., Induced plastic deformation of zirconia. In Deformation of ceramic materials II, ed. R.E. Tressler and R.C. Bradt, Plenum Press, New York, 1984, pp 695-708.

5. Veyssière, P., Rabier, J., Jaulin, M., Demenet, J.L., Castaing, J., Instrumental modifications for compressive testing under hydrostatic confining conditions. Rev. Phys. Appl., 1985, **20**, 805-811.

6. Veyssière, P., Dislocation core effects in plasticity. Rev. Phys. Appl., 1988, **23**, 431-443.

7. Skrotzki, W., Haasen, P., Hardening mechanisms of ionic crystals on {110} and {100} slip planes. J. Phys., 1981, **C3**, 119-148.

8. Hund, F., Anomie Michkristalle in System ZrO_2-Y_2O_3. Z. Elektrochem, 1951, **55**, 363-66.

RESULTS OF THE VAMAS CERAMICS HARDNESS TESTING ROUND-ROBIN

R Morrell, D M Butterfield, D J Clinton
National Physical Laboratory, Teddington, Middlesex, TW11 OLW, UK.

ABSTRACT

The results of the VAMAS Ceramic Project round robin on hardness testing of high-alumina ceramics is reported in summary form. The objectives were to establish the level of scatter and possible biases between individuals as a precursor to standardisation of test procedures. The results show that in order to guarantee resolution of differences between different materials tested by different individuals on different machines, the difference in hardness number has to be typically 10-15%. This level of error needs to be taken into account in interpreting hardness data and using hardness in specifications for hard ceramics.

INTRODUCTION

Hardness measurements on hard ceramics are in widespread use both for scientific and for commercial purposes. However, the small size of indentations leads to possible large errors in hardness measurement, posing problems if hardness is to be used for specifying a material. These conclusions were deduced from some earlier NPL work (1,2), from which this VAMAS study was initiated. The VAMAS round-robin had several aims, but was principally designed to determine typical distributions of data and machine and/or operator biases when conventional metallurgical tests are used under the extreme limits posed by ceramics. Following participation by 20 organisations in the UK, France, F R Germany, CEC (JRC Petten), US and Japan, the results have been analysed by NPL, and the potential errors in test results quantified,

ROUND-ROBIN DESIGN

Two high-alumina ceramics were prepared as a series of test discs with carefully polished surfaces, which were then divided into four zones. The two materials were chosen such that one, A, by virtue of its very small grain size (< 2 µm) and very low residual porosity, posed the minimum of observational or microstructure-limited difficulties, while the second, B, was a conventional medium grain size two-phase material with about 3-4% of closed porosity. NPL made a series of HR45N, HV1.0, HV0.2 and HK0.2 indentations and recorded its data on the complete set of test discs

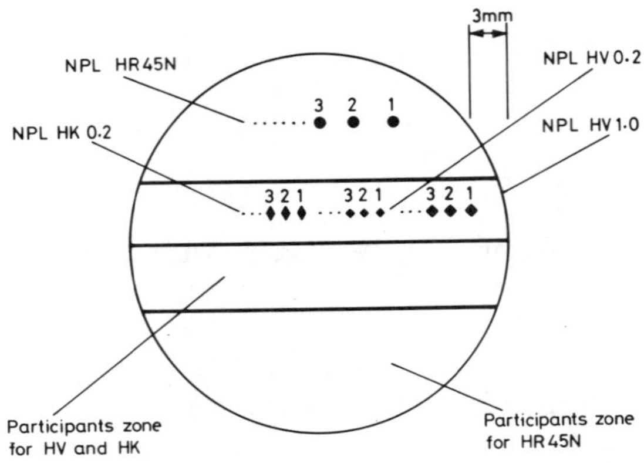

Figure 1. Layout of test-piece as received by participants showing zones for NPL and participants' indentations.

(Figure 1). The participants were then asked to remeasure the HV1.0, HV0.2 and HK0.2 indentations with their own system, to make their own series of indentations and to report their results. Some of these second sets were then remeasured by NPL on return of the test discs, especially in cases where results deviated considerably from those originally made by NPL. The NPL indentations were used as a reference set with which to compare the participants individually with the NPL observers, and to ensure that the set of discs behaved similarly. A comparison of NPL and participants' hardness test equipment can be made by comparing the two sets of participants' results. Analysis of the results has been performed to ascertain the biases and measurement errors likely in a typical population of users, few of whom had attempted in the past to make routine measurements of this kind on ceramics.

RESULTS AND DISCUSSION

The full results are reported in a VAMAS Technical Report(3), and comprise an analysis of about 7000 individual measurements. A summary of the ranges and the averages of the data is given in Table 1. Most of the participants were able to make their own HV1.0 and HV0.2 indentations, but less than half were able to make HR45N and HK0.2 measurements. Nevertheless, all remeasured NPL's indentations.

The possible sources of error are as follows. With the optical reading methods (Vickers, Knoop), there are random errors due to real variations in true indenter penetration in the local microstructure, random errors of positioning microscope eyepiece crosswires, systematic errors due to variations between diamond indenter geometries, and also personal biases of judgement of the position of the indentation corners. Only the first and third of these sources are present in Rockwell tests, due to the mode of operation of the test machine, and since such indentations cannot be remeasured, simple averaging and determination of standard deviations are the most appropriate techniques. With the Vickers and Knoop tests it is desirable to establish whether individual participants, when compared with the experienced NPL operators, were able to follow size variations in indentations in the same way, or whether the random errors of measurement of either or both parties outweighed the real material variations. This was explored using a covariance test on pairs of NPL and participants' results on individual indentations placed by NPL. Correlation coefficients obtained varied from near 1 to near -1, with the material B generally showing much

TABLE 1
Summary of results

	Material A HR45N	HV1.0	HV0.2	HK0.2	Material B HR45N	HV1.0	HV0.2	HK0.2
NPL indentations:								
Mean indentation size, NPL, μm	-	31.0	13.4	38.8	-	38.9	15.9	43.6
Std. dev. of means, μm, ±		0.35	0.24	1.5		0.60	0.60	2.1
Mean NPL hardness no.	88.2	1935	2058	1897	78.4	1228	1494	1494
Typical std. deviation, ±	0.3	60	70	100	0.5	70	100	120
Range of participants' mean results, μm	-	29.6-32.6	12.1-14.2	35.2-42.9	-	36.9-41.3	15.0-17.7	41.2-48.2
Range of std. devs, μm, ±		0.2-1.0	0.3-0.7	0.3-1.4		0.3-3.3	0.4-2.1	1.2-3.0
Mean participants' result, μm	-	31.4	13.4	38.8	-	39.4	16.1	44.2
Std. dev. of means, μm, ±		0.9	0.6	2.3		1.2	0.6	2.2
Mean participants' hardness no.	-	1885	2062	1917	-	1202	1462	1370
Range of std. devs., ±		20-129	59-203	30-172		21-253	96-355	84-191
Participants' indentations:								
Range of mean indent sizes, μm	-	29.8-34.1	11.6-14.3	36.0-40.4	-	37.9-42.8	11.8-17.9	42.3-47.1
Range of std. deviations, μm, ±		0.1-2.4	0.2-0.8	0.2-1.6		0.5-5.5	0.5-3.8	1.3-6.7
Overall mean indent size, μm	-	31.7	13.6	38.2	-	39.7	15.8	44.5
Std. dev. of mean, μm, ±		1.1	0.6	1.2		1.4	1.3	1.6
Overall mean hardness no.	89.0	1857	2038	1953	78.3	1190	1529	1470
Range of std. devs., ±	0.1-0.9	19-259	29-207	22-168	0.3-0.7	24-246	72-1242	82-372

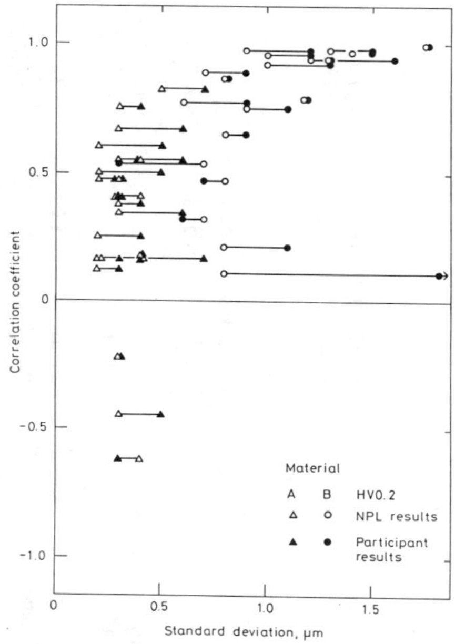

(a)

Figure 2. Relationship between correlation coefficients and standard deviations for NPL and participant measurements on individual NPL-made indentations using (a) HV0.2 and (b) HK0.2 tests. Good correlation is obtained only for large standard deviations.

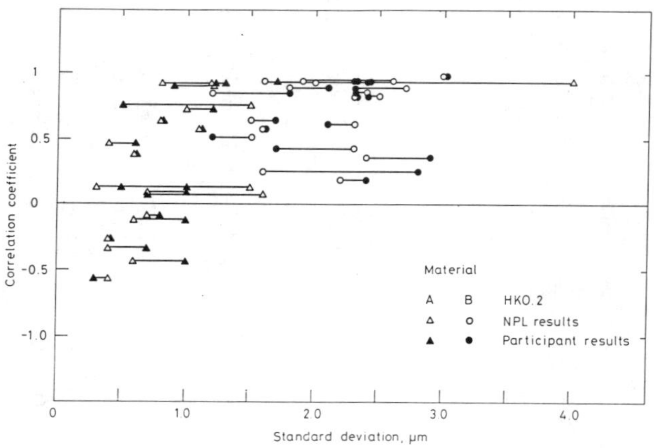

(b)

better correlation than A. Thus, if there is a large variation in true indentation size as a consequence of microstructural inhomogeneity, then two independent observers are more likely to show the same trends of measurement than in the case of only small true variations, when random errors predominate. Further, only when the standard deviation of diagonal measurements exceeded about ±1 μm for HV or about ±2 μm for HK indentations could two observers follow the same trend (Figure 2). Correlation coefficients less than +0.5 imply a high level of randomness in the measurements, while negative values have to be treated as freak cases of randomness.

Table 2 summarises the analysis. Material variability was low for the fine-grained alumina A, but significantly higher for material B. Similarly, the difference between participant's and NPL's average measurements was significantly less for material A than for B. If it is assumed that the NPL

TABLE 2
Resolvability of differences in hardness

	Material A HR45N	HV1.0	HV0.2	HK0.2	Material B HR45N	HV1.0	HV0.2	HK0.2
Material variability as determined by NPL indentations, μm	±0.4	±0.5	±0.4	±1.5	±0.3	±1.0	±0.7	±2.0
Number of specimens employed	20	20	20	20	20	20	20	20
Single participant variability (typical standard deviations), μm	±0.4	±1.0	±0.4	±1.0	±0.5	±1.5	±1.0	±2.0
Number of indentations employed	5	5	10	10	5	5	10	10
Single participant bias, μm (typical NPL/participant difference)	±0.8	±1.0	±0.5	±0.8	±0.5	±1.5	±0.5	±1.5
Number of participants	6	20	22	21	6	20	22	21
Machine bias, μm, (difference between NPL's and participant's machines as measured by participants)	±0.8	±0.5	±0.3	±1.0	±0.5	±0.5	±0.3	±2.0
Difference in size needed to be resolvable by any two persons, μm	±0.9	±1.5	±0.7	±1.6	±0.7	±2.2	±1.2	±3.2
Number of indentations employed	5	5	10	10	5	5	10	10
Difference as % of mean size	±7.5	±4.6	±5.4	±4.3	±3.2	±5.7	±7.5	±7.1
Difference in hardness number	±0.9	±180	±220	±180	±0.7	±150	±230	±180

Note: The differences in Rockwell hardness number shown above are exactly equivalent to the same value in μm, owing to the relationship HRN = 100 - δ where δ is the indentation in μm.

observers were consistent in their measurement criteria (their results were central in the spread from all participants (Table 1) suggesting their criteria were appropriate), then systematic participant biases could be as large as the typical standard deviations about their mean results. In contrast, differences between NPL and participant machines were small, as determined by the differences between participants' measurements of NPL's and their own indentations, except in the case of Knoop tests in which alignment of the diamond and orthogonality of loading direction to specimen surface are much more critical. The final figures in Table 2 are estimates of the true difference in mean indentation size needed before it can be declared resolvable by most participants on any test machine. These figures are a measure of the overall reliability of hardness data from any source. Possible combined errors in the visually measured tests are >4% in indentation diagonal length, up to >7% in microhardness tests on material B. Such errors are doubled in calculation of the hardness number, giving the typical allowance that will have to be made in agreeing measurements or specifications. In the Rockwell measurements, the penetration (δ) of the indenter under the major load is recorded as the hardness number, i.e. HR45N = 100 - δ. With increasing material hardness, penetration becomes less, and the hardness number becomes more dependent on the exact shape of the indenter at its tip, and on the microstructure of the specimen under the indenter, increasing potential errors. This is confirmed by the typical differences between NPL tests and participants' tests being greater for the high-hardness material A than for material B. This bias is a significant part of the total possible variation, given in the last line of the Table. Thus for tests at less than 78 HR45N, the potential variation of results is the lowest of all the tests in this study, whereas at 88 HR45N, penetration is only one half of that at 78 HR45N, and the overall errors are similar to the maxima from all the other tests.

CONCLUSIONS

The VAMAS round-robin has demonstrated the sources of error in the measurement of hardness of ceramic materials. The combination of material variability and machine bias in HR45N tests results in possible uncertainties of about ±0.8 in the hardness scale, tending to be larger for hardness numbers approaching 90 than for those less than 80. In tests in which the operator has to make a visual judgement of the correct positions of the measuring cross-wires in a microscope, true indentation sizes in two materials must be different by at least 1 µm under good observational conditions, rising towards 2 µm or more for multiphase, inhomogeneous materials, especially when using the Knoop test. These factors combine in the calculation of a hardness number to give possible total errors (random observer and material errors plus participant bias) of typically ±10%. These limitations need to be borne in mind if any attempt is made to standardise hardness testing for the purposes of classification or specification of ceramic materials. Further consideration should be given to the development of high-hardness reference materials, and to the examination of alternative methods of defining hardness of ceramics, e.g. automatic microhardness testers.

ACKNOWLEDGEMENT

The authors would like to express their thanks to the many participants who took part in the round robin, without whom it would not have been possible to assess all the factors involved.

REFERENCES

1. Clinton, D J, Morrell, R. "The hardness of alumina ceramics", **Proc.Brit.Ceram.Soc.**, 1984, **34**, 113-27.
2. Clinton, D J, Lay, L A, Morrell, R. "The microstructure dependence of hardness in high-purity alumina ceramics". **Proc.Brit.Ceram.Soc.**, 1986, **37**, 217-27.
3. Butterfield, D M, Clinton, D J, Morrell, R, The VAMAS hardness test round robin on ceramic materials, VAMAS Technical Report 3, National Physical Laboratory, Teddington, UK, 1989.

THE HOT HARDNESS OF CERIA PARTIALLY STABILISED ZIRCONIA (Ce-TZP)

R Morrell, W P Byrne, N J McCormick, M J Reece, M G Gee
National Physical Laboratory, Teddington, Middlesex, TW11 OLW, UK
S Blackburn, P Greenwood, P G Senhenn
Foseco plc, Ceramic Materials Division, Stafford, ST16 1EA, UK

ABSTRACT

The hot hardness of a 13.5 wt % CeO_2 partially stabilised ZrO_2 (Ce-TZP) fired to three different grain sizes has been measured and compared with conventional Mg-PSZ. Transformation zone sizes are large compared with those of other zirconias, and correlate well with the concept of extensive stress-induced transformation just above the M_s temperature.

INTRODUCTION

Zirconias partially stabilised with ceria show remarkable behaviour in regard to toughness and phase transformation [1]. Not only is the toughness high (~ 15 MN $m^{-3/2}$), but the material appears to show significant permanent strain before failure. This present work has been performed to establish whether the material continues to behave in the same way at elevated temperatures, or whether the transformation effect is reduced. Hot hardness measurements have been performed on a 13.5 wt % CeO_2-TZP and compared with those on a conventional 3 wt % MgO-PSZ.

EXPERIMENTAL

Specimens were pressed at about 70 MPa into discs from powder produced by electro-refining and comminution to a mean particle size of 0.6 µm [2]. They were fired at 1400 °C/2 h and 1500 °C/2 h. A larger grain size material was prepared by a prolonged firing at 1400 °C/60 h. Specimens were then ground flat and carefully polished to a metallographic finish.

Hot hardness indentations were made using a motor-driven diamond indenter in a heated stage under vacuum. Loads of about 1 N and about 4 N were used (i.e. HV0.1 and HV0.4). Indentations were subsequently measured using a Leitz Miniload II microhardness machine. Indentations at room temperature were made at the same loads in the microhardness tester, and at about 300 N in a Vickers tester (i.e. HV30).

Specimens were examined optically and by SEM. Optical images obtained were enhanced using conventional and Nomarski interference techniques.

RESULTS

The grain size of the fired ceramic discs increased with increasing firing temperature and time. Material A fired at 1400 ^{o}C/60 h had the largest grain size (about 3 μm), but the lowest density of 6.12 Mg m^{-3} (Figure 1). Materials C and F fired at 1400 ^{o}C/2h and 1500 ^{o}C/2h respectively had smaller grain sizes, around 1.5 and 2.2 μm respectively, and high densities of 6.16-6.19 Mg m^{-3}. X-ray diffraction showed all specimens to be almost completely tetragonal on the polished surfaces.

(a) (b)

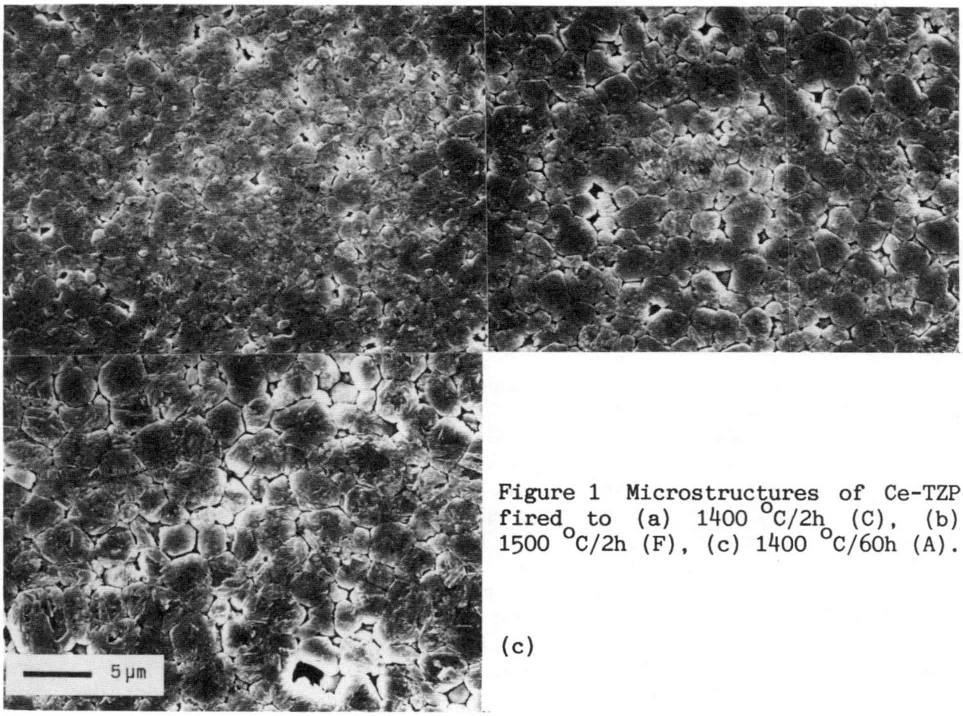

Figure 1 Microstructures of Ce-TZP fired to (a) 1400 ^{o}C/2h (C), (b) 1500 ^{o}C/2h (F), (c) 1400 ^{o}C/60h (A).

(c)

The hot microhardness fell for all three prepared specimens as the indentation temperature was raised, but there was little change above 500 ^{o}C. The fall over the temperature range 25-300 ^{o}C was steeper than for an MgO-PSZ (Feldmühle ZN40) (Figure 2). There was no evidence of significant radial cracking until the test temperature exceeded 500 ^{o}C, but at higher temperatures cracks began to develop as typically observed in most ceramic materials (Figure 3). There was a limited amount of very localised fracture immediately adjacent to the indentation edges, mostly running parallel to the edges.

In the HV30 tests at room temperature, material A showed larger indentations than C or F, with much larger diameter associated regions of surface uplift (Figures 4 and 5). This uplift had a granular appearance, of roughness increasing with increasing grain size. In addition there were starfish-like near-radial arms to the uplifted area, similar to those observed by Hannink and Swain [3] in a 12 mol % CeO_2 material at -120 ^{o}C.

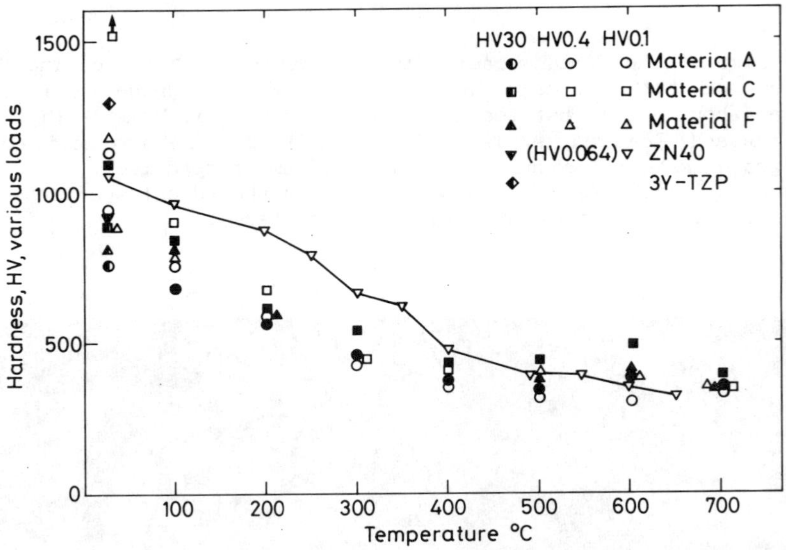

Figure 2 Microhardness as a function of temperature for Ce-TZP specimens, compared with a MgO-PSZ. Data at room temperature for HV30 are also shown.

DISCUSSION

The M_s temperature for Ce-TZP depends on composition and grain size. Hannink and Swain show indirectly than the M_s temperature for a 12 mol % CeO_2 material is at about -173 °C, and Coyle et al.[4] discuss the evidence that the tetragonal phase is fully stable at room temperature for a 16 mol % material. The present material has substantially less CeO_2, 10.8 mol %, and in sintered form should thus possess an M_s temperature between room temperature and -173 °C. The equivalent appearances of the high-load hardness indentations at room temperature in this work and at -120 °C in the Hannink and Swain work suggest that the M_s temperature for material A is at about -10 °C, and those of the finer-grained materials somewhat lower than this. These temperatures compare with the phase stability temperature from the phase diagram [5] of about 400 °C. In terms of the hot-hardness data, the appearance of cracking at temperatures above about 500 °C and the loss of significant uplift despite the larger size of indentation at a given load correlate with the absence of any effective phase transformation caused by the high imposed local indentation stresses. The materials are essentially behaving in a normal brittle ceramic fashion. As the temperature is reduced, increasing amounts of tetragonal-to-monoclinic phase transformation occurs, the transformation zone size increasing considerably as the level of stress required to effect transformation declines with increasing metastability. The appearance of the indentations suggests that the more metastable the material, the greater the proportion of material that transforms, and the greater the volume change and hence uplift around indentations. The appearance of Y-TZP HV30 indentations (Figure 4) shows that this material is much less easy to transform. The uplift is less, and zone size is much smaller. These features correlate with high equilibrium transformation temperatures but low or non-existent M_s temperatures reported for Y-TZP.

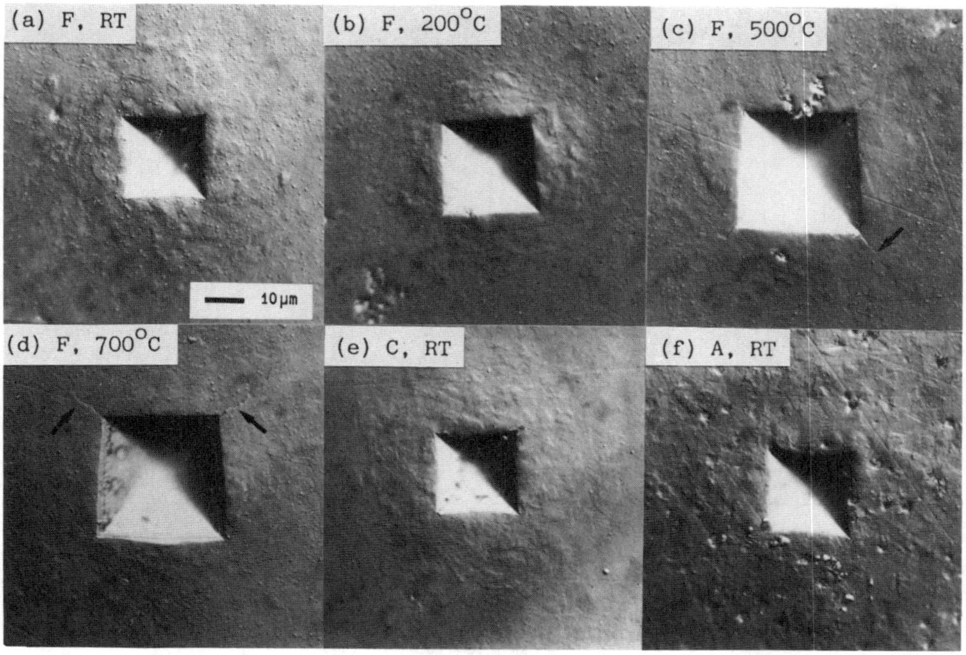

Figure 3 HV0.4 indentations observed by Nomarski interference.

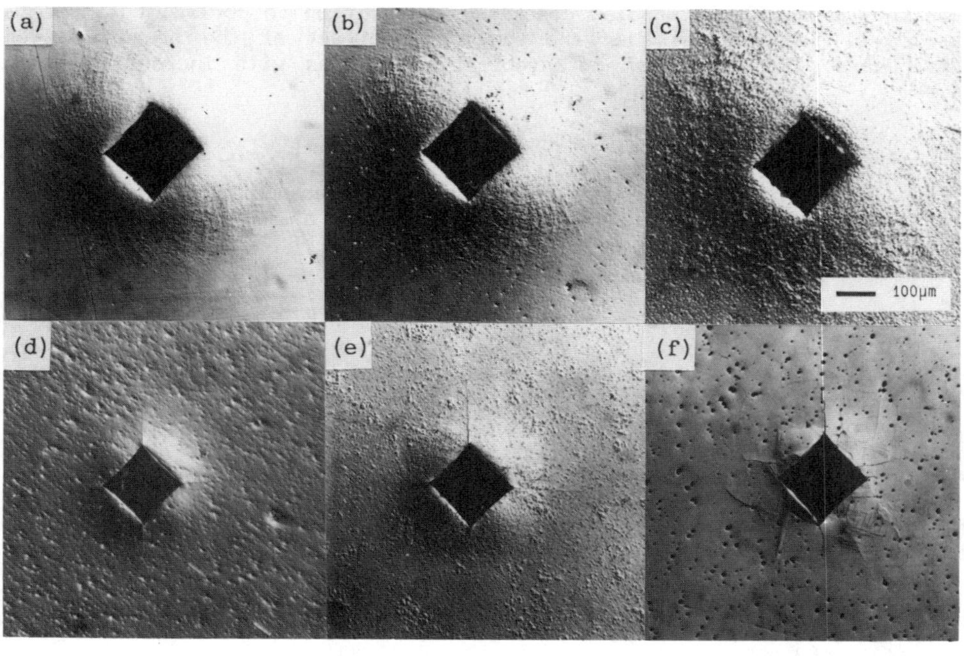

Figure 4 Room-temperature HV30 indentations in Ce-TZP: (a) C, (b) F, (c) A, compared with (d), (e) two commercial Y-TZP ceramics, (f) an MgO-PSZ.

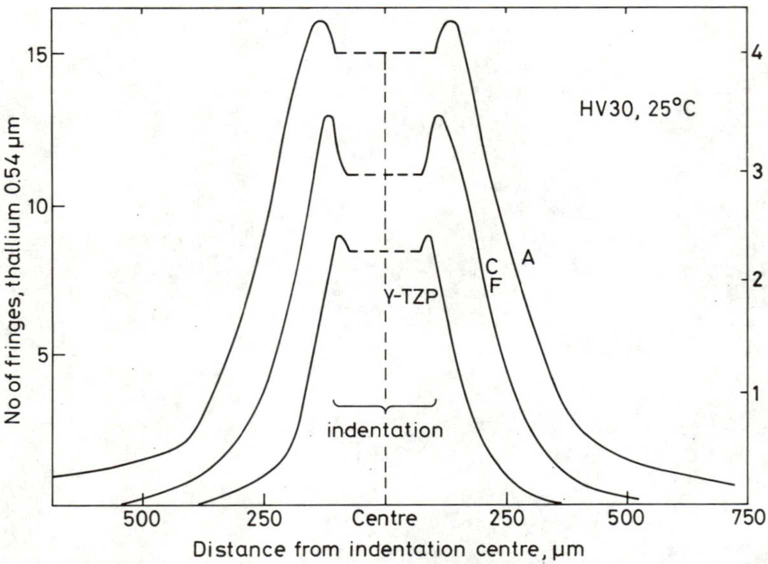

Figure 5 Uplift from interference micrographs as a function of distance from centre of HV30 indentations at room temperature for Ce-TZPs and Y-TZP.

CONCLUSIONS

The hardness of Ce-TZP falls more sharply with increasing temperature than does an MgO-PSZ. The surface uplift due to the t → m transformation vanishes above 500 °C. Radial cracking is absent up to 500 °C, but appears at higher temperatures when the toughening effect of the transformation disappears. The degree of metastability increases with increasing grain size.

ACKNOWLEDGEMENTS

Thanks are due to the Directors of Foseco plc, Ceramic Materials Division for permission to publish, and to FCPG staff for assistance with material preparation.

REFERENCES

1. Tsukuma, K, Shimada, M, "Strength, fracture toughness and Vickers hardness of CeO_2-stabilized tetragonal zirconia polycrystals (Ce-TZP)", **J.Mater.Sci.**, 1985, **20**, 1178-84.
2. Blackburn, S, Kerridge, C R, Senhenn, P G, "Electrorefined PSZ powder - an alternative zirconia for dense engineering components", Science and Technology of Zirconia III, edited by Somiya, S, Yamamoto, N, Hanagida, H, **Advances in Ceramics 24**, 193-9, 1988.
3. Hannink, R H J, Swain, M V, "Metastability of the martensitic phase transformation in a 12 mol % ceria-zirconia alloy: I, deformation and fracture observations", **J.Amer.Ceram.Soc.**, 1989, **72**(1), 90-98.
4. Coyle, T W, Coblenz, W S, Bender, B A, "Transformation toughening in large-grain-size CeO_2-doped ZrO_2 polycrystals", **J.Amer.Ceram.Soc.**, 1988, **71**(2), C88-C92.
5. Duwez, P, Odell, F, "Phase relationships in the system zirconia-ceria", **J.Amer.Ceram.Soc.**, 1950, 33(9), 274-83.

ELASTIC PROPERTIES AND CRYSTALLIZATION IN SIYALON GLASSES AND CERAMICS

TANGUY ROUXEL, JEAN-LOUIS BESSON, CHRISTIAN GAULT
UA CNRS 320 - E.N.S.C.I. 87065 LIMOGES CEDEX FRANCE
PAUL GOURSAT
UA CNRS 320 - UFR des Sciences 87060 LIMOGES CEDEX FRANCE

ABSTRACT

The high temperature mechanical properties of nitrogen ceramics are strongly dependent on the intergranular phases. Crystallizing these phases, which are vitreous after sintering, improves creep resistance. In order to have a better understanding of the secondary phases, nitrogen glasses with varied compositions in the Si-Y-Al-O-N diagram are studied. In addition to usual characterizations, the elastic properties are determined using an ultrasonic method. Young's modulus is very sensitive to structural changes. Its evolution with temperature allows to localize the onset of the glass transition range and the crystallization domains. Isothermal experiments, associated with XRD, bring information on the crystallization kinetics. The results permit an optimal choice for post-sintering treatments.

INTRODUCTION

The high temperature behaviour of Si_3N_4 based ceramics is controlled by the properties of secondary intergranular phases (1,2). But, in spite of the considerable number of studies dealing with these ceramics and with nitrogen glasses (3,4), very few reports are devoted to the rheology of nitrogen glasses at high temperature. The aim of our work is to show how the behaviour of the glasses themselves can help us understand that of the sintered silicon nitride ceramics.

MATERIALS

Glasses were elaborated by melting mixed powders of Si_3N_4, SiO_2, Y_2O_3 and Al_2O_3 in boron nitride crucibles in a purified nitrogen atmosphere at 1700°C during one hour, and quenching. The compositions are given in table 1. The nitrogen content was verified by oxidation and Kjeldhal method. An oxide glass with the same cationic ratios was also fabricated. No crystalline phase was detected using routine X-ray analysis.

The silicon nitride ceramic was pressureless sintered (1 hr at 1700°C) with alumina and 4 wt % yttria leading to the β'sialon solid solution with z = 3.

TABLE 1
Glass compositions

Grade	equivalent % (theoretical) from /3/					weight %					
	Y	Si	Al	O	N	Y	Si	Al	O	N	N exp.
G_1	28	56	16	100	0	15	30	8.6	46	0	0
G_2	28	56	16	83	17	17	34.2	9.8	34.7	4.2	3.7
G_3	28	56	16	75	25	17.3	34.7	9.9	31.9	6.2	4.8

METHODS AND RESULTS

Glass transition temperatures were first determined using classical methods : dilatometry and differential thermal analysis (DTA). The dilatometric runs and the DTA tests were performed in argon at a heating rate of 50°/min and 10°/min respectively. The data are in Table 2. The mean thermal expansion coefficient, measured between 50 and 800°C decreases when the nitrogen content of the glass increases. On the D.T.A. curves, the glass transition domain is evidenced by an endothermic peak. At higher temperatures, exothermic signals associated with crystallization phenomena appear. These peaks are better defined for the oxide glass than for the nitrogen containing glasses. The glass transition domain shifts to higher temperatures when the nitrogen content increases as already reported in the litterature (3).

Creep tests allow to study the evolution of viscosity with temperature (5). The experiments were conducted in air between 800 and 1000°C in 3-point bending on bars 25 x 4 x 3 mm^3. The tensile stress on the outer fibre ranges from 5 to 40 MPa. The stress exponent, derived using the incremental stress step technique, was equal to one, that is characteristic of a newtonian behaviour. The viscosity, η, is then given by :

$$\eta = \sigma / 3\dot{\epsilon}$$

where $\dot{\epsilon}$ is the mid-point deflection rate and σ the maximum stress on the outer fibre. The strain point (T_s) at $\eta = 10^{13.5}$ Pa.s and the glass transition temperature (T_g) at $\eta = 10^{12}$ Pa.s were determined from the viscosity-temperature curves (Fig. 1). The results are collected in Table 2, together with the values for the β'Sialon ceramic.

Young's modulus was measured in Ar-7 % H_2 gas using an ultrasonic method (6). The heating rate was 1°/mn. The curves, reported in Fig. 2, show a departure from linearity in the temperature range corresponding to the glass transition.

TABLE 2
Experimental data

		G_1	G_2	G_3	β'Sialon
T_g	Dilatometry	863	911	926	
	DTA	905	960	965	982
	Creep	896	945	966	
T_c	DTA	1062	1085	1080	
		1190	1180	1170	
		1295	1285	1270	
Thermal expansion coeff.		$6,60.10^{-6}$	$5,96.10^{-6}$	$4,59.10^{-6}$	$3,1.10^{-6}$.

DISCUSSION

For each experimental technique, the temperatures of the transition points are determined through a conventional procedure. Under these circumstances, it would be risky to compare absolute values that are further sensitive to the heating rates. However, the different methods lead to similar values for each material and to evolutions consistent with each other for the different materials. The thermal expansion coefficient decreases as the nitrogen content increases but remains superior to that of the β'sialon ceramic. The glass transition domain shifts to higher temperature as the nitrogen content of the glasses increases. However, the shift is only 70°C for the highest nitrogen content. The sialon ceramic has a glass transition close to that of glass G3. This temperature corresponds to the onset of the degradation of the mechanical properties of silicon nitride ceramics. The viscosity is enhanced by nitrogen. Replacing bivalent oxygen by trivalent nitrogen increases the degree of interconnexion of the network which explains the increased rigidity.

From the viscosity curves, the activation free energy for viscous flow can be derived assuming an Arrhenius approximation between two successive temperature steps (Fig. 3). As temperature increases, the energy increases up to a maximum corresponding to the strain point temperature, then slowly decreases. Although this evolution is not yet clearly understood, it shows a stricking analogy with that observed for atactic glassy polymers (namely PS and PMMA) for temperatures ranging on both sides of Tg (7). This point calls for further work for clarification. Nevertheless, it can be noted that the activation free energy above Tg falls in the apparent activation energy range for creep in nitrogen ceramics (8).

Samples of glass 2 were heat treated at various temperatures in nitrogen. The different crystalline phases detected by XRD are reported in Table 3.

TABLE 3
Crystalline phases after heat treatment at various temperatures

Temperature °C	1050	1100	1150	1200	1250	1300
Soaking time hrs	90	20	15	7	7	1
Compounds	$\alpha Y_2Si_2{0}_7$ traces	$^{+}\alpha Y_2Si_2{0}_7$	$\alpha Y_2Si_2{0}_7$ traces	$\delta Y_2Si_2{0}_7$	$\beta Y_2Si_2{0}_7$	$\beta Y_2Si_2{0}_7$.
			$\delta Y_2Si_2{0}_7{}^{++}$	$\beta Y_2Si_2{0}_7{}^{+++}$	$Si_2N_2{0}$ traces	$Si_2N_2{0}$

These results agree with the exothermic DTA peaks (Table 2) : the 1080°C, 1180°C, 1270°C signals correspond respectively to the formation of $\alpha\, Y_2Si_2{0}_7$, $\delta\, Y_2Si_2{0}_7$ and $\beta Y_2Si_2{0}_7$ plus $Si_2N_2{0}$.

Above Tg, the evolution of Young's modulus is complex and results from the competition between the rapid decrease in viscosity and the consolidation due to the successive sequences of crystallization (Fig. 2). For the oxide glass, G_1, the crystallization is easy and the modulus increases. In the case of G_2 and G_3, the viscosity is higher and crystallization is more difficult. The moduli keep decreasing until crystallization of α-$Y_2Si_2{0}_7$ has proceeded enough to balance the loss in stiffness, leading to a plateau at about 1050°C. For higher temperatures, the moduli drop again up to 1150°C where $\beta\, Y_2Si_2{0}_7$ and $Si_2N_2{0}$ appear. The sialon ceramic exhibit an evolution quite similar to that of G_3.

+ ASTM n° 21-1457 ; ++ ASTM n° 20-1460 ; +++ ASTM n° 22-1103

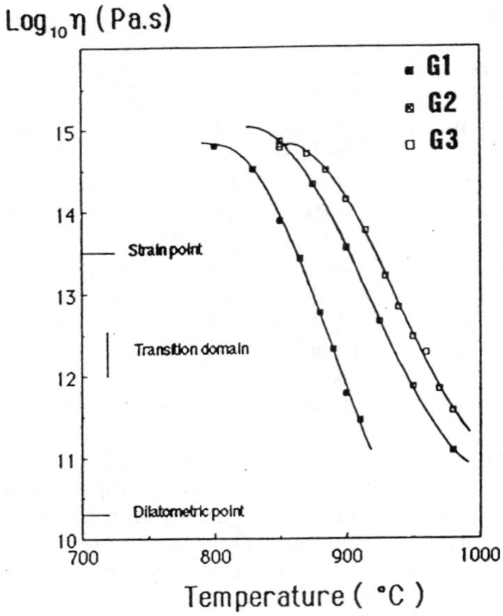

Figure 1 : Evolution of viscosity versus temperature

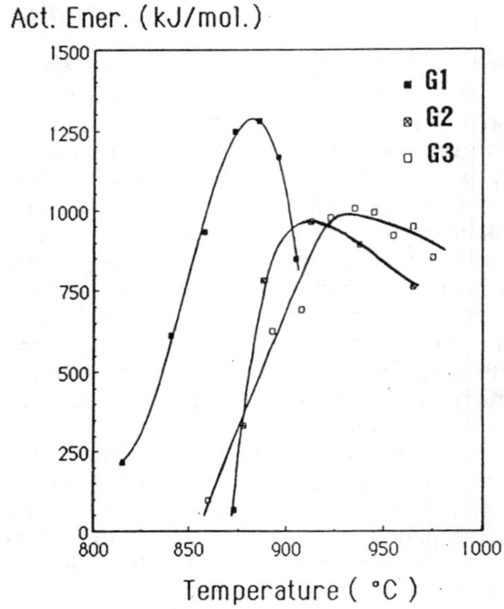

Figure 3 : Activation energy for viscosity

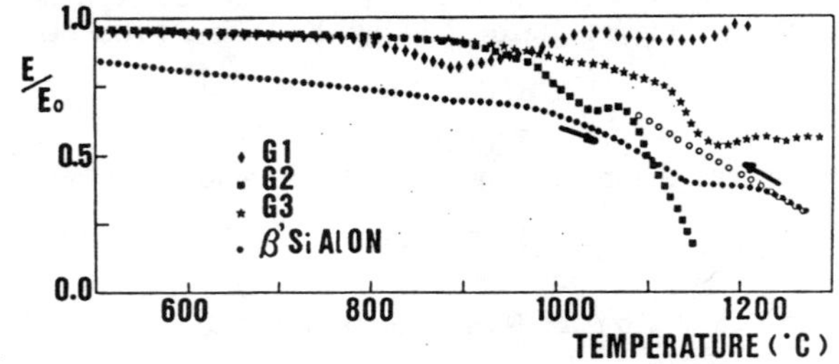

Figure 2 : Young's modulus evolution versus temperature

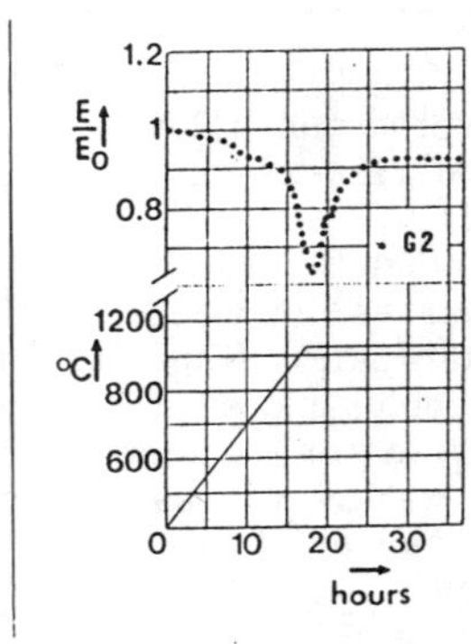

Figure 4 : Evolution of Young's modulus of G_2 during aging.

Isothermal studies of Young's modulus in the crystallization domains allow to follow in situ the kinetics of the transformation as is illustrated in figure 4 for G_2 at 1050°C. After 15 hrs of heat treatment, the modulus reaches a nearly constant value, close to the room temperature initial value.

CONCLUSION

It has been shown that the study of creep of nitrogen glasses can provide knowledge on their rheology. Work is in progress in order to identify the mechanisms controlling the deformation on both sides of the transition temperature domain.

It is confirmed that the mechanical properties of silicon nitride ceramics are linked to the behaviour of the intergranular phases. In addition, Young's modulus measurements are well suited to detect the different transformations and to follow the crystallization of amorphous phases. Isothermal studies should allow the optimization of the post-sintering heat treatments that are known to greatly improve the high temperature properties of silicon nitride ceramics.

Acknowledgement

The authors are endebted to Dr. S. Hampshire, N.I.H.E., Limerick Ireland, for supplying the samples.

REFERENCES

1. Lange, F.F., Davis, B.I. and Clarke, D.R., Compressive creep of Si_3N_4MgO alloys. J. Mater. Sci., 1980, 15, 601-18.

2. Chartier, T., Besson, J.L., Goursat, P., Microstructure, oxidation and creep behaviour of a -Sialon ceramic. Int. J. High Tech. Ceram., 1986, 2, 33-45.

3. Hampshire, S., Drew, R.A.L. and Jack, K.H., Oxynitride glasses. Physics and chemistry of glasses, 1985, 26, 182-86.

4. Verdier, P., Pastuszak, P. and Laurent, Y., Verres et Refract., 1982, 36, 547-56.

5. Hagy, H.E., Experimental evaluation of beam bending method of determining glass viscosities in the range 10^8 to 10^{15} Poises. J. Amer. Cer. Soc., 1986, 46, 93-97.

6. Gault, C., Ultrasonic non destructive evaluation of microstructural changes and degradation of ceramics at high temperature. M.R.S. Fall Meeting, symposium U, Boston, Nov. 1988. To be published.

7. Cavrot, J.P., Haussy, J., Lefebvre, J.M., and Escaig, B, Mater. Sci. Eng., 1978, 36, 95-103.

8. Besson, J.L. and Goursat, P., Optimization of SiAlYON ceramics. Relations : processing - microstructure - properties, in Technical Ceramics, ed. H. Nosbusch and I.V. Mitchell, Elsevier Applied Science Publishers, London, 1988, pp. 127-35.

HIGH TEMPERATURE MECHANICAL SPECTROMETRY ON WC-Co CERMETS.

MARTIN GARDON, SERGE ETIENNE, GILBERT FANTOZZI.
Groupe d'Etudes de Métallurgie Physique et de Physique des Matériaux, U.A. 341
I.N.S.A. de Lyon
F69621 Villeurbanne cedex FRANCE.

ABSTRACT

Ceramic-metal composite materials (WC-25wt%Co) have been studied by mechanical spectrometry from room temperature to 1273K.

After mechanical treatment such as grinding, the αCo(fcc) of the binder phase is transformed to εCo(hcp). The εCo--->αCo allotropic transition has been shown and, by measurement of internal friction spectra as a function of temperature, the temperature range of the transformation has been estimated.

During an annealing over 24 hrs at 1270K, the evolution of the internal friction spectrum has been associated with formation of Co_6W_6C η phase detected by X-ray diffraction.

INTRODUCTION

Widely used as cutting tools, (WC-Co) cermets are subjected to severe mechanical and thermal stresses[1]. In order to understand macroscopical behaviour of WC-Co, we have made some measurements from room temperature to 1273K by mechanical spectrometry. This method is a very sensitive one and is particulary suited to observe microstructural phenomena such as phase transformation, dislocation gliding and climbing, dislocation interaction with defects, allotropic transition, grain boundary effects, etc...

We have measured the internal friction (Q^{-1}) and modulus (G) as a function of temperature for a few frequencies.The spectra are mainly composed of a relaxation peak around 900K and a complex phenomenon above 1070K superimposed over a background increasing nearly exponentially with temperature.

MATERIALS AND METHODS

Used since thirties as cutting tools, WC-Co cermets show both opposite qualities: hardness and toughness, respectively due to carbide phase and cobalt binder phase.

Cermets studied here have been sintered by CERAMETAL, Ltd.. Their composition is 15wt% Co and 85% WC with 1.3 μm grain size.

Samples were prepared as little platelets (50x5x1.2 mm^3) which were then ground by diamond wheel to 0.4 mm thickness.

In order to study WC-Co cermets whose eutectic is near 1590K, we have designed a new internal friction pendulum working under forced oscillations at high temperature. This apparatus works in the temperature range between room temperature and 1273K in a vacuum (<10^{-3} torr). The internal friction and modulus measurements were made at several frequencies during the same thermal treatment.

Complementary characterization methods:

Samples have also been observed by Scanning Electron Microscope (S.E.M.) and X.Ray diffraction.

To observe their microstructure in S.E.M., samples have been polished (3 μm diamond paste) and etched by Murakami reagent in an Ultrasonic cleaner.

To observe the cobalt phase by X-Ray diffraction, tungsten carbides have been electrolytically etched in a caustic soda solution[2].

RESULTS

Samples were studied by mechanical spectrometry (frequency: 1 Hz) from room temperature to 1120K (heating rate: 2K/min.). We obtained a spectrum mainly composed of a peak around 910K and an exponentially mounting background[3]. When the sample is cooled, the peak shifts towards a lower temperature of 860K (fig.1). We repeated the same thermal treatment (heating from room temperature to 1120K then cooling). The obtained spectrum is the same as the first cooling spectrum. When the sample is abraded again and heated in the same way as before, we obtained the same results as in the first heating and cooling.

X-Ray diffraction of an as-sintered sample and a 1273K-annealed sample gives the following results (fig.2): in the first case (abraded sample) we see the preponderence of εCo(hcp) over αCo(fcc), where as in the second case (annealed sample) αCo(fcc) is the only Co present phase, we conclude that the latter is due to a εCo--->αCo allotropic transition.

By treatments at increasing temperatures, the beginning and the end of this allotropic transition range have also been determined (fig.3). We considered that, transformation begins as soon as there is a shift of the curve, around 770K, between heating and cooling spectra and finishes when the heating and cooling spectra became identical. Then we studied the transformation in the temperature range 920K-1170K.

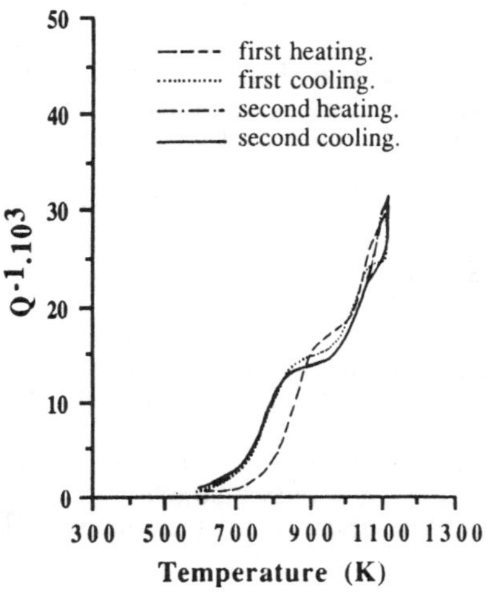

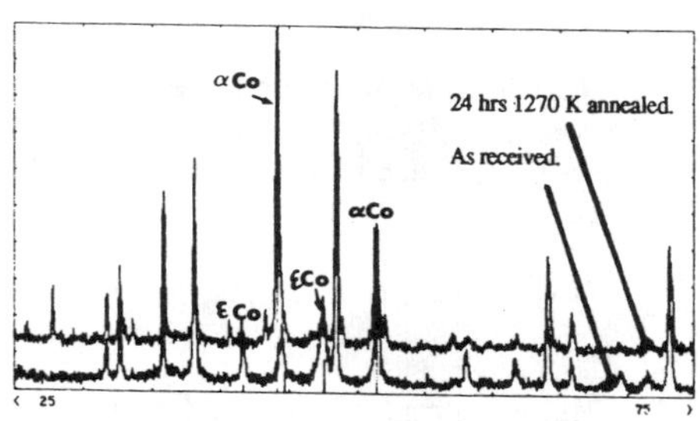

fig.2: X-Ray diffraction spectra of electrolytically etched samples.

fig.1: Evolution of the internal friction spectrum corresponding to εCo--->αCo transition. (frequency: 1 Hz)

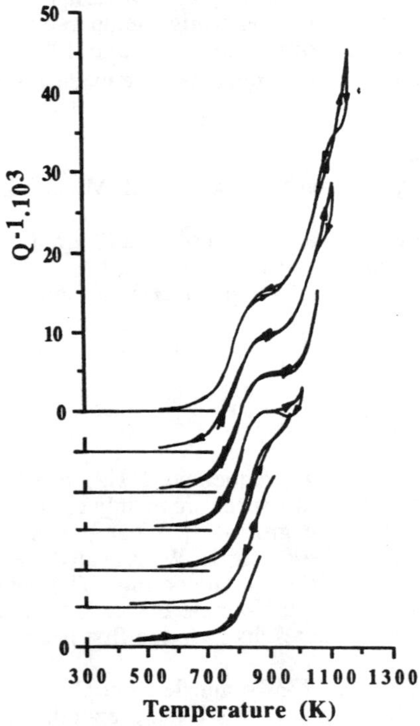

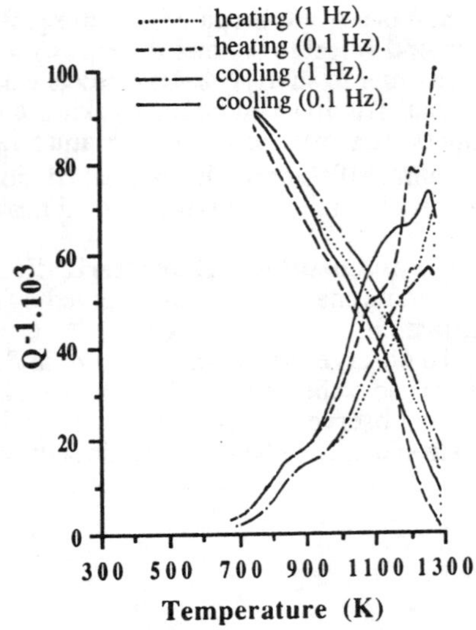

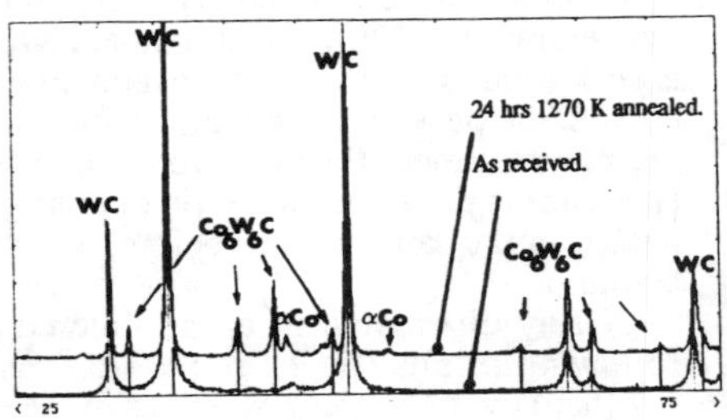

fig.3: determination of the εCo--->αCo temperature transition by increasing temperature treatments.

fig.4: Int. friction(Q^{-1}) and modulus versus temperature. Effect of 24 hrs annealing.

fig.5: X-Ray diffraction spectra. Presence of the Co_6W_6C η phase.

Near high temperatures, (around 1120K and 1190K) two phenomena were observed in the spectra (fig.4). By X-Ray diffraction made on a 1273K annealed sample, a new Co_6W_6C η phase is present (fig.5), as has seen before by other workers also[4-5-6].

DISCUSSION

Many internal friction studies have been done on pure cobalt[7-8-9]. One known result is that of an allotropic transition εCo(hcp)--->αCo(fcc) near 690K which is completely reversible. On the contrary, this transformation εCo--->αCo in WC-Co, if it appears, is located at higher temperature 1050K, but for the reverse transition (αCo--->εCo) to happen mechanical activation is necessary. Differences between pure cobalt transition temperature and WC-Co binder phase transformation is understood by stress interaction of cobalt with WC skeleton[10-13]. Mechanical activation could be obtained by grinding[11-12] or by stress which leads to a strain >1%[14].

In the range above 1020K, the spectrum shows several phenomena caused on one hand by appearance of a new η phase Co_6W_6C and on the other hand by microplasticity decrease during annealing for a few hours at 1273K. This plasticity decrease could be due to precipitate formation (η type, not observed until now on our samples) in the binder phase which could cause the pinning of the dislocations. During cooling some metastable precipitates can disappear to form more Co_6W_6C η phase, which is observed by X-Ray[6].

A more systematic study is in progress which would determine the importance of the binder phase composition (Co content, binder phase components, granulometry, etc...) on high temperature microplasticity.

CONCLUSION

By mechanical spectrometry, the presence in the WC-Co binder phase of a εCo--->αCo allotropic transition has been confirmed near 1050K, and it was observed to be a reversible transformation by mechanical strain at room temperature.

In the high temperature range (above 1020K), results suggested a precipitation phenomenon and a phase transformation accompanied by formation of Co_6W_6C.

AKNOWLEDGEMENTS

We would like to thank Mr. BARBIER (CERAMETAL, Mamer, Luxemburg L8201) for preparation of the samples, helpful discussions and the permission to publish these results.

REFERENCES

1. NAERHEIM, Y., Determining the temperature of cemented carbides from the amount of tungsten dissolved in the binder. Powder metallurgy international, vol. 11, n°1, 1979, pp 31-33.

2. TUMANOV, V.I., TRUKHANOVA, Z.S., FUNKE, V.S. and SCHERBAKOV, V.G., The electrochemical separation and investigation of the connecting and carbide phases of hard tungsten cobalt alloys. Zavodskaya Laboratorya, 1963, vol. 29, n° 3, pp 277-280.

3. AMMANN, J.J., MARI, D., SCHALLER, R. and BONJOUR, C., High temperature behaviour of WC-Co hard metal studied by internal friction, Proc. 9 th Int. Symposium on metallurgy and material science, 1988, RISO.

4. JAYARAM, V., SINCLAIR, R. and ROWCLIFFE, D.J., Deformation enhanced decarburization of WC-Co. Scripta Metallurgica, 1986, vol. 20, pp 55-60.

5. GAHM, H., KARAGÖZ, S. and KOMPEK, G., Metallographic methods for the characterisation of the microstructure of cemented carbides. Practical metallography, 18, 1981, pp 14-30.

6. POLLOCK, C.B. and STADELMAIER, H.H., The eta carbides in the Fe-W-C and Co-W-C systems. Metallurgical transactions, 1970, vol. 1, april, pp 767-770.

7. SELLE, J.E., Le frottement interne du cobalt. Cobalt, 1969, 45, pp 186-189.

8. WINTERHAGER, H. and KRÜGER, J., Le cobalt pur et ses propriétés. Cobalt, 1966, 30, pp 27-38.

9. BIDAUX, J.E., SCHALLER, R. and BENOIT, W., Study of the H.C.P.-F.C.C. phase transition in cobalt by accoustic measurements. Acta Metallurgica, 1989, 37, n°3, pp 803-811.

10. GIAMEI, A.F., BURMA,J., RABIN, S., CHENG, M. and FREISE, E.J., The role of allotropic transformation for cobalt alloys. Cobalt, 1968, 40, pp 140-155.

11. SUZUKI,H., YAMAMOTO,T. and SAKANOUE, H., Binder phase transformation in WC-Co cemented carbides. J. Japan Inst. Met., 1968, 32, pp 993-997.

12. WIRMARK,G. and DUNLOP, G.C., Phase transformations in the binder phase of Co-W-C cemented carbides. Science of hard materials, WISWANADHAM, R.K., ROWCLIFFE, D.J. and GURLAND, J., 1983, Eds Plenum Pub. Corp., New York, pp 311-327.

13. LE ROUX, H., The martensitic transformation and the transverse rupture strength of heat treated WC 25 wt % Co Hardmetals. 10 th Plansee Seminar, 1981, vol.1, Metallwerk Plansee, Reutte, Austria, pp 529-534.

14. MANLANG, L., XIAOYING, H., SHITIAN, D., DAOIN, S., YUMEI, C. and ZHENMEI, Y., Diffraction-contrast study of microstructure and deformation process of WC-Co cemented carbide. Int. J. Refract. and Hard Met., september 83, pp 129-132.

CONTROLLED FRACTURE EXPERIMENTS ON SIC-WHISKER REINFORCED ALUMINA

Christian Plappert, Hartmut Frei, Georg Grathwohl
Universität Karlsruhe, Institut für Keramik im Maschinenbau
Haid und Neu Straße 7 · D-7500 Karlsruhe

ABSTRACT

A miniaturized four-point bending device is used to study crack propagation in a SiC-whisker reinforced Al_2O_3/ZrO_2 ceramic under simultaneous observation in a scanning electron microscope. Crack resistance measurements and their interpretation using photographs of the microstructure under load are presented.

1. INTRODUCTION

The progress in the development of advanced structural ceramics is characterized by a remarkable increase of their strength and fracture toughness. Further improvement of these essential mechanical properties is still necessary and requires a fundamental understanding of the crack propagation processes. In the new types of ceramic microstructure, e.g. whisker-, particle- or platelet-reinforced ceramics the relevant crack growth processes are not understood in an adequate manner. These processes are responsible e.g. for the *R-curve* behaviour which is tried to be explained by the formation of a process zone around the crack tip or by wake effects of interacting forces between the crack surfaces. In order to understand the formation and extension of the relevant micro- and macrocracks, SEM-studies offer a powerful tool due to the ample range of magnification and large depth of focus.

2. DESIGN OF THE TEST DEVICE

In order to avoid any mechanical, electromagnetic or hydraulic arrangement for load transfer into the SEM vacuum chamber, a piezoelement transducer has been used.

The maximal expansion of 45 µm of the piezoelement used is achieved at a voltage of 1000 V. The expansion is measured with high accuracy by application of strain gauges

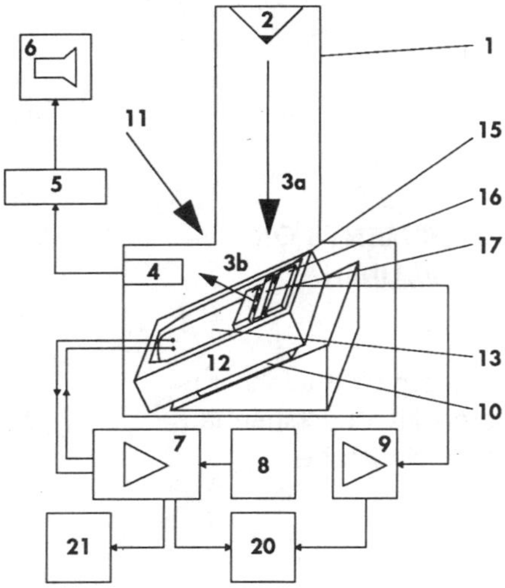

Figure 1. Schematic diagram of the arrangement of the bending device

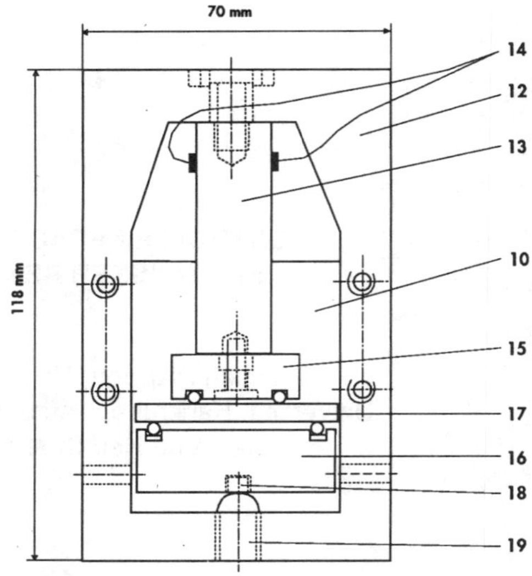

Figure 2. Four-point bending fixture with specimen.

1 SEM column
2 filament
3a primary electron beam
3b secondary electrons
4 electron detector
5 signal processing
6 TV-screen
7 amplifier and control unit for the piezo-electric displacement transducer
8 function generator
9 amplifier for the force measurement quartz crystal transducer
10 commercial stage of the SEM
11 view of Fig. 2
12 frame
13 piezo-electric displacement transducer
14 electrical connections to amplifier and controller
15 inner support
16 outer support
17 specimen
18 quartz crystal transducer for force measurement
19 prestressing screw
20 x-y-recorder
21 oscilloscope

to the stack. Thus, the control unit allows the piezoelement to be positioned reproducibly with a deviation of less than 0.1 μm. Due to this control unit, hysteresis effects and drifting phenomena are overcome; thus, a linear relation between applied voltage and expansion is achieved throughout the whole working range of the translator even under the action of variable counteracting forces.

The inner loading fixture (15) with a distance of 20 mm between the two loading rollers, is mechanically connected to the piezotranslator. The other part of the fixture which has the two outer loading rollers (16) at a distance of 40 mm from each other, can be moved in all directions; it operates as a self-aligning system upon preloading of the specimen by the screw (19) shown in figure (2). By this arrangement, a pure bending loading mode is reached in the specimen with the dimension 3,5 x 4,5 x 45 mm^3 as they are also used for tests in normal mechanical testing machines. Thus, the results of the *in situ* experiments can be compared with the more conventional mechanical test results.

The material used for the loading rollers is sintered silicon carbide. This ceramic material is favoured due to its high level of hardness, stiffness and resistance against deformation. In contrast to hardened steel it also has the advantage that the influence of ferromagnetic forces on the electron beam can be excluded. There are several reasons to give preference to a four-point bending support over a three-point one. For very long cracks (relative to the specimen size) the superposition of tensile stresses at the crack tip and compressive stresses under the loading roller are encountered in three-point arrangements, influencing crack propagation and crack resistance measurements. Another advantage of the four-point bending system is the constant bending moment in the inner part of the specimen (here over 20 mm). This allows a quick and easy specimen change because exact positioning of a precracked specimen relative to the single loading roller is not necessary.

The maximum displacement of 45 µm of the piezotranslator leads to a midpoint deflection of the specimen of about 62 µm in this fixture. This value is sufficient for most experiments with high strength ceramics, although it can be increased further by prestressing the specimen with the screw (19) before the fixture is mounted in the SEM chamber. This can be continued up to the maximum load of 1000 N piezotranslator.

A quartz load transducer is applied between the fixture (16) and the prestressing screw (19). The charge generated by this miniaturized transducer during loading is amplified and changed into a voltage which is directly proportional to the load. The small size of the transducer (5 mm ø x 5 mm) is advantageous; it also exhibits a high stiffness with a compression of only 1 µm under a load of 300 N. A resolution of 0.1 N is achieved.

The frame (12), which incorporates all the parts described is made of a bulk piece of non-magnetic steel. With this rigid design it was possible to minimize the deformation of the device during loading of a specimen.

The small size of the whole device (118 x 70 x 18 mm^3) allows the utilisation of the commercial stage with many SEM models. Expensive and time-consuming modifications are not necessary. Experiments have been successfully conducted not only with a SEM ISI 60 (Akashi Corp., Japan) (figure 1) but also with a SEM Stereoscan 360 (Cambridge Instruments, UK) and a DSM 940 (Zeiss, Germany) after simple plug connection to the x, y, z stage. There is no need for additonal mechanical feedthrough. The electrical connections necessary for the piezoelectric displacement transducer and the force measurement were put together on a blank flange in the form of vacuum sealed BNC feedthroughs.

In addition to static or manually controlled bending experiments there is the possibility of creating arbitrary load time relations by using a function generator. It allows cyclic tests in a frequency range of $1 \times 10^{-4} - 3 \times 10^{2}$ Hz. The upper limit of the frequency is given by the specific form and amplitude of the cycle and the applied load. This is due to the capacity of the piezoelectric displacement transducer which requires time to change its state of charge. It is also possible to superimpose a stationary displacement to the cycling part of the piezo displacement. In this way oscillations around a fixed value of midpoint deflection of the specimen is provided. By observing the displacement signal on an oscilloscope (21) the movement of the displacement transducer can be controlled and stopped at each required position. It is then possible to view the specimen not only in the TV mode but also to photograph stationary images on the high resolution monitor screen. Load and dispacement are recorded by an x-y recorder. With this equipment even experiments such as controlled fracture at deformation velocities of a few μm h^{-1} are also realised as fatigue experiments at 10^6 cycles h^{-1}.

3. RESULTS

For the experiments in the bending device the specimens of whisker reinforced alumina were precracked by the bridge method (Brugger) to get a naturally sharp crack about 3 mm length. These specimens were then loaded in the SEM with a deformation velocity of 200 nm min^{-1}. The record of the load and displacement of the alumina specimen (figure 3) shows a linear elastic function in the beginning and there was no crack propagation visible on the SEM screen. Later, there is a coincidence between the deviation from the straight line and the visible crack propagation. The load withstood by the specimen decreases and the bending displacement has to be increased to obtain further crack propagation. The crack propagates in a fully controlled manner through the specimen and it is possible to stop the crack at any time.

The measurement of the maximal stress σ_B and the crack length a allows to determine the stress intensity factor K_{IC}:

$$K_{IC} = \sigma_B \cdot \sqrt{a} \cdot Y(a/W) \quad (1)$$

W is the specimen height and Y is a dimensionless geometry factor. The stress intensity factor at each point of a new crack initiation was then calculated and related to the dimensionless crack length a/W. This allows to determine 10-20 K_{IC} values from a single specimen test. The results were plotted in figure 4 as crack growth resistance curves (*R-curves*) in terms of the critical stress intensity factor.

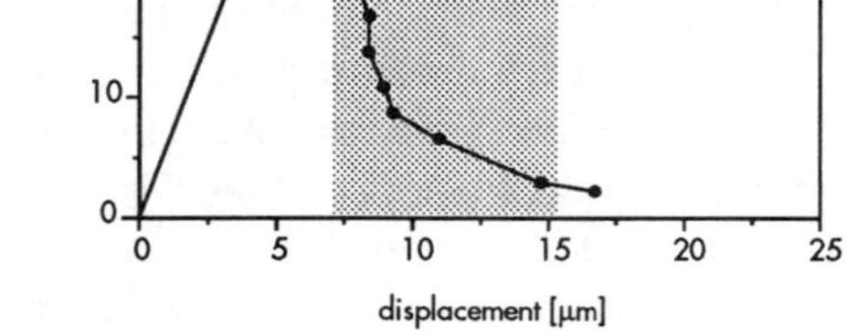

Figure 3. Load-displacement diagram of a controlled fracture experiment on SiC reinforced alumina.

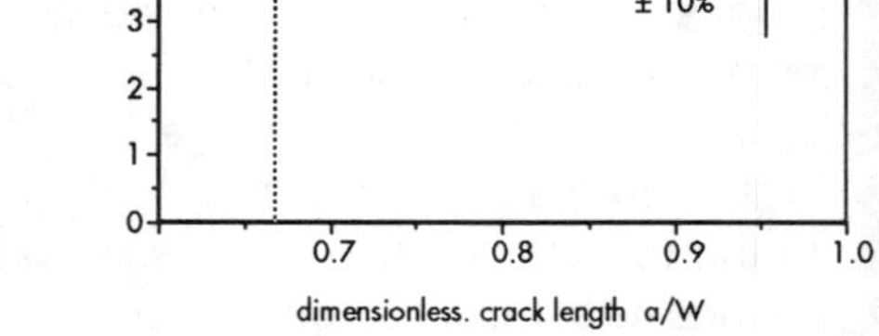

Figure 4. Stress intensity factors for increasing crack length for a SiC reinforced alumina.

The unexpected low value of K_{IC} of 4,3 $MPam^{1/2}$ for this modern material is due to the lack of reinforcing efficiency of the SiC-whiskers. Scanning electron microscopy examination of the crack-microstructure interaction revealed limited whisker pull-out and crack bridging, which would be responsible for enhanced fracture toughness. Possible reasons for the low crack resistance curve might be problems in the fabrication process, especially in the incorporation of the SiC-whiskers to the alumina matrix and low whisker quality. In our case the bonding of the whisker is to strong, so that whisker fracture occurs before whisker pull-out and crack bridging can be observed. Such pull-out processes dissipate more energy than does whisker fracture.

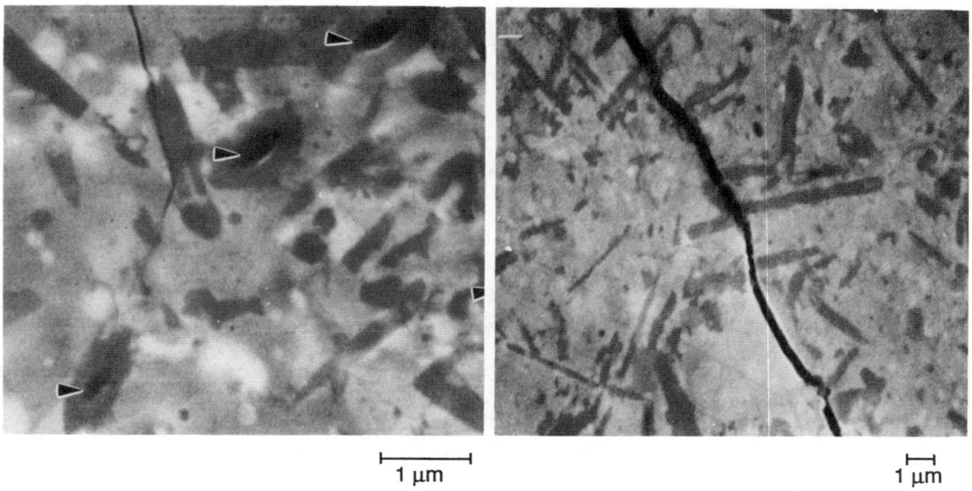

Figure 5. Crack tip at a magnification of 20.000 x. No microcracking zone in front of the crack tip visible. Cavities in the middle of the whisker axes confirm the low whisker quality and the low K_{IC} values. The other picture shows the crack path with broken whisker. No whisker pull-out is obseved.

An example for the low whisker quality in the tested material is shown in figure 5. Cavites in the middle axis of the whisker were observed, so the crack breaks the whisker instead of deflecting and whisker pull-out. The picture shows the crack tip under load at a magnification of 20.000 x. The proposal of a frontal microcracking zone, the so called prozess zone, cannot be confirmed.

4. CONCLUSIONS

Controlled fracture experiments in a miniaturized four point bending machine provided multiple data points for generation of a *R-curve* from a single specimen test. Simultaneous observation in a scanning electron microscope as well as in an optical microscope and under various surrounding conditions such as vacuum and normal atmosphere allow the correlation between quantitative values and the microstructure of the material. The determination of the stress intensity factor under vacuum in a SEM microscope have the result in an unexpected low value of 4,3 $MPam^{1/2}$. Possible reasons are problems in the fabrication process as well as low whisker quality, which were observed by the tested specimens.

Brugger, N. "Zum Verhalten von Rissen in keramischen Werkstoffen unter statischer, langsam ansteigender und schwingender Belastung". Dissertation Universität Karlsruhe, 1986.

HIGH TEMPERATURE MECHANICAL BEHAVIOUR OF SiC-SiC COMPOSITE MATERIALS

Moussa **GOMINA**, Pascal **FOURVEL**, Marie-Hélène **ROUILLON**
LERMAT, URA 1317, ISMRa-Université
Bd du Maréchal Juin, 14032 CAEN Cedex, FRANCE

ABSTRACT

Three point bending tests have been performed on flatwise specimens of a SiC-SiC laminar composite material to check the influence of specimen thickness and temperature (22°C to 1200°C in air) on the strength and the elastic modulus and the fracture mechanisms. It appeared an important modification due to the oxydation effects on the shear stress and the fibre/matrix interface.

INTRODUCTION

Today a few fibrous composite materials are available for specific applications under high stress, high temperature or severe environment conditions. The most promising of them are made of carbon or silicon carbide matrix.
The contribution of the wake region is shown to be an important factor to the toughening of these composites at room temperature (1). Since these materials are destined to high temperature utilizations, the question is whether the effects of the wake region will remain important ; that is will a rising R curve be preserved. We intent to check these points for a SiC(Nicalon)/CVI-βSiC matrix composite. But the first step in such a program is to deal with the evolutions of the fracture stress, elastic modulus, loading curves behaviour and fracture mechanisms with test temperature and specimen depth in a severe condition, i.e. in air from 22°C to 1200°C. That is the matter of this paper.

MATERIALS AND METHODS

This report concerns SiC-SiC materials in which the reinforcement is a two directional isotropic tissue made of Nicalon SiC fibres. These so-called SiC fibres really contain SiC (≃ 65 wt%) and carbon as aggregates and SiO_2 deeply present in the fibre. The oxygen is introduced at the beginning of the process when the starting polymer is treated at low temperature in air. The matrix deposited using the CVI method is a β-SiC type of good mechanical quality. The porosity is the third phase in this material ($\simeq$ 15 vol%). Its size distribution, the localization and the orientation of the pores (2) are of great influence on the failure modes depending on the specimen orientation. The material is designed to contain 38 vol% fibres with a final density between 2.4 to 2.6. Extensive descriptions of the materials are now available in the litterature (3).

Only flatwise orientation specimens were investigated. All the bending specimens were 70 mm long and 9.5 mm wide. Using a span of 60 mm, the span to depth ratios were 6.3 (thickness 9.5 mm with 23 laminates), 12 (thickness 5 mm with 16 laminates) and 24 (thickness 2.5 mm with 7 laminates).

Three point bending tests were performed on a INSTRON machine at a cross head speed of 20 μm/min, using a 10 KN load cell. The displacement of the load application point was measured under the upper knife using two linear variable differential transducers (LVDT), through alumina rods.

The push rods, the rollers and the bearing plates were made in polycrystalline alumina (AF 997, DESMARQUEST) and were permanently set in the heating system.

The specimens were put in the furnace once the test temperature was reached. The excellent thermal shock resistance of the material allows this procedure which shortened the duration of exposure at high temperature.

RESULTS AND DISCUSSION

Measurements of the flexural strength and the elastic modulus of unnotched specimens were performed in order to check the influences of specimen thickness and temperature. These two parameters, when associated to the loading rate and duration, are very important for parts survival predictions.

Figure 1a shows the load versus deflection curve for a specimen tested at 700°C ; this is the general behaviour for the temperature values $T \leqslant 700$°C. This non-linearity is less pronounced at higher temperatures (Fig. 1b).

The maximum flexural tensile stress σ_R was calculated at fracture using simple elastic beam theory and the resultant data are represented in figure 2a as a function of temperature for the three groups of specimens studied. The strength increases slightly for temperature range 22°C $< T \leqslant 700$°C, except for the thinner specimens, and then continuously drops off.

These results look very different from the one obtained by BERNHART et al. when testing this material under vacuum (4) or by DAUCHIER et al. when testing in an $Ar-H_2$ atmosphere (5).

The elastic modulus E measured from the linear part of the load-deflection curve appears to be a slightly decreasing function of the test temperature (Fig. 2b), although the measured values on thick specimens are to be taken with care. The initial value of 210 GPa at 22°C for the composite (with dimensions 70*9.5*5mm³) is identical to the fibres modulus and the decrease with temperature beyong 900°C may be due to a structural modification of the fibres or, more likely to a not so good fibres/matrix adhesion.

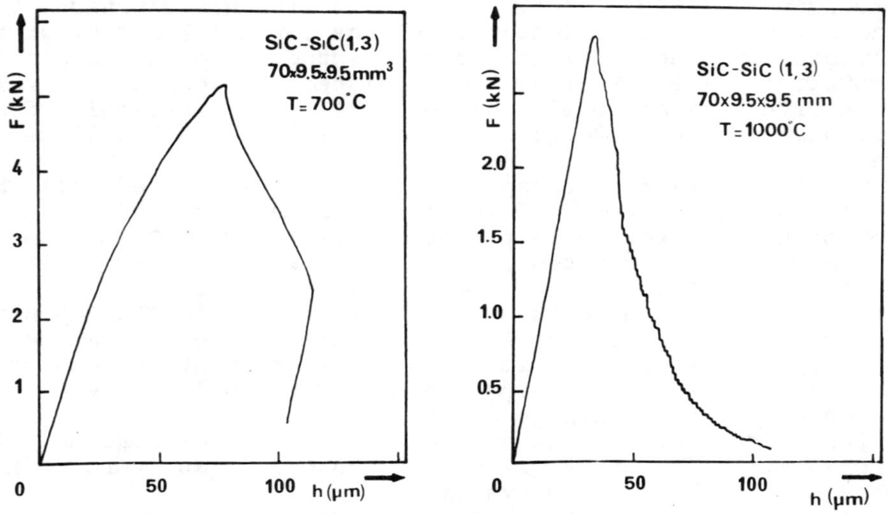

(a) (b)

Figure 1. Three point bending monotonic loading curves of SiC-SiC materials tested in air : a) non linearity before maximum load at 700°C - b) total linearity at 1000°C.

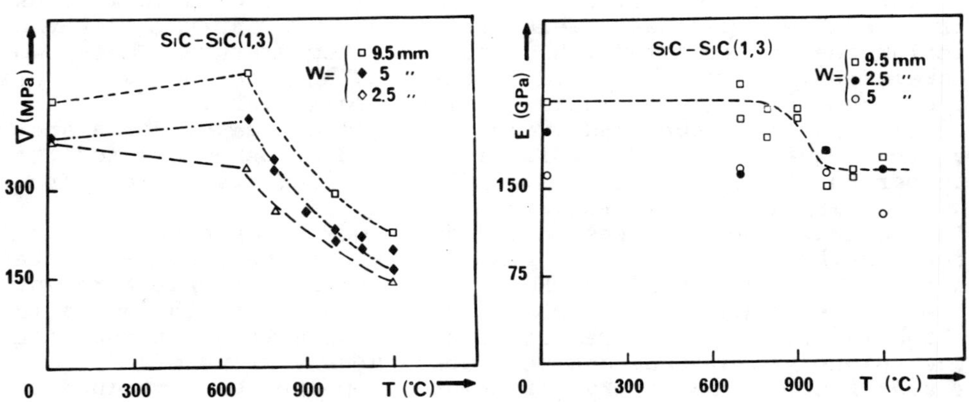

(a) (b)

Figure 2. Flexural strength (a) and elastic modulus (b) of SiC-SiC materials as a function of test temperatures in air for the three specimens depths, W.

A question arises about using three point bending tests to evaluate flexural strength and Young modulus for composite materials made of laminates.
Depending on the ratio of the span to the specimen depth, the shear stress effects can be appreciable. This question have been recently addressed by RIEF et al. (6).
The usual shear stress τ is increased by an amount τ_L generated by the laminated structure of the material with a non-perfect bound between the laminates :

$$\tau_L = \frac{3}{2} \frac{PL}{BW^2} \times \frac{\Delta W}{W} \qquad (1)$$

The total shear stress $(\tau+\tau_L)$ and the measured tensile stress σ_R are represented as a function of the geometrical ration L/W on figures 3(a) and 3(b).

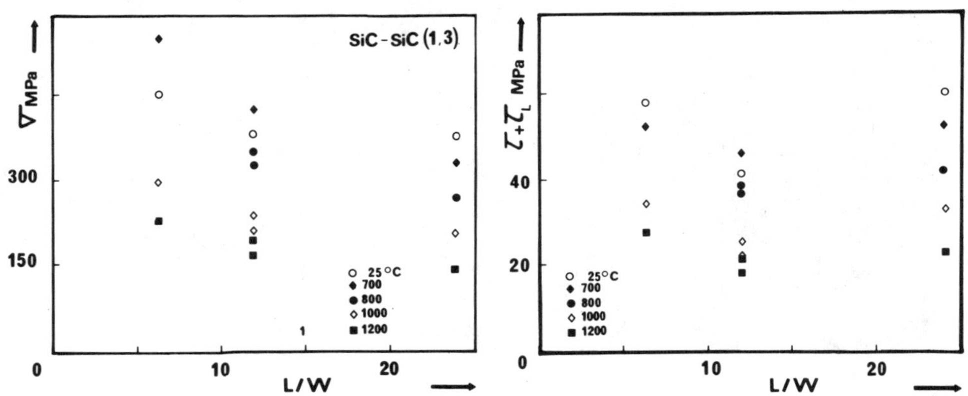

(a) (b)

Figure 3. Flexural strength (a) and total shear stress (b) of SiC-SiC materials as a function of the geometrical ratio L/W, for test temperature in air.

It appears that the tensile stress σ_R is a decreasing function of L/W whereas $(\tau+\tau_L)$ is almost constant. Over the temperature range investigated, the decrease of the tensile stress is less pronounced (380 MPa at 22°C and 180 MPa at 1200°C) than the decrease of the total shear stress (60 MPa at 22°C and 22 MPa at 1200°C).
The variations of the tensile stress and elastic modulus with temperature coupled with a pronounced decrease of the total shear stress $(\tau+\tau_L)$ denote a deep structural modification of the material.
The proposed sequences of the rupture of notched specimens are :

- At relatively low temperatures (from room temperature to 700°C), in a first stage the specimen deforms elastically due to the progressive loading of the fibres (the measured composite modulus corresponds to the fibres modulus). The non-linear part of the P-h curve should correspond to the fibres sliding in the matrix (shear stress effects) and to the matrix cracking. Ahead of the crack, the matrix fails first and the fibres break beyond P_{max} ; appreciable pull-out lengths are observed (figure 4a).

- At higher temperatures (T > 800°C) the main feature is the interface modification in air (it grows hard) which prevents the fibres sliding. This results in less important total deformation and residual displacements. The material behaves brittle (figure 4b).

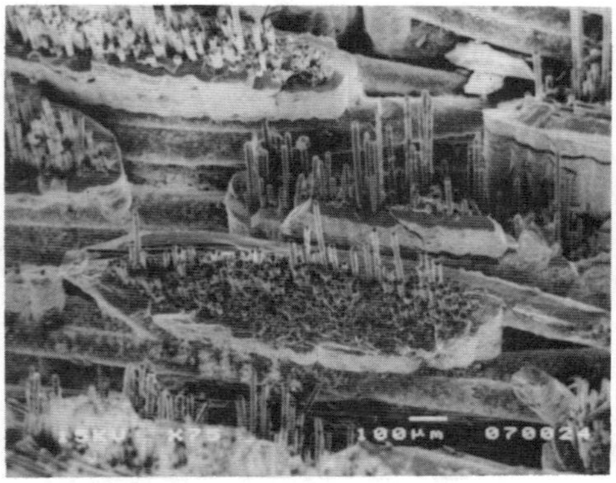

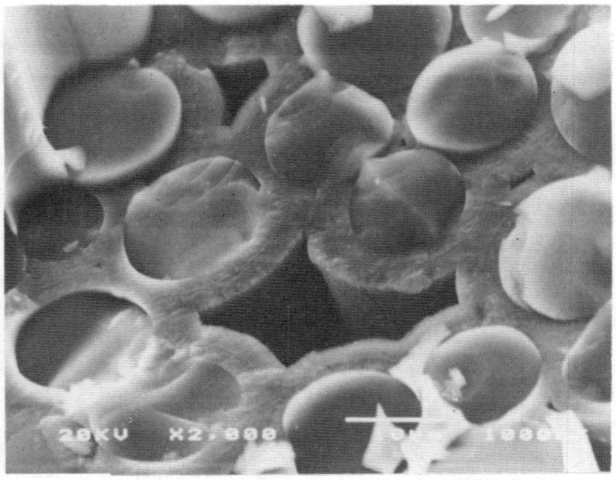

(a) (b)

Figure 4. Scanning electron micrographs of the rupture surfaces of SiC-SiC composites : a) from 22°C to 700°C - b) at 1300°C.

To confirm this structural modification, transmission electron microscope observations were performed on specimens just annealed in air at 700°C, 900°C and 1300°C. The results indicate no modification of the fibre matrix interface for T ⩽ 900°C, but a deep modification was observed at 1300°C : decohesions appear between the fibre and the carbonaceous interphase primarily designed to increase the toughness. Then the fibres are exposed to oxydation. This is the reason why the SiC-SiC materials are coated when designed to be used in oxydizing environments.

CONCLUSIONS

We have studied the thermomechanical behaviour of a SiC-SiC material in conditions far from those they are designed for. Deep modifications of the mechanical properties are due to the reduction of the total shear stress and to the oxydation of the carbonaceous fibre/matrix interphase at high temperatures in air.

ACKNOWLEDGMENTS

Parts of this work has been performed under the BRITE Program of the European Commission, Project P-1348-6-85, Contract RI 1B-0098.

REFERENCES

1. Pan, H.C., Sakai, M., Warren, J.W. and Bradt, R.C., Tailoring multiphase and composite ceramics. The Pennsylvania State University, University Park, Penn., USA July 17-19, 1985 ; ed. R.E. Tressler, G.L. Messing, C.G. Pantano and R.E. Newham, Plenum Press, Mat. Sci. Res., 1986, 20, pp. 631-638.

2. Gomina, M., Chermant, J.L. and Coster, M., Radial distribution of the fibres in composites materials. Acta Stereol., 1983, pp. 179-184, 2 suppl. I.

3. Lamicq, P., Bernhart, G.A., Dauchier, M.M. and Mace, J.G., Amer. Ceram. Soc. Bull., 1985, 64, 298.

4. Bernhart, G., Lamicq, P. and Mace, J., Fiabilité des composites céramiques-céramiques. Ind. Céram., 1985, 790, 1/85.

5. Dauchier, M., Lamicq, P. and Mace, J., Comportement thermomécanique des céramiques-céramiques. Rev. Int. Htes Temp. Refract., 1982, 19, pp. 285-299.

6. Rief, C., Lindner, M. and Kromp, K., Experimental investigations and model proposal on damage mechanisms in a RCC-material. Submitted to ASTM.

AGEING OF AN Al_2O_3 - ZrO_2 - SiC COMPOSITE

R. MOLINS, N. DE DAVE, A. THOREL
Ecole Nationale Supérieure des Mines de Paris
Centre des Matériaux, B.P. 87, 9003 Evry Cedex, FRANCE

ABSTRACT

Al_2O_3-ZrO_2-Si C composite belongs to the new generation of high performance materials devoted to thermomechanical applications. Using analytical microscopy, we investigate in this paper the microstructure for the as sintered material+, the composite reinforced with preoxidized fibers+ and the composite after ageing at high temperature.

INTRODUCTION

Ceramic cutting tools must display high strength as well as high toughness during a limited life time. Though most of them exhibit an acceptable strength level, they often suffer a lack in toughness. Thoughening mechanisms have been recently reviewed [1]. They mainly involve the presence of second phase particles in the material which can dissipate elastic energy either through an allotropic transformation or by particles decohesion in the stress field associated with the propagating crack [1, 2, 3]. Achievement of toughening at higher temperature requires the coupling between two phases with interfaces that give rise to a non linear response to the sollicitation.

These requirements are found in Al_2O_3-ZrO_2-SiC whiskers ceramics where elastic energy dissipation occurs in the process zone associated with extending cracks via three principal mechanisms [4] : crack deflection, fiber pullout, wake toughening or bridging and transformation toughening [5, 6, 7, 8].

+ **provided by Desmarquest**

EXPERIMENTAL

The basic material under consideration (A) has been elaborated from a mixture of α-Al_2O_3 powder, ZrO_2 + 3% mole Y_2O_3 powder and β Sic whiskers according to the ratio $\frac{SiC + ZrO_2}{Al_2O_3} = 0.7$. This leads to a fracture toughness KIC = 7 MPa $\sqrt{m}$ and to a flexural strength $\simeq$ 1000 MPa up to 1000°C [9]. For the material B, prior to sintering, the SiC whiskers have been submitted to a treatment at 800°C during one hour. Material C is identical to mat A, but has undergone a post elaboration heat treatment at 1400°C during 30 mn associated with drastic heating and cooling (300°C/mn).

Microstructural observations have been achieved with an analytical TEM-SEM Philips EM 430 equipped with X-ray and electron energy loss spectrometers.

RESULTS AND DISCUSSION

The observations on the <u>material A</u> show that the SiC whiskers are always associated with at least one ZrO_2 particle (Fig. 1), and that ZrO_2 and SiC inhibit the Al_2O_3 grain growth. Fig. 2 shows a SiC fiber in the grain growth <111> orientation, the {112} planes being then viewed edge on. Fig 3 shows a SiC fiber close to a <112> orientation; it is seen that the {112} planes are rough with small facets on alternating {111} planes and with probable emergent polytypoïds phases. According to thermodynamical considerations drawn from elaboration conditions, no intermediate layer could be detected at the fiber matrix interface.

The thermal expansion coefficients of Al_2O_3, SiC and ZrO_2 are respectively $8,8.10^{-6}/°C$, $9,6\,10^{-6}/°C$ and $4,7\,10^{-6}/°C$. Then the fiber is under radial and longitudinal compression whereas the matrix is under a hoop tension, an axial tension and a radial compression. Then any crack is attracted to the fiber : microcracking and crack deflection can occur but the effective shear resistance at the interface is increased. Using Shetty expression [11], we estimated the critical whisker length for pullout and found it equal to ~ 3.5 μm. Then, considering this low value as well as the roughness of the {112} growth planes, it is reasonable to think that whisker pullout is possible but must be limited. We verified by electron diffraction and in situ transformation that a certain proportion of the ZrO_2 particles was in the tetragonal form. Consequently whiskers bridging, crack deflection and to a lesser extend transformation toughening, seem to be the most probable toughening mechanisms in mat. A.

For the <u>material B</u>, the aim of the fiber preoxidation treatment at 800°C was to slightly debase the fiber-matrix interface and then enhance the fiber pullout mechanism, the probable chemical reaction being :

$SiC \rightarrow Si + C$, $Si + O_2 \rightarrow SiO_2$

This ageing treatment is expected to give rise to a flattening of the facetted Al_2O_3 / {112} β SiC interfaces, through an evaporation and condensation process and to the appearance of a very thin silica film that blunts the crack initiation notches provided by the faceting. But, Fig. 4 shows that no film is present at the SiC/Al_2O_3 as well as SiC/ZrO_2 interfaces. Fig. 5 gives evidence of silica rich glassy pockets, confirmed via electron induced effects and microanalyses. Furthermore, we have seen triple junctions with a semi crystalline structure which is compatible with that of graphite (Fig. 6). A vitreous film was also suspected at an Al_2O_3/ZrO_2 interface : this can lead to a spontaneous transformation of the ZrO_2 particles [11]. This treatment seems to be insufficient to obtain a continuous silica layer at the SiC/matrix interface [12, 13]. During sintering, the films retracted probably because of dielectric or crystallographic considerations. Fiber pullout is probably favoured by the smoothing of the SiC surfaces.

A general view of <u>material C</u> is displayed on Fig. 7, showing that most of the interfaces are debased. The degradation observed cannot be explained only in terms of mechanical sollicitation of interfaces.

The chemical interactions at SiC/Al_2O_3 interfaces could be expressed as follows [14] :

$$\left\{\begin{array}{l} 2\,Al_2O_3 + 3\,SiC \leftrightharpoons 3\,SiO_2 + Al_4C_3 \\ 2\,SiO_2 + 3\,Al_2O_3 \leftrightharpoons 3\,Al_2O_3\,.\,2\,SiO_2 \end{array}\right.$$

leading to the formation of a glassy film and to a fine precipitation of Al_4C_3. (Fig. 8). At the SiC/ZrO_2 interfaces, similar reaction could occur :

$$SiC + ZrO_2 \leftrightharpoons SiO_2\,.\,ZrO_2 + ZrC \text{ (or C)}$$

Although no mechanical testing have been performed after such a treatment, it seems clear that the fracture strength has been weakened even if the toughness remains at an acceptable level.

CONCLUSION

Interfaces in Al_2O_3-ZrO_2-SiC_w composite with various treatment have been accurately studied. Interfaces in the as sintered material have been found second phase free. Pre-oxidizing treatment on fibers at 800°C probably forms a thin layer of oxide that retracts from Al_2O_3/SiC and ZrO_2/SiC interfaces during the sintering process. Small silica rich glassy pockets are then formed as well as 2 nm wide vitreous films at many Al_2O_3/ZrO_2 grain boundaries. For that material, an enhancement of fiber pullout and a diminishing of the transformation toughening is to be expected. A drastic treatment simulating the thermal sollicitation during the cutting of metals is found to debase mechanically and chemically the bonding of interfaces.

These first results show that microstructural informations down to this scale are necessary to understand the final behaviour of such complex materials.

REFERENCES

[1] Evans, A.G., Mat. Sc. Research, vol 21, Edited by J.A. Pask and A.G. Evans, p. 775-794.

[2] Claussen, N., Advances in Ceramics, vol 12, Edited by N. Claussen, M. Rühre and A.H. Hener, pp 325-51.

[3] Lamon, J. et al, J. Mat. Sci. (21) 2277-2282 (1986).

[4] Rice, R.W., Ceram. Eng. Sci. Proc., 6(7-8)589 - 607 (1985).

[5] Fowlkes, C.W., J. Adhes., 4, 1-36 (1973).

[6] Holmquist, G.A. et al, J. Am. Ceram. Soc., 59(9) 384-86 (1976).

[7] Sueh, H. et al, J. Am. Ceram. Soc., 71(11) 929-33 (1988).

[8] Becher, P.F. et al, J. Am. Ceram. Sic., 71(12) 1050-61 (1988).

[9] Mathieu, P. et al, Silicates Industries; (9-10)143-146 (1988).

[10] Shetty, D.K., Current awareness Bulletin Metals and Ceramics information Center, Batelle Columbus Labs., 118 (12), 1982.

[11] Westmacott, K.H., et al, Ultramicroscopy [22] 15-6 (1987).

[12] Tiegs, T.N., Becher, P.F. and Harris, L.A., Mat. Sc., Research vol 21, 911-97.

[13] Kriven, W.M., Vantenderloo, G., Tiegs, T.N. and Becher, P.F., Mat. Sc. Research vol 21, 939-947.

[14] Luthra, K.L., J. Am. Ceram. Soc. 71 [12] 1114-20 (1988).

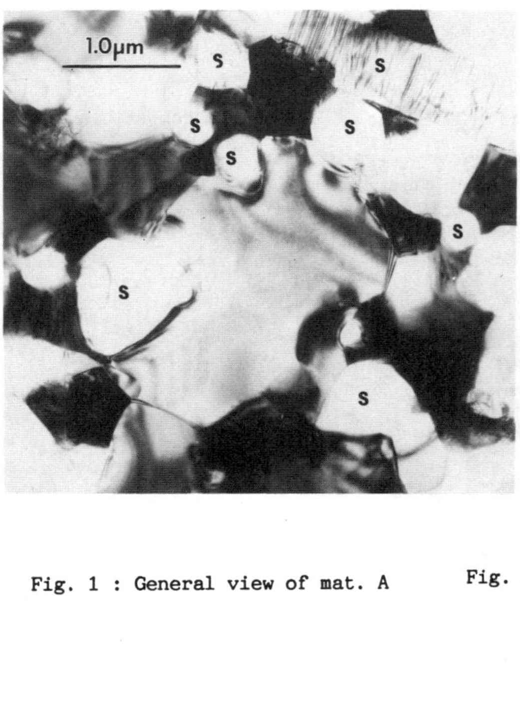

Fig. 1 : General view of mat. A

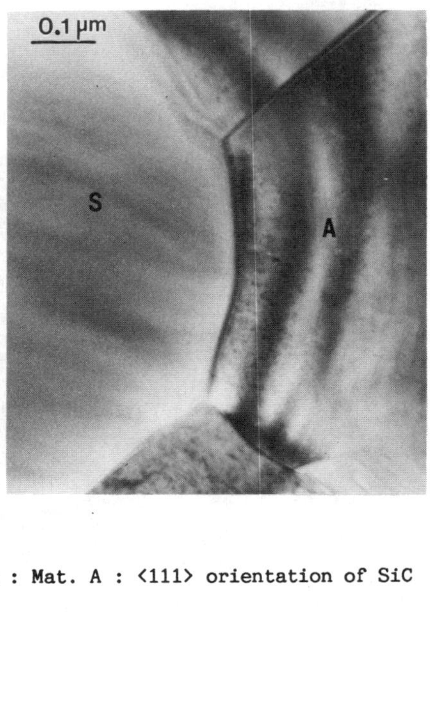

Fig. 2 : Mat. A : <111> orientation of SiC

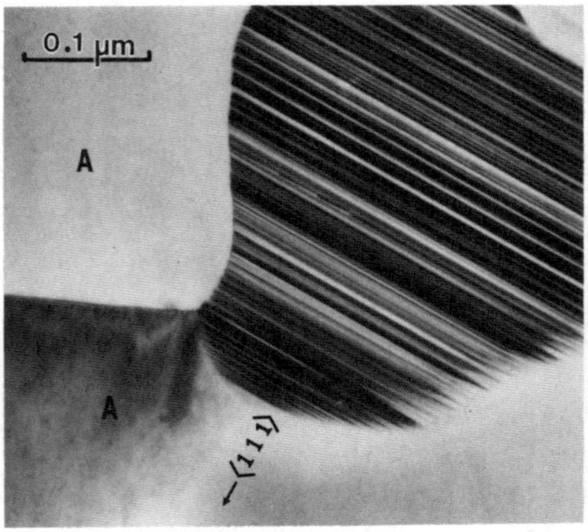

Fig. 3 : Mat. A : SiC near <112> orientation

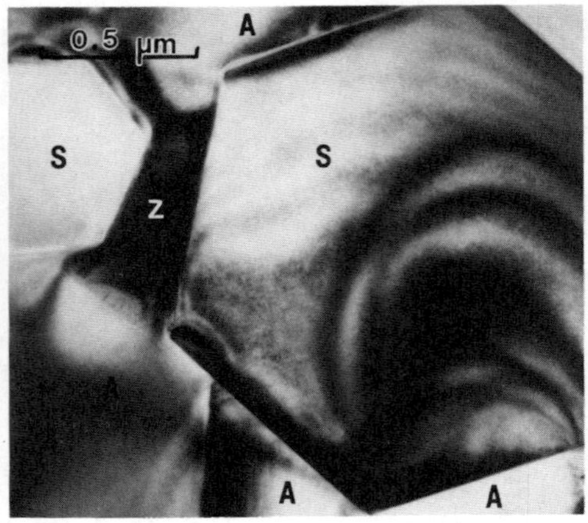

Fig. 4 : Mat B : SiC/Al_2O_3 and SiC/ZrO_2

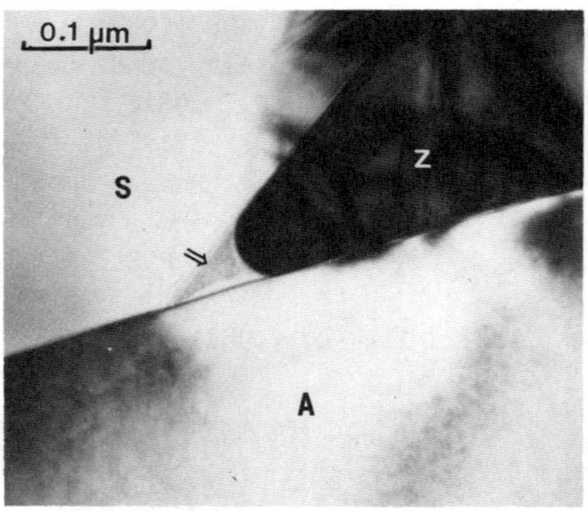

Fig. 5 : Mat. B : Silica glass pocket

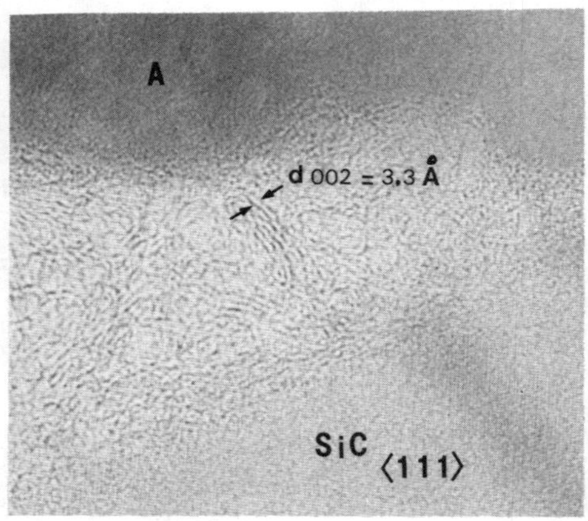

Fig. 6 : Mat. B : Graphite compatible structure

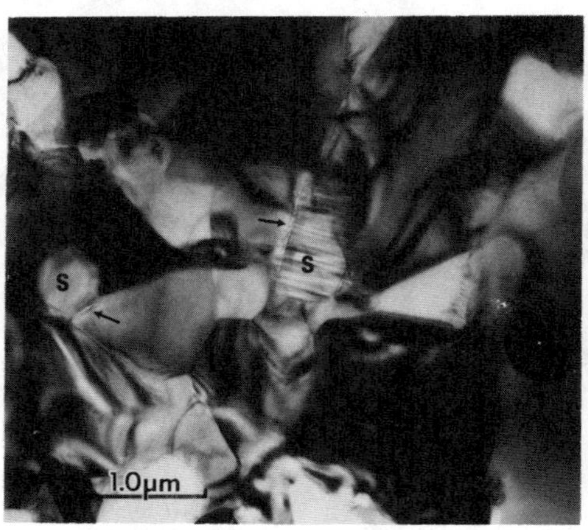

Fig. 7 : Mat C. : debased interfaces

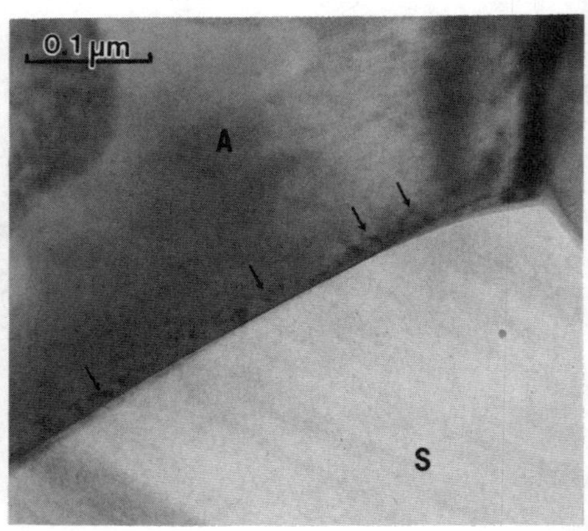

Fig. 8 : Mat. C : SiC/Al_2O_3 interface

STRUCTURE AND FRACTURE BEHAVIOR OF Al_2O_3/(Ce)-STABILIZED ZrO_2 COMPOSITES

S. Maschio, O. Sbaizero and S. Meriani
Istituto di Chimica Applicata e Industriale
Università di Trieste - ITALY

ABSTRACT

In this investigation a series of Al_2O_3-ZrO_2 composite materials were prepared using unstabilized ZrO_2 or ZrO_2 stabilized in its metastable tetragonal form with different amounts of either Y_2O_3 or CeO_2. The mechanical properties (hardness, bend strength and toughness) were measured and the influence of the different microstructures obtained as well as the role of phase transformation and microcracking was assessed

INTRODUCTION

Zirconia-Toughened-Alumina materials are difficult to tailor because dispersed ZrO_2 particles must be smaller than a critical diameter to be useful from a practical point of view. The most common dopant, Y_2O_3, can be replaced by CeO_2 which forms a wider tetragonal solid-solution than Y_2O_3 does. It lowers the ZrO_2 t→m transformation temperature close or below room temperature being larger the grain size required to avoid it during process cooling. The combination of Ce-stabilized ZrO_2 and Al_2O_3 should give good materials because the former is known for its relatively high toughness but moderate strength, while the latter has high hardness and good strength if its microstructure is sufficiently fine.

The aim of this paper has been to prepare different ZTA composites, one containing an unstabilized zirconia, the other containing zirconia stabilized with yttria or ceria, pointing out the influence of the chemical stabilizer on both microstructure and mechanical properties.

EXPERIMENTAL PROCEDURE

In the present study, sintered ZrO_2-toughened Al_2O_3 ceramics (ZrO_2 content ranging from 15% to 30% vol. in the monoclinic form or stabilized with Y_2O_3 or CeO_2) were prepared by two methods: solutions of yttrium nitrate or cerium nitrate and zirconyl chloride in which an alumina powder (ALCOA A16) was dispersed, were mixed in appropriate proportions. Small amounts of H_2O_2 and NH_4OH were added to accelerate the precipitation of ZrO_2. To assure complete hydrolysis the slurries were refluxed, at the boiling point, for five days (1) and then NH_4OH was added again increasing the pH to 8 at 1 which value $Y(OH)_3$ and CeO_2 precipitated. The resulting slurry was filtered, washed with alcohol and diethylether, dried, calcined at 900 °C, milled with binder and lubricant in plastic jar with zirconia balls, dried, sieved, then uniaxially pressed into bars of 50x10x5 mm at 110 MPa. The third composite was prepared following the method proposed by Lange at al.(2); a slurry of alumina and zirconia was obtained suspending the two commercial powders into distilled water (powder content 25% vol.). With the addition of reagent grade HCl, the H^+ concentration was brought to a pH value of 2. The slurry was rapidly stirred (10 min.), aged 2 hours, stirred again (10 min.) and then flocced by addition of NH_4OH. The clear supernatant was removed and the solid was washed several times with distilled water to remove chloride ions. The material was dried, sieved and formed as described here above. The three kinds of specimens were pressureless sintered, in air at 1500, 1530, 1580 °C for 1 to 12 hours. The bulk densities of the resulting billets were determined by water-displacement technique. Microstructure of the polished and thermally etched bodies were examined using the scanning electron microscopy. The average grain size of the materials was determined by the linear intercept method. X-ray diffraction analysis was carried out on both polished and fracture to identify phases, and to assess the tetragonal to monoclinic ratio using the procedure proposed by Garvie and Nicholson (3). Hardness was measured by Vicker's indentation with loads ranging from 90 to 200 N, Young's modulus was determined by Knoop indentation as developed by Marshall et al. (4). Modulus of rupture measurements were made using a 4-point bend jig with 30 mm outer span, 10 mm inner span and a cross-head speed of 0.1 mm/min. The fracture toughness was measured by indentation fracture in bending (ISB) technique using a Vicker's indenter, applying 200 N load, then breaking the specimen in the above 4-point bending test (5)

RESULTS AND DISCUSSION

Relative densities above 96% of theoretical values were obtained within 2 hours at 1580 °C, Fig. 1. This seemed to be the optimum heat treatment schedule; lower temperatures required a too long soak time while higher temperature increased the grain size depleting the mechanical properties. Moreover the residual porosity of all the composites fired at 1580 °C was approximately the same; its effect on the transformability of t-ZrO_2 particles and on the materials properties could be considered similar. The main characteristics obtained with the chosen sintering schedule are listed in Table I.

Table I Characteristics of pressureless sintered Al_2O_3/ZrO_2 composites (after 2h at 1580 °C)

Composition	ρ %	tetr. %	d_{ZrO2} μm	d_{Al2O3} μm
Al_2O_3/ZrO_2(15vol.%)	98	70-80	0.5	1.7
Al_2O_3/ZrO_2(15vol.%)+3Y	97	95-100	0.3-0.6	1.7
Al_2O_3/ZrO_2(15vol.%)+12Ce	96.5	95	0.8-0.9	1.8
Al_2O_3/ZrO_2(20vol.%)+12Ce	97.5	97	1.1	1.4
Al_2O_3/ZrO_2(25vol.%)+12Ce	96.5	100	1-1.3	1.35
Al_2O_3/ZrO_2(30vol.%)+12Ce	98	100	1.5(+)	1.1

Y=Y_2O_3, Ce=CeO_2, +=presence of clusters

The resulting microstructures showed Al_2O_3 grains with a dispersion of irregular inter- and intragranular ZrO_2 particles; the former are larger and more irregular than the latter. With low addition of ZrO_2 some fine entrapped porosity is still present. Alumina grain size is reduced as the ZrO_2 content increases, therefore zirconia particles are responsible for a grain-boundary pinning effect, however, 15 vol.% addition still shows several abnormally-grown grains. The inhibition of Al_2O_3 grain growth by addition of more than 15 vol.% of zirconia is of a striking evidence, it gave an homogeneous microstructure where exaggerated grain growth was scarce. This should be a secondary effect of the toughening particles which contribute to further improve mechanical properties, as it has been previously reported by Lange (2) Table I shows that the mean size of the ZrO_2 inclusions increased with its volume fraction and even if the ZrO_2 grain size is still small, for the 30 vol.% composition (Fig. 2), the particles coalesced to form large clusters, thus ZrO_2 and Al_2O_3 particles had comparable size.

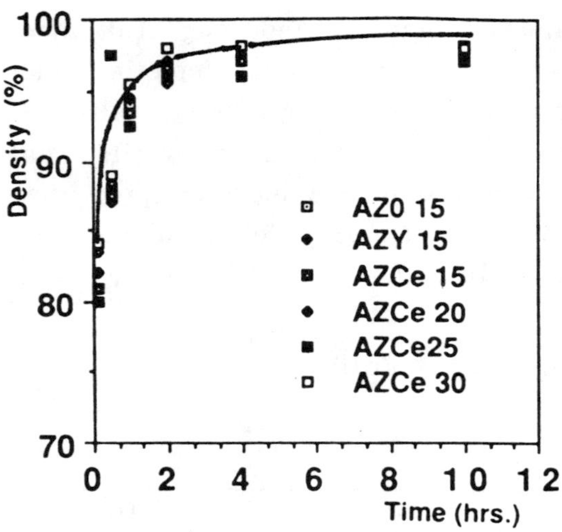

Fig. 1 Relative densities obtained for different ZTA materials sintered in air at 1580 °C

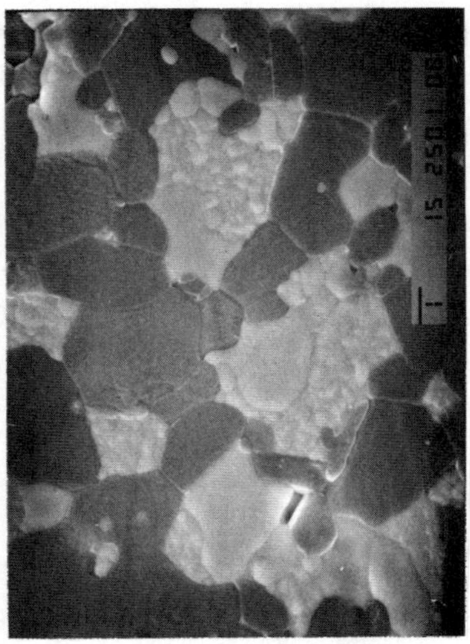

Fig. 2 Ce-stabilized 30%mol ZrO_2-Al_2O_3 microstructure with ZrO_2 clusters 1μm

The amount of intragranular ZrO_2 particles was reduced as the ZrO_2 increased, owing to the fact that as long as the ZrO_2 addition was low the breakaway grain growth occurred if the zirconia particles were not given enough time to coalesce (2,6) or if the clusters remained smaller than a critical size. In the latter case the dragging force exerted by the precipitated particles was not enough to counteract the driving force for boundary movement; the Al_2O_3 grain boundary moved away and led to intragranularly-located ZrO_2 particles. When the ZrO_2 amount increased, the distances between individual particles were reduced and the pinning effect was increased enough to exert effective dragging. We also feel that the degree of clustering could be affected by the way starting powders were mixed. Using either Y_2O_3 or CeO_2 as stabilizer, the resulting ZrO_2 crystalline phase in the composites was almost fully tetragonal while using unstabilized ZrO_2 a mixture of tetragonal and monoclinic phase was obtained. Bending strength (σ_f), hardness (H_v) and toughness (K_{Ic}) values of the sintered ZTA are given in Table II.

Table II Mechanical properties of pressureless sintered ZTA (after 2h at 1580 °C)

Samples	σ_f MPa	HV GPa	K_{Ic} MPa$\sqrt{m}$
Al_2O_3	250	18	3.5
Al_2O_3/ZrO_2(15vol.%)	310	16	5.5
Al_2O_3/ZrO_2(15vol.%)+3Y	350	15.5	4.2
Al_2O_3/ZrO_2(15vol.%)+12Ce	345	14.7	5.7
Al_2O_3/ZrO_2(20vol.%)+12Ce	350	14.2	6
Al_2O_3/ZrO_2(25vol.%)+12Ce	410	13.9	6.2
Al_2O_3/ZrO_2(30vol.%)+12Ce	470	13.5	6.8

Y=Y_2O_3, Ce=$Ce0_2$

From these values it can be seen that the ZrO_2 addition led to composites with improved mechanical properties if compared to pure Al_2O_3; only hardness is depleted and it appears to follow a rule of mixtures: as the hardness of zirconia is lower than that of alumina, the hardness of the composites decreased with ZrO_2 increase. The presence of higher CeO_2 content (12 mol.%) compared with Y_2O_3 (3 mol.%) further on reduced the hardness' values. It is significant to note that in all composites both bending strength and fracture toughness increased by adding ZrO_2. Without stabilizing agent, the content of t-ZrO_2 was low and it appears, therefore, that the t-ZrO_2 particles enhanced toughness which proportionally increased bending strength. On the other hand the m-ZrO_2 particles did not increase strength as much as they enhanced toughness; the major toughening mechanism in this latter material is probably the microcracks extension and branching being the contribution of phase transformation toughening relatively small. The monoclinic ZrO_2 particles during the cooling stage of the sintering process, introduced microcracks which led to some toughness increase but also to a larger critical flaw size. In fact, assuming that all the monoclinic ZrO_2 particles reside at Al_2O_3 grain corners, each alumina grain boundary will be subjected to high local stresses which may lead to grain boundary cracking. With the presence of a stabilizing agent to ZrO_2, the content of metastable tetragonal phase increased (cf. Table 1), in this way a larger volume fraction of ZrO_2 could be added prior to introducing significant grain boundary microcracks, but at the same time, the chemical free energy for the t → m transformation was increased, giving rise to a decreased level of toughening for the same total volume content of ZrO_2 expecially when stabilized with Y_2O_3. The initial increase in K_{Ic} with ZrO_2 content is a result of two factors: first, the increase in the frequency of intergranular tetragonal particles that may be transformed, second, the size dependence of the ZrO_2 for transformation, e.g. finer particles do not transform as readily as larger do. Using CeO_2, being the stabilizer amount fixed, the K_{Ic} behaviour is dominated by the increase in the number of tetragonal particles that are available for transformation at the crack tip rather than by the chemical free energy required for the transformation itself. Consequently, in the case of Ce stabilizer the stress-induced transformation toughening effect became preponderant in comparison with microcracks toughening, so both bend strength and toughness have been remarkably enhanced. The results showed that K_{Ic} increased monotonically from 5.7 to 6.8 MPa $m^{1/2}$ and bending strength from 345 to 470 MPa with ZrO_2 addition up to 30 vol%. These values were larger than those obtained using Y_2O_3 probably because, in the latter case, both the critical grain size and the transformation zone-size, are smaller and the chemical free energy required for the t → m transformation is higher. Furthermore with higher ZrO_2 content, clusters are present which can also increase toughness by deflecting the crack out of the plane normal to the applied stress, thereby reducing the stress intensity at the crack tip. The model proposed by Faber et al. (7)

suggests that the K_{Ic} enhancement is a function of the volume fraction of the dispersed phase. Moreover in the Ce-stabilized ZrO_2/Al_2O_3 composites we did not observe a maximum in the K_{Ic} as previously reported by some authors for other ZTA materials (8,9). This behavior could be probably explained in terms of R-curve effects.

CONCLUSIONS

In this investigation a series of Al_2O_3-ZrO_2 composites materials were prepared using unstabilized ZrO_2 or different amount of either Y_2O_3 or CeO_2 for stabilizing the ZrO_2 in its metastable tetragonal form. The mechanical properties (hardness, bend strength and toughness) were measured and the influence of the different microstructures obtained as well as the role of phase transformation and microcracking was assessed. Using CeO_2 the hardness decreased but both strength and toughness increased due to the fact that the critical grain size for the t--m transformation is larger, therefore the proportion of transformable particles is larger, and in the case of 30 mol.% of ZrO_2 the presence of zirconia clusters might introduce an additional toughening effect due to crack deflection. Also the manner in which the zirconia is spatially distributed within the alumina matrix appears to influence the toughness achievable in these composites. For low ZrO_2 addition the resulting microstructures showed Al_2O_3 grains with a dispersion of irregular inter- and intragranular ZrO_2 particles. The fine intragranular ZrO_2 particles are more stable and they do not readily transform reducing the number of particles that can undergo transformation under an applied stress, thus the toughening effect is diminished.

REFERENCES

1. Y. Murase, E. Kato, K. Daimon - J. Amer. Ceram. Soc. 69(2)83-7(1986)
2. F.F. Lange, M.M. Hirlinger - J. Amer. Ceram. Soc. 67(3)164-68 (1984)
3. R.C. Garvie, P.S. Nicholson - J. Amer. Ceram. Soc. 55(6) 303-5 (1972)
4. D.B. Marshall, T. Noma, A.G. Evans - J. Amer. Ceram. Soc. 65(10) C175-C176 (1982)
5. P. Chantikul, G.R. Anstis, B.R. Lawn, D.B. Marshall - J. Amer. Ceram. Soc.64(9)539-43(1981)
6. B.W. Kibbel, A.H. Heuer - J. Amer. Ceram. Soc. 69(3)231-36(1986)

ACKNOWLEDGEMENTS: Work performed under C.N.R. contract

ALUMINA-ZIRCONIA COMPOSITES; FABRICATION AND PROPERTIES

TUIJA RYTKÖNEN and KARI KESKINEN
Helsinki University of Technology
Vuorimiehentie 2 K, SF-02150 Espoo, FINLAND

PEKKA LINTULA
Tampere University of Technology
P.O. Box 527, SF-33101 Tampere, FINLAND

ABSTRACT

Alumina - zirconia composites were fabricated and their properties studied in the composition range Al_2O_3 = 0, 20, 40, 60, 80 and 100 vol.-% starting from commercial powders. Good mixing was achieved by ball-milling.

Scanning electron microscopy showed that the dispersion homogeneity of these composites was good (no large agglomerates present) and the achieved grain sizes were relatively fine.

INTRODUCTION

To achieve a homogeneous mixture of the two starting components, several ways to produce Al_2O_3-ZrO_2 composites have been reported in litterature. Many of the publications dealt with the addition of a small amount of the other end-member to the other, but only a few articles covered the whole composition range, studying the transformation toughening(1) or the densification behaviour(2) of Al_2O_3-ZrO_2 composites.

In this present work the mixing behaviour of two commercial ceramic powders was studied to achieve a homogeneous composite structure with good mechanical properties.

EXPERIMENTAL

Materials
The powders used were commercial zirconia (TZ-3Y, Tosoh Co., av. part. size 0.1-0.3 μm, doped with Y_2O_3 (5.3 wt.-%)) and alumina (CT 3000 SG, Alcoa Chemicals, av. part. size 0.5 μm) powders. For comparison one commercial ZrO_2-Al_2O_3 powder (TZ-3Y20A, Tosoh Co., av. part. size 0.3

μm, doped with Y_2O_3 (4.2 wt.-%)) was used in the experiments.

Processing of alumina - zirconia composites

The composites as well as the pure end-members and the reference powder were fabricated according to the schematic flow chart in Fig. 1. The starting powders were mixed in a ball-mill for approximately 20 hours with ZrO_2-balls in a plastic container and ultrasonication was used in helping the dispersion homogeneity. When making mechanical test bars, lubricants were added and mixing was continued for further an hour. After drying the powder cake was milled and sieved to a size range of 63 $\mu m \leq d \leq 250$ μm.

Powders without lubricant addition for dilatometric studies and powders with lubricant addition for mechanical testing were pressed uniaxially using pressures of 80 and 150 MPa, respectively. Compacts for dilatometric studies were billets (Ø ≈ 1.1 cm and h ≈ 0.6 cm) and for mechanical testing bars (≈ 9 cm · 0.9 cm · 0.4 cm in the green state).

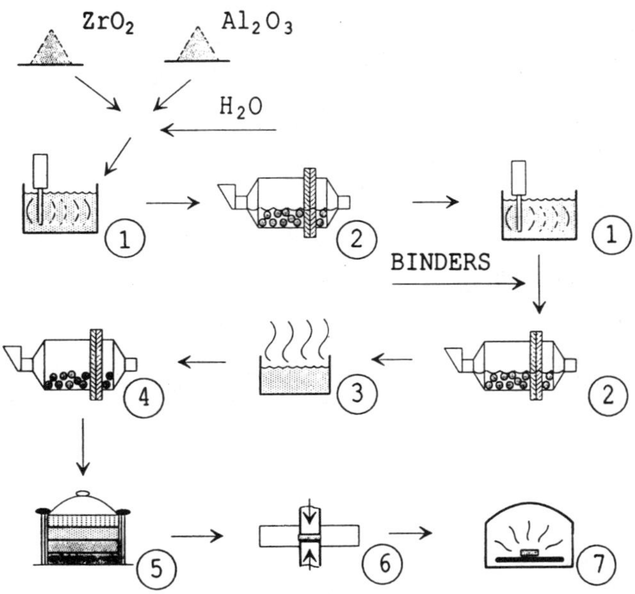

Fig. 1. **Fabrication route for Al_2O_3 - ZrO_2 composites, 1) ultrasonication, 2) wet ball-milling, 3) dewatering, 4) dry ball-milling, 5) sieving, 6) die-pressing, 7) sintering.**

Sintering

The compacts were sintered with a rate of 1 °C/min and holding times of 1 h at 80 °C (removal of excess water), 2 h at 350 °C (binder removal), 2 h at 600 °C (removal of excess carbon), 2 h at 800 °C (phase transformation) and with a rate of 2 °C/min from 800 °C to T_S. The sintering temperature and holding time of the composites ZrO_2/Al_2O_3 = 100/0 and 80/20 were 1600 °C and 2 hours and of the rest 1650 °C and 4 hours, respectively.

Mechanical testing
Flexural strength of the test bars was measured with 4-point bending and fracture toughness with SENB-method.

RESULTS AND DISCUSSION

The results of all the composites and pure end-members are collected in Table I. Green densities were calculated from the measurements of the billets and the sintered densities by using Arkhimedes' principle. The monoclinic and tetragonal phase contents were measured from X-ray diffraction patterns of the polished surfaces of the billets. The ZrO_2 and Al_2O_3 grain sizes were measured from SEM-micrographs of thermally etched surfaces of the billets.

TABLE 1
Results of the composites fabricated.

SAMPLE ZrO2/Al2O3	FIRING TEMP. (°C) *	DENSITIES GREEN %TD	DENSITIES FIRED %TD *	t - ZrO2 PHASE (%) *	ZrO2 GRAIN SIZE µm	Al2O3 GRAIN SIZE µm
100/0	1500 (1600)	46	99 (98)	100 (100)	0.4	-
80/20	1550	43	98	100	0.45	0.7
80/20	1550	51	97	100	0.5	0.8
80/20	1550	50	97	100	0.5	0.7
80/20	1600 (1600)	46	98 (97)	100 (100)	0.6	1.0
60/40	1550 (1650)	49	95 (99)	92 (90)	0.7	1.4
40/60	1600 (1650)	55	92 (97)	80 (89)	0.8	1.6
20/80	1600	55	93	58	0.6	1.8
20/80	1600 (1650)	60	91 (96)	76 (84)	0.6	2.0
0/100	1600 (1650)	59	87 (96)	-	-	2.0
TZ-3Y20A	1550 (1650)	49	89 (96)	84 (100)	0.6	0.6

* Values in parenthesis represent the ones of the mechanical test bars

Phase structures
The cubic phase content of the composites fabricated was very small if detected at all. As seen in Table 1. the amount of the monoclinic phase increased along the increase of the alumina content in the composites. This, in spite of the rather small grain size of ZrO_2, may be caused by the lower density of the material. It may be possible that at increasing porosity the Al_2O_3 grains cannot pin the ZrO_2 grains as well as in the case of nearly theoretical density.

Microstructure
The final microstructures of the composites fabricated are presented in Fig. 2. and the measured grain sizes in Table 1. The ZrO_2 grain size

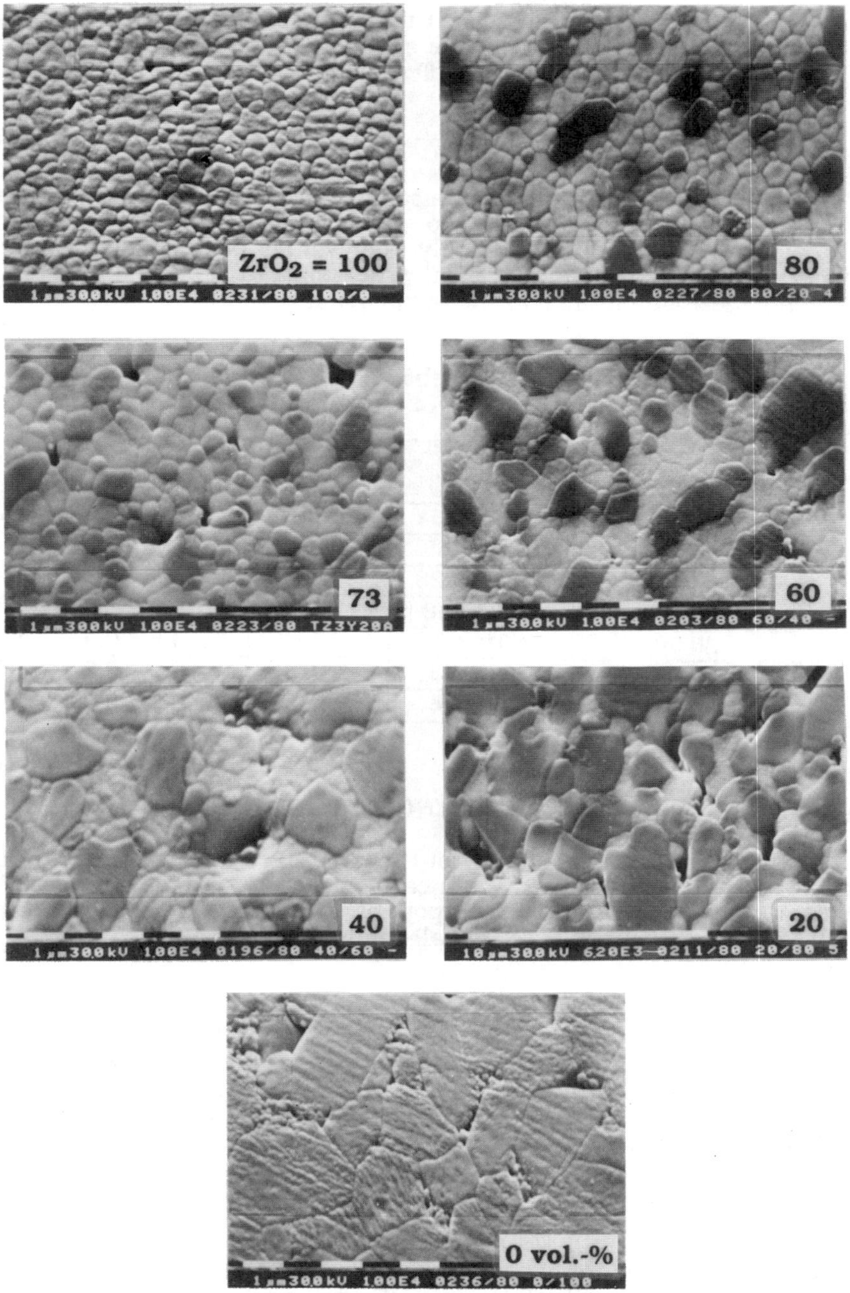

Fig. 2. Scanning electron micrographs (secondary electron image) of thermally etched surface of sintered Al_2O_3-ZrO_2 composites, showing the microstructure.

increases as the amount of ZrO_2 in the composite decreases as does the Al_2O_3 grain size. It seems possible and also confirmed by TEM that the Al_2O_3 grains are located between ZrO_2 grains.

Mechanical properties

Flexural strength of the composites, Table 2. varied with composition from 360 MPa to 1110 MPa, the best value achieved at composition ZrO_2/Al_2O_3 = 60/40. The fracture toughness also varied along the composition from 3.9 MPa$\sqrt{m}$ for pure alumina to 14.9 MPa$\sqrt{m}$ for the composition ZrO_2/Al_2O_3 = 80/20. The relatively poor values of the Weibull modulus can be improved by a more careful processing to remove the remaining monodisperse agglomerates in the suspension.

Table 2
Mechanical properties of the composites fabricated.

ZrO2/Al2O3 (vol.-%)	Flexural strength/MPa	Weibull modulus	Fracture toughness/MPa$\sqrt{m}$
100/0	779 ± 93	9.7	12.2 ± 1.5
80/20	875 ± 165	6	14.9 ± 2.1
60/40	1113 ± 226	6	11.8 ± 2.0
40/60	748 ± 168	5	6.6 ± 1.2
20/80	501 ±80	7	4.6 ± 0.5
0/100	361 ± 43	10	3.9 ± 0.2
73/27 (TZ-3Y20A)	647 ± 74	10	8.8 ± 0.2

CONCLUDING REMARKS

The good dispersion homogeneity of the Al_2O_3-ZrO_2 composites fabricated is beleived to be a consequence of nearly the same particle size of both the powders. Good mixing of the components, resulting in good properties of the fired bodies, was achieved by ball-milling and ultrasonication.

ACKNOWLEDGEMENTS

The authors wish to thank the Technology Development Centre of Finland for financing this study, which is a part of the Finnish National Programme on Engineering Ceramics coordinated by the Federation of Finnish Metal and Engineering Industries.

REFERENCES

1. Lange, F.F., Transformation toughening. Part 4: Fabrication, fracture toughness and strength of Al_2O_3 - ZrO_2 composites. J. Mater. Sci., 1982, **17**, 247-54.

2. Majumdar, R., Gilbart, E. and Brook, R.J., Kinetics of densification of alumina - zirconia ceramics. Br. Ceram. Trans. J., 1986, **85**, 5, 156-60.

ELECTROCONDUCTIVE Si_3N_4-BASED COMPOSITES

A.Bellosi, A.Fiegna, G.N.Babini.
CNR-IRTEC, Research Institute for Ceramic Technology,
via Granarolo 64, Faenza - Italy.

ABSTRACT

A class of electroconductive composites, based on Si_3N_4, have been recently developed, with interesting properties and perspectives. The effect of the addition of a dispersed phase (TiN, TiB_2, TiC) on microstructure, electrical and mechanical properties has been evaluated. Additions of the dispersoids in amounts of about 30% lead to a minimum resistivity of 1.4×10^{-2} Ωcm, and the materials have been found suitable for electrical discharge machining.

INTRODUCTION

An increasing attention has been devoted to particulate additions for the production of structural ceramics composites, with the aim to increase mechanical properties and reliability. Recently this approach has been considered for some specific applications in the field of heaters, igniters, heat exchangers and complex- shaped mechanical components, and has stimulated the development of reinforced SiC or Si_3N_4-based ceramics with electrical conductive secondary phase (TiC, TiN, TiB_2, ZrB, etc.) (1-4). The new type of composites have two main advantages: the first is the use of electrical discharge machining (EDM) (5,6) to manufacture complex shapes and the second is the potential availability of materials suitable for high temperature heaters or igniters. Some preliminary results are presented based on Si_3N_4 composites, with the addition of TiN, TiC, TiB_2 that have been densified through hot pressing and pressureless sintering techniques.

EXPERIMENTAL METHODS

The main characteristics of the starting powders (Si_3N_4 and TiN, TiC, TiB_2 as dispersoids) are shown in table 1.

TABLE 1
Characteristic of the starting powders.

POWDERS	SPECIFIC SURFACE AREA m^2/g	AVERAGE PARTICLE SIZE μm	MAIN IMPURITIES wt%
Si_3N_4	18.8	0.10	O=1.98; Ca=.008; Fe=.008;
TiN	3,8	0.20	O=.9; C=.06; Fe=.02;
TiB_2	3.0	0.44	O=1.7; C=.16; N=.17;
TiC	2.6	0.47	O=.5; Cfree=.18; N=.054.

Silicon nitride powder and sintering aids (3wt% Al_2O_3 and 8wt% Y_2O_3) were homogenized in water for 48 hours and then freeze-dried. The second phase, ranging from 10 to 40 vol%, was added to the matrix mix, and mixed in isobutyl alcool for 48 hours. The composites were hot pressed in vacuum at 1700-1800°C with a pressure of 30MPa. Pressureless sintering tests have been performed on all the composites, but only Si_3N_4-TiN composites. can be densified to a density higher than 90%, (table 2). Densities have been measured with the Archimede's technique; microstructural characteristics have been studied through X-rays diffraction, scanning electron microscopy and microanalysis.
Electrical conductivity has been measured on test bars (10x4x1mm), gold plated contacts, connected with copper wires to a Keithley 195 DMM instrument (two points). Bend strength (four points), Vickers hardness (0.5 Kg load), K_{IC} (indentation method), Youngs'modulus (resonance frequency method) and oxidation resistance have been evaluated.
In table 2 compositions, densities and properties are shown.

RESULTS AND DISCUSSION

The typical microstructures of Si_3N_4-30 vol% TiN and TiC (fig.1a,d) show low Si_3N_4 grain size and rather good dispersion of the second phase. Grain size of TiN and TiC particles range from 0.2 to 2.0 μm, but easily agglomerate when added in the amount of 40 vol%.
As crystal phases, in addition to the costituent components, the presence of low amounts of Y_2TiO_5 in Si_3N_4-TiN and of traces of SiC in Si_3N_4-TiC composites have been detected.

Electrical behaviour.
Electrical resistivity decreases with the increasing of the content of the second phase, reaching a maximum of resistivity of about $1.4x10^{-2}$ Ωcm for 40 vol% TiC addition. The increase of electrical conductivity, changing the dispersoids content between 30 and 40 vol%, appears lower than the expected and

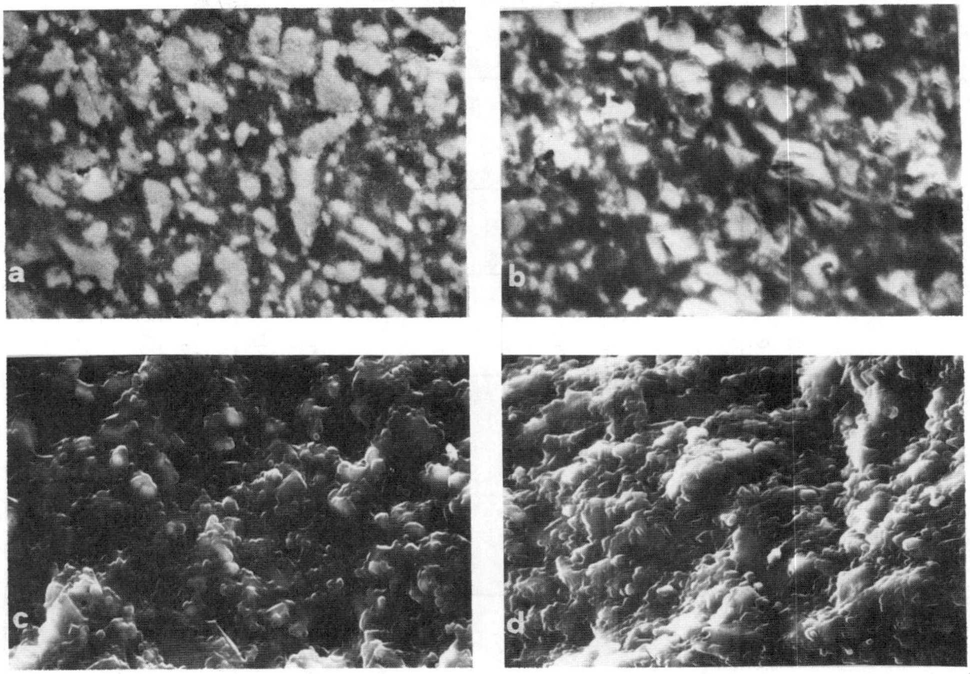

Figure 1. Morphology of polished surface (**a** and **b**) and of fracture surface (**c** and **d**) showing grain size and distribution of the dispersoids and microstructure of the composites. **a** and **c**: Si_3N_4+30% TiN; **b** and **d**: Si_3N_4+30% TiC. Magnifications 3000x.

seems to be affected by:
- possible chemical reactions between the second phase and the matrix, giving complex interfaces components, with unidentified electrical characteristics and physical properties;
- dispersion and size of the second phase.

Appropriate and deep analysis of these problems are necessary to produce reliable and taylored materials.

Mechanical properties.
A noticeable increase in the fracture toughness is measured and maximum value corresponds to 30 vol% of the dispersoids.
Bend strength shows a decrease, with the increase of the secondary phase content, as already observed (1). The effect can be mainly attributed to the porosity, to defects at the second phase particles-matrix interface and to inhomogeneity of the material, overall to the agglomeration of the dispersoids.
The value of E increases with the addition of the dispersoids, being the elastic modulus of these phases higher than the matrix one.
Hardness decrease with the increase of TiN content, but does not vary with the addition of TiC.

TABLE 2

Compositions and properties of the tested materials .

SAMPLE	H.P. Conditions			DENSITY g\cm^3		Hv (0.5)	K_{IC}	σ	E	$\overline{\alpha}$ x10^{-6}	ρ	WEIGHT
	T°C	P(MPa)	t(min)	D.exp.	D.rel.	(G.Pa)	(G.Pa m$^{-1/2}$)	(M.Pa)	(G.Pa)	(°C^{-1})	cm Ω	GAIN mg/cm^2
Si_3N_4*	1700	30	30	3.28	100	20.7 ± 0.9	4.8	895 ± 35	340.0	3.25	3.6 x 10^{13}	0
+ 20 TiN	1800	"	10	3.68	99.4	17.8 ± 1.5	6.4	545 ± 172	331.5	4.42	5.7 x 10^{13}	0.44
+ 30 TiN	"	"	"	3.90	99.6	19.2 ± 0.4	9.2	613 ± 134	351.28	4.68	4.1 x 10^{-2}	1.17
+ 35 TiN	"	"	"	4.00	99.4	18.4 ± 1.1	9.9	585 ± 77	363.53	4.83	1.8 x 10^{-2}	
+ 40 TiN	"	"	"	4.10	99.4	15.2 0.3	6.9	529 ± 61	359.30	5.80	1.7 x 10^{-2}	1.59
+ 20 TiB_2	"	"	"	3.46	98.1	20.2 ± 0.9	9.2	701 ± 50	117.0	3.75	1.5 x 10^{13}	0.07
+ 40 TiB_2	"	"	"	4.03	—	— —	—	230 ± 26	—	5.30	2.6 x 10^{-2}	—
+ 30 TiC	"	"	15	3.82	97.3	19.9 ± 0.7	8.3	658 ± 98	344.0	5.07	3.7 x 10^{-2}	0.91
+ 40 TiC	1850	"	30	4.07	—	20.7 ± 0.8	6.6	474 ± 36	351.0	—	1.4 x 10^{-2}	1.20

* Si_3N_4 + 3 wt.% Al_2O_3 + 8 wt % Y_2O_3

PRESSURELESS SINTERING

SAMPLE	DENSITY D:g /cm^3							
	Green		1750°C 1h		1800°C 2h [8]		1850°C 1h	
	D	%	D	%	D	%	D	%
+ 20 TiN	2.25	62.7	3.36	90.6	--	--	--	--
+ 30 TiN	2.36	59.6	3.54	90.4	3.69	94.0	3.82	97.6
+ 35 TiN	2.45	60.2	--	--	3.76	93.5	3.78	94.0
+ 40 TiN	2.49	59.7	3.76	91.2	3.78	91.7	3.89	94.2

Electrical-discharge machining.
Tests have been performed using EDM wire technique on materials with the addition of 30-40 vol% TiN. A cutting speed of about 1.5 mm/min has been measured. The roughness of the as-cut surface is about 4.2 and 1.7 μm in the materials with 30 and 40 TiN respectively. A second run on the surface at lower frequency reduces the roughness to about 3.5 and 0.9 μm respectively.
The analysis of the worked surface show the presence of a scale of about 10-20 μm thickness, whose composition is mainly glassy and could contain resolidified melt formation droplets, as previously observed (6).

CONCLUSION

Electroconductive Si_3N_4-based composites can be produced with the addition (at least 30 vol%) of TiN, TiC, TiB_2. The most attractive properties of these composites are the improved fracture toughness and the possibility to apply EDM to make complex shaped components. The size and content of conductive phase particles and the processing parameters have to be carefully controlled and the composition must be adjusted to find the best compromise among mechanical properties, EDM machinability and surface quality of the composites.

REFERENCES

1. Suzuki Kariya, H., Yoshida, H. and Yamaguki, S., Ceramic heater and a method for its production. United States Patent n. 4,613,455, Sept. 23 1986.

2. Martin, C., Mathieu, P. and Cales, B., Elecrical discharge machinable ceramic composites . Proceedings of Symposium on Ceramic Materials Research, E-MRS Spring Conference. Strasbourg, 31, May-2 June 1988. Ed. by R.J.Brook.

3. Mc Murtry, C.H., Boecker, W.D.G., Seshadri, S.G., Zanghi, J.S. and Garnier, J.E., Microstructure and material properties of SiC-TiB_2 particulate composites. Am. Ceram. Soc. Bull. **66**, 1987, 325.

4. Higuchi, M., Miyake, M., Kakeuchi, H. and Kamjo, E., Electrically conductive sintered compact of Si_3N_4 Machinable by Electrical Discharge Machinable and process of producing the same. United States Patent n. 4,659,508, Apr. 21,1987.

5. Ramulu, M., EDM Sinker Cutting of Ceramic Particulate Composite, SiC-TiB_2. Adv. Ceram. Mat., **3**, 1988, 324.

6. Petrofes, N.F. and Gadalla, A.M., Electrical Discharge Machining of Advanced Ceramics. Am. Ceram. Soc. Bull., **67**, 1988, 1048.

THE MECHANICAL PROPERTIES OF CORDIERITE-MULLITE COMPOSITES AS A FUNCTION OF TEMPERATURE

D.L. Monroe, J.B. Wachtman, Jr., Rutgers University, Piscataway, NJ, USA; and C. Gault, ENSCI, Limoges, France

ABSTRACT

The mechanical properties of cordierite-mullite and glass-bonded cordierite-mullite composites for substrate applications were investigated. Mixtures of cordierite-mullite-glass frit powders were sintered below the melting temperature of cordierite. The elastic moduli increased with mullite content. The strength showed a general increase, but dropped off at very high mullite contents due to the poor sinterability of the mullite. Porosity was taken into account by an e^{4P} factor. The 10% glass additions raised the strength, but decreased the elastic moduli. The relative Young's modulus behaved as most oxides do at high temperatures, exhibiting a slow decrease of about 1%/100°C. The compositions with glass underwent an abrupt decrease in Young's modulus at about 1150°C and in strength at about 1000°C due to the softening of the glass. The strength decrease at high temperatures increased with the percentage of cordierite.

INTRODUCTION

Composites of cordierite ($2MgO{\cdot}2Al_2O_3{\cdot}5SiO_2$) and mullite ($3Al_2O_3{\cdot}2SiO_2$) represent a technically important class of compositions which are applicable in a variety of areas. In the regime of microelectronic packaging, these materials are alternatives to alumina as substrates because in addition to a lower dielectric constant and processing temperature, they offer the ability to tailor the coefficient of thermal expansion to match that of the silicon chip.[1] Cordierite is employed as kiln furniture in rapid firing cycles because of its excellent thermal shock resistance, and mullite is added to the body to extend the maximum temperature of use.[2] For the same reasons, cordierite-mullite bodies may also find applications as catalyst supports. The nature of these applications demands a knowledge of the mechanical properties of the system not only at room temperature, but at elevated temperatures as well. Such an investigation is the purpose of this study.

Composites of cordierite and mullite have been fabricated from a variety of starting materials: oxide powders,[3] cordierite and mullite powders,[3,4] mullite and glass,[5] glass frits,[4] and even organo-metallic precursors.[1,3] Dry pressing milled powders of cordierite and mullite was chosen as the processing route for this study because of its simplicity. Because Anderson[4] found additions of a barium aluminosilicate glass to enhance the sintering and lower the sintering temperature, small amounts were added to certain compositions here.

PROCEDURE

Five compositions ranging from pure cordierite to pure mullite were chosen to adequately investigate the system. Glass was added to three compositions: cordierite, mullite, and the 50-50 mixture of the two. Ten percent by weight was added because Anderson found that amount to give the maximum strength; further additions decrease the mechanical properties.[4] Cordierite and mullite powders[a] were attrition milled for 24 h in mullite media and water. In those compositions containing 10% glass, a frit (63% SiO_2, 11.2%

---

[a] Baikowski Intl., Annecy, France

Al_2O_3, and 25.8% BaO by weight) was milled with the crystalline powders. After milling, the suspension was poured through a 50 μm sieve and dried. Three percent by weight of polyvinyl alcohol was added to the cake as a binder. The mixture was granulated, dried, and pressed uniaxially at 150 MPa into disks and bars.

The intimate mixing and fine starting particle size (~1 um) enabled the bodies to be sintered below the melting temperature of cordierite, as Anderson[4] demonstrated. All were sintered for 1 h below 1455°C, except for the pure mullite, which was soaked for 3 h at 1650°C. The faces of one thick disk of each composition were ground parallel, and the bulk density of each was determined geometrically. Characterization by XRD and SEM was then performed.

The velocities of shear and longitudinal ultrasonic waves were measured in each thick disk. At room temperature, the "pulse-echo overlap" method[6] was employed at frequencies of 10 - 20 MHz. Poisson's ratio (ν), shear modulus (G), and Young's modulus (E) were then calculated from the standard equations.

Young's modulus was measured at high temperatures by measuring the velocity of low frequency (~200KHz) longitudinal waves in bar-shaped samples. One bar of each composition was coupled to an alumina waveguide and heated in an Ar-7%H_2 atmosphere at a rate of 60°C/h to 1300°C and cooled to room temperature at the same rate. Young's modulus was thus expressed by

$$E = \rho V_{LB}^2$$

where ρ is the specimen density. The relative Young's modulus was calculated by dividing by the room temperature value.

The strengths of the bodies were measured in piston-on-ring biaxial flexure[7] on an Instron universal testing machine[b]. The radius of the loaded area was 1.9 mm and the load was applied at a rate of 0.2 mm/min. At room temperature, 9 to 11 disks of each composition were broken. At temperatures of 800°, 1000°, and 1100°C, at least 5 samples of each composition were broken.

RESULTS AND DISCUSSION

No crystalline phases in the bodies other than mullite and cordierite were detected by XRD. No reaction with the glass was detected. Quantitative analysis by the "auto flushing" method[8] indicated that there was little or no change in composition during sintering.

SEM revealed microstructures consisting of fine grains of cordierite and mullite ranging in size from about 0.5 to 3 μm. The mullite grains often exhibited an elongated morphology. Porosity was submicron to about 15 um in diameter, and became less spherical as the amount of mullite in the bodies increased. This behavior has previously been observed in composites of this type[5], and is attributed to the difficulty in sintering mullite. In fact, porosity in the pure mullite bodies was crack-like due to incomplete sintering, even though they were soaked for 3 h at 1650°C.

----

[b] Instron Ltd., Buckinghamshire, England

The length of these cracks extended up to 100 um at times.

Sintering data for the composites is given in Table I. The nomenclature used to express the composition is weight percent mullite/cordierite/glass. Ten percent additions of glass lowered the sintering temperature. All compositions were sintered to greater than about 95% theoretical density. It can be seen that as the percentage of mullite increased, the percent theoretical density of the samples generally tended to decrease. It was easier to sinter compositions higher in cordierite.

The values of Poisson's ratio for pure cordierite and mullite agreed excellently with published values[5], and composite values fell between those of the end-members. The shear and Young's moduli exhibited an increasing trend with mullite content (see Table II and Fig. 1), as expected. The error is about $\pm 0.5\%$, about equal to the size of the symbols which make the points. The results are much like those of Mussler and Shafer.[5] Though Musser and Shafer used a porosity correction of e^{3P}, a correction of e^{4P} was found to be more appropriate for this study (concurring with Anderson[4]). The porosity-corrected values fall on an almost straight line. The elastic moduli of the composites with 10% glass displayed similar behavior but were slightly lower than those of the glass-free composites.

Typical examples of the behavior of the relative Young's modulus as a function of temperature are seen in Fig. 2. The error on these points is about 1%. All compositions not containing glass underwent a gradual,

Table I

Sintering Data for Mullite-Cordierite Composites

Composition* (M/C/Glass)	Sintering Temperature (^oC)	Soak Time (h)	Bulk Density (g/cm^3)	Theoretical Density (g/cm^3)	% Theoretical Density
0/90/10	1410	1	2.49	2.55	97.1
45/45/10	1410	1	2.69	2.83	95.0
90/0/10	1580	1	3.01	3.16	95.2
0/100/0	1430	1	2.48	2.52	98.4
25/75/0	1425	1	2.64	2.66	99.1
50/50/0	1445	1	2.71	2.81	96.3
75/25/0	1450	1	2.87	2.98	96.5
100/0/0	1650	3	3.07	3.18	96.5

*Weight Percent

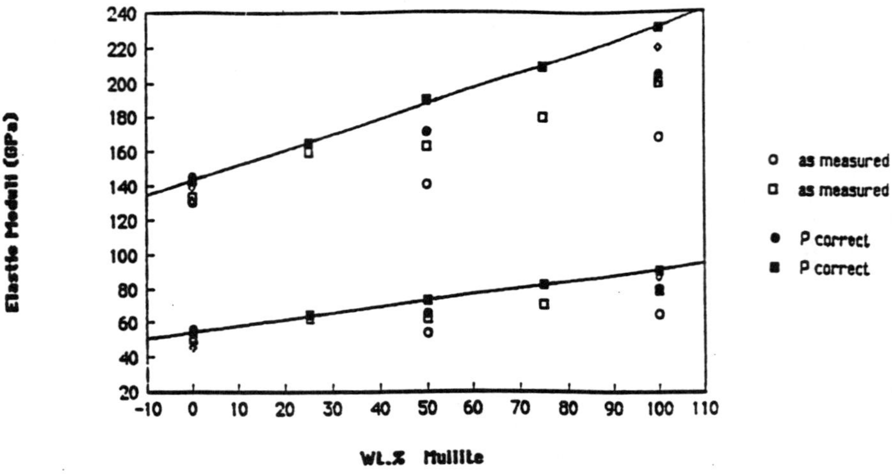

Fig. 1 - Elastic Moduli of Cordierite-Mullite Composites

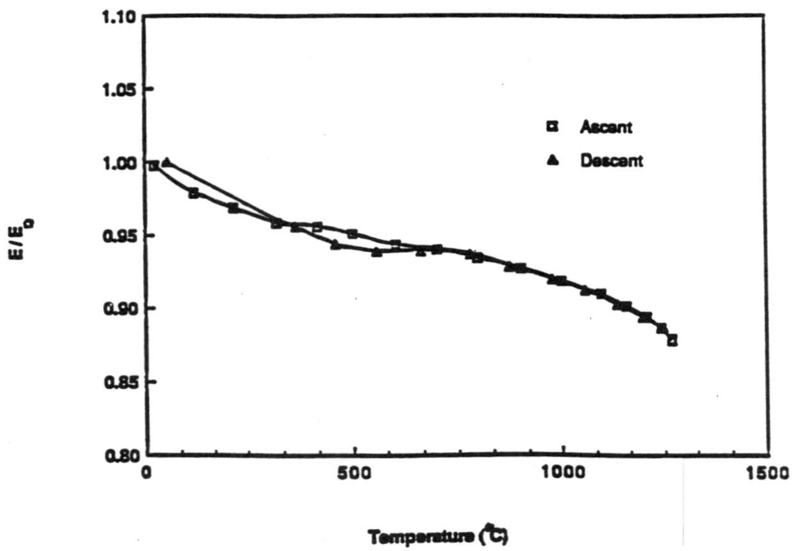

Fig. 2a - Relative Young's Modulus as a function of temperature of 50/50/0

Table II

Elastic Moduli of Composites

Composition (M/C/G)	Poisson's Ratio	Shear Modulus (GPa)	Young's Modulus (GPa)
0/90/10	0.303	50	130
45/45/10	0.307	54	141
90/0/10	0.282	66	169
0/100/0	0.305	51	134
25/75/0	0.286	62	160
50/50/0	0.292	63	164
75/25/0	0.266	71	180
100/0/0	0.269	79	201

roughly linear decrease in relative Young's modulus of about 1%/100°C as temperature increased (Fig. 2a). This is a trend which has been observed for most oxides[9]. The three glass-containing compositions demonstrated this behavior up to about 1100°C, above which a rapid, non-linear decrease occured (Fig. 2b). At 1300°C Young's modulus of all three of these had fallen to 76-77% of the initial value. This is believed to be a result of grain boundary sliding due to a decrease in the viscosity of the glass at the grain boundaries. In each case the values for decending temperature were the same as those for ascending temperature, and the final Young's modulus for all was the same or nearly the same as the initial value, indicating a stable structure up to 1300°C.

The strengths of the composites as a function of composition are plotted in Fig. 3. In both the 10% and 0% glass range of compositions, the strength was higher for mixtures of mullite and cordierite than for bodies containing only one crystalline phase. The initial increase in strength due to the addition of a higher-modulus, higher-strength phase (mullite) is quite expected, but the reduction in strength at high mullite contents is not. The low strength of the pure mullite samples in this case can be attributed to the poor sinterability of the mullite powder. The large, non-spherical surface porosity with sharp edges is responsible for the low strengths.

Even though the glass additions improved the sintering

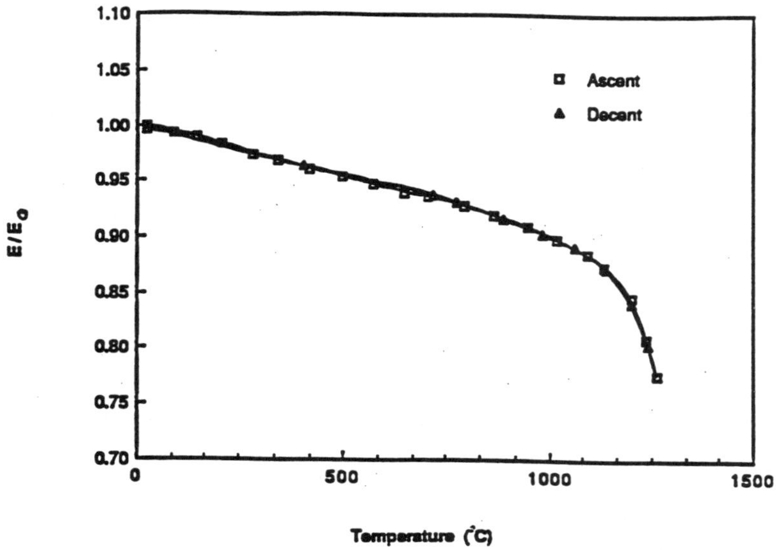

Fig. 2b - Relative Young's Modulus as a function of temperature of 45/45/10

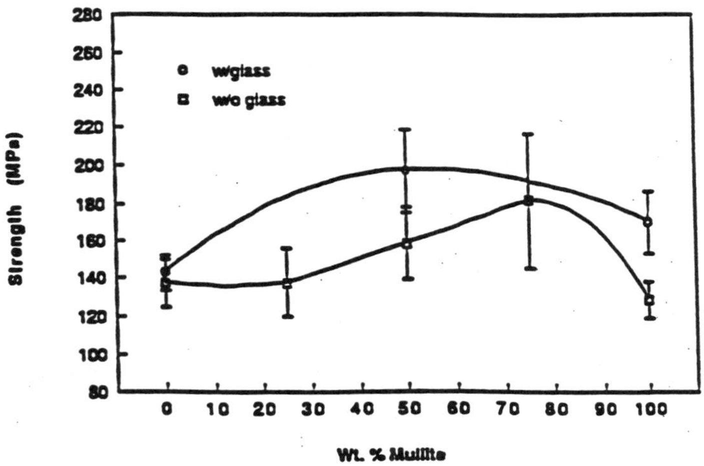

Fig. 3 - Strength of Cordierite-Mullite Composites

of composites and resulted in smaller, more spherical porosity, the same general behavior was observed in the 10% glass samples. Their strengths were higher than those of their glass-free counterparts because of the better sintering. When corrected for porosity, the graphs had the same shape and the values were 15-20% greater.

The room-temperature biaxial strengths of the 0% glass bodies are similar to those found by Anderson.[4] Ikawa et al.[10] measured the strengths of cordierite-mullite bars in 3-point bending. Because the critical flaw can be oriented in any direction in a biaxial flexure test, the values thus obtained are conservatively 80% of what would result from a 3 or 4-point bend test[11]. To more readily compare these measurements with those of Ikawa, the results of this study were divided by 80%. For up to 75 wt.% mullite, the result is a line which is almost identical to Ikawa's data.

The biaxial strengths of each composition at room temperature, 800°, 1000°, and 1100°C are listed in Table III. Two trends are apparent from the data: presence of the glass causes the strength to drop at high temperatures, and the greater the mullite content, the lesser the decrease in strength as the temperature increases.

Fig. 4 demonstrates the typical behavior of the composites as a function of temperature. In Fig. 4a, it can be seen that the strength of the 45/45/10 composition does not decrease much up to 1000°C, above which it decreases abruptly. The same composition without the glass, 50/50/0, does not exhibit this abrupt decrease in the temperature

Table III

Strength of Cordierite-Mullite Composites at Various Temperatures

Composition (M/C/G)	Biaxail Strength (MPa) 25°C	800°C	1000°C	1100°C
0/90/10	143.0±10.1	117.4±3.4	109.1±14.5	79.5±4.7
45/45/10	197.3±22.8	187.0±25.8	159.7±12.4	111.8±6.7
90/0/10	170.2±17.5	152.0±36.3	188.9±17.8	138.1±4.3
0/100/0	138.0±12.7	88.0±8.5	90.8±4.5	87.6±13.1
25/75/0	137.9±17.8	107.7±21.3	1123±18.6	98.0±7.1
50/50/0	158.5±18.8	133.2±8.8	155.8±26.0	135.0±17.3
75/25/0	181.1±35.8	207.0±20.2	180.5±19.6	156.4±26.0
100/0/0	129.0±10.0	111.6±10.9	128.2±26.8	132.5±21.6

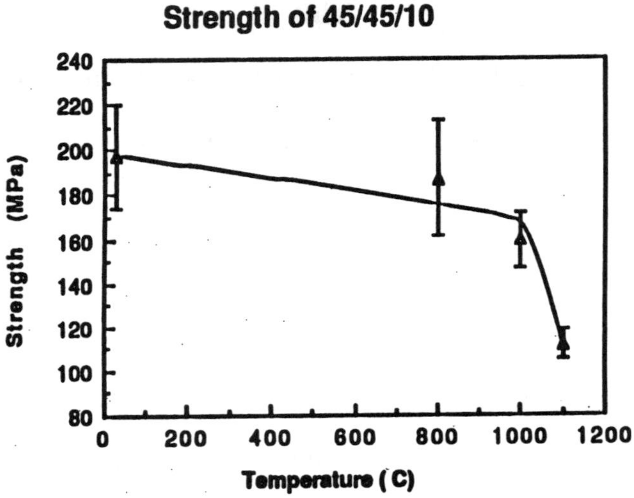

a)

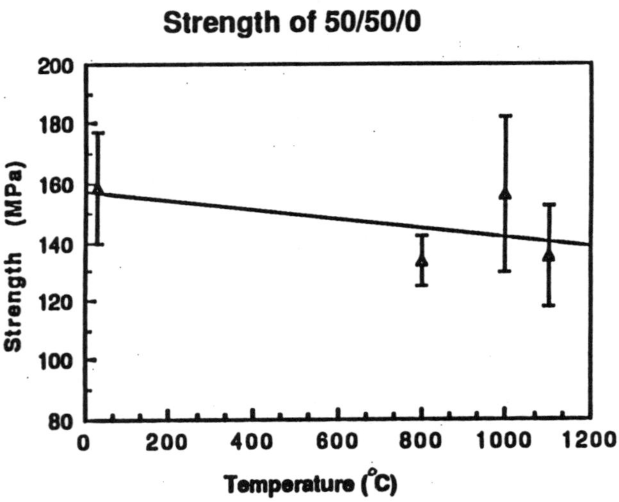

b)

Fig. 4 - Strength of 45/45/10 and 50/50/0 as a function of temperature

range under consideration (Fig. 4b). The other two compositions containing 10% glass also experience the drop in strength at about 1000°C at this loading rate.

The composites not containing glass did not experience this diminution in strength at high temperatures. Their change in strength with temperature, $\Delta \sigma_f/\Delta T$, was fairly regular over the temperatures measured and can be approximated by a straight line. The slopes of these lines became steeper as the cordierite content increased. For pure mullite, almost no change in strength with temperature was observed; for pure cordierite the drecrease is significant. The composites in between have intermediate slopes. The reasons for this behavior are not clear at this time. Measurements of K_{Ic} at high temperatures may offer some insight into this phenomenon.

Examination of the fracture surfaces and fracture origins of every composition revealed that all samples broke in brittle transgranular fracture at all temperatures except for the samples with glass at 1100°C. These first underwent a region of intergranular fracture in which the crack tip followed the glass at the grain boundaries (slow crack growth). It is believed that after the crack reached a critical size, the crack velocity increased greatly and the fracture mode became transgranular.

REFERENCES

1. C. Gensse and U. Chowdhry, "Non-Conventional Route to Glass-Ceramics for Electronic Packaging," Materials Research Society Symposia Proceedings, Electronic Packaging Materials Science, 72, Materials Research Society, Pittsburgh, PA, 297-307 (1986).

2. P. Buduer, H. Liebmann, H. Rump, C. Schneider, "Cordierite-Mullite Kiln Furniture for Firing of Ceramics," Silikattechnik, 36 [10] 307-9 (1985).

3. J.D. Hodge, "Densification and Microstructural Aspects of Mullite-Cordierite Ceramics," Advances in Ceramics, 19, American Ceramic Society, Westerville, OH, 117-29 (1987).

4. R.M. Anderson, R. Gerhart, J.B. Wachtman, Jr., D. Onn, and S. Beecher, "The Thermal, Mechanical, and Dielectric Properties of Cordierite-Mullite Composites," to be published in Advances in Ceramics, 26 (1989).

5. B.H. Mussler and M.W. Shafer, "Preparation and Properties of Mullite-Cordierite Composites," Am. Ceram. Soc. Bull., 63 [5] 705-10 (1984).

6. E.P. Papadakis, "New compact instrument for pulse-echo overlap measurements of ultrasonic wave transit times," Rev. Sci. Instrum., 47 [7] 806-13 (1976).

7. J.B. Wachtman, Jr., W. Capps, and J. Mandel, "Biaxial Flexure Tests of Ceramic Substrates," J. Mat., 7 [2] 188-94 (1972).

8. F.H. Chung, "Quantitative Interpretation of X-ray Diffraction Patterns of Mixtures. I. Matrix-Flushing Method for Quantitative Multicomponent Analysis," J. Appl. Cryst., 7 519-25 (1974).

9. J.B. Wachtman, Jr., "Young's Modulus of Various Refractory Materials as a Function of Temperature," J. Am. Ceram. Soc. 42 [5] 254-60 (1959).

10. H. Ikawa, T. Watanabe, K. Urabe, and S. Udagawa, "Thermal Expansion and Microstructure of Cordierite and Mullite Composite," Yogyo Kyokai Shi, 93 [12] 762-7 (1985).

11. R.W. Davidge, Mechanical Behaviour of Ceramics, Cambridge University Press, 1979.

ELASTIC PROPERTIES OF CERAMIC COMPOSITES AT HIGH TEMPERATURES

R. Wagner, G. Ziegler
Deutsche Forschungsanstalt für Luft- und Raumfahrt (DLR)
Institut für Werkstoff-Forschung
D-5000 Köln 90, FRG

ABSTRACT

This paper deals with the elastic properties, Young's Modulus, Shear Modulus and Poisson's ratio, of whisker and particle reinforced composites as a function of temperature up to 1400 °C. The study was carried out with ceramic composites based on alumina, silicon nitride and mullite with varying amounts of SiC-whiskers and SiC-particles. Young's Modulus E and the Shear Modulus G increase with higher SiC-content while the elastic properties decrease almost linearly with rising temperature. There is no difference between the elastic properties of whisker or particle reinforced materials. A good agreement between the experimental results and theoretical considerations was found. The small difference in elastic properties between whisker and particle reinforced composites is explained by orientation effects of the whisker in the hot-pressed materials.

INTRODUCTION

For using ceramic composites for engineering design, the knowledge of their elastic properties is important. Therefore, experimental data at various temperatures should be available. Moreover, microstructural effects on elastic properties should be understood. The aim of this investigation was to study the influence of amount and morphology (whisker, polycrystalline particles) of silicon carbide as a secondary component on the elastic properties (Young's Modulus, Shear Modulus, Poisson's ratio) of the ceramic composites as a function of temperature.

MATERIALS AND METHODS

Measurements were carried out on whisker and particle reinforced ceramics, based on alumina, mullite and silicon nitride matrices, which contain amounts of SiC-whiskers and SiC-particles between 10 and 50 vol%, and 10 and 30 vol%, respectively. Additionally, the size of the SiC-particles was varied between 2.5 and 46.5 μm. For reinforcement of composites, SiC-whiskers (Tokamax) and SiC-particles (ESK) were used. The composites were prepared by slip casting after dispersion with special dissolvers. All specimens were densified to full density (>99% TD) by hot pressing at a temperature of 1650 °C (t=30 min, p=40 MPa).
The elastic properties (Young's Modulus E, Shear Modulus G) were measured by the resonant frequency technique using rectangular bars 4.5x3.5x45 mm in dimensions. Young's Modulus E and the Shear Modulus G were calculated from the

flexural and torsional resonant frequencies, using the well known equations for E and G. Due to internal damping, measurements were limited to temperatures of about 1200 °C (for mullite and silicon nitride) and 1400 °C (for alumina).

RESULTS

The results of the high temperature measurements are shown in Figure 1. Young's Modulus (and the Shear Modulus) of the composites increase with higher SiC-content (Figure 1 and 2). In the temperature range investigated, Poisson's ratio was constant. There is no difference between the elastic properties of particle and whisker reinforced materials. Nor has any influence of the size of the SiC-particles been observed (see Figure 2). The high temperature measurements of Young's Modulus of the composites show a nearly linear decrease with temperature increase. The temperature behaviour can be described by the temperature coefficient T_E ($T_E = 1/E \cdot dE/dT = dlogE/dT$) . The values are summarized in Table 1. For alumina, the temperature coefficient T_E was determined to be $T_E = -1.17\ 10^{-4}/°C$. The incorporation of 30 vol% SiC-whiskers and SiC-particles results in a decrease of $T_E = -1.019\ 10^{-4}/°C$, caused by the low temperature coefficient of SiC ($T_E = -0.478\ 10^{-4}/°C$ [1]).

Table 1
Temperature coefficient of SiC reinforced alumina and mullite

Material	1/E dE/dT [$10^{-4}/°C$]	Material	1/E dE/dT [$10^{-4}/°C$]
Al_2O_3	-1,171	Mullite	-0,895
Al_2O_3 + 10% SiC-Wh	-1,170	Mullite + 10% SiC-Wh	-0,876
Al_2O_3 + 20% SiC-Wh	-1,090	Mullite + 20% SiC-Wh	-0,864
Al_2O_3 + 10% SiC-P	-1,179	Mullite + 10% SiC-P	-0,862
Al_2O_3 + 20% SiC-P	-1,102	Mullite + 20% SiC-P	-0,787
Al_2O_3 + 30% SiC-P	-1,019	Mullite + 30% SiC-P	-0,809

DISCUSSION

Due to the high values of $E_{whisker}$ ($E_{SiC-whisker}$ = 578 GPa [2], $E_{SiC}(1/s_{33})$ = 556 GPa [3]) a strong increase of the elastic properties of the composites with rising whisker content is expected. Moreover, a large difference between whisker and particle reinforced materials should be observed.
According to the equations of Paul [4] and Hashin [5] E-values of 450 GPa for 30 vol% SiC-whisker and 490 GPa for 50 vol% SiC-whisker are obtained. However, the experimental results show only small changes from 400 GPa for Al_2O_3 to 413 GPa (30 vol% SiC) and 432 GPa (50 vol% SiC), respevtively [1].

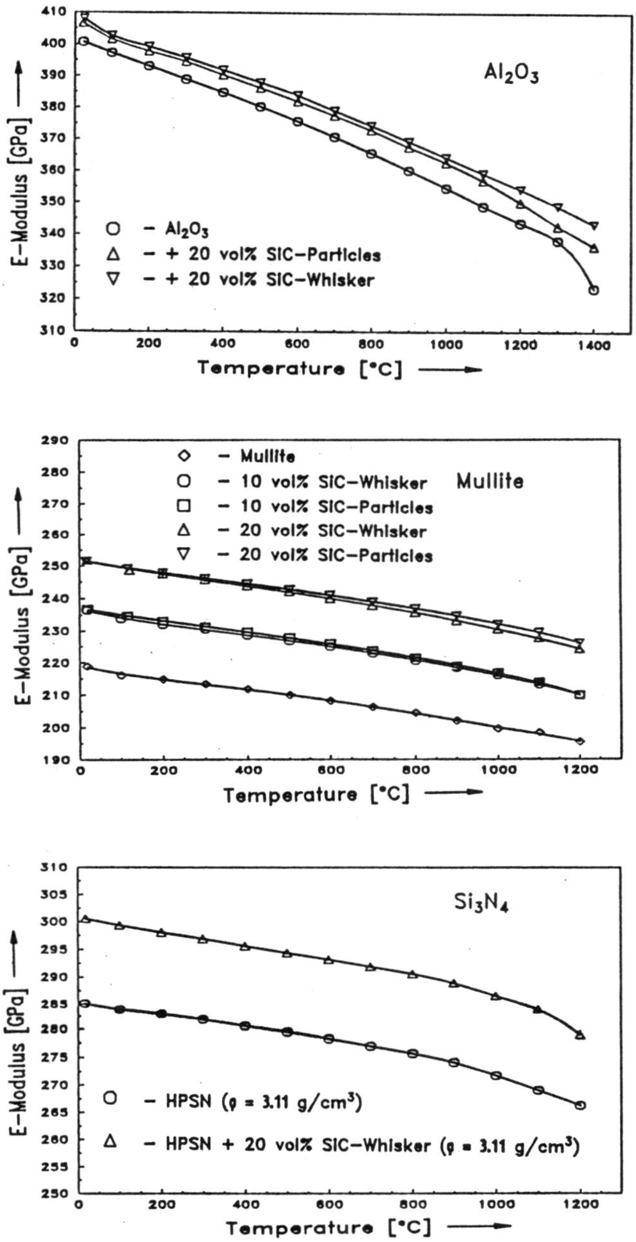

Figure 1. Temperature dependence of Young's Modulus of various ceramic composites: Al_2O_3, *mullite*, Si_3N_4.

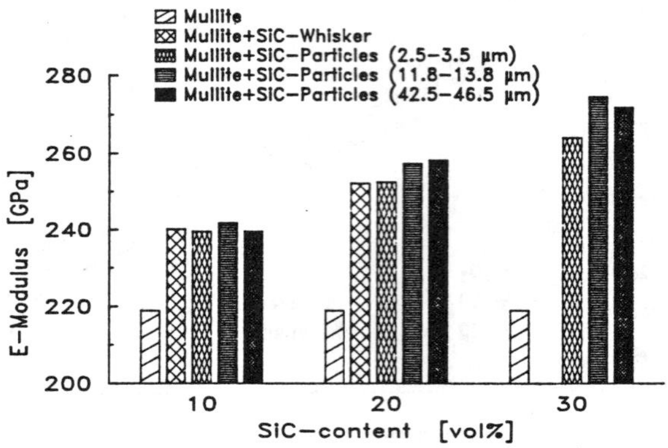

Figure 2. Influence of SiC-content and SiC-particle size on Young's Modulus E of reinforced mullite.

This discrepancy can be explained with the fact that the high value of $E_{whisker}$ can only be used for the calculation of E_c if there is a complete orientation of the whisker in the [001] direction in the composite. Microstructural analysis of the hot-pressed composites proves that nearly all whiskers are orientated on the plane parallel to the hot-press direction, but the whiskers are distributed randomly on the perpendicular plane. Thus, in order to consider the real microstructure of the composite, the average value of the elastic properties of the SiC single crystal in this plane has to be used (eq. (1) [6]).

$$\frac{1}{E} = s_{11}\sin^4\theta + s_{33}\cos^4\theta + (s_{44} + 2s_{13})\sin^2\theta\cos^2\theta, \qquad (1)$$

Based on the data of [3], this value is $\bar{E}_{whisker} = 469$ GPa. Putting this value in the equation of Paul, good agreement with the experimental results is obtained for the whisker content >30 vol% [1].

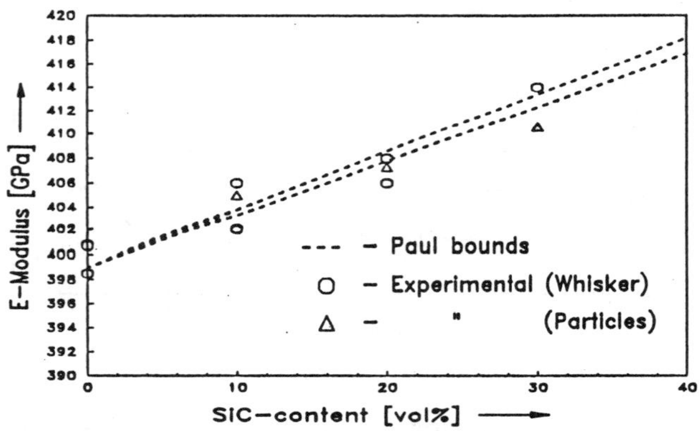

Figure 3. Comparison of experimental data and bounds based on considerations of Paul for alumina.

In the case of lower whisker concentrations, however, only little orientation of the whisker is obtained. Thus, the calculation has to imply all possible orientations, i.e. the elastic properties of polycrystal has to be calculated on the basis of the single crystal data which results in $\bar{E}_{SiC} = 447$ GPa. Using this value for the calculation of Paul boundaries a good agreement between the calculated values and the experimental data is found (Figure 3). These results are confirmed by the measurements on polycrystalline SiC-particle reinforced composites. These considerations are supported by the experimental results in the mullite-SiC system (Figure 4).

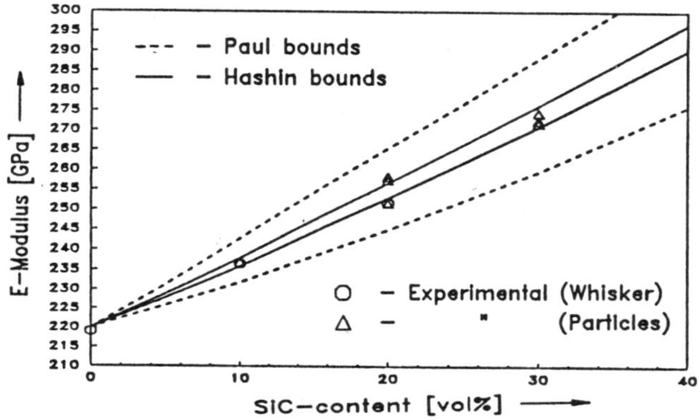

Figure 4. Comparison of experimental data and bounds based on considerations of Paul and Hashin for mullite.

REFERENCES

1. R. Wagner: Elastische Eigenschaften von keramischen Verbundwerkstoffen bei hohen Temperaturen. Dissertation to be printed 1989
2. J.J. Petrovic, J.V. Milewski, D.L. Rohr, F.D. Gac: Tensile Mechanical Properties of SiC Whiskers. Journal of Material Science 20 (1985) 1167-1177
3. Landolt-Börnstein: Kristall- und Festkörperphysik. Gruppe III, Band 2, Springer Verlag, 1969, p. 8
4. B. Paul: Prediction of Elastic Constants of Multiphase Materials . Transactions of the Metallurgical Society of AIME 218 (1960) 36-41
5. Z. Hashin, S. Shtrikman: A Variational Approach To The Theory Of The Elastic Behavior Of Multiphase Materials. J.Mech.Phys.Solids 11 (1962) 127-140
6. J.F. Nye: Physical Properties of Crystals. Oxford Univ. Press, London, New York 1957

THERMAL SHOCK OF MULLITE-ZIRCONIA BASED COMPOSITES

CARMEN BAUDIN, JOSE S. MOYA
Instituto de Cerámica y Vidrio
Ctra. de Valencia km. 24.300, Arganda del Rey, 28500 Madrid

ABSTRACT

The thermal shock behaviour of mullite-alumina-zirconia composites is studied in relation to microstructure. The materials have been prepared by reaction sintering of alumina and zircon with and without MgO, this last used as a sintering aid.

INTRODUCTION

Mullite is a candidate for high technology applications due to its good high temperature properties but it lacks of hardness, toughness and fracture strength (1).

In this work, the thermal shock behaviour of mullite-Al_2O_3-ZrO_2 composites prepared by reaction sintering of Al_2O_3 and $ZrSiO_4$ is studied. Zirconia aditions are to reinforce the mullite matrix, and Al_2O_3 is to increase its hardness(2-3).

Acoustic emission detections revealed the importance of the interaction of the crack with the microstructure during the fracture of these materials (3). In order to determine the role played by microstructure in relation to thermal shock resistance, a comparison is stablished between a material prepared using MgO as sintering aid and one prepared without such additive. The microstructure of the materials is greatly changed by low Mgo additions even if the chemical composition -basic thermal shock parameters- remains nearly the same.

EXPERIMENTAL

Mixtures of alumina (CT 300 SG, Alcoa, U.S.A), zircon (OpazirS Quiminsa, Spain) and magnesia (Magchem 10, Martin Marietta,

U.S.A) in relative quantities following the equation:

$$2ZrSiO_4+6.4Al_2O_3+X(Al_2O_3+MgO) \text{--}\ 2Zr_2O_3+3.4Al_2O_3+XAl_2MgO_4 \quad (1)$$

with X=0, 0.3, were attrition milled with alumina balls in isopropyl alcohol for 1.5 hours, dried, sieved, and isostatically pressed (200 MPa) to form blocks (~50x20x10 mm^3). Thermal treatments of 1.5 h at 1450° C and of 0.5 h at 1400° C followed by 4.5 h at 1570 for the mixtures with X=0.3, 0 respectively were performed in air in a furnace with superkanthal bars. The materials will be named X(M+A), X=0, 0.3.

The thermal shock resistance of these composites was obtained by measuring the three-points bend strength (Instron machine, span=20 mm, head cross speed=0.005 mm/min) retained by test bars (~4.5 x 3.5 x 40 mm^3) which were first held at selected temperatures (100-600° C) for 20 min , then quenched into water at room temperature. The surface of the bars to be in tension was polished (down to 6 μm) after machining. For each ΔT six measurements of σ_f were performed. For the ΔT for which standard deviation in the values of residual strength was a maximum, Weibull analysis using 25 values was done.

Average thermal expansion coefficient up to 600° C was determined in a LVDT dilatometer Adamel Lhomargy DI-24 and E from ultrasounds velocity in the materials.

RESULTS AND DISCUSSION

The microstructure of the 0.3 (M+A) material (fig.1a) is made of a skeletton of large (~20 μm) mullite grains and glassy pockets at the triple points. Al_2O_3 and ZrO_2 particles are found embedded in the mullite matrix as well as in the glassy phase. Mullite grain growth in the 0 (M+A) material has been lower (~ 5 μm), ZrO_2 particles are located mainly in intergranular positions and no glassy pockets are found (fig.1b).

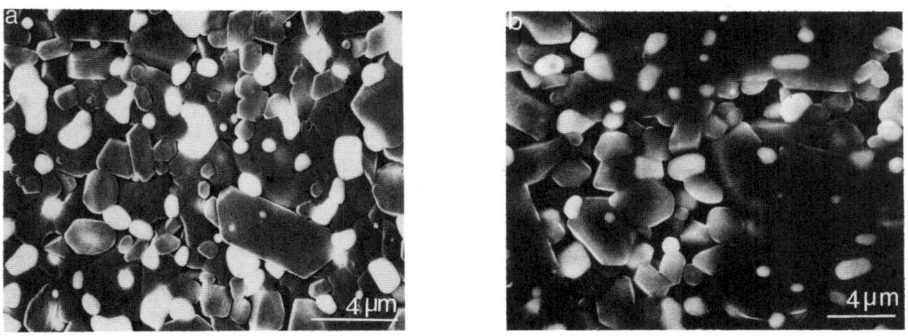

Figure 1. SEM: a.- 0(M+A). Thermally (1400° C, 10 min) and chemically (HF 7%, 1 min) etched. b.- 0.3(M+A). Chemically (HF 7%, 0.5 min) etched.

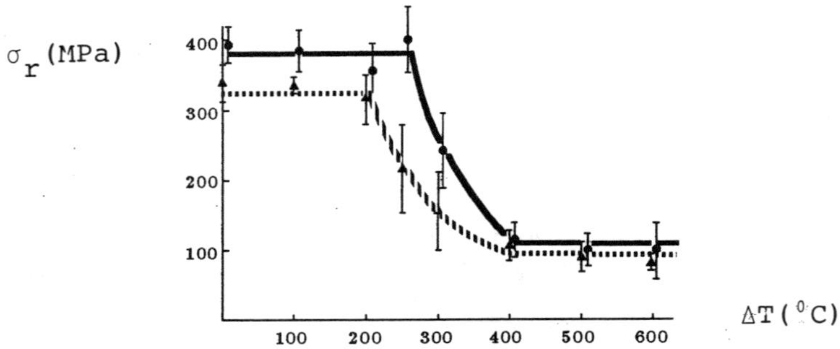

Figure 2. Residual strength versus temperature increment:
▲ .- 0.3(M+A) ● .- 0(M+A)

The variation of residual strength with ΔT (fig.2) shows a gradual decline from ΔT=250 and 300°C for X(M+A), X=0.3 and 0 respectively and up to ΔT=400° C, remaining constant from this last ΔT up to 600° C. Accordding to (4-5), the critical temperature increment for fracture initiation due to thermal shock is given by:

$$\Delta T_c = \frac{\sigma_f (1-\upsilon)}{E \alpha f(\beta)} \qquad (2)$$

where E is the Young's modulus, υ is the Poisson's ratio, and $f(\beta)$ is a function of heat transfer conditions.

The strength of ceramics is not characterized by a unique value of σ_f, but by a distribution of strengths, corresponding to the distribution of sizes of the internal flaws. Thus, a range of values of ΔT_c, related to the initial distribution of strengths is expected from eq. (2) and, this fact may be responsible for the gradual decline in σ_r observed in fig.2.

Performance of a sufficiently large number of tests shows the actual evolution of the σ_r values which is a change from a narrow distribution at $\Delta T < \Delta T_c$ to a bimodal distribution at $\Delta T \sim \Delta T_c$ and back to a narrow distribution at $\Delta T > \Delta T_c$. Thus a sensitive measure of ΔT_c is the point at which a sudden increase in the standard deviation in strengths is noted (6).

TABLE 1
Statistical analysis of σ_r at ΔT=250,300 for X(M+A), X=0.3,0

X	y = a x + b				y = a'x + b'				y = W x + C			
	a	b	R	σ_{r1}	a'	b'	R'	σ_{r2}	W	C	R	σ_r
0.3	5.5	-26	0.99	86± 12	1.1	-5.4	0.92	220± 93	2	-10	0.93	166± 98
0	7.1	-28	0.99	188± 21	2.7	-15	0.97	289± 53	4	-23	0.96	244± 66

W and C are obtained using all the σ_r values; a, a', b and b' correspond to the bimodal distribution. σ_r data are in MPa

Standard deviation in σ_r values shows a sudden increase for ΔT=250, 300 ^{0}C for x(M+A), x=0.3, 0 respectively corresponds to clearly defined bimodal strength distributions centered in σ_{r1} and σ_{r2} (table 1). From eq.(2), taking f(β) and equal for both materials and substituing the experimental values of α and E, a 20% increase should be seen in the critical temperature to initiate thermal stress failure from 0.3(M+A) to 0(M+A), which agrees with ΔT_c=250 and 300^0 C respectively. For 0.3(M+A), σ_{r1} coincides with the retained strength for ΔT>300^{0}C; for 0(M+A) σ_{r1} is higher than the retained strength for ΔT> 350^0 C (table 1, fig 2).

Neither for 0(M+A) nor for 0.3(M+A) the value of σ_r corresponding to the global Weibull distribution may be considered as the residual strength at ΔT_c; a sensitive value for this parameter would be σ_{r1} (table 1).

There are two parameters that describe the degree of damage of the material when fracture due to thermal shock initiates (9), these are: R'''- minimum available elastic strain energy at fracture - and R''''- minimum extent of crack propagation with the initiation of fracture-. The higher value of these parameters represents the lesser damage which should occur from thermal shock.

Calculations using the experimental values (α= 6.5x10^{-6}, 6.2x10^{-6} ^{0}C^{-1}, for X=0.3, 0; E= 240 GPa, σ_f from fig.2 for both materials) show that R'''does not correctly describe the thermal stress behaviour in the initiation of fracture region since the 0(M+A) material showed considerably less damage and R'''is lower (~25%) for this material than for the 0.3(M+A). The effect of the fracture surface energy reflected in R'''' should be extremely important in describing the differences between the thermal shock behaviour of these materials.

Figure 3 shows typical fracture surfaces of samples tested at ΔT=250 and 300 ^{0} C for the 0.3(M+A) and the 0(M+A). Fracture is: transgranular through the mullite matrix, trans/intergranular through the zirconia particles embedded in the mullite matrix and intergranular through the mullite-Al_2O_3, Al_2O_3-Al_2O_3 and ZrO_2-Al_2O_3 interfaces. There exist large zones of intergranular fracture in the glassy pockets found in the 0.3(M+A) samples.

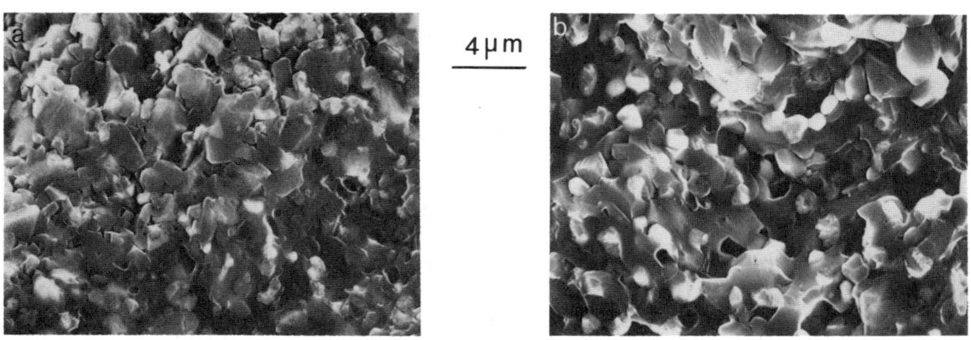

Figure 3. Typical fracture surfaces: a.- 0.3(M+A), b.- 0(M+A)

In the 0.3(M+A) samples, the fracture initiation of thermal shock cracks must take place through the glassy interstices where γ_f is much lower than in the mullite matrix (fig.3a).

In the 0(M+A), cracks must propagate through the ZrO_2-reinforced mullite matrix. Moreover, crack deflexion phenomena take place (fig.3b). Fracture surface energy in this material is expected to be much higher. In fact, the sudden decrease in σ_f values predicted by Hasselman may not exist for materials with high fracture energies in which crack propagation occurs primarly in a quasi-static manner in contrast to the kinetic crack propagation predicted by this author (8).

CONCLUSIONS

The thermal shock behaviour of two mullite-alumina-zirconia composites with substantially different microstructures has been studied. It has been concluded that:

- A sensitive measurement of ΔT_c is the ΔT for which standard deviation in residual strength is a maximum.
- Consideration of just the values of $\overline{\sigma}_r$ at ΔT_c can overestimate the real value of the retained strength for ΔT_c.
- The changes in strength with thermal shock for these materials are directly related to their microstructure.
- This relation is due to the role played by the fracture surface energy at initiation of fracture by thermal shock.

REFERENCES

1. First International Workshop on Mullite, Nov. 1987, Tokyo, Japan.
2. C. Baudín, F. Cambier, L. Delaey, "Fractographic Study of the Alumina and Zirconia Particles embedded in Mullite Prepared by Reaction Sintering" J. Mater. Sci.,1986,21,4024-4028.
3. C. Baudín, F. Cambier, L. Delaey, Fractographic and acoustic emission studies of mullite-Al_2O_3-ZrO_2 composites prepared by reaction sintering, J. Mater. Sci.,1987,22,4398-4402.
4. Hasselman, D.P.H., Unified theory of thermal shock fracture initiation and crack propagation in brittle ceramics, J. Am. Ceram. Soc.,1969,52,600-4.
5. Hasselman, D.P.H., Thermal stress resistance parameters for brittle refractory ceramics: A compendium, Ceram. Bull., (1970) 49, 1033-1037.
6. Lewis III, D., Thermal shock and thermal shock fatige testing of ceramics with the water quench test, Fracture Mechanics of Ceramics, vol.6, 1983, 487-496, Plenum Press, N. York.
7. Coppola, J.A., Bradt, R.C., Thermal shock damage in SiC, J. Am. Ceram. Soc., 1973, 56, 214-8.
8. Gupta, T.K., Strenght degradation and crack propagation in thermally shocked alumina, J. Am. Ceram. Soc., (1972), 55, 249-53.

PROPERTIES OF ALUMINIUM NITRIDE DOPED WITH LANTHANUM OXIDE.

J.- P. BAZIN, A. KRANZMANN and G. PETZOW
Max- Planck- Institut für Metallforschung
Institut für Werkstoffwissenschaft
Pulvermetallurgisches Laboratorium
Heisenbergstraße 5, 7000 Stuttgart 80, F.R.G.

ABSTRACT.

AlN is valuable as a substrate material for electronic devices because of its high thermal conductivity. To trap the oxygen which is always present in commercial powders, the AlN has been doped with La_2O_3 (from 0 to 10 wt.%) and pressureless sintered at temperatures from 1850 to 2000°C. The influence of oxygen on the microstructure has been investigated by additional doping with alumina. Densities higher than 98% of the theoretical value were obtained. The influence of phase composition and oxygen content on the mechanical properties and the heat conductivity of the material has been investigated.

INTRODUCTION.

AlN is a good candidate for heat sinks, especially in electronics because of its good thermal conductivity and electrical insulation, or for heat exchangers in regard to its good chemical resistance. In order to machine the artefacts without the risk of damaging them, and also for some special applications, a good mechanical strength is needed. All trials to strengthen AlN through oxynitride platelets [1], SiC [2] or Si_3N_4 whiskers lower the thermal conductivity because of solid solution in the SiCAlON system. On the other hand, the AlN grains are often losely bonded together, which is obvious on many micrographs where the fracture is intergranular. Therefore, a compound has to be found, which traps the alumina always present on the surface of the AlN grains without dissolving in the AlN lattice, and which is able to produce a phase promoting the sintering of AlN and bonding it well without acting as a thermal barrier. Perovskites of the $LnAlO_3$ type have a relatively high thermal conductivity; the influence of compounds in the system (La,Al)O on the sintering and the thermal and mechanical properties of AlN have been investigated.

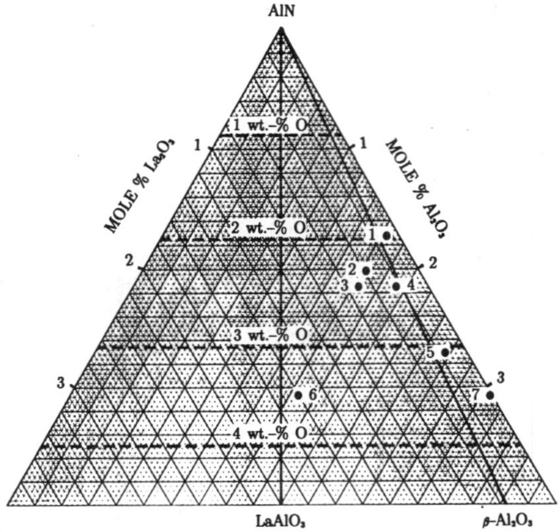

Figure 1 . Position of the chosen mixtures in the AlN rich corner of the quasi ternary system AlN- Al_2O_3- La_2O_3.

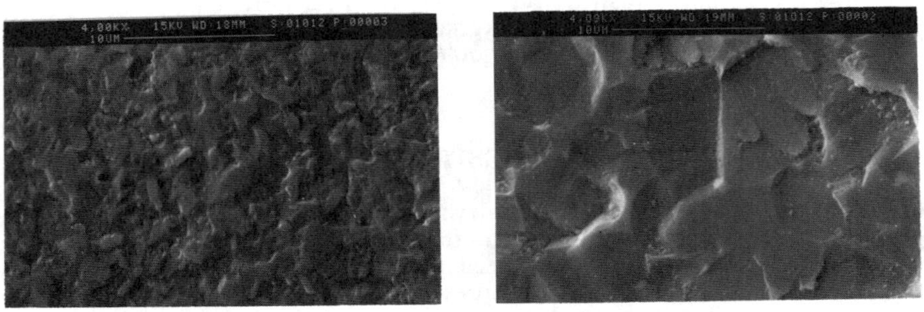

Figure 2 . Etched surfaces of samples 3 (left) and 4 (right).

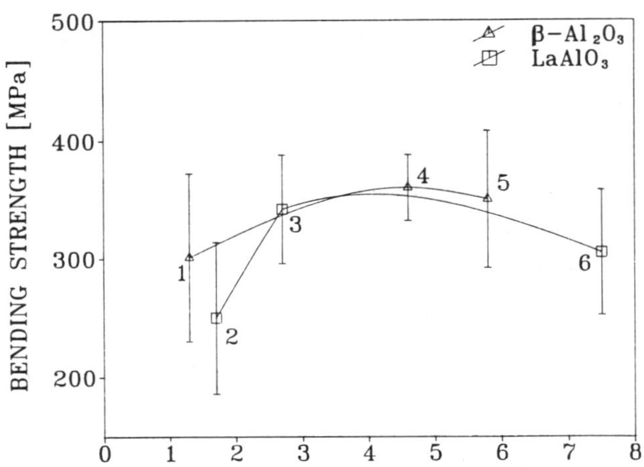

Figure 3 . Bending strength as a function of the volume fraction of the second phase. The maximum bending strength is achieved at about 4 vol.- % additives.

MATERIALS AND METHODS.

AlN Powders (H.C. Starck Grade A) were mixed with La_2O_3 (Ventron, 99.9%) and Al_2O_3 (Alcoa A16) in the proportions showed in fig. 1 and attrition milled for 150 minutes in isopropanol at 700 rpm with alumina balls, then dried in air at 70°C for 6 hours. After isostatical pressing at 200 MPa, the samples were sintered at 1850°C or 2000°C for 5 minutes (heating rate of 12 K/min). The phases were investigated with X- Ray diffraction and the oxygen content of the samples was measured with inert gas extraction method; the thermal conductivity was investigated using a laser flash apparatus (length of specimens ≥ 6 mm) and the bending strength with a hydraulic machine (Carl Schenck AG, speed 0.5 mm/s, samples 45 x 3.5 x 4.5 mm, 4 points bending method on a 40- 20 mm span).

RESULTS.

Three phases were found in the AlN rich corner of the quasi ternary system at temperatures between 1850 and 2000°C : AlN, $LaAlO_3$ perovskite in cubic form (with a= 0.3795 nm), and the hexagonal (a= 0.5582 nm, c= 2.2031 nm) $La_2O_3 \cdot 12.2Al_2O_3$ after [3]. No compositions showed traces of γ- AlON ($5AlN \cdot 9Al_2O_3$) or 27R- polytype ($7AlN \cdot Al_2O_3$) when lanthanum was present.

TABLE 1

Secondary phases found in the specimens and densities obtained at 1850°C (except for sample 7 at 2000°C).

Sample number	PHASE COMPOSITION AlON	 $LaAlO_3$	 β- Al_2O_3	REL. DENSITY (% of theor.)
1	-	vvw	vw	98.8
2	-	w	vw	99.3
3	-	w	-	99.5
4	-	vvw	w	98.6
5	-	-	m	98.4
6	-	s	-	99.3
7	s	-	-	96.5

vvw= very very weak; vw= very weak; w= weak; m= medium; s= strong.

At 2000°C, the densities were lower and the X- ray peaks of lanthanum containing phases weaker, so that it may be concluded that the lanthanum species were volatilising, like in yttria containing AlN [4]. The sintering rate ($3\ \% \cdot min^{-1}$ at a heating rate of 12 K/min) with 3 vol.- % $CaAl_4O_7$ was similar to that of AlN with 3 vol.- % $LaAlO_3$ and slightly higher than that with 5 vol.- % β- Al_2O_3. Schrinkage began with $LaAlO_3$ at about 1625°C, in the two other cases 200°C lower. The relative densities were all over 98 % and increase when the molar ratio La:Al increased. In the same time, grain growth was observed in the samples with lower lanthanum content (fig. 2).
The bending strength of the pressureless sintered material was 350 MPa with a Weibull modulus of 12.3 (CaO doped samples treated in the same way show

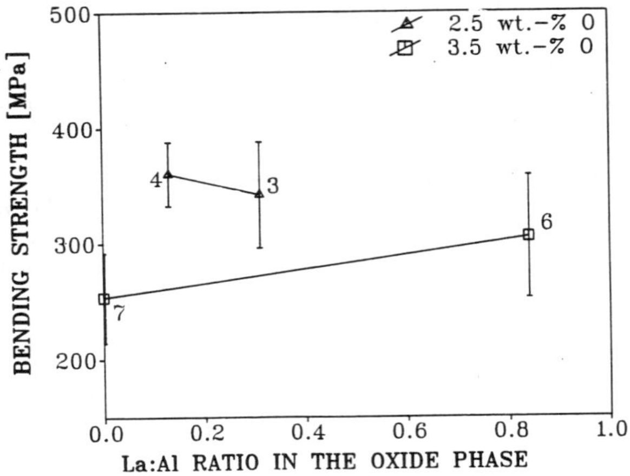

Figure 4 . Bending strength as a function of the molar ratio La:Al.The strength increases when the oxygen content decreases.

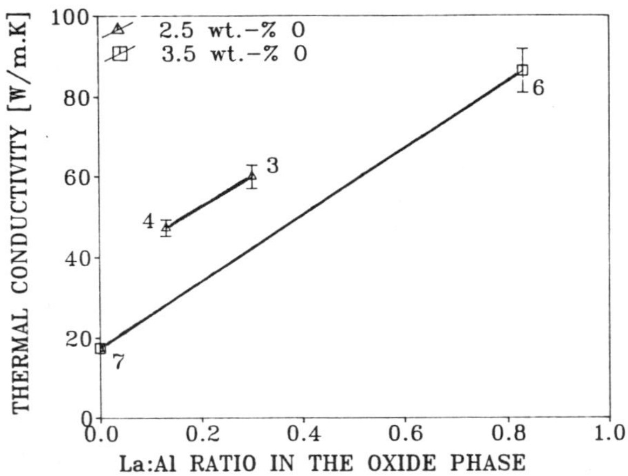

Figure 5 . Thermal conductivity as a function of the molar ratio La:Al, for the two different oxygen contents. λ increases if the oxygen content decreases and if the La:Al ratio increases.

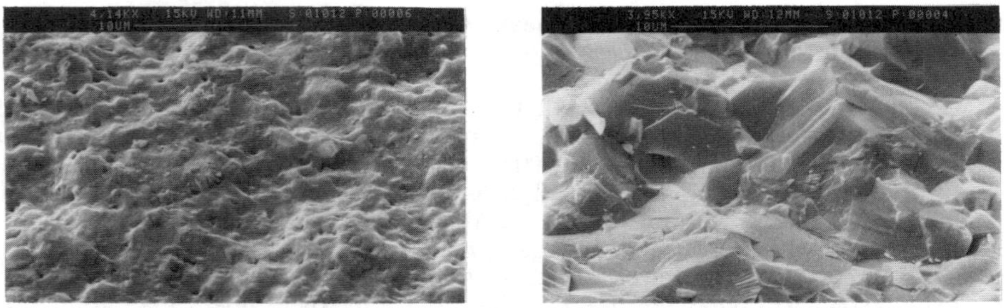

Figure 6 . Scanning electron micrographs of the fracture surfaces of the samples 3 (left) and 4 (right). The fracture mode is mainly transgranular in 4; in 3, notice the good wetting of the perovskite phase.

values of 250 and 8 respectively [5]) at about 4 vol.- % of second phase (fig. 3), and is higher at 2,5 wt.- % oxygen (fig. 4). However, the thermal conductivity of these materials, which increases when decreasing oxygen content and increasing lanthanum content (fig. 5), was less than that of calcium oxide doped AlN (about 150 W/m·K) and virtually the same as commercial yttria- - doped AlN.

DISCUSSION.

The good wetting of the grains by a lanthanum rich second phase explains the sintering behaviour of these compounds, and their mechanical properties. It should be noticed that the similar bending strengths of the samples 3 and 4 proceed of two different fracture mechanisms : in 3, the fracture goes through the good wetting oxide phase, between the small grains; in 4, it is strongly transgranular (fig. 6). The β- Al_2O_3 containing samples began to sinter at a lower temperature; consequently, the sintering finished at a lower temperature. This may explain the grain growth in these samples. The relatively high thermal conductivity of sample 6, compared to the other samples, may be explained by the fact that the conductivity of the second phase is high despite its good wetting, or more generally because the impurities picked up during sintering may dissolve preferentially in the perovskite than in the AlN lattice; the thermal conductivity decreases with increasing volume of second phase, but not as drastically as when AlN solid solution occurs [5], which probably occurs in the sample 4 where apparently there were good contacts between the grains.

CONCLUSIONS.

Oxynitrides were not found in AlN based materials doped with La_2O_3 containing more than 2 wt.- % oxygen, but only $LaAlO_3$ and β- Al_2O_3. Lanthanum oxide promotes sintering and grain growth of AlN; relative densities higher than 98% are attained with the same sintering rate as with calcium oxide. The mechanical strengths are slightly higher than materials sintered in the same conditions with calcium oxide (about 350 MPa). and increases when the oxygen content decreases, independently of the nature of the second phase. The low thermal conductivity (less than 100 W/m·K, compared to more than 150 for CaO doped material) may be explained by the good wetting of the AlN grains or by the impurities picked up during attrition milling and dissolved in the AlN lattice. In order to achieve a high sinterability and good mechanical properties, a high La:Al ratio is needed (good wetting), which produces a low thermal conductivity.

REFERENCES.

[1] T. Sakai, M. Kuriyama, T. Inukai and T. Kizima, Yogyo Kyokai Shi **86** (1978) 174- 179.
[2] W. Rafaniello, K. Cho, A. Virkar, J. Mater. Sci. **16** (1981) 3479- 3488
[3] J. Dexpert- Ghys, M. Faucher and P. Caro, J. of Solid State Chem. **19** (1976) 193- 204
[4] F. Ueno, Seramikkusu **23** (1988) 220- 222
[5] A. Kranzmann, PhD thesis, Stuttgart 1988

THE INTERACTION BETWEEN SiC AND METALS

R.C.J. Schiepers, J.A. van Beek, F.J.J. van Loo and G. de With,
Centre for Technical Ceramics, Eindhoven University of Technology
P.O. Box 513, 5600 MB Eindhoven, The Netherlands.

ABSTRACT

Diffusion bonding between SiC and metals has been studied from a thermodynamic and kinetic point of view. In solid-state diffusion couples the reactions have been studied between SiC and Ni, Fe and (Fe-Ni) alloys in the temperature range 700 - 1000 °C. In SiC-Fe couples the layer consists of α-(Fe,Si) with random carbon precipitates. In SiC-Ni couples the phases Ni_2Si, Ni_5Si_2 and Ni_3Si are formed. The carbon is present as precipitates in regular bands in the Ni_2Si and Ni_5Si_2 layers. In SiC-Fe_xNi_{100-x} couples a ternary compound $\tau = Fe_5Ni_3Si_2$ is formed for $20 \leq x \leq 60$. The kinetics of the foregoing reactions have been studied. To control the rate of the reactions, diffusion barriers are needed.

INTRODUCTION

In structures where ceramics have to be applied in combination with metals, a good adherence between the metal and the ceramic is required. However, severe reactions at the interface may negatively influence the quality of the joints. In order to understand and to control the reactions, the thermodynamics and the kinetics of ceramic-metal interactions are subject of investigations in our laboratory. At present we are primarily interested in SiC. From previous work the isothermal sections of the Ni-Si-C and Fe-Si-C phase diagrams at 850°C are known [1].

In this paper we present the results of diffusion experiments between SiC and pure Ni, Fe or (Fe-Ni) alloys. The experimental set-up and preparational procedure have been described extensively in ref. [1]. The metals used in this investigation have a purity > 99.95 %. For SiC we used hot isostatically pressed SiC without sintering additives and HIP-SiC with

0.2 wt.% Al. Fe-Ni and Fe-Ni-Si alloys have been made by argon-arc melting the proper amounts of the constituents (up to 10 gram), and the resulting alloys were annealed during one week at 850 °C. The diffusion couples were annealed in a vacuum furnace at 10^{-4} Pa under a pressure of 13 MPa for various times. The couples and the equilibrated alloys were investigated by optical microscopy and electron probe micro-analysis (JEOL Superprobe 733).

INTERACTIONS

- In SiC-Ni diffusion couples at 850 °C, the compounds Ni_2Si, Ni_5Si_2 and Ni_3Si are formed in regular layers. Carbon precipitates are present in the Ni_2Si and Ni_5Si_2 layers as regular bands parallel to the original interface. By means of marker experiments nickel is found to be virtually the only diffusing component [1]. The morphology and composition of the reaction layer are independent of the presence of Al as a sintering additive.

- In SiC-Fe diffusion couples at 850 °C the α-(Fe,Si) solid solution was formed, with carbon precipitates randomly dispersed in the layer except for a thin, carbon-free zone of α-(Fe,Si). Fe turns out to be virtually the only diffusing component [1]. At 850 °C the reaction zones show the same morphology and composition independent of the Al-content of the SiC ceramic.

- In SiC-(Fe-Ni) diffusion couples at 850 °C complex reactions occur. The diffusion paths can be plotted in the quaternary Fe-Ni-Si-C diagram at 850 °C with Fe, Ni and Si at the base and C on the vertical axis (fig.1a). However, it is more convenient to give the projections of the diffusion paths on the isothermal section of the Fe-Ni-Si phase diagram at 850 °C (fig. 1b). We determined the Fe-Ni-Si phase diagram at 850 °C on the basis of the analysis of 30 equilibrated alloys. Our results globally agree with the cross-sections of the Fe-Ni-Si phase diagram at temperatures between 600 and 1000 °C, proposed by Raynor [3].

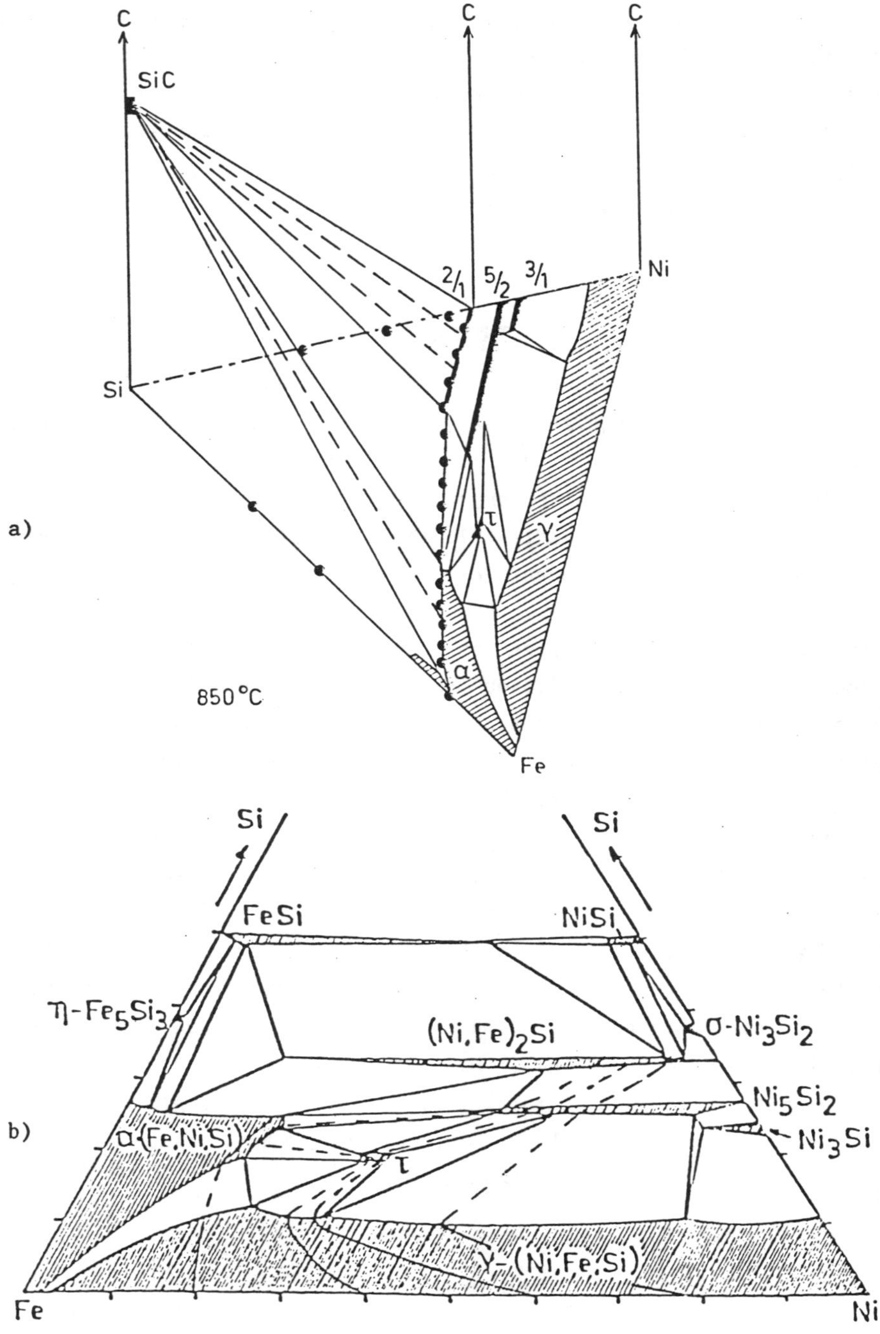

Figure 1a) Isothermal section of Fe–Ni–Si–C phase diagram at 850 °C.
b) Projections of the diffusion paths of SiC–(Fe–Ni) diffusion couples on the Fe–Ni–Si isotherm at 850 °C. [2].

KINETICS

The kinetics of the foregoing reactions were studied. SiC reacts with Ni without an incubation time and the layer growth follows the parabolic growth law. The presence of Al in SiC seems to accelerate the reactions: thicker reaction zones are formed [2].

In the kinetics of SiC-Fe [2] and SiC-(Fe-Ni) diffusion couples an irreproducible incubation time is present, probably caused by a reaction barrier at the initial interface. Diffusion experiments to elucidate the origin of the incubation time are in progress. The presence of Al in this case also seems to accelerate the reactions.

DISCUSSION

It is shown that severe reactions occur between SiC and Ni, Fe or (Fe-Ni) alloys. Therefore, joints between SiC and these metals will degradate fast at high temperatures. Moreover, the large difference in thermal expansion coefficient between SiC and these metals may cause cracking of the joint during cooling. Diffusion barriers should cope with these two problems. Copper is useful as a diffusion barrier material for SiC. However, in SiC containing free Si, we found an excessive formation of Cu_3Si. Therefore, other materials have to be considered as well.

Using a model developed by van Loo et al. [4] it is possible to predict, from the shape of the phase diagram, the type and sequence of the phases which are formed during the reaction between SiC and the metal. First, only phases below the dotted line in fig. 1 can be formed, because all other phases are already in equilibrium with SiC. (This is the reason that only a part of the Fe-Ni-Si-C diagram had to be investigated!). Further, the sequence of the products formed, i.e. metal silicides MSi_x and carbon, can be predicted by comparing the two hypothetical extreme situations after a short diffusion time (fig. 2).

Figure 2. Two hypothetical extreme situations after a short diffusion annealing of a couple SiC - Metal.

In SiC the activity of carbon is less than one, if no free carbon is present. If the situation of figure 2a would be present, then carbon should diffuse through a metal-silicide layer towards a pure carbon layer with an activity equal to 1. Thermodynamically it is impossible for an atom species to intrinsically diffuse upward its own activity gradient. Therefore, the situation in fig. 2a is impossible.

On the other hand, in fig. 2b the carbon layer is formed at the SiC-side of the couple. The increase of the activity of carbon from SiC to the value 1 in the graphite layer is now imposed upon carbon by the intrinsic diffusion of the metal atoms and, in fact, carbon does not move. This is thermodynamically allowed and in our experiments we indeed always see this initial sequence: in all couples a carbon-free layer is formed next to the metal. After longer annealing, the brittle carbon layer breaks down and is dispersed as more or less coherent particles in the reaction layers.

CONCLUSIONS

- Due to the severe reactions between the SiC ceramic and the metals, diffusion barriers are needed to get good joints between the ceramic and the metals.
- The layer products and sequence found in SiC - metal diffusion couples can be predicted by the model of van Loo et al. [4].

ACKNOWLEDGEMENT

This work has been financially supported by the commission Innovative Research Program Technical Ceramics (IOP-TK) of the Ministery of Economic Affairs in the Netherlands. The authors are indebted to mr. J.T. Klomp for many valuable suggestions.

REFERENCES

1. Schiepers, R.C.J., van Loo, F.J.J., and de With, G., Reactions between α-Silicon Carbide Ceramic and nickel or iron, J.Am.Ceram.Soc., 1988, 71, C-284 - C-287.
2. Schiepers, R.C.J., van Beek, J. A., de Giacomoni, E., Valla, B., van Loo, F.J.J. and de With, G., The interaction between SiC and Ni or Fe and their alloys, Scripta Metallurgica (1989), in print.
3. Raynor, G.V., Rivlin, V.G., Critical evaluation of constitution of Co-Ni-Si and Fe-Ni-Si alloys, Int.Metals Reviews, 30, 1985, nr.4, 181-208.
4. van Loo, F.J.J., van Beek, J.A., Bastin, G.F. and Metselaar, R., The role of thermodynamics and kinetics in multiphase ternary diffusion, from: Diffusion in Solids, recent developments (1985), pp. 231-259.

JOINING OF ALUMINUM TITANATE WITH NIOBIUM

H. WOHLFROMM, P. PENA and J.S. MOYA
Instituto de Cerámica y Vidrio, C.S.I.C.
285000 Arganda del Rey, Madrid, Spain

A.P. TOMSIA and G. THOMAS
Lawrence Berkeley Laboratory,
Materials and Chemical Sciences Division
Berkeley CA 94720, USA

ABSTRACT

Aluminum titanate was joined with niobium by hotpressing with the aim to study the reactions at the metal/ceramic interface. Scanning electron microscopy, electron-probe microanalysis and indentation measurements were used to characterize the interface. Several reactions were found to take place during the bonding involving partial decomposition of aluminum titanate and formation of niobium oxides. It was shown that the bonding conditions have to be chosen in a way that prevents the formation of Nb_2O_5 which is detrimental to the bonding strength.

INTRODUCTION

Joining of metals to ceramics is a challenging field of ceramic science as well as a technological issue with growing interest. In the present work bonding in the system Nb-Al_2TiO_5 was studied. Aluminum titanate is an interesting candidate for many structural applications which is known because of its low coefficient of thermal expansion and elevated thermal shock resistance (1). Niobium was chosen because of its refractoriness and high ductility (2). Although much work has been done on the similar system Al_2O_3-Nb (3), up to this day no data are available for the system Al_2TiO_5-Nb.

EXPERIMENTAL

A 127 μm thick niobium foil, 99.8 % pure (Johnson Matthey 10261), and 1.5 mm thick discs of hotpressed aluminum titanate (94 % dense) were used for the bonding experiments. After polishing and cleaning, Al_2TiO_5/Nb/Al_2TiO_5 "sandwich" type specimens were prepared by hotpressing in vacuum of $2*10^{-4}$ Torr. 10 MPa pressure was applied during 2 hr soaking at a) 1500 °C, specimen labeled J1, and b) 1450 ° C, labeled J2. In both cases a highly reducing atmosphere was present due to the gettering effect of the graphite die. After bonding, the specimens were cut perpendicularly to the interface, polished and examined by scanning electron microscopy (SEM). Compositional line scans across the interface were made by electron-probe microanalysis (EPMA). In sample J2 cracks were generated close to the interface and caused to propagate using a Vickers indenter which was cyclically loaded at 50 N. The propagation of these cracks after several cycles was examined by scanning electron microscopy.

RESULTS AND DISCUSSION

General Observations

In specimen J1, bonding was achieved only in few areas (Fig. 1a). Large cracks can be seen along and perpendicular to the interface which in some areas even led to failure of the metal foil. Conversely, in specimen J2, bonding was achieved over practically the whole interfacial area (Fig. 1b).

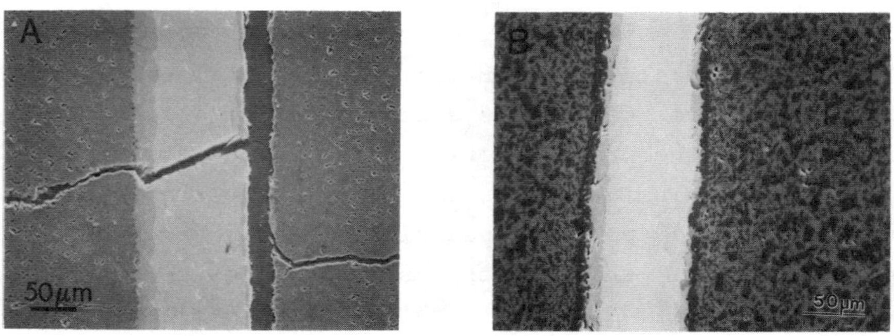

FIGURE 1. Cross section of the Al_2TiO_5/Nb/Al_2TiO_5 interface, a) J1, b) J2

In both specimens, the formation of several reaction layers between ceramic and metal-foil can be observed. Adjacent to this reaction layer a relatively broad zone, 60-80 µm thick, is found where Al_2TiO_5 decomposed to Al_2O_3 and TiO_2. The microstructure of this Al_2O_3/TiO_2-layer is much finer in J1 than in J2 (Fig. 2). A smaller decomposition layer, 35-60 µm thick, can be appreciated at the surface of the ceramic, which is due to the reducing atmosphere (4).

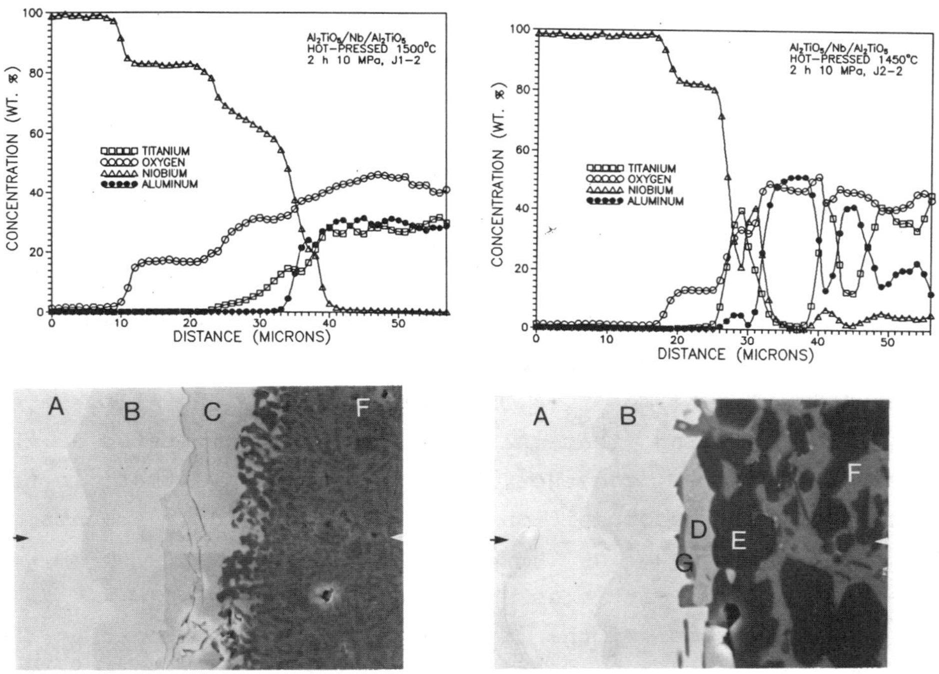

FIGURE 2. Cross section of the Nb/Al_2TiO_5 interface with compositional profiles, a) J1, b) J2.

Interface Microchemistry

Fig. 2a shows the compositional profile of specimen J1 determined by EPMA in an area where bonding was achieved. Adjacent to the metalic Nb (A) is an oxide layer, 10 µm thick, which was identified as NbO (B). The next layer (C), 10-12 µm, corresponds to the nominal composition $Nb_xTi_yO_z$; y and z are increasing with increasing distance from the interface. The outer zone of C is characterized by a constant oxygen content, and is practically Nb_2O_5 with a small amount of oxygen deficient TiO_{2-x} in solid solution. Zone (F) is the above-mentioned area of decomposed Al_2TiO_5. The dark particles are Al_2O_3, the brighter matrix is probably oxygen deficient TiO_{2-x}. It is noteworthy that there is significant diffusion of 10 μm of Nb into the AlO_3/TiO_{2-x} layer.

In specimen J2 (Fig. 2b) similar to J1, an NbO layer (B), 8-14 μm, is formed adjacent to the metal foil (A), that is, the metal is partially oxidized. However, contrary to J1, there is no Nb_2O_5 layer formed in J2. That is, Nb oxidation stopped at a lower oxidation state of Nb than in the case of J1. This fact could be explained considering that the oxidation kinetics is lower at 1450° C (J2) than at 1500°C (J1). But it should also be taken into account that a hypothetic redox reaction involving reduction of TiO_2, stemming from Al_2TiO_5-decomposition, and oxidation of Nb is thermodynamically more favourable at higher temperature (4). The next continuous layer (D) corresponds to the nominal composition $Ti_{25}Al_5Nb_7O_{63}$. The morphology of the Al_2O_3-layer (E) is suggesting that Al_2O_3-particles precipitated at the interface and grew together. It is noteworthy that in the coarse grained decomposition zone (F) appreciable amounts of Al and Nb are found in the TiO_2-rich matrix, but no Nb was detected in Al_2O_3-particles.

In both samples, the morphology of the zone next to the niobium oxide, e.g. phase G in J2, which is discontinuously distributed at the interface, suggests that glassy phases are involved in reactions taking place place at the interface (5).

Mechanical Evaluation of the Interface

The poor bonding in sample J1 is evident from Fig. 1a and 3. Large stresses are obviously generated during bonding and cooling producing cracks radial and parallel to the interface. The presence of an Nb_2O_5-rich layer is likely to be responsible for the poor strength of the interface in J1. This layer is strongly microcracked (Fig. 2a and 3a) due to the

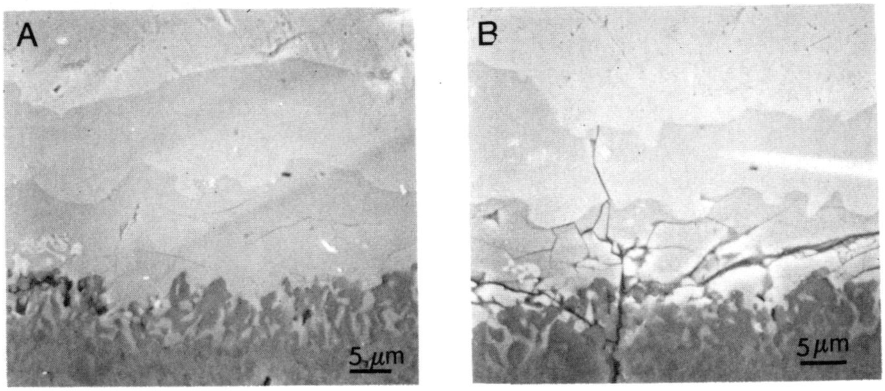

FIGURE 3. Details of the Nb/Al_2TiO_5 interface in specimen J1, a) microcracks in Nb_2O_5-layer, b) failure of the Nb_2O_5-layer.

thermal anisotropy of Nb_2O_5 (6) and therefore most sensitive to failure. In addition , large stresses will arise between Al_2O_3+TiO_2 (CTE 7-8*$10^{-6}K^{-1}$) and Nb_2O_5 (CTE $\leq$ 2*10^{-6} K^{-1} (6)) and NbO (CTE unknown but probably > CTE of Nb_2O_5) due to the thermal expansion mismatch which can finally cause failure of the Nb_2O_5-layer (Fig. 3b). On the contrary the stresses which could arise form the thermal expansion mismatch at the Al_2O_3+TiO_2/Al_2TiO_5 interface are supposed to be less severe since there is no "sharp" interface formed but a gradual transition from decomposed over partially decomposed to stable Al_2TiO_5.

In specimen J2 good bonding was achieved which can be attributed to the lack of Nb_2O_5. That is, the lower temperature of 1450°C is more suitable for bonding Nb to Al_2TiO_5 since it only permits a limited oxidation of the metal foil. A qualitative measure of the interface mechanics is given by the observation of cracks generated by a Vickers indenter in the ceramic close to the interface. Fig. 4 illustrates typical features of the interfacial zone. Cracks propagating towards the interface penetrate the brittle NbO-layer but are stopped when reaching the ductile metal foil (Fig. 4a). Further loading is necessary to initiate secondary

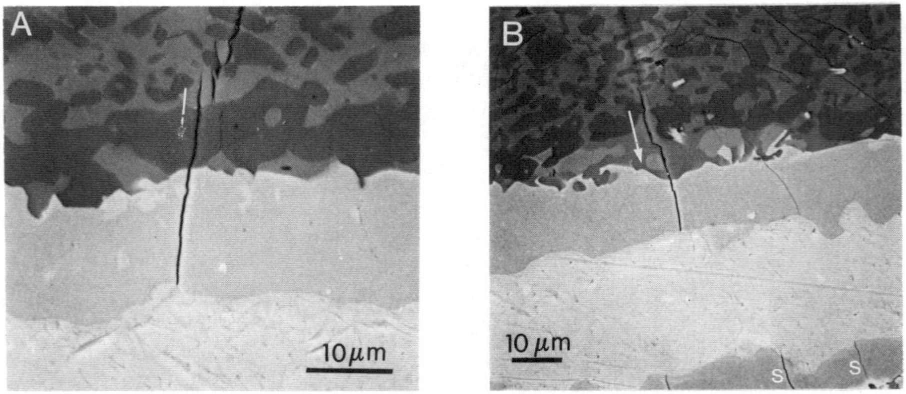

FIGURE 4. Crack propagation at the interface in specimen J2, a) crack stopped at the metal foil, b) secondary cracks (s) are generated.

cracks in the NbO at the opposed face of the metal. That is, the metal foil is bridging the crack but withstanding failure by deforming plastically.

CONCLUSIONS

This study demonstrates the possibility of achieving good metal ceramic bondings in the system Nb/Al_2TiO_5. Contrary to similar systems, like e.g. Nb/Al_2O_3, the system Nb/Al_2TiO_5 is very reactive. This can be attributed to the presence of Ti, which can easily change its oxidation state permitting it to react with Nb under the indicated experimental conditions.

An interface reaction mechanism is proposed which involves partial decomposition of Al_2TiO_5 permitting the formed TiO_2 to participate in a redox reaction with Nb. The oxidation state of the NbO_x formed is a critical parameter which has to be controlled by the choice of adequate bonding conditions. At higher temperatures (1500 °C) Nb_2O_5 whose properties are detrimental to the development of high strength joints was formed in addition to NbO. At lower temperatures (1450°C) only NbO is formed resulting in favourable mechanical properties.

REFERENCES

1. Buessem, W. R., Thielke, N. R., Sarakauskas, Thermal expansion hysteresis of aluminum titanate, Ceramic Age, 1950, 60, 38 - 40.

2. Smithells, L.J., Metals Reference Book, Butterworth, 1976.

3. Klomp, J.T., Ceramic-metal raections and their effect on the interface microstructure. In Microstructures '86. Role of Interfaces, ed. Pask, J., Evans, A.G., Plenum Press, New York and London, 1987, pp. 307-317.

4. Wohlfromm, H., unpublished research.

5. a) Levin, E.M., Robbins, McMurdie, H.F., Phase Diagrams for Ceramists, Am. Cer. Soc., Westerville, 1964, fig. 372; b) ibid. supplement 1975, fig. 4159; c) ibid. vol. VI, fig. 6453.

6. Manning, W.R., Hunter, O., Calderwood, F.W., Stacy, D.W., Thermal expansion of Nb_2O_5, J. Am. Cer. Soc., 1972, 55, 342-347.

ACKNOWLEDGEMENTS

This work was supported by CICYT, Spain (proyect number MAT88-0156) and NSF, USA (Grant DMR-83-1317239). One of the authors (H.W.) thanks the Commission of the European Communities for the award of a fellowship.

IN SITU SYNTHESIS OF SILICON CARBIDE WHISKERS WITHIN AN ALUMINA OR ALUMINA/ZIRCONIA MATRIX POWDER

J.-P. ERAUW ° and F. DELANNAY
Dept des Sciences des Matériaux et des Procédés
Université Catholique de Louvain
Place Ste Barbe, 2 - B - 1348 Louvain-la-Neuve (Belgium)

ABSTRACT

In-situ synthesis of silicon carbide whiskers within an alumina or alumina/zirconia matrix powder was investigated. The syntesis reaction consists in a carbothermal reduction of either silica or zircon in presence of metallic aluminum.

INTRODUCTION

Alumina-based ceramics are promising structural materials exhibiting high mechanical strength and excellent corrosion and wear resistance. However, their application is still limited because of their brittle nature and low strength at high temperature. These properties may be improved by the dispersion of a second phase within the matrix, either as particles or whiskers. It has been shown for instance [1] that a dispersion of fine silicon carbide particles enhances by 40% the fracture toughness and mechanical strength of pure alumina. The incorporation of silicon carbide whiskers was also demonstrated to improve significantly the fracture toughness of monolithic oxide ceramics [2].

Yet the obtention of a uniform distribution of a second phase within the matrix remains a major problem in the preparation of ceramic-matrix composites, especially when this second phase presents a fibrous morphology. In this respect, the in-situ synthesis of second phase particles or whiskers within the matrix appears an attractive solution to this problem. In the present work we applied this approach to the preparation of an alumina/silicon carbide composite powder. It is indeed possible to obtain a mixed powder of alumina and silicon carbide by reacting a mixture of silica and carbon in the presence of aluminum [3]. The overall reaction may be formulated as

$$3\ SiO_2 + 4\ Al + 3\ C \rightarrow 3\ SiC + 2\ Al_2O_3 \qquad (1)$$

Calculations from relevant thermodynamic data show that this reaction is exothermic and brings about a negative free energy change at the temperatures involved ($\Delta G°_{298}$=-808 KJ/mol ; $\Delta G°_{1000}$=-729 KJ/mol ; $\Delta H°_{298}$=-839 KJ/mol ; $\Delta H°_{1000}$=-890 KJ/mol).

- - - - - - - - - - - - - - - - - -

° aspirant du F.N.R.S.

In this work, we studied the progress of the above reaction as a function of temperature and analysed the microstructure developed.

EXPERIMENTAL

The silica used in this study was an amorphous precipitated silica with primary particles in the range 10-60 nanometers and a BET surface area of about 200 m^2/g (Neosyl ET from Crosfield Chemicals); the carbon source was a special carbon black with a DPB value of about 400 ml/100g, a particle size around 35 nanometers and a BET surface area of 1000 m^2/g (Degussa); aluminum was an atomized powder from Alcoa with a size distribution ranging from a few micrometers up to 30-40 µm. The major impurity detected by ICP analysis of this powder was iron (about 0.1%). In order to study the effect of iron on the synthesis of silicon carbide we also made use either of an aluminum powder containing 3% iron (with particle sizes of the order of 100 µm), either of silica preliminary impregnated with an iron nitrate solution and treated one hour at 700 °C in air.

Homogeneous powder blends of $Al/C/SiO_2$ were prepared by ball milling in ethanol for several hours in polyethylene jars. The proportions of the reactants corresponded to the stoichiometry of reaction (1). After drying and screening, the powders were deposited in a graphite crucible covered by a graphite lid, and heat treated at various temperatures in a tube furnace for one hour under flowing argon. The temperature ranged from the melting point of aluminium up to 1400 °C. Chemical transformations of the samples were assessed by X-ray diffraction using Cu-Kα radiation. The microstructure of the composite powders was characterized by SEM, TEM and EPMA.

Some experiments were also done by replacing silica by zircon in order to synthesize an alumina/zirconia matrix powder.

RESULTS

Chemical transformations

Figure 1 shows typical diffraction patterns of the products obtained after heat treatment at different temperatures. The observations may be summarized as follow.

- Heat treatment of the reactants blend leads to the formation of α alumina above 900°C and of silicon carbide above 1000 °C;
- Silicon appears as an intermediate product of the reaction;
- Above 1400°C, only α alumina, α silicon carbide and β silicon carbide are detected.

Approximatively the same chemical transformations occured in the iron-doped blends except that reactants are still detected even after treatment at 1400°C . This results probably from, on the one hand, a lower homogeneity of the blend due to the coarser grain size of the aluminum powder and, on the other hand, from a decrease of the reactivity of the silica due to the preliminary heat treatment.

The alumina observed consists mainly of α alumina although η and θ alumina were also detected after treatments at temperatures $\leq$ 1000 °C. Those transition aluminas transform into α alumina with increasing temperature.

Both α and β silicon carbide were formed. The α modification has been identified as the 2H polytype. Its percentage relative to the total silicon carbide present in the sample has been calculated.. It amounts to approximatively 30% at 1400 °C.

When zircon substituted silica, the reaction was complete above 1300°C with the formation of zirconia, alumina and silicon carbide. Zirconia was present in both the monoclinic and quadratic form.

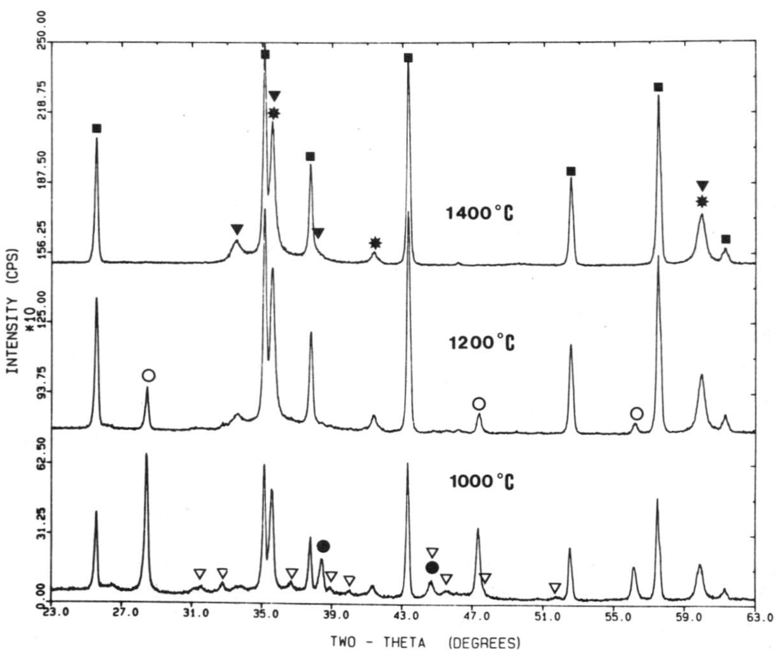

Figure 1. X-ray powder diffraction patterns of the Al-SiO_2-C after heat treatment; ○ :Si ●: Al, ■ : α-Al_2O_3, ▽: η and θ-Al_2O_3, ✸ : β-SiC, ▼: α-SiC.

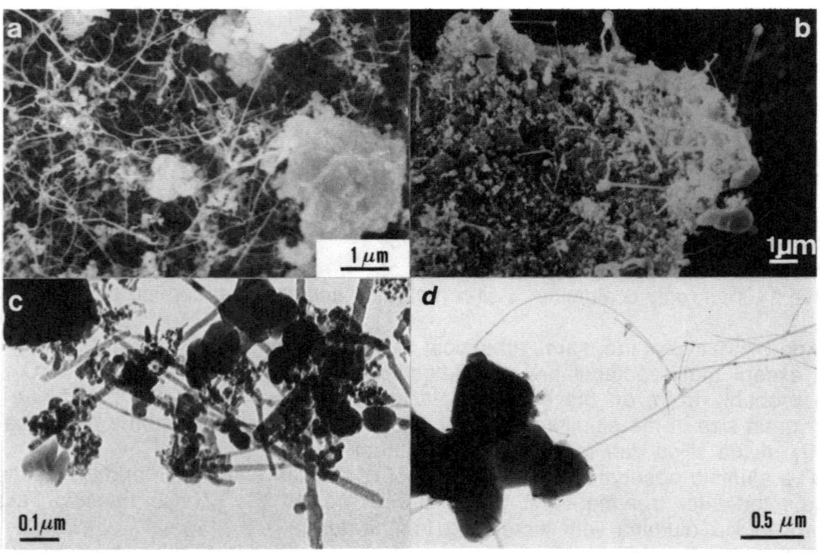

Figure 2. (a)(b) SEM micrographs of an Al-SiO_2-C powder treated one hour at 1400°C; (c)(d) TEM micrographs of the same sample.

Microstructural observations

The microstructure of the samples was studied by SEM, TEM and EPMA. Typical scanning electron micrographs of samples treated one hour at 1400 °C are shown in figure 2a and b. One observes the presence of agglomerates of about 5 to 10 microns size among which numerous whiskers have grown. These whiskers present a high aspect ratio. EPMA indicated that the agglomerates were composed of both alumina and silicon carbide particles.

More detailed structural informations on the products formed are visible on the transmission electron micrographs (fig 2c and d). Alumina particles appear as equiaxed particles with a size in the 0.2-1 micron range. Silicon carbide particles appear either in clusters or distributed among the whiskers. Their size is of the order of 0.05 microns. As for the whiskers, they were identified by electron diffraction as β silicon carbide with a growth direction along <111>. The electron diffraction patterns also indicated the presence of thin {111} twins and planar faults on close packed planes normal to the whiskers axis, both types of defects being commonly observed in silicon carbide whiskers [4].

In samples treated below 1400 °C, one could observe in several instancies the presence of a little sphere at the tip of whiskers (fig. 2b). These spheres were too small to be identified confidently but it is anticipated that they result from a liquid drop responsible for a VLS growth mechanism (see below).

Analogous microstructures have been observed in samples from the iron-doped blends. Work is in progress in order to assess quantitatively the influence of the amount of iron in the sample on the proportion of whiskers.

A dispersion of silicon carbide whiskers among alumina, zirconia and silicon carbide particles was also observed in the samples obtained from blends containing zircon.

DISCUSSION

On thermodynamic grounds, the main possible reactions ($\Delta G<0$) likely to occur during thermal treatment of the blends, are the following ones:

$$4\,Al + 3\,SiO_2 \rightarrow 2\,Al_2O_3 + 3\,Si \quad (2)$$
$$Si + C \rightarrow SiC \quad (3)$$
$$3\,SiO_2 + 3\,C \rightarrow 3\,SiO + 3\,CO \quad (4a)$$
$$3\,SiO + 6\,C \rightarrow 3\,SiC + 3\,CO. \quad (4b)$$

We have also to consider the alloying of silicon with aluminum to give a dispersion of Si particles in a Si-Al liquid, and the evaporation of aluminum. Aluminum carbide and aluminum silicate could form at low temperatures but should decompose in the higher temperature range.

The fact that silicon peaks show up simultaneously with alumina peaks indicates that the formation of alumina proceeds primarily from reaction (2), consistently with previous studies of this reaction [5]. The size of the alumina particles is thus mainly dictated by the size of the oxygen source i.e. by the size of the silica particles.

The synthesis of silicon carbide results probably from both reactions (3) and (4). Reaction (3) being a reaction between two solid phases should be quite slow. However, according to ternary diagram Al-Si-C proposed by Andersson and Warren [6], silicon carbide particles should also form by a reaction-precipitation at the interface between carbon black particles and the Si-Al liquid. This reaction should proceed at a higher rate as it is anticipated that this formation of SiC should induce wetting of carbon by the liquid. The fineness of the silicon carbide particles observed in our samples result apparently from the fine particle size of carbon we used.

The presence of little sphere at the tips of the whiskers indicates that the whiskers were most probably grown by a VLS mechanism as suggested by previous authors [7,8].

In the VLS mechanism, an impurity (usually a transition metal) acts as a catalyst by forming a liquid interface between the crystalline material to be grown and the vapour source of this same material. This liquid interface constitutes a preferred site for deposition of feed from the vapour which causes the liquid to become supersaturated. Crystal growth occurs by precipitation from the supersaturated liquid at the solid-liquid interface. This mechanism requires the solubility of the constituent atoms of the whiskers (Si and C) into the molten catalyst which is especially the case for iron alloys.

We believe that, in the system under study, the iron present as impurity in the aluminum powder acts as a catalyst promoting this mechanism of whisker growth. The Si and C vapour feeds result presumably from the direct reduction of silica by carbon according to reaction (4a).

It appears thus possible to synthesize simultaneously silicon carbide particles and whiskers within an alumina matrix, by reacting a mixture of silica and carbon in presence of aluminum. The proportion of whiskers relative to that of particles should depend on the competition between reactions (3) and (4) and, consequently, on the stoichiometry of the reactants. It is noteworthy that aluminum plays a rôle in the synthesis of both the particles and the whiskers. The benefit of using metallic aluminum is indeed multiple. First, aluminum constitutes the source for the alumina matrix powder. Secondly, by reducing silica, it involves the formation of silicon that reacts with carbon and forms silicon carbide particles. Through alloying with silicon it also probably permits a more rapid diffusion of this latter to the carbon sites. Finally it acts as an iron impurity source either because of its iron content, either by reducing the iron oxide deposited on silica from iron salts solutions. In this way, it promotes the growth of silicon carbide whiskers.

CONCLUSION

The present study has demonstrated the faisability of the in situ synthesis of silicon carbide within an alumina or alumina/zirconia matrix powder. The silicon carbide was synthesized both as submicronic particles and as whiskers. Both morphologies are susceptible to contribute to an enhancement of the mechanical properties of the ceramic. Work is in progress to gain a better control of the microstructure of the products, in particular for optimizing the aspect ratio of the whiskers, and to assess the densification behaviour of the composite powders by hot uniaxial pressing.

REFERENCES

[1] Nakahira, A., Niihara, K. and Hirai, T., Yogyo-Kyokai-Shi, 1986, **94**, 767-772.

[2] Wei, G.C. and Becher, P.F., Am.Cer.Soc.Bull., 1985, **64**, 298-304.

[3] Cutler, R.A., Virkar, A.V. and Holt, J.B., in the proc. 9th an.conf.cer.mat., Florida, The American Ceramic Society ed., 1985, 715-728.

[4] Nutt, S.R., J.Am.Cer.Soc., 1984, **67**, 429-431.

[5] Standage, A.E. and Gani, M.S., J.Am.Cer.Soc., 1967, **50**, 101-105.

[6] Andersson, C.H. and Warren, R., Composites, 1984, **15**, 101-111.

[7] Milewski, J.V., Gac, F.D., Petrovic, J.J. and Skaggs, S.R., J.Mater.Sci., 1985, **20**, 1160-1166.

[8] Bootsma, G.A., Knippenberg, W.F. and Verspui, G., J.Cryst.Growth, 1971, **11**, 297-309.

TOUGHNESS ANISOTROPY IN A C-SiC COMPOSITE MATERIAL

M. GOMINA
LERMAT - URA 1317 - ISMRa-Université
Bd du Maréchal Juin - 14032 CAEN Cedex - FRANCE

ABSTRACT

Models based on a few modifications of Linear Elastic Fracture Mechanics (LEFM) methodologies are used to check the toughness anisotropy of a laminar 2D C-SiC material.

INTRODUCTION

More than the fundamental problem arising from the significance of K_{IC} value, the toughness anisotropy is a great handicap to a large scale utilization of fiber reinforced composite materials. In the general case of long-fiber-reinforced materials with very pronounced principal directions of reinforcement, the anisotropy is intrinsic. PAN et al. [1] have shown that the toughness varies an order of magnitude for a 2D laminar SiC-SiC material. For CFC materials, KIM et al. [2] found that K_R results were invalid when the crack propagation direction was normal to the laminate plane (flatwise), because of severe crack blunting and delamination. This problem is often encountered when fibrous composite materials are studied in the flatwise orientation. The purpose of the present paper is to briefly discuss key aspects of the fracture of a C-SiC material in the three principal orientations and particularly to address methods for toughness measurements suitable for each specimen orientation ; using three point bending tests.

MATERIAL AND EXPERIMENTAL TECHNIQUES

The C-SiC material investigated was made of a 2D woven texture of PAN precursors treated to obtain a filamentary carbon frame. These frames are pilled-up in a furnace and the porosities between them or inside the bundles of fibres are progressively filled with a CVI-processed SiC matrix. The resulting C-SiC material (28 vol% fibres) has a density d=2.2 to 2.4, a residual porosity $V_V(P) \simeq 20\%$ a Young modulus E=130 to 160 GPa and a four point flexural strength σ_r = 230 to 330 MPa. Three principal orientations are distinguished :

- in the interlaminar orientation the tensile stress is normal to the plane of the laminates,
- in the flatwise orientation the notch plane is normal to the plane of the laminates,
- in the edgewise orientation the crack propagation direction and the tensile stress direction lie in the plane of the laminates.

Different dimensions of SENB specimens and compact tension specimens (CT) were tested at room temperature on a 1185 INSTRON machine or a SCHENCK machine using a 10 KN load cell. The load point displacement was measured using a LVDT and the load-displacement curve (P-h) was directly recorded to be worked out using a digitizer connected to a computer. Acoustic emission signals were recorded using a DUNEGAN 3000 set for qualificative correlations with the P-h curves and optically measured crack lengths.

RESULTS AND DISCUSSION

a) Interlaminar orientation specimens

Although the C-SiC material is not available for structural applications in this orientation, it may happen that the stress level is reached for crack propagation to occur between the layers.

Monotonic loading curves for specimens of dimensions 50*10*5 mm^3 are linear up to near maximum load value and then fully controled crack propagation is observed whatever the relative notch length value a_o/w. One may expect LEFM methodologies could apply for toughness evaluation. The results obtained when using the usual compliance curve for crack lengths estimation along the P-h curve are shown in Table 1.

TABLE 1
Linear Elastic Fracture Mechanics parameters characterizing rupture of interlaminar C-SiC specimens.

a_o/w	P_{max} (N)	K_{IC} (MPa$\sqrt{m}$)	G_c (J/m^2)	R_{max} (J/m^2)	K_{Rmax} (MPa$\sqrt{m}$)	$(a/w)_{R_{max}}$
0.30	152.0	1.80	48	77	2.3	0.45
0.40	115.2	2.10	68	90	2.5	0.47
0.44	92.8	1.83	61	64	2.0	0.54
0.49	92.8	1.83	54	64	2.0	0.56
0.50	93.6	1.90	57	65	2.0	0.57

Evaluations of the instability points on the resistance curves lead to G_c values ranging from 48 J/m^2 to 65 J/m^2 consistent with J_c = 50 J/m^2 obtained when using the J integral method of

LANDES and BEGLEY [3]. These values reflect quite a good quality of the SiC matrix, comparable to usual polycristalline ceramics.

Under load cycling experiments, it appeared residual displacements and hysteresis loops (Fig. 1a). We have observed that the compliance lines met at a unique point M ($P=P_o$, $h=o$). Then we have proposed a calculation of R as :

$$R = \frac{1}{2B} (P + P_o)^2 \frac{dC}{da} \qquad (1)$$

The result of such a calculation is shown in figure 1b where a plateau value R = 65 J/m^2 is followed by a steepper increase. BURNS and SWAIN [4] and SHAH [5] have later proposed a more complete expression of the type of equation (1).

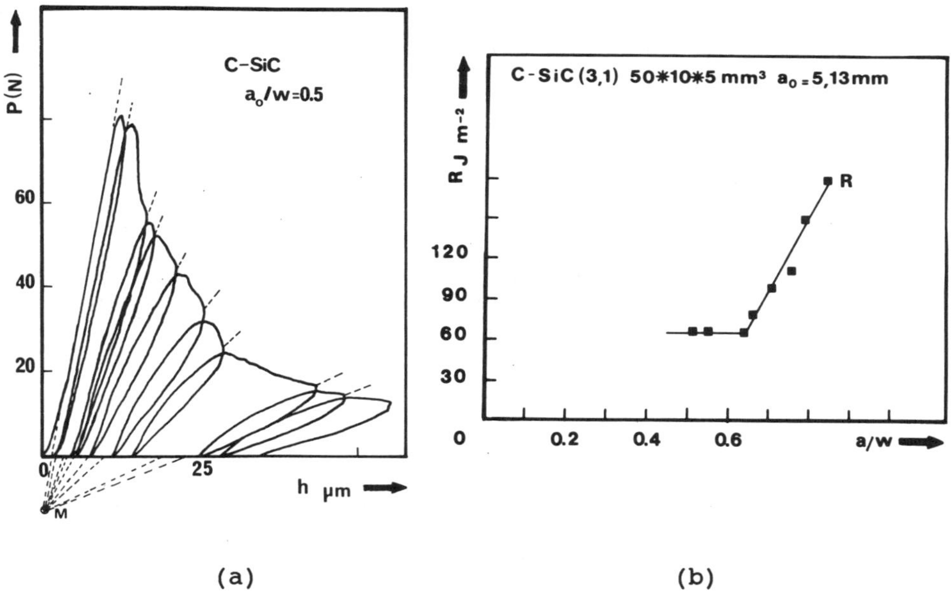

Figure 1. a) Loading unloading curve of an interlaminar C-SiC specimen, b) associated resistance curve estimated using equ.1

b) Edgewise orientation specimens

Different dimensions of SENB specimens and CT specimens have been tested in this orientation ; we shall just outline the main features of the behaviour of the C-SiC material in this section.

Because of the woven structure of this material and in reason of the small size of the tested specimens in comparison with the macrostructure, any particular points in the mechanical behaviour have to be addressed : **i)** Is it the proper way to notch a fibrous composite material in the aim to check mechanical parameters ? **ii)** What is the significance of a crack length in such a material and what is the value to be used for rupture-description ? **iii)** What are the methods to be used for toughness evaluation ?

i) The answer to this first point is of course no. Even in metallic materials it has been necessary to realize fatigue cracks to simulate initiation conditions. But no satisfactory way is yet available for introducing a fatigue crack in a fibrous composite material.

ii) The significance of a crack length depends on the type of material and specially on its microscopic state. Very often when the fibre-matrix interface is designed for a high contribution to the fracture energy, the definition of a crack length fails and usual compliance calibration curve becomes obsolete. For the edgewise orientation of the C-SiC material we have measured crack lengths through a microscope (a_{opt}) on the polished surfaces during loading-unloading experiments. These crack lengths were then compared to those derived from the compliance calibration curve when the compliances are estimated as the tangent lines to the reloading loops [6]. The compatibility was quite good. The main reason is that in this material, despite the pronounced deformation observed before the maximum load P_{max} is reached, crack propagation starts only near P_{max}. This is confirmed by the correlation of the total number of acoustic emission counts with the P-h curve. Other reasons are that during crack propagation the effects of fibres bridging the crack mouths are not very pronounced and delamination is absent ; crack lengths measurements on the polished surface are then possible.

TABLE 2
Fracture energies estimated by different methods for the SENB specimens of C-SiC material in the edgewise orientation.

L = 50 mm ; W = 10 mm ; B = 5 mm

a_o/W	GARWOOD J^G (J/m^2)	GARWOOD J^{Gc} (J/m^2)	SAKAI R_c (J/m^2)	SAKAI J_s (J/m^2)	RICE J_R (J/m^2)
0.3	2260	1080	1600	700	920
0.4	2440	1100	1800	810	1030
0.5	1440	730	1260	610	720
0.54	2160	1000	1630	700	730
0.6	1850	720	1200	450	690

iii) These measured crack lengths values have been used in a few methods to work out resistance curves. Table 2 shows the energy values obtained when separating the work of fracture R_c in a quasi-elastic part, J_s, and a non-elastic contribution (SAKAI method [7]), or when using GARWOOD method and the correction to residual displacement (J^G and J^{Gc}) [8], or when using the well known RICE J-integral [9]. For these specimens, the plateau of the resistance curve is attained after an amount of crack growth $\Delta a \simeq$ 1mm and the crack initiation energy is $G_c^o \simeq 700\ J/m^2$, that is $K_{Ii} \simeq 9.5\ MPa\sqrt{m}$.

c) Flatwise orientation specimens

For most fibrous composite materials, the flatwise orientation specimens are unlikely to be discribed in term of LEFM concepts. In fact, usually the loading curves of these specimens look very irregular and denote the lay-out of the laminates. Under load, microcracks develop in the matrix from the notch root and from the sharp angles of the pores. A few competitve macrocracks form from the notch root well before the maximum load value is reached. But further the crack propagation can be stopped when the crack tip falls in a region of fibres perpendicular to the notch plane. Microcracks perpendicular to the plane of the laminates develop : the acoustic emission signal increases continuously, all the volume under stress is damaged. Thus a direct crack length measurement is impossible to perform ; even the definition of an equivalent crack length by using a compliance calibration curve is questionnable. The first parameter affecting the roughness of the crack path is the number of laminates in the width of the specimen. Figure 2 shows the differences in the crack paths for two specimens of different sizes.

(a) (b)

Figure 2. Crack path observed on the surface of flatwise orientation specimens of C-SiC material : a) dimensions $50*10*5mm^3$ - b) dimensions $100*20*10mm^3$.

In lake of a resistance curve, we evaluate apparent K_{IC}^{app} assuming that the maximun stress attained corresponds to the resistance of the remaining ligament, $W-a_o$ (stress concentration criteria) :

$$P_{max} \simeq P_f = 2 \frac{B(W-a_o)^2}{3L} \sigma_f \qquad (2)$$

and $$K_{IC}^{app} \text{ (max)} \simeq \sigma_f \ (W-a_o)^{1/2} \left(\frac{a_o}{W}\right) \Pi_M \qquad (3)$$

with : σ_f, the failure stress of an unnotched specimen,
Π_M, a geometrical factor depending on a_o/W.

The results of the theoritical (equ. 3) and experimental calculations are shown on figure 3 as function of the relative notch lengths. In the range $0.3 \leqslant a_o/W \leqslant 0.65$, the apparent toughness is $K_{IC}^{app} \simeq 6$ MPa$\sqrt{m}$. This approach is only based on a stress criteria but it may allow comparisons between specimens made of the same material.

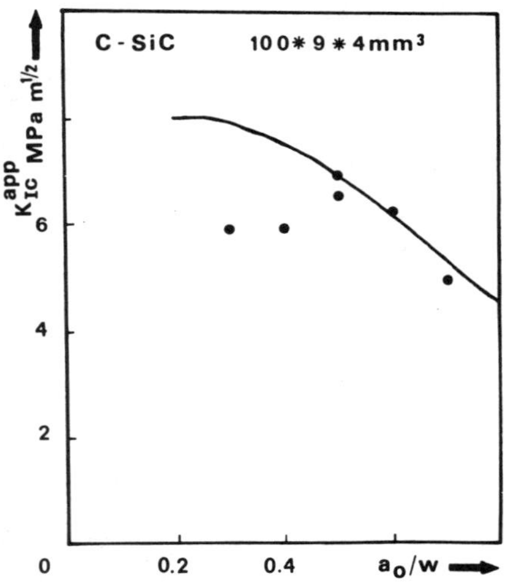

Figure 3. Apparent toughness values for the flatwise specimens of C-SiC material. The line corresponds to the expression (3).

CONCLUSIONS

The principal orientations of a C-SiC material have been studied. Due to the absence of fibres bridging the crack mouths, for the interlaminar and edgewise specimens crack resistance parameters can be easily worked out. But the methods proposed up to now are not suited for the flatwise specimens.

REFERENCES

1. Pan, Y.M., Sakai, M., Warren, J.W. and Bradt, R.C., Toughness anisotropy of a SiC-SiC laminar composite. Mat. Sci. Res., Vol. **20**, Ed. R.E. Tressler, G.L. Messing, C.G. Pantano and R.E. Newnham, pp. 631, Plenum Press, New-York and London, 1986, pp. 631-638.

2. Kim, H.C., Yoon, K.J., Pickering, R. and Sherwood, P.J., Fracture toughness of 2d carbon fibre reinforced carbon composites. J. Mat. Sci., 1985, **20**, 3967-3975.

3. Landes, J.D. and Begley, J.A., ASTM STP **632**, American Society for Testing and Materials, 1977, pp. 57-81.

4. Burns, S.J., Swain, M.V., Fracture toughness of Mg-O - Partially-Stabilized ZrO_2 specimens with K_R curve behaviour from transformation toughening. J. Amer. Ceram. Soc., 1986, **69**, pp. 226-230.

5. Shah, S.P., Fracture of cement and concrete. Advances in Fracture Research, Vol. **1**, Sixth International Conference on Fracture, New Delhi, India, Pergamon Press, Dec. 4-10, 1984, pp. 495-514.

6. Gomina, M., Crack length measurements in a C-SiC composite material. Int. J. Fract., 1987, **35**, R69-R74.

7. Sakai, M., Urashima, K. and Inagaki, M., Energy principle of elastic-plastic fracture and its application to the fracture mechanics of a polycristalline graphite. J. Amer. Ceram. Soc., 1983, **66**, pp. 868-874.

8. Bouaouadja, N., Thèse de Doctorat Spécialité Sciences des Matériaux, INSA de Lyon, 1986.

9. Rice, J.R., Transactions of the American Society of Mechanical Engineers. J. Appl. Mech., 1968, **35**, pp. 379-386.

FRACTURE BEHAVIOUR RELATED TO MICROSTRUCTURE IN SiC-SiC AND C-SiC COMPOSITES

GILLES NAVARRE, DOMINIQUE ROUBY, GILBERT FANTOZZI
Groupe d'Etudes de Métallurgie Physique et de Physique des Matériaux,
U.A. CNRS n° 341 - I.N.S.A. de Lyon
F69621 Villeurbanne cedex FRANCE

ABSTRACT

Fracture behaviour of two ceramic-ceramic composites was studied by the method of crack growth resistance curves (R-curves). The significance of each parameter, specially the crack growth is analyzed by different approachs : crack marking, X-ray radiography, pull-out modellization. The materials reveal very large process zones : the consequences about R-curves are discussed.

INTRODUCTION

Ceramic materials reinforced with ceramic fibres exhibit generally high toughness due to several mechanisms appearing during crack growth. These energy absorbing mechanisms determine a large process zone at crack front and consequently, the materials reveal non-linear and non-elastic behaviour. Better understanding or characterization of the fracture behaviour of such materials needs a global approach taking into account the macroscopic behaviour (fracture parameters) and the micromechanisms (effect of the reinforcement phase). The aim of this paper is to point out the signification of the crack growth resistance curves (R-curves) for SiC-SiC and C-SiC fibre composites with the help of observations and measurements about the process zones and, at finer scale, about fibre mechanisms.

MATERIALS

The materials studied were processed by the Société Européenne de Propulsion (Bordeaux, France) and were of two types. The SiC-SiC composite consists of superimposed woven cloths (two directional) with the same orientation (Fig. 1, a) ; the bundles contain nearly 500 SiC-Nicalon filaments (from Nippon Carbon Co).

For the C-SiC material, the reinforcement is a three-directional structure named Novoltex^R (SEP's patent), made with PAN precursor Carbon fibres (Fig. 1, b). For both materials the SiC matrix was deposited by chemical vapor infiltration process ; the open porosity was about 10% and the fibre volume fraction was about 40% for SiC-SiC and 25% for C-SiC.

Fracture tests were performed on SENB specimens by three points bending (typical dimensions : L x W x B = 70 x 9.5 x 5 mm^3, span : 60 mm) ; the notch was cut normally to the lamina planes (edgewise orientation, see Fig. 1) ; notch length : a_0.

a   b

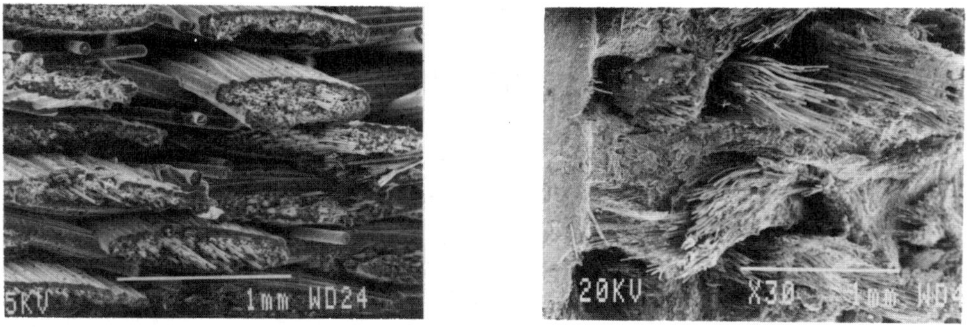

Fig. 1 : Scanning electron microscopy of fracture surfaces :
a : SiC-SiC composite ; b : C-SiC composite.
(the notch front is parallel to left side of each picture)

CRACK GROWTH RESISTANCE CURVES

The curves were established using the geometrical method proposed by Sakaï (1). The specimen undergoes a sucession of loading-unloading cycles at increasing peak displacement. After crack initiation, between two subsequent loadings the crack propagates over a given increment and the energy needed can be calculated from the area limited by the two loading curves (2). The average slope of each loading curve decreases progressively and the associated compliance increase allows us to calculate at each cycle, by an iterative expression the "effective crack length" ($a_0 + \Delta a$) or the "effective crack increment" Δa (2).

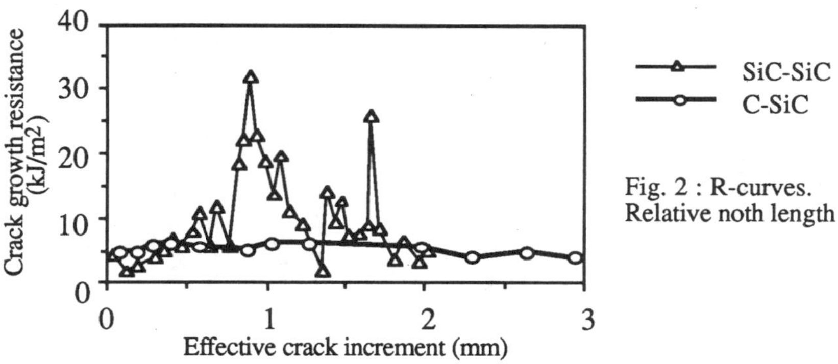

Fig. 2 : R-curves.
Relative noth length a_0/W = 0.4

Fig. 2 shows typical R curves for SiC-SiC and C-SiC composites. First of all, specially for SiC-SiC, the curves are serrated and reveals large peaks ; this feature changes from one specimen to another and is probably due to the reinforcement geometry. In fact, in the SiC-SiC composite, half of the bundles are perpendicular to the crack path (Fig. 1, a) and nearly arranged on rows. The fracture of each row needs an increase of energy, responsible of each peak. For the C-SiC materials, the R curve is more smooth, probably because there are bundles oriented obliquely to the crack plane and the crack path is more homogeneous (Fig. 1, b).

However it is worth mentionning that mean energy of fracture is very higth (5 to 10 kJ/m^2) as regard to classical bulk ceramics (100 J/m^2). The initial value (at $\Delta a = 0$) is not very precisely defined and depends on the position of notch front relative to the reinforcement structure (the row of bundles perpendicular to the crack plane).

More, the R curve tends to decrease when the "effective crack increment" is larger than 1 mm. This is probably the consequence of an interaction between the process zone and the rear surface of the specimen. For this test the specimen ligament seems to be too short.

For R curves, the crack increment is a decisive parameter and then it must be analysed in details. The micromechanisms controlling the fracture (matrix microcracking, crack bridging, fibre breaking, ...) are responsible for the existence of different zones along the crack length (see Fig. 3) with each zone showing a different stiffness degree and therefore, the global result, i.e. the "effective crack length", measured by compliance change appears to be not adequate.

CRACK AND DAMAGE ZONES

In this section, we briefly describe two methods for determining dimensions of the differents zones shown on Fig. 3 ; the material tested here was the SiC-SiC composite in the edgewise orientation. For microscopic obvervations, half of the bundles are perpendicular to the lamina plane.

It is well known that the Nicalon fibre can be oxidized at elevated temperature (3) and this feature can be an opportunity to obtain the marking of the different bridging zones. In fact for a given cracking stage, oxygen penetrates in the main crack as better as crack lips are free. Several specimens were cracked at room temperature at different damage degrees (different Δa's), then heat treated and finally completely fractured at room temperature again. Three zones parallel to notch front can be pointed out by SEM observation of the fracture surface. Each zone reveals a specific aspect, particularly concerning the pull-out length. Near the notch front, the weakly or not bridged crack is relatively open and the fibres are likely oxidized, leading to characteristic flat surface; we assume that this first zone (Z1) corresponds to b and c zones on Fig. 3.

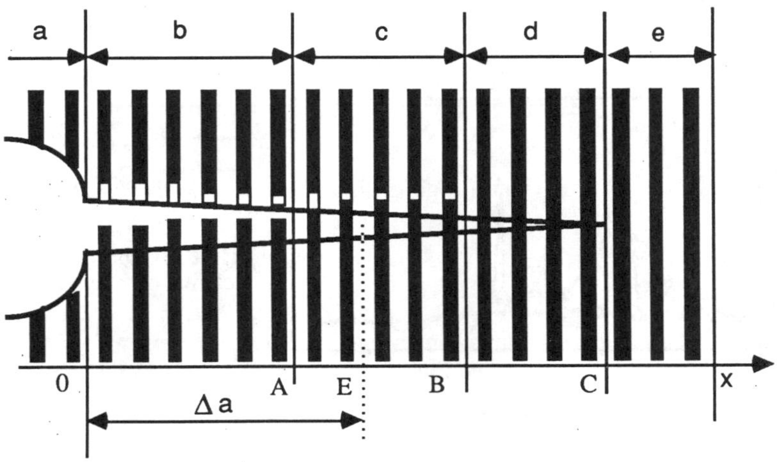

Fig. 3 : Schematics of cracking in unididirectional composite. a : notch, b : unbridged crack, c : bridged crack with brocken fibres, d : unbrocken fibres, e : undamaged zone.

The next zone (Z2), assumed to be corresponding to zone d (Fig. 3) which is bridged by unbrocken fibres presents after heat treatment an intermediate pull-out.The last zone exhibits typical pull-out length as an uncracked heat treated specimen (corresponding to the undamaged zone e (Fig. 3)). Fig. 4 shows the size changes of Z1 and Z2 versus effective crack increment Δa.

During a R-curve test at different cracking stages, the specimen was removed from testing machine and observed by X-rays. Radiographs were obtained by means of opacifiant (zinc iodide) ; due to porosity, a small quantity of opacifiant was kept in the porosity and subsequently diffused into the newly created cracks. Careful analysis of the radiograms reveals straight and parallel lines growing from notch front. Each line corresponds to the cracking of one or several adjacent cloths ; the cloths do not break exactly in the same plane. After splitting of the specimen between to lamina planes, SEM observation shows that those lines corresponds to the main matrix crack (zones b, c and d on Fig. 3). The lengths of the X-ray lines are reported on Fig. 4 and are very close to the Z2 zone.

As shown on Fig. 4, the effective crack increment Δa is approximatively the half of Z1 zone, where the fibres are unbroken. For an ideal homogeneous materials, the effective crack length corresponds to an unique crack with free surfaces (zero stiffness at the crack and nominal stiffness ahead the crack tip). In our case, the stiffness increases gradually from zero (zone b) to nominal value (zone e), so the "effective" Δa is probably located in the c zone (point E, Fig. 3) ; unfortunately the location of the b and c zones border is unknown. The distance between Z2 zone front and notch front (the main matrix crack length) increases more and more rapidly with Δa (Fig. 4). For an effective crack increment of about 1 mm, the measured crack growth energy is due to fibre fracture and pull-out, modified by the specimen end-effect. To calculate the whole energy absorbed during crack growth, the knowledge of only the "effective crack growth increment" appears no sufficient. In fact, for each zone, it corresponds to a specific absorbed energy and the Δa integrates mechanically all the mecanisms of different energy inportance. In addition, due to statistical aspects (fibre strength, pull-out length) the zones shown on Fig. 3 are largely overlapping in real materials.

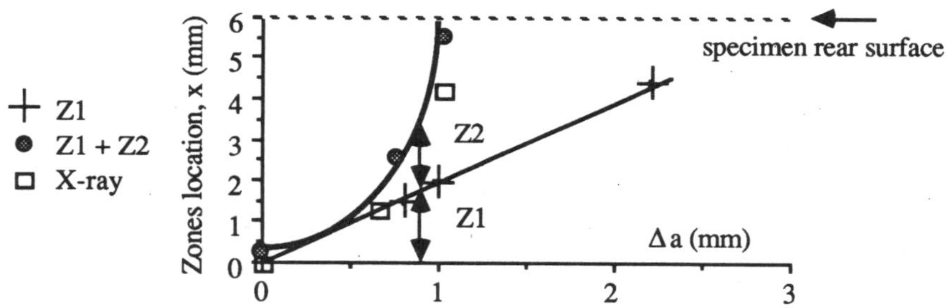

Fig. 4 : locations of zone fronts (origin at notch front) vs effective crack increment.

FIBRE PULL-OUT

It is known that for long fibre ceramic composites, most part of crack growth energy absorbed is due to fibre pull-out. That is why it is interesting to analyse quantitatively the fracture surface.

In the case of a matrix crack bridged by unbrocken fibres, the fibres undergo overload in a region around the matrix crack. Due to a distribution of the local fibre strength (Weibull statistic), the fibres have a non-zero probability for breaking at a given distance from the matrix crack and then can be pulled out. Formal analysis of this mechanims (for example : Sutcu (4)) shows that average pull-out length L_p depends on fibre strength, fibre Weibull's modulus and critical interfacial shear stress. Therefore, observation of fracture surface leads to complementary informations about these parameters. In addition, Sutcu have shown that the non dimensional pull-out length distribution (see Fig. 5 : probability density fontion times L_p versus relative pull-out length) is not really sensitive to the above parameters.

This non dimensional pull-out length distribution is reported on Fig. 5 and compared with experimental non dimensional distribution obtained by measuring individual pull-out length on typical fracture surface of SiC-SiC composite (Fig. 6) ; except for very short length, the agreement is quite good. This confirms that Sutcu's model is valid and can be an interesting tool to analyse the fracture surface of composites.

a

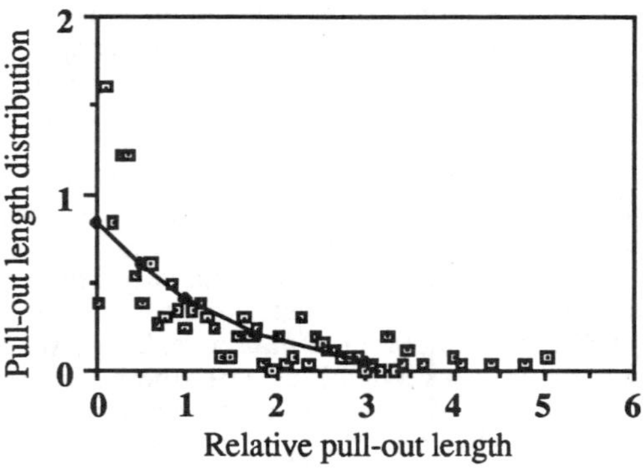

b

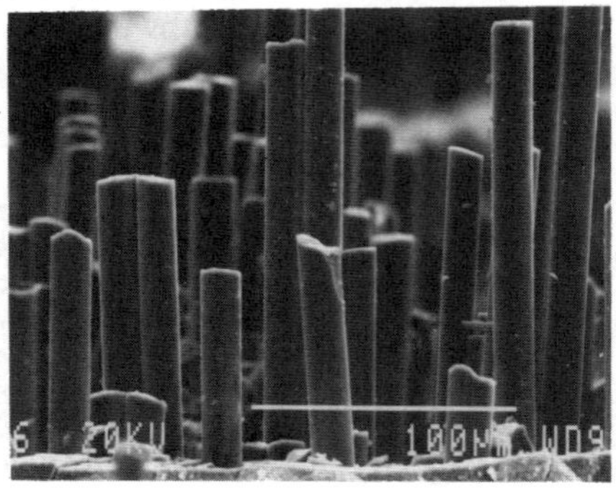

Fig. 5 : SiC-SiC composite :
pull-out length distribution, — : theory; □ measured

Fig 6 : typical SEM picture for pull-out length measurement

For C-SiC composite, the R-curves seems not reveals an edge effect. Due to the reinforcement structure (oblique bundles relative to the crack), the above crack and pull-out modelling cannot be used.

CONCLUSION

SiC-SiC and C-SiC composites reveals complicated fracture behaviour associated with a very large process zone. This phenomenon can lead to specimen-end effect before steady state crack propagation and in all cases sets a problem concerning the significant crack area for R-curve calculation. In the case of fibres normal to main crack plane, the fibre pull-out can be easily modellized, so the analysis of the fracture surfaces is very useful for better knowledge and understanding of micromechanical parameters. Further work needs calculations of stress field and absorbed energy in the process zones in order to determine the pertinent values and the appropriate methods involved in the crack growth resistance measurements.

We thank Messrs Lamicq and Jouin from S.E.P. for helpful discussions. We also thank Mr Rouais for his collaboration about the X-ray radiography.

This work is a part of the research program BRITE n° P-1348-6-85.

REFERENCES

1. Sakaï, M. and Bradt, R. C., Graphical methods for determining the non linear fracture parameters of silica and graphite refractory composites. 4th Int. Conf. Fract. Mech. Ceramics, VPI, June 19-21, 1985. U.S.A. Plenum Press, 1986, vol. 7, p 127-47.

2. R'Mili, M., Application de la mécanique de la rupture au composite carbone-carbone bidirectionnel. Thesis, INSA de Lyon, Lyon, 1987.

3. Simon, G. and Bunsell, A. R., Mechanical and structural characterisation of the Nicalon silicon carbide fibre. J. of Mater. Sci., 1984, **19**, pp 3649-62.

4. Sutcu, M., Weibull statistics applied to fiber failure in ceramic composites and work of fracture. Acta Metall., 1989, **37**, pp 651-61.

INTERFACIAL FRICTION AND DEBOND STRENGTH OF ALIGNED CERAMIC MATRIX COMPOSITES

N. SHAFRY, D.G. BRANDON AND M. TERASAKI
Department of Materials Engineering
Technion-Israel Institute of Technology, Haifa 32000, Israel

ABSTRACT

A quantitative test has been developed for the measurement of interfacial friction stresses and debond strength in aligned fiber-reinforced ceramic matrix composites.

The test involves the compression of a lapped, polished slice of the aligned composite cut normal to the reinforcement. The bottom surface of the slice is compressed at constant strain, while the top surface is compressed at constant stress. Debonding of the fibers occurs at the top surface, due to the strain mismatch between the fibers and the matrix, and results in fiber protrusion. On removing the load, the fibers partially relax back into the matrix, depending on the frictional stresses at the fiber-matrix interface.

The extent of fiber protrusion under load and the residual protrusion of the fibers after load relaxation are measured, and the relation between the measured protrusion and the mechanical properties of the fiber-matrix interface are determined by stress analysis.

INTRODUCTION

The strength and toughness of ceramic matrix composites has been shown to be related to the mechanical response of the interface between the reinforcement and the ceramic matrix (1). The interfacial debond strength and the frictional characteristics of the ceramic matrix/fiber interface are key factors in the analysis of the mechanical properties of the composites (2,3).

Two basic techniques have been developed to study interfacial debonding in these materials. Marshall et al (4) have used a microhardness indenter, accurately positioned at the center of the exposed cross-section of the fiber, to push the fiber into the matrix. Jurewicz (5) has developed a "pull-out" test, which is suitable only for large diameter fibers.

The Slice Compression Test described here is both simple to perform, and independent of the dimensions of the reinforcement. In addition, the test is applicable to all aligned fiber or whisker reinforced materials, at both room and elevated temperatures.

EXPERIMENTAL METHOD

The test specimen is a lapped and polished slice of the composite, cut normal to the direction of alignment of the reinforcement. This slice is uniaxially compressed between two plates. The bottom plate is a polished, hot pressed Si_3N_4 tile, which imposes a condition of approximately uniform strain at the bottom surface of the slice. The top plate is a polished, annealed commercial purity Al (1100 grade), which imposes a condition of uniform stress at the top surface. On loading the test slice, debonding of the reinforcement initiates from the top surface, where the elastic mismatch is a maximum. At the end of the test, the Al retains a "negative image" of the maximum extent of fiber protrusion, while the fibers at the top surface of the composite partially relax back into the matrix.

Preliminary experiments were performed on polished slices cut from Nicalon SiC fiber reinforced lithium aluminium silicate (LAS). Fig.1 shows the loading assembly.

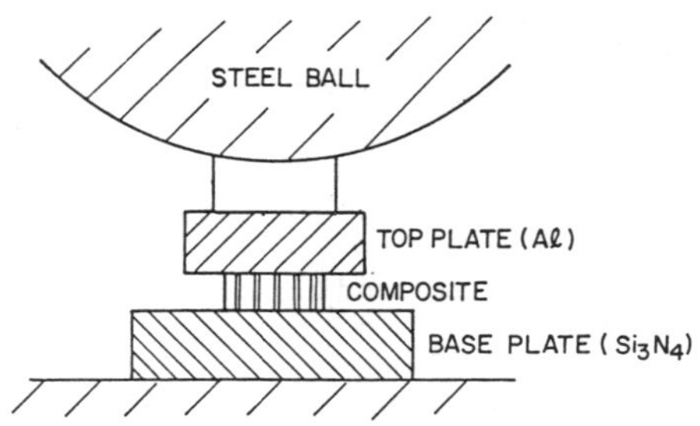

Fig.1. Loading assembly

The depth of the fiber indentations in the Al top plate, and the extent of residual fiber protrusion after unloading, were measured from a single scanning electron micrograph, photographed at a tilt angle of 45-65°. The extent of residual fiber displacement and the depth of the indentation from the same fiber in the aluminium were calculated from the measurements as indicated in Fig.2. An example is shown in Fig.3.

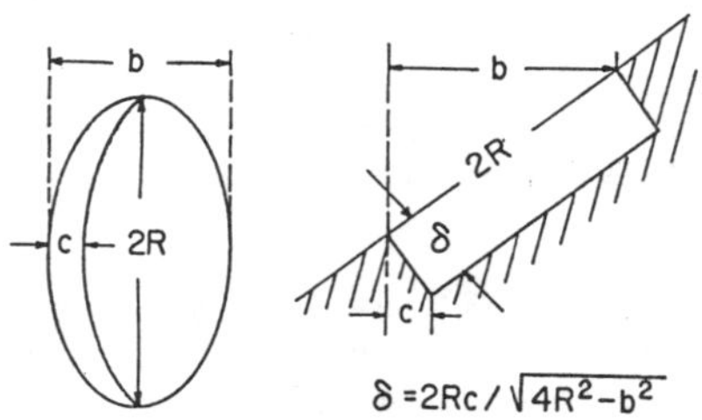

Fig.2. Analysis of indentation depth and residual protrusion from SEM micrographs of tilted specimens

a. 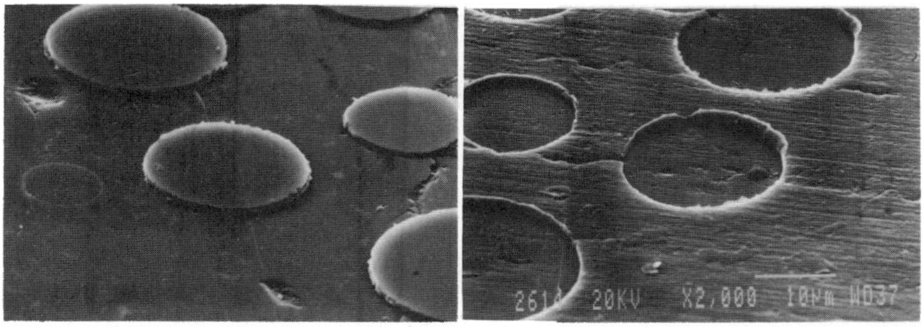 b.

Fig.3. Residual fiber protrusion (a) and indentations due to the same fibers in the Al replica (b).

Theoretical Analysis

The analysis used for the present calculations follows closely that of Marshall and Oliver (4). At the top surface of the composite, the axial stress in both matrix and fiber is equal to the applied stress - σa. At the bottom surface, the axial strains in matrix and fiber are identical. The shear stress, τ, in the debonded region is assumed to be constant and localized at the interface. Using the law of mixtures to relate the elastic modulus of the composite E_c to the component moduli, $E_c=E_fV_f+Em(1-Vf)$, we arrive at a relation between the shear stress τ at the interface, the debond length L, the applied stress σ_a and the fiber/matrix modulus mismatch.

$$(1) \quad 2\tau L/R = (1-V_f)(E_f-E_m)\sigma a/Ec$$

The extent of fiber protrusion δ_o is obtained by integrating the strain mismatch over the debond length:

$$(2) \quad \delta_o = \tau L^2E_c/[E_fF_mR(1-V_f)]$$

Equations (1) and (2) are combined to yield separate expressions for both the debond length, and the interfacial frictional shear stress:

$$(3) \quad L = 2\delta_oE_fE_m/[\sigma_a(E_f-E_m)]$$

$$(4) \quad \tau = R(1-V_f)\sigma_a^2(E_f-E_m)^2/(4\delta_oE_mE_fE_c)$$

Fig.4 shows the expected compressive stress and strain distribution in the loaded fiber and matrix, while the expected stress and strain distributions after unloading are shown in Fig.5.

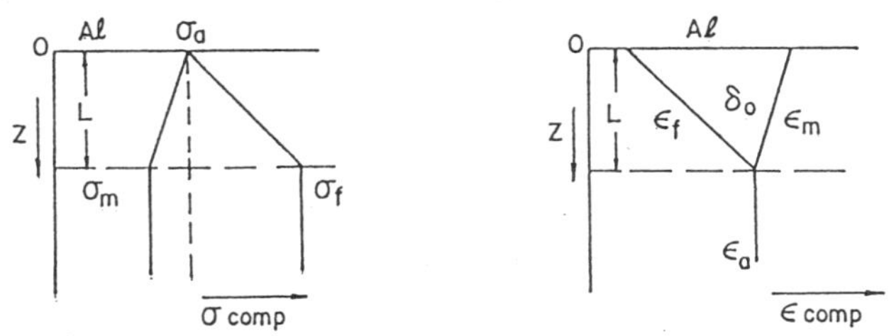

Fig.4. Predicted stress and strain distributions in the fiber and matrix beneath the loaded aluminium contact surface.

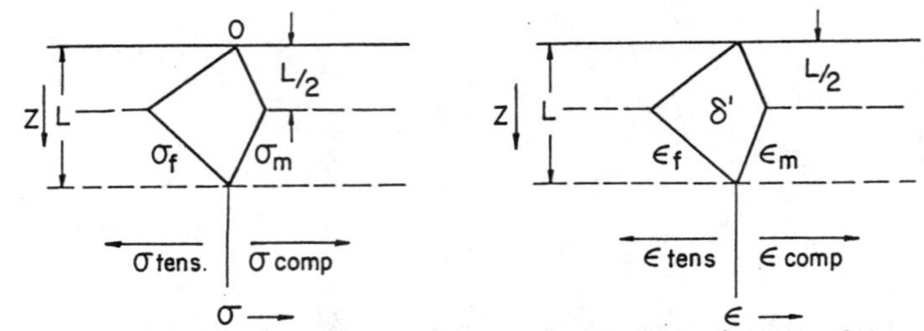

Fig.5. Predicted stress and strain distributions in the fiber and matrix beneath the aluminium contact surface after unloading.

RESULTS AND CONCLUSIONS

The tests were performed on slices prepared from uniaxial and biaxial reinforced LAS III laminates. The slices were loaded to stresses of 90-150 MPa. Measured fiber displacement and calculated values of τ are shown in Table 1.

TABLE 1

Summary of experimental results

LAS III + Nicalon Alignment	Stress MPA	Indentation Depth (μm)	Residual Protrusion (μm)	Calculated Debond Length (μm)	Calculated Shear Stress (KPa)
Uniaxial as-pressed	100	2.27	1.6	4.8	54
	100	2.9	1.2	6.2	68
	100	2.5	1	5.4	48
	100	2	1	4.3	85
Uniaxial ceramed 1150°C 16 hrs in air	107	0.6	0.28	1.7	111
	100	0.43	0.34	1.3	132
Biaxial caramed	140	0.53	0.46	1.2	91
	108	0.76	0.62	2.2	40

Unceramed composites show high values of debond length which exceed the slice thickness, implying that the fibers were fully debonded throughout the slice. However, in the ceramed specimens bonding is incomplete. In the biaxial 0/90° Nicalon reinforced LAS, the protrusion of the fibers parallel to the loading direction varied across each layer of fibers, with fibers at the outer edge of the layer showing the greatest displacement (Fig.6). The values of the frictional shear stress are much lower than those measured by Marshall and Oliver (4), presumably because of a higher radial compression frictional constraint.

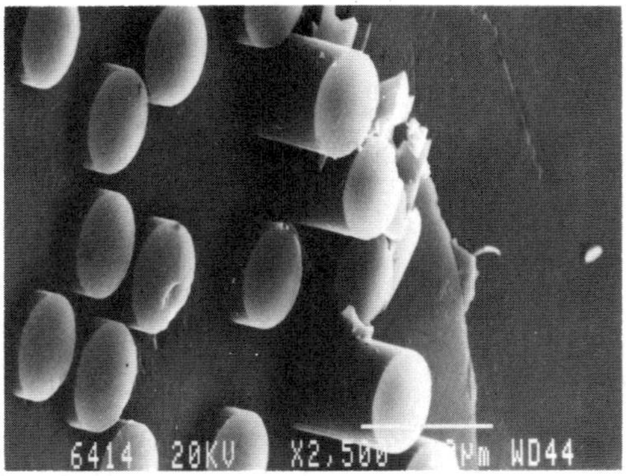

Fig.6. Distribution of residual fiber protrusion across a layer of fibers in a biaxial laminate.

ACKNOWLEDGEMENTS

We thank Dr. J.J. Brennan (UTRC) for providing us with the ceramic composite specimens and E.R. Fuller (NIST) for his help with the analysis of data.

REFERENCES

1. D.B. Marshall and A.G. Evans, J. Am. Ceram. Soc., 1985, 68, 225.
2. J.J. Brennan and K.M. Prewo, J. Mater. Sci., 1982, 17, 2371.
3. T. Mah, M.G. Mendiratta, A.P. Katz and K.S. Mazdiyasni, Cer. Bul., 1987, 66, 304.
4. D.B. Marshall and W.C. Oliver, J. Am. Ceram. Soc., 1987, 70, 542.
5. A. Jurewicz, seminar, NIST, Washington, July 1988.

MECHANICAL PROPERTIES AND AGING BEHAVIOUR OF HOT ISOSTATICALLY PRESSED Y-ZrO_2 CERAMICS MADE OF HYDROTHERMALLY PRODUCED AND SUPERCRITICALLY DRIED POWDERS

TAPIO LEPISTÖ, TAPIO MÄNTYLÄ
Tampere University of Technology
P.O. Box 527, 33101 Tampere, Finland

GUDMUNDUR GUNNARSSON, EDDA LILJA SVEINSDOTTIR
Technological Institute of Iceland
Keldnaholt, IS-112 Reykjavik, Iceland

ANNA-KARIN WESTMAN
ABB Cerama
S-91500 Robertsfors, Sweden

ABSTRACT

In this study Y-TZP ceramics were made of hydrothermally produced and supercritically dried powders which were cold isostatically pressed and hot isostatically sintered. The materials were mechanically tested by three-point bending and Vickers indentation methods. The stability of the structure was evaluated by exposing the materials to water vapour at 150 ^{o}C for up to 1000 hours. HIPing of the powders resulted in high density materials with strength values comparable to those of the materials made of commercial powders. Aging experiments showed that HIPing procedure is a feasible way to improve the structural stability of TZP ceramics against water induced phase transformation.

INTRODUCTION

Tetragonal zirconia polycrystals (TZP) have potential mechanical properties to make these materials possible structural materials at room and slightly elevated temperatures. However, the structural degradation under humid conditions at temperatures of 70-400 ^{o}C has greatly limited the use of these materials. The main factors which improve the stability of the tetragonal phase against water induced phase transformation are small grain size and high stabilizer content.

Zirconia powders with particle size of the order of 10-20 nm can be produced by hydrothermal methods resulting in good sintering properties. For certain forming methods the particle size may, however, be too small thus requiring additional calcination procedure. This may lead to the formation of strong agglomerates which decrease the sinterability of the powder and decrease the strength of the sintered material.

In order to decrease agglomerate formation upon calcination we have dried hydrothermally produced powders with the supercritical method. We have also produced zirconia powders by supercritically drying zirconium hydroxide. The powders produced are reactive and even after calcination at 1000 ^{o}C they sinter to high densities at low temperatures, thus resulting in small grain size in the material. Hot isostatic pressing was used to further decrease the sintering temperature. Also the stabilizer content was varied to study the interrelationship between toughness and structural stability for degradation.

MATERIALS AND METHODS

Raw materials for the powder production were zirconium oxychloride solution (Magnesium Elektron), yttrium oxide (Rare Earth Products) and concentrated ammonia (Merck). Yttrium oxide was dissolved in hydrochloric acid to form yttrium chloride solution. The flow scheme for powder production and powder compaction is shown in Fig. 1.

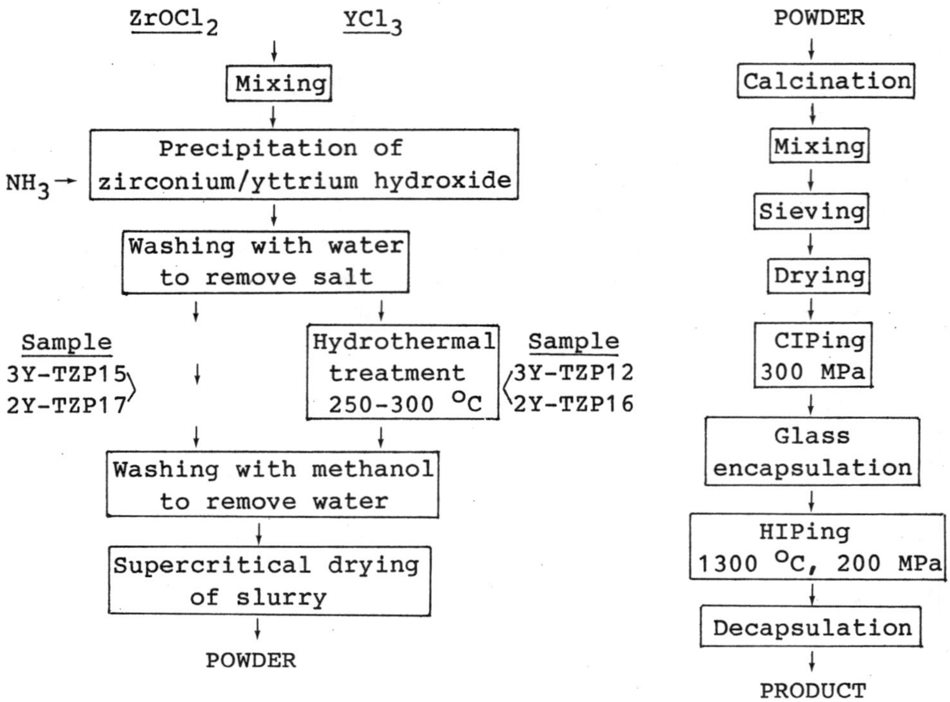

Figure 1. Flow scheme for powder production (1) and powder compaction.

For HIPing the powders were calcined to eliminate easily vaporized species and to obtain pure oxides. The powders were then wet-sieved in methanol to remove particles larger than 10 μm. Methanol was evaporated and the dried powders were cold-isostatically pressed at the pressure of 300 MPa. For HIPing the samples were glass encapsulated and hot isostatically pressed at 1300 °C at the pressure of 200 MPa.

The materials were mechanically tested by three-point bending and fracture surfaces were analyzed by SEM+EDX. Vickers indentation method was used to determine the fracture toughness of the materials. The average grain size of the samples was determined by SEM using line intersect method. The stability of the tetragonal phase was studied by exposing the materials to argon-water vapour mixture at 150 °C for up to 1000 hours. Phase fractions were determined by XRD using CuKα-radiation and graphite secondary monochromator.

RESULTS AND DISCUSSION

Relevant data for the studied materials are shown in Table 1. In 3Y-TZP materials the average grain size was approximately 0.25 μm whereas in 2Y-TZP materials the average grain size was of the order of 0.35 μm.

Vickers hardness (10 kg load) and fracture toughness of the materials were inversely related to each other. Lower stabilizer content and larger grain size in 2Y-TZP materials yielded higher fracture toughness compared to 3Y-TZP materials.

Three point bend strengths of the studied materials were of the order of 1000 N/mm^2 except for the material 2Y-TZP16 which had a strength value of 745 N/mm^2.

The monoclinic phase content in the surface of the samples as a function of time of exposure in water vapour are shown in Fig. 2. In 2Y-TZP materials phase transformation rate from tetragonal to monoclinic structure was higher than in 3Y-TZP materials though in both 2Y-TZP16 and 3Y-TZP12 materials the monoclinic phase contents reached the same level after prolonged time. In 2Y-TZP17 material monoclinic content reached 100 % already during 500 hours and the sample cracked after 800 hours of exposure. In 3Y-TZP15 material phase transformation was very limited and the monoclinic phase content in the surface of the sample was less than 10 % after 1000 hours of exposure. The stability of the structure in 3Y-TZP15 material is believed to be due to the small grain size of the material.

TABLE 1
Relevant data for the studied materials.

Material	Relative density (%)	Average grain size (μm)	Fracture toughness ($MPa\sqrt{m}$)	Vickers hardness (GPa)	3-point flex. strength (N/mm^2)
3Y-TZP12	99.5	0.25	8.6	13.3	995
3Y-TZP15	99.3	0.23	6.5	13.8	1030
2Y-TZP16	99.3	0.35	17.4	12.9	745
2Y-TZP17	99.5	0.36	15.5	12.3	1040

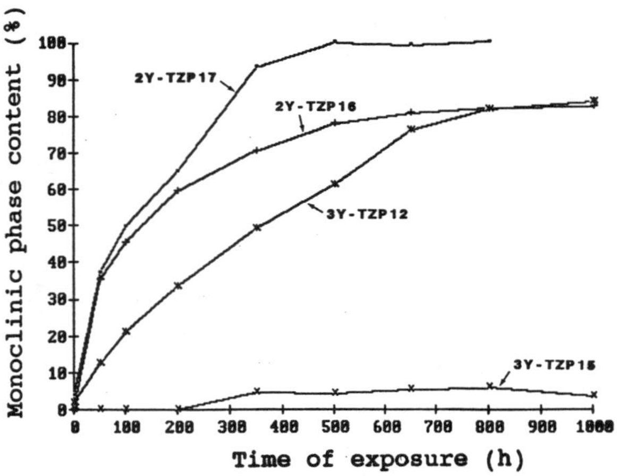

Figure 2. Monoclinic phase content in the surface of the samples as a function of time of exposure in water vapour at 150 °C.

CONCLUSIONS

1) Hydrothermally produced and supercritically dried powders can be sintered to high densities at low temperatures resulting in small grain size.

2) Mechanical properties of the HIPed samples made of hydrothermally produced and supercritically dried powders are comparable to those of the materials produced of commercial powders.

3) By HIPing it is possible to produce TZP materials with high structural stability against water induced phase transformation.

REFERENCES

(1) Gunnarsson, G., Sveinsdottir, E.L., Westman, A-K., Lepistö, T.T., Mäntylä, T., Sörensen, O.T., Production of zirconia powders by hydrothermal methods and supercritical drying and their properties, presented at the 2nd International Conference on Ceramic Powder Processing Science and Technology, Oct. 12-14, Berchtesgaden, FRG, 1988.

Corrosion of Alumina in Acids

W. GENTHE *, H. HAUSNER
Technische Universität Berlin
Institut für Nichtmetallische Werkstoffe
Englische Straße 20, D — 1000 Berlin 12

ABSTRACT

The corrosion of aluminum oxide in various acids has been investigated at elevated temperature and pressure. The influence of composition, the difference between mono- and polycrystalline material and the grain size dependence of the corrosive attack is being discussed.

INTRODUCTION

In general ceramics have a high resistance against chemical attack. Nevertheless, problems can arise under certain conditions, when ceramics are in contact with acids. In order to investigate the most important influential factors, aluminum oxides of different compositions have been prepared and their behaviour in a corrosive environment has been studied.

EXPERIMENTAL

High purity alumina powders (Baikalox CR6 AS2 and Sumitomo AKP 50) were mixed with precipitated hydroxides, the mixture freeze dried, dry pressed und sintered at 1550 °C (AKP 50) or 1650 °C (CR6 AS2).
The samples were exposed to various acids in an autoclave in the temperature range from 80 to 250 °C. The corroded samples were investigated by SEM and the metal content of the leaching solutions was determined by ICP-OES. In Figure 1 reaction vessels (stainless steel with teflon insert) and samples are shown.

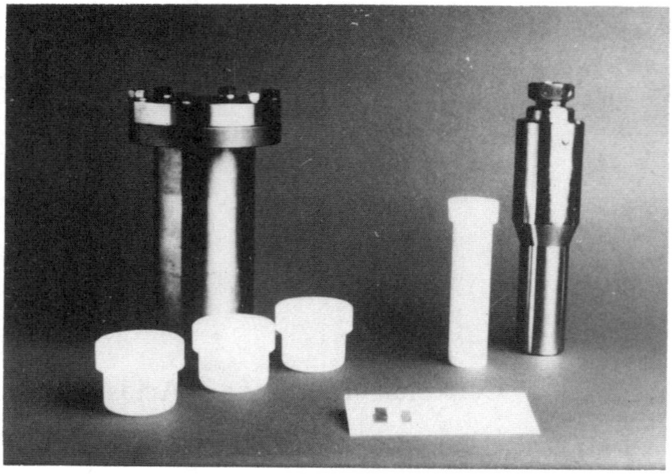

Figure 1: Reaction vessels and samples

RESULTS AND DISCUSSION

Figures 2 to 4 show surfaces of alumina samples after different exposure time. The attack starts at the grain boundaries and the grain boundaries are dissolved at a faster rate than the grains themselves. After a certain time the grains are washed out of the matrix with continuing dissolution.

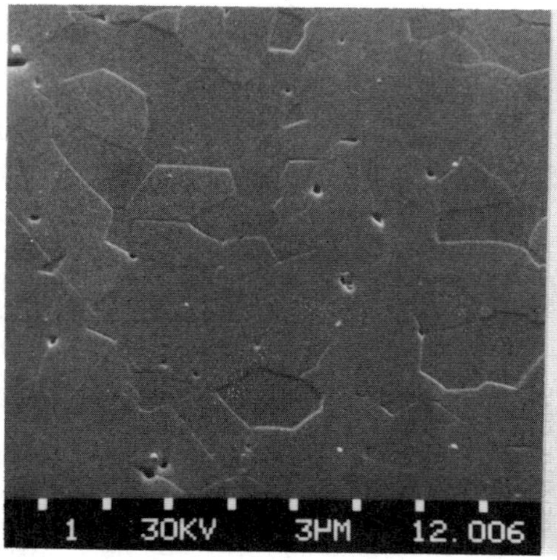

Figure 2: Surface of Al_2O_3 (450 ppm MgO, 170 ppm SiO_2), HCl, 150 °C, 24 h, dG/A = 0.09 mg/cm²

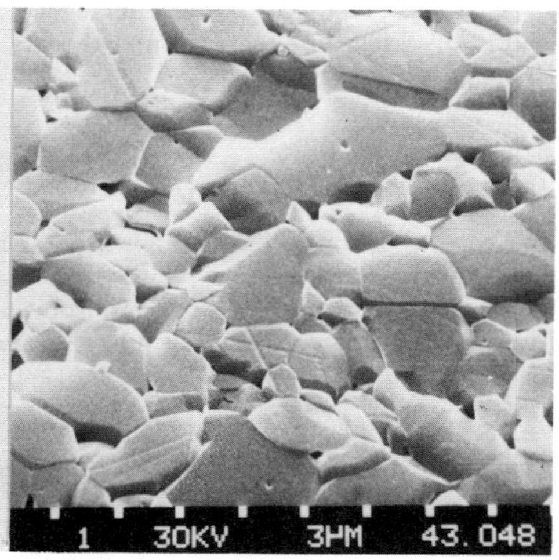

Figure 3: Surface of Al_2O_3 (450 ppm MgO, 170 ppm SiO_2), HCl, 150 °C, 96 h, dG/A = 0.49 mg/cm²

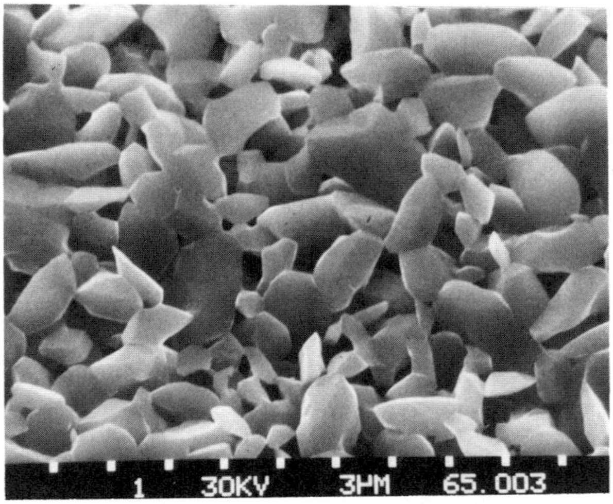

Figure 4: Surface of Al_2O_3 (450 ppm MgO, 170 ppm SiO_2), HCl, 150 °C, 192 h, dG/A = 13.25 mg/cm²

In Table 1 and 2 some results of the corrosion experiments are shown. "dG/A" is the weight loss per unit area, and "C_{leach}/C_{bulk}" is the ratio of the metal concentration in the leaching solutions and the sample itself.

TABLE 1
Influence of SiO_2 on the corrosion of Al_2O_3 (HCl, 150 °C,96 h)

SiO_2 ppm	MgO ppm	dG/A g/cm²	C_{leach}/C_{bulk} Al_2O_3	SiO_2	MgO
50	520	0.31	0.91	n.d.	1.09
170	450	0.49	0.83	3.73	1.10
2920	500	4.78	0.85	3.29	1.10
34020	560	8.13	0.79	2.38	1.13

TABLE 2
Influence of Cr_2O_3 on the corrosion of Al_2O_3 (180 °C, 168 h)

Al_2O_3	+ 1140 ppm Cr_2O_3			+ 6320 ppm Cr_2O_3		
	dG/A	C_{leach}/C_{bulk}		dG/A	C_{leach}/C_{bulk}	
	mg/cm²	Al	Cr	mg/cm²	Al	Cr
HCl	16.2	1.06	1.19	3.7	0.96	1.11
H_2SO_4/H_3PO_4	81.0	0.93	1.12	10.5	0.90	1.78
HNO_3	10.3	0.96	1.2	6.6	1.00	1.25
HF	8.4	1.10	2.31	10.4	1.11	1.90

In the case of aluminas containing a silicate phase more SiO_2 is found in the leaching solution than could be expected from the bulk composition of the material. This result supports the fact that the silicate phase is mainly located at the grain boundaries, which are attacked to a higher extent.
Figure 5 shows a cross section of a corroded alumina sample with an in depth attacked portion. By using EDX-microanalysis a significant decrease in the Si-concentration of this portion compared with intact parts of the sample can be shown.

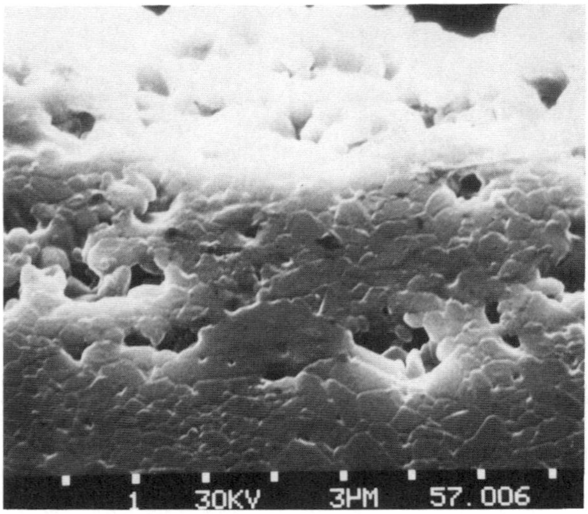

Figure 5: Cross section of Al_2O_3 (560 ppm MgO, 34030 ppm SiO_2), HCl, 150 °C, 96 h, dG/A = 8.13 mg/cm^2

In most of the cases shown in Table 3 the C_{leach}/C_{bulk} ratio is close to 1 indicating that the grain boundary and the bulk composition is similar. The high value of 1.78 obtained for the H_2SO_4/H_3PO_4 corrosion requires further investigation. The results obtained with HF may be caused by the formation of an aluminium fluoride layer with a low solubility.
The C_{leach}/C_{bulk} values can only be used for a semi-quantative evaluation of the results. Errors may arise from the depostion of reaction products and from the formation of insoluble compounds. In addition the different parameters responsible for the corrosion behaviour cannot be seen indipendently: the same chemical composition of the bulk may result in a different composition of the grain boundary if different sintering conditions are used; the influence of temperature and pressure cannot be separated under the applied experimental conditions (isochoric process); the density of the sample varies with processing conditions; the grain size and the grain size distribution of the sintered samples depend on the powder characteristics.

A comparison between polycrystalline and single crystal material (sapphire and ruby, Comadure sa.)shows clearly, that the corrosion resistance of single crystals is higher.

TABLE 3
Corrosion behaviour of mono- and polycrystalline material (180 °C, 168h)

Sample		Cr_2O_3 ppm	dG/A mg/cm^2	C_{leach}/C_{bulk} Al	Cr
Single crystal	HCl	6270	0.8	1.09	1.03
	H_2SO_4		0.5	1.02	1.01
Polycrystalline material	HCl	6320	3.7	0.96	1.11
	H_2SO_4		10.4	1.11	1.90

In the case of the H_2SO_4 attack a prefered leaching of Cr has been observed in the case of the polycrystalline material. Single crystals without chromium oxide show a higher corrosion resistance than the doped material.

A possible microstructural influence on the corrosion behaviour was investigated with hot-pressed pure and MgO doped aluminas. Material of different grain sizes was obtained by a heat treatment of hot- pressed samples at 1550 °C for various time intervals.

TABLE 4
Influence of grain size on corrosion behaviour (HCl, 180 °C, 168 h)

HP 1400 °C/15 min	Hours at 1550 °C	Grain Size µm	dG/A mg/cm^2
Al_2O_3	0	0.5 ... 1	26.8
	2	4 .. 5	25.2
	4	5 .. 6	21.0
	12	7 .. 8	16.8
Al_2O_3 + 500 ppm MgO	0	0.5 .. 0.8	17.8
	2	2 .. 3	17.6
	4	3 .. 4	14.2
	12	4 .. 5	6.2

It can be seen from Table 4 that the specific weight loss is much higher for pure aluminium oxide than for the MgO-doped samples. The reason may be the more irregular grain size of the pure oxide. The corrosion resistance increases with increasing grain size in both cases.

CONCLUSIONS

Aluminia in an acidic enviroment is corroded by grain boundary attack. The chemical composition of the grain boundary has a major influence on the corrosion resistance. Polycrystalline samples have a lower corrosion resistance than single crystal material. The corrosion resistance ist grain size dependent.

INTERPHASES IN PVD-COATED TiN/STEEL SYSTEMS

L. DE SCHEPPER[(1)], L. M. STALS[(1)], M. VAN STAPPEN[(2)], J. P. CELIS[(3)], J. R. ROOS[(3)]

[(1)] Materials Physics Laboratory, Limburgs Universitair Centrum, B-3610 Diepenbeek (Belgium); [(2)] Scientific and Technical Centre of the Metal Working Industry, Universitaire Campus, B-3610 Diepenbeek (Belgium); [(3)] Dept. of Metallurgy and Materials Engineering, Katholieke Universiteit Leuven, B-3030 Leuven (Belgium)

ABSTRACT

AISI 304 and AISI 440C steel substrates have been PVD-coated with titanium nitride. The coating deposited was either a TiN layer, or a TiN layer on a thin intermediate Ti layer. The deposited layer, and in particular the interface region between layer and substrate, have been investigated with transmission electron microscopy (TEM). TEM of the TiN layer on the AISI 440C substrate revealed that TiN forms a homogeneous polycrystalline layer (grain size about 25 nm), whether a Ti intermediate layer is present or not. The structure of the TiN layer on AISI 304 was observed to be more complicated: the TiN layer consists of micron-size groups of small TiN grains (typical size 25 nm) with nearly the same crystallographic orientation. These groups of TiN grains are denoted as 'super-grains'. From interface observations it was concluded that the crystallographic orientation of the super-grains is determined by the orientation of the austenite grain on which it is formed. It is was also found that the orientation of the super-grains is influenced by the presence of a Ti intermediate layer.

INTRODUCTION

In this paper we concentrate on the microscopic crystallographic structure of a PVD deposited TiN layer on AISI 440C martensitic stainless steel and AISI 304 austenitic stainless steel, and on the structure of the interface between the TiN layer and the substrate.

Special attention is given to the influence of a Ti intermediate layer. The present paper deals with transmission electron microscopy (TEM) observations. X ray diffraction results are described elsewhere [1].

MATERIALS AND METHODS

2 micrometer thick TiN layers were deposited on AISI 440C martensitic stainless steel, and on AISI 304 austenitic stainless steel substrates in an industrial size Balzers triode ion plating system. Prior to the deposition, the substrates were mechanically polished, ultransonically and chemically cleaned, and argon sputter cleaned at 400 °C.

Two types of coatings were produced: TiN layers deposited directly on the substrate by starting the evaporation of Ti in an argon-nitrogen plasma, and TiN layers deposited on a substrate precoated with a thin intermediate Ti layer (thickness about 25 nm). The latter layer combination was obtained by starting the evaporation of Ti in an argon plasma.

TEM samples were produced by an Iontech or Balzers ion milling apparatus. Argon ion milling was performed in two steps, in order to assure that the thinned areas contained the interface zone between substrate and coating: the TiN coating was first perforated by ion bombardment until the underlying substrate became visible; next the sample was bombarded from the substrate side until complete perforation occurred.

TEM observations were made in a Philips EM 420 microscope, operating at 120 kV, and equipped with an EDAX energy dispersive X ray analyser.

RESULTS AND DISCUSSION

AISI 440C martensitic stainless steel

From TEM pictures and electron diffraction patterns of the TiN coating on AISI 440C substrates with and without Ti intermediate coating it was concluded that the TiN layer is in both cases an homogeneous polycrystalline layer, with a typical grain size of 25 nm.

TEM of the AISI 440C martensitic stainless steel substrate shows that it consists of a finely grained polycrystalline martensite structure (typical martensite grain size in the order op 50 nm), in which metal-carbide (M-C) precipitates (typical diameter 1 micrometer) are embedded. Since the volume ratio of M-C precipitates to martensite is low (estimated to be only a few percent), it can be expected that the crystallographic structure of the TiN layer is mainly determined by the structure of the interphase between the coating and the martensite grains. Therefore the TEM observations were concentrated on thinned regions where the martensite-coating interphase was visible in the microscope.

A typical TEM observation of the interphase region between martensite (with an intermediate Ti layer) and the TiN coating is shown in fig. 1. Some interface defects (voids and/or bubbles) are indicated by the arrows. The corresponding electron diffraction pattern

(EDP), shown in the inset of the figure, reveals diffraction rings from both martensite and TiN. It demonstrates that even the early TiN layer in the interface region is a homogeneous polycrystalline structure.

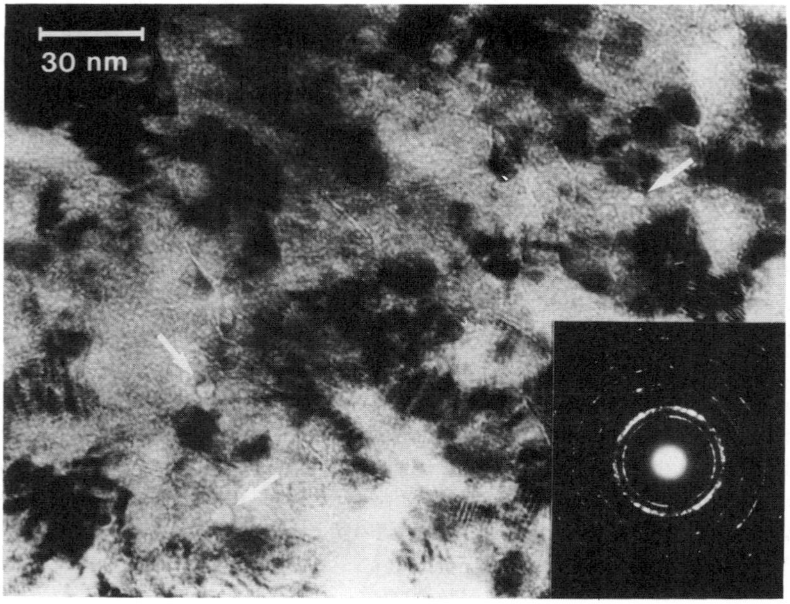

Figure 1. TEM bright field image of the structure of the TiN-martensite interface. The picture is taken slightly in underfocus, in order to reveal voids and/or bubbles at the interface (indicated bij arrows). The inset shows the corresponding EDP, in which the two inner rings belong to TiN, and the third ring (very close to the second TiN ring) to martensite.

AISI 304 austenitic stainless steel

TEM observations on the TiN layer formed on AISI 304 substrates show that, in contrast to the TiN layer formed on AISI 440C substrates, the layer does not form an homogeneous polycrystalline layer. The layer on AISI 304 consists basically of small TiN grains (grain size in the order of 25 nm, as it was for the layer on AISI 440C), but these grains are now grouped together in micron-size entities of TiN grains with nearly the same crystallographic orientation. Such entities are referred to as 'super-grains'. The common crystallographic orientation of the TiN grains in a super-grain can be characterized by an fcc crystal direction vector $\boldsymbol{B}$ perpendicular to the surface of the substrate. TEM pictures of such super-grains are published elsewhere [2]. The super-grain structure was observed in the TiN layer on AISI 304 substrates with and without a Ti intermediate coating.

The super-grains are formed because of a kind of epitaxial growth of the basic TiN grains on the austenite grains of the substrate. Therefore, the grain size of the super-grains is in the order of that of the austenite grains (typically 1 to 10 micrometer). A typical example of the interface between a super-grain and an austenite grain without Ti intermediate coating is shown in figure 2.

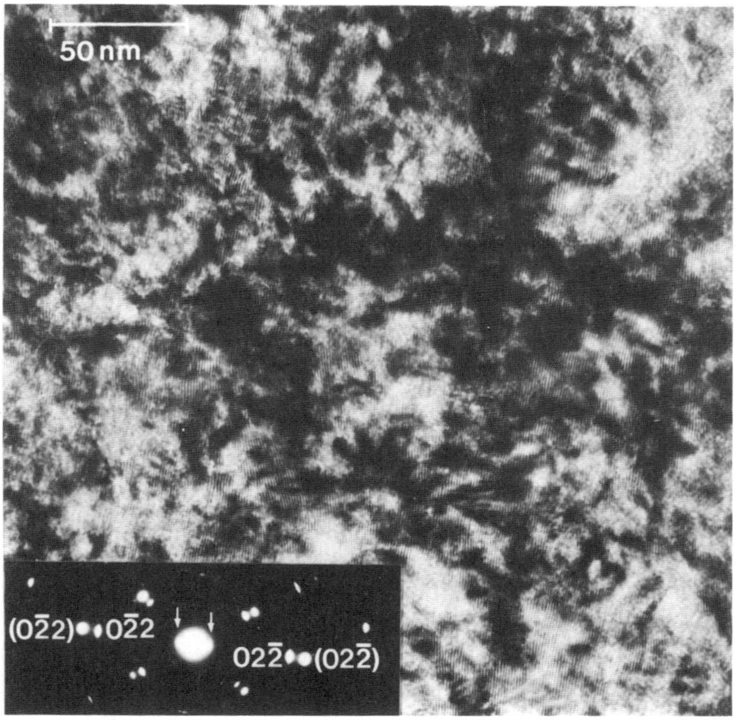

Figure 2. TEM image of the interface between a TiN super-grain and the underlying austenite grain (without Ti coating). The inset shows the corresponding EDP (indices in brackets refer to austenite, the others to TiN). Both the austenite grain and the TiN super-grain have a ***B***=[011] crystal orientation. Note parrallel Moiré fringes running North-South, caused by the double diffracted beams indicated by arrows in the EDP.

The EDP in the inset of fig. 2 demonstrates that all the TiN grains in the super-grain have nearly the same orientation characterized by the fcc crystal direction vector ***B***=[011], which is the same crystal orientation vector as that of the austenite grain. One could denote this as full epitaxy between the super-grain and the austenite grain, although the Moiré fringes indicate slight differences in orientation between the basic TiN grains.

It was found that for austenite without Ti coating, full epitaxy between super-grains and austenite grains occurs. Therefore, the early TiN layer close to the interface has a tendency to develop a [011] texture, since this is the texture of the austenite substrate. This was confirmed by X ray diffraction [1]. Further away from the interface, the TiN coating gradually developes its normal [111] texture. This is indeed the texture usually observed by X ray diffraction on a TiN layer with a thickness of a few microns.

For austenite with intermediate Ti coating, the situation is more complicated: the presence of the Ti layer disturbs the full epitaxial growth, and super-grains can be formed with a different ***B*** vector than the underlying austenite grain. The case of a ***B***=[001] super-grain on a ***B***=[011] austenite grain was often observed. It was indeed confirmed by X ray diffraction that in this case a [002] peak of TiN is observed, which is absent for substrates without Ti coating [1]. Also in this case the coating converts to its usual [111] texture further away from the interface.

It is obvious that the formation of super-grains in TiN coatings on austenitic stainless steel, and the induced texture of the TiN layer near the interface, which is different from the [111] texture usually observed in sufficiently thick coatings, can have important consequences for the functional properties of the coating (e.g. adhesion and internal stresses).

CONCLUSIONS

The microscopic crystallographic structure of TiN layers on martensitic (AISI 440C) and austenitic (AISI 304) steel substrates has been investigated with transmission electron microscopy. It was found that the TiN layer forms a homogeneous polycrystalline layer on AISI 440C substrates, whether a Ti intermediate layer is present or not. On AISI 304 substrates, the TiN layer is built up of so-called super-grains. Their crystallographic orientation, which induces a texture in the TiN layer close to the interface, is related to the orientation of the underlying austenite grain. If no intermediate Ti layer is present, full epitaxy between super-grains and austenite grains occurs. If a Ti intermediate layer is present, the crystallographic orientation of the super-grain can be different from that of the underlying austenite grain.

REFERENCES

[1] Van Stappen, M., Malliet, B., De Schepper, L., Stals, L.M., Celis, J.P., Roos, J.R., submitted to Surface Engineering, 1989

[2] De Schepper, L., D' Olieslaeger, M., Knuyt, G., Stals, L.M., Van Stappen, M., Malliet, B., Celis, J.P., Roos, J.R., Thin Solid Films, 1989, in press

ADHESION AND DUCTILITY OF PLASMA SPRAYED THERMAL BARRIER COATINGS.

A.T.J. VERBEEK, J.M. HOUBEN, J.A. KLOSTERMANN
Materials Group, Faculty of Mechanical Engineering,
Eindhoven University of Technology,
Den Dolech 2, 5612 AZ Eindhoven, The Netherlands

ABSTRACT

In this paper the development of a new Tensile Adhesion Test, operating without glue, for Plasma Sprayed Coatings is described. First some general information about bond strength and adhesion tests is given. Next, a description about the new test and some test results of this test are given, together with the results of a conventional Tensile Adhesion Test. On testing the coatings, the failure behaviour has been followed by acoustic emission monitoring.

INTRODUCTION

One of the most important problems one will encounter on applying plasma sprayed (ceramic) coatings, is the bond strength of these coatings. The mechanical behaviour is strongly dependent on the bondstrength. When a coating is subjected to a mechanical, thermomechanical or combined load, failure will often occur at the interface between substrate and coating.

Principles of adhesion

In general, there are assumed to be three principles of adhesion of plasma sprayed coatings: Mechanical Anchoring The coating fixes itself by anchoring on the peaks and holes at the substrate surface. Adsorption; this is merely a surface effect. It can be divided into three types of bonding: Chemical bonding, Physical bonding or Chemisorption. Metallurgical interactions; diffusion of the coating atoms into the substrate material and also the reverse process.

Adhesion tests

The most widely used test for bond strength testing is the so called Tensile Adhesion Test. There are various kinds of this test, but they all are based on the same principle. A specimen is coated and a metal body is glued to the coating. This construction will be tested in a tensile testing machine. The bondstrength is defined as the fraction of the force at failure and the coating area under tensile stress.
According to Strompen [1], four types of coating failure can be determined using tensile adhesion tests. These failure modes are: delamination, breaking down of the glue film. failure in the coating and mixed failure. The latter is a combination of delamination and failure in the coating.

As already mentioned, there are several types of tensile adhesion tests. Only one of these tests, the DIN 50160 is standardized. (figure 1) This test is very easy in use however it has some major disadvantages:
The glue penetrates into the coating, changing the characteristics of this coating. The deposition circumstances vary with the radius of the specimen and the Poisson effect plays an important role at the coating boundary.
Two other tests [2], however not standardized, can be used to avoid the problems involved with the varying deposition circumstances and Poisson effect (figure 1). These are the so called TNO-test and the TUE test, the latter developed at Eindhoven University of Technology.

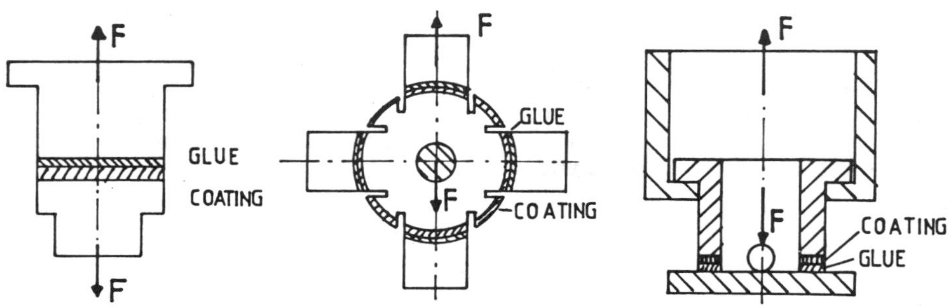

Figure 1. DIN test (a), TNO test (b) and TUE test (c)

DEVELOPMENT OF A NEW TEST

Because of the problems involved with the use of glue that penetrates into the coating and influences the coating characteristics, a new test without glueing, according to an idea of J.M. Houben, has been developed. This test is based on the following principle:. A hollow cylinder is loaded as stated below. (figure 1) In the areas, indicated by the little arrows, a tensile stress will occur. This stress tends to seperate the concentric thin cylinders that form the total cylinder. The stress state in the cylinder can be described by using an Airy stress function [3]. This gives us the following stresses:

radial stress $\sigma_r = f_1(r)*\sin\theta + f_{11}(r)$

tangential stress $\sigma_\theta = f_2(r)*\sin\theta + f_{22}(r)$

shear stress $\sigma_{r\theta} = - f_1(r)*\cos\theta$

$f_1(r)$, $f_2(r)$, $f_{11}(r)$ and $f_{22}(r)$ are functions of the radius

The tangential and radial stresses reach their maximums at $\theta = 90°$, whereas the shear stress is maximum at $\theta = 0°$. In figure 2 the principle of this test and the stress distribution are shown

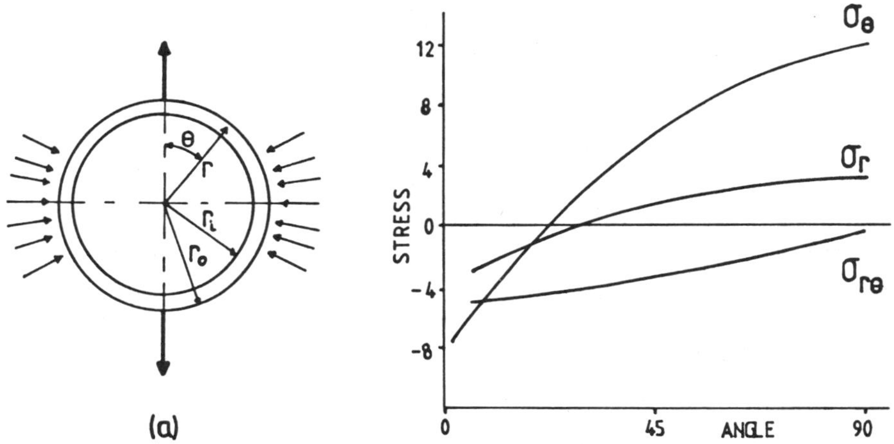

Figure 2. Hollow cylinder loaded by two equal, opposite forces (a) and stress distribution in this cylinder (b)

When this hollow cylinder is coated, the tensile stress around $\theta = 90°$, will try to delaminate the coating from the cylinder if we assume that the adhesion strength of the coating is less than the cohesion strength of the substrate or coating material. Further, the test specimens have two, oppositely placed joints, just at the points the specimen is loaded in the tensile testing machine. At these joints, the coating is removed to avoid cracking of the coating during the early stages of the adhesion test. During the tensile adhesion test, delamination can be observed in the force vs. replacement curve of the tensile testing machine. At the point of delamination, the stiffness of the coated cylinder decreases, resulting in a dip in the force vs. replacement curve. With the help of the finite element methode, it is now possible to determine the stress at which the coating delaminates. When the Young modulus of the coating has the same value as the young modulus of the substrate, the stress at delamination easily can be determined by applying the already mentioned analytical formulas. In figure 3 the test principle, together with a typical force vs. replacement curve is shown.

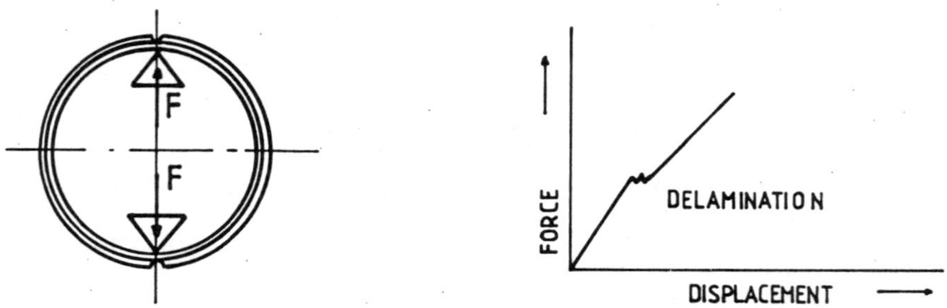

Figure 3. Testprinciple of new tensile adhesion test and a typical force vs. replacement curve.

TENSILE ADHESION TESTING OF THERMAL BARRIER COATINGS

Thermal Barrier coatings are ceramic coatings with a very low thermal conductivity. Usually they are produced by means of powder plasma spraying. As coating material, partially stabilized ZrO_2-8wt%Y_2O_3 is used.
To test the adhesion strength of the Thermal Barrier Coatings, the new test and the TNO test were used.
The coatings were sprayed with an arc current of 600 Amps, a Ar to H_2 ratio of 150 to 15, a spraying distance of 100 mm and a powder grain size of 22.5 to 45 μm. This resulted in a very dense coating of about 0.3 mm thickness on the disks and a coating of about 1 mm thickness was sprayed onto the cylinders. The coating on the cylinders showed cracks, perpendicular to the coating surface at regular distances.
The substrates were gritblasted before spraying.
The metal bodies were glued to the disks with a one component epoxy glue with a adhesive strength of about 70 N/mm².
During the tensile adhesion test the failure process was monitored by acoustic emission evaluation.

The coating failure observed at the TNO test was coating delamination and sometimes mixed failure. The bond strength of the coatings varied from 31.4 to 38 N/mm².
During the test a continuous Acoustic Emission Activity was measured, indicating that crack formation occurred not only at the final delamination of the coating, but already before this delamination. At the moment of delamination, however, the Acoustic Emission activity strongly increases.

On testing coatings with the new developed test, two types of coating failure were observed. The coating only delaminated around $\theta = 90°$, a gap between the coating and the cylinder can be observed, or a piece of the coating around $\theta = 90°$ is totally removed. At one specimen, the coating delaminated next to the joint. The acoustic emission signal shows very sharp peaks at the moment of delamination. Before the delamination also acoustic emission activity is measured.
The duration of the events, measured before the delamination, varies from 1 μs until 500 μs, while the events measured at

delamination vary between 200 and 5000 μs. The beginning of the delamination can be observed by increasing acoustic emission activity (hits vs. time ratio) and an increasing duration ot the hits. The final delamination of the coating can be heard as a dry "plopping" sound, and is seen as very high acoustic emission peaks. The amplitudes of these final peaks reach up to 100 dB.
After testing, the failed coatings were examined by light microscopy. It was shown that the perpendicular cracks, already present in the coating had not been growing. So the measured acoustic emission signal must be caused either by microcracks (those couldn't be observed) or cracks at the interface coating substrate.

When the acoustic emission signals of the cylinder test are compared to the signals obtained by the TNO-test, it can be remarked that the first one shows a more reproducable signal. At the cylinder test, failing can be observed as increasing acoustic emission activity followed by a sharp peak. During the TNO test no direct relationship between acoustic emission activity and failure mode was found. The signals measured at the mixed failure mode, were sometimes the same as the signals measured at a coating totally delaminating.

CONCLUSIONS

However the bondstrengths that have been measured by the two tests, are very different and cannot be compared, the TNO test as well as the cylinder test deliver very reproducable results. Delamination has shown to be a process that does not occur suddenly but is preceded by the formation of little cracks. The absence of glue at the cylinder test is a great advantage, the coating characteristics are not changed due to penetrating glue. Further the failure mode is very reproducable, no mixed failure occurs. Also the acoustic emission signal of the coating is very reproducable.

ACKNOWLEDGEMENT

The authors would like to express their gratitude to the IOP Technical Ceramics for supporting the research programme on Thermal Barrier Coatings.

REFERENCES

1. Strompen N., Plasmagespritzte Metalloxid- und Oxidschichten. PhD. Thesis Technische Hochschule Aachen, Aachen, 1986

2. Houben J.M., Oppervlaktebehandelingen, synopsis of a lecture, Eindhoven University of Technology, Eindhoven, 1985.

3. Verbeek A.T.J., Ontwikkeling van een nieuwe methode voor het beproeven van plasmagespoten coatings. M. Thesis, Eindhoven University of Technology, Faculty of Mechanical Engineering, Eindhoven, 1988

PLASMA SPRAYED TiC COATINGS FOR FIRST WALL PROTECTION IN FUSION DEVICES

P. GROOT, J.G. VAN DER LAAN, L. LAAS
Netherlands Energy Research Foundation, ECN,
P.O. Box 1, 1755 ZG PETTEN, the Netherlands
M. MACK, M. DVORAK
ISOT GmbH, Dortmund, FRG

ABSTRACT

For protection of plasma facing components in nuclear fusion devices thick titanium carbide coatings are being developed. Coatings have been produced by plasma spraying at atmospheric pressure (APS) and low pressure (LPPS) and analyzed with respect to microstructure and chemical composition. Thermo-mechanical evaluation has been performed by applying short pulse laser heat flux tests. The influence of coating thickness and porosity on the resistance to spalling by thermal shocks appears to be more important than aspects of chemical composition.

INTRODUCTION

The in-vessel components of a large fusion plasma experiment like the Joint European Torus (JET, UK) are exposed to high heat fluxes [1]. For the Next European Torus (NET) the design heat loads are up to 0.5 MW/m² during normal operation. Heat fluxes on the first wall due to off-normal events (plasma disruptions) may have energy densities up to 2 MJ/m² in periods lasting 0.1- 50 ms. An unprotected stainless steel vessel will suffer from cracking, melting and erosion under such conditions. Candidate wall protection materials must have a low atomic number, high melting point, low vapour pressure, low sputtering yield and good chemical compatibility even at high temperatures. In addition to carbon materials, carbides are being considered. TiC and SiC have a lower sputtering yield than carbons under plasma ion bombardment. Several researchers have developed titanium carbide coatings for fusion applications [2-5]. Brossa and coworkers produced TiC-coatings by chemical vapour deposition (CVD), atmospheric plasma spraying (APS) and low pressure plasma spraying (LPPS) onto stainless steel AISI 316 [2-4]. The response to thermal shocks was studied using electron beam. The APS-coatings (thickness 30-100 µm) appeared to have a higher resistance to thermal shock than the dense CVD-coatings (thickness 10-30 µm), due to the considerable porosity which offers a better thermal barrier [3]. LPPS-coatings (thickness 10-120 µm, porosity about 6%) showed similar response as the CVD-coatings, thus appearing to be too dense and too brittle [4].

Dallaire and coworkers produced several TiC-coatings by means of plasma spraying in an inert atmosphere (Inconel substrate, thickness 0.1-0.4 mm, porosity 17-29%) [5, 6]. Results from electron beam tests indicate that the resistance to thermal shock damage decreases as the coating porosity increases. It was stated that the resistance to thermal shocks is maximum for a 10-20 % coating porosity [5].
In the framework of the European Fusion Technology Programme, ECN contributes the development of titanium carbide coatings as a possible protection of metal components, with a minimum thickness of 0.5 mm. Additional research was required to optimize the thermal shock resistance (tested by laser beam) of such thick coatings, with a particular emphasis on porosity. Initial results are presented.

COATING PRODUCTION AND CHARACTERIZATION

Coatings have been produced by plasma spraying at atmospheric pressure (APS) and low pressure (LPPS). APS TiC coatings were made by ISOT (20-40 kW plasmagun) and ECN (40 kW), while LPPS coatings were made by ISOT (93 kW), in close collaboration with the institute of Materials Technology Dortmund, Prof. H.D. Steffens.
A commercial TiC powder (Starck Amperit) was used. Several ranges of particle sizes were selected, since particle size and distribution are critical parameters in plasma spraying of TiC [5]. Substrates (AISI 316 for APS-coatings and mild steel St. 37 for LPPS) were grit blasted before spraying to improve adherence. The spraying conditions are given in table 1.
The microstructure of the coatings was characterized as follows:
- C, H and N contents by classical element analysis
- O content by neutron activation analysis
- phase identification by X-ray powder diffraction
- porosity measurements by Texture Analysis System (TAS)
- microstructure by SEM and optical microscopy.

The quantitative results are given in table 1 and 2. In atmospheric plasma spraying carbon depletion takes place, probably due to oxidation. In addition, all APS-coatings contain oxygen in the range 1-10% and nitrogen up to a few percent which are present in solid solution TiC,N,O and as TiO_2. The mean porosity ranges from 16-28%, although denser areas are present (>11%). A smaller size of the spray particles seems to reduce the mean porosity, in agreement with results of Brunet & Dallaire [6].

THERMAL SHOCK TESTS WITH LASER

The thermo-mechanical behaviour of the titanium carbide coatings under transient heat loads similar to plasma disruptions has been determined by applying a heat flux using a pulsed Nd:YAG laser, as described elsewhere [7]. The tests have been performed in a vacuum better than 0.01 Pa in order to minimize environmental effects. The pulse duration was 10.0 ms. The energy content of a single incident laser pulse was 54 J, and the energy density was varied by changing defocus conditions. A typical picture is given in figure 1. The damage has been characterized in terms of melting and degree of spalling. In table 2 the results are given. For each coating/substrate the incident energy density on spot 1 was increased in steps from 0.64, 0.72, 0.82 to 1.0 MJ/m^2 (table 2, columns 6,7). On spot 2 energy densities of 1.1 and 2.2 MJ/m^2 were applied (columns 8,9). For ECN-P, LTC-6 and LTC-7 spot 2 was taken identical to spot 1 since no failure was observed after the 1.0 MJ/m^2 pulse. An energy density of 5.9 MJ/m^2 was applied to spot number 3 (columns 9,10). Thermal fatigue conditions were obtained by 100 shots of equal energy density 0.64 MJ/m^2 with a repetition rate of 0.5 Hz (columns 11,12). The highest heat load causes melting of the coating surface in all cases. To prevent substrate melting a coating thickness of about 0.7 mm for an incident energy density of 5 MJ/m^2 is needed, according to the results of a detailed numerical transient heat flow model [8]. However, in none of the cases melting of the substrate has been observed. Possible explanations for the discrepancy are : the absorption coefficient for the 1.064 µm laser light is less than unity (TiC 0.8- 0.9); the thermal conductivity of a porous plasma spray layer is much less than 40 W/mK (i.e. the literature value for pure TiC in the range 10-3000 K) [8]; the heat flow is not really one-dimensional because of the limited spot size, so lateral heat losses will reduce the maximum temperatures.

RESULTS AND DISCUSSION

To quantify the degree of spalling damage the maximum crack penetration is given relative to the coating thickness in figures 2a-d. The results on the LPPS-coatings are not really directly comparable to the APS-coatings since they have different substrate and substrate thickness, and LPPS coated specimens have been machined, resulting in very smooth surfaces with respect to as-sprayed conditions. Nevertheless, the results show a trend of improved thermal shock resistance with increasing thickness of the coating for single shot laser pulses. Severe spalling has been observed for thicknesses less than 0.5 mm. The porosity distribution of a coating has an effect on its thermal shock resistance, see figures 3a-d. The present results do not indicate a relation with the mean porosity, but there is evidence of a trend in the relation with the minimum value of the porosity. These figures suggest that a minimum porosity of about 10-20% is favourable, which confirms the results from Dallaire & Saint Jacques [5]. Indications of a lower spalling resistance of coatings with porosities less than 10% as obtained by Brossa et al. do not contradict our present results [2-4]. Oxygen contents and stoichiometry (C/Ti atomic ratio) do not seem to have a clear influence on the performance of present coatings.

CONCLUSIONS

Conclusions from the evidence obtained so far :

- The damage threshold to thermal shocks with a laser beam of present best performing plasma sprayed TiC coatings is about 1 MJ/m^2 incident energy density in 10 ms.
- The degree of thermal shock damage depends on coating thickness and minimum porosity. A larger thickness and porosity in the range 11-22% appears to result in a lower relative crack penetration.

ACKNOWLEDGEMENT

Several discussions with W. van Witzenburg an H.T. Klippel were very fruitful. Also the assistance of H. Kooistra and J. Bakker is greatfully acknowledged.

REFERENCES

[1] Dietz, K.J., J. Nucl. Mat. 155-157 (1988) 8-14.

[2] Brossa, F., J. Bohdansky, J. Roth & P. Martinelli, J. Nucl. Mat. 93-94 (1980) 474-8.

[3] Brossa, F., C. Ferro & E. Franconi, Proceedings 13th Symposium On Fusion Technology, Varese, 1984, 1267-73.

[4] Brossa, F., G. Rigon & B. Looman, J. Nucl. Mat. 155- 7(1988) 267-72.

[5] Dallaire, S. & R.G. Saint Jacques, Surf. & Coat. Techn. 33(1987) 319-326.

[6] Brunet, C. & S. Dallaire, Surf. & Coat.Techn. 31(1987) 1-10.

[7] Van der Laan, J.G., J. Bakker, H.T. Klippel, Proc. 15th Symposium on Fusion Technology, 19-23 sept. 1988, Utrecht, to be published.

[8] Klippel, H.T., Proc. International Symposium on Fusion Nuclear Technology, 4-8 april 1988, Tokyo, to be published.

technique/ substrate/ coating	powder size (mu)	spray distance (mm)	Ar/H2	C,N,O-contents C (w/o)	N (w/o)	O (w/o)	atomic ratio C/Ti	X-ray diffraction + 15-30%,tr 5-15% TiCO,N	TiO2
ECN J	-25+5	70	85/15	13.7	1.6	9	0.73	+	tr
ECN P	-25+5	80	80/20	13.3	1.9	9.3	0.71	+	+
ECN X	-25+5	100	75/25	10.4	2.3	8.5	0.53	+	tr
ECN VI	-25+5	90	75/25	12.3	2.1	1.4	0.58	+	-
TC 24	>56	100	80/20	14.9	1.2	5	0.75	tr	tr
TC 25	>56	100	80/20	16.2	0.8	3.2	0.81	+	+
TC 26	>56	100	80/20	16	1.0	4.3	0.82	+	tr
TC 27	-20+5	100	80/20	11.9	2.1	5.2	0.59	+	tr
LTC 6	-56+36	255	82/18	18.9	0.1	0.1	0.93	-	-
LTC 7	-56+36	255	56/44	20.2	0.05	0.15	1.01	-	-

Table 1. Spraying conditions of present coatings and chemical and microstructural characterization. The stoichiometric ratio has been derived from the C, N and O concentration taking Ti as a rest element.

technique/ substrate/ coating	thickness (mm)	porosity mean	s.d.	min	damage expressed as melting(m)/no melt(n.m), and relative crack propagation (rcp, in %) -incident energy density (MJ/m2) E = 1.0 m/nm	rcp	E = 2.2 n/nm	rcp	E = 5.9 n/nm	rcp	E = 0.64 100 pulses m/nm	rcp
ECN J	0.82	19.9	2.0	15	n.m	34	m	30	m	47	n.m	18
ECN P	1.32	23.3	3.7	12	n.m	0	m	6	m	45	n.m	26
ECN X	0.3	25.3	1.5	20	n.m	100	n.m	100	m	100	n.m	30
ECN VI	1.1	23.2	2.6	14					m	45	n.m	30
TC 24	0.8	22.8	1.9	18	n.m	16	n.m	50	m	50	n.m	14
TC 25	0.46	26.8	1.3	24	n.m	50	n.m	75	m	90	n.m	100
TC 26	0.47	25.4	1.5	23	n.m	100	m	100	m	100	n.m	100
TC 27	0.67	16.2	2.5	11	n.m	20	m			60	n.m	40
LTC 6	0.53	22.8	2.3	16	n.m	0	m	34	m	54	n.m	0
LTC 7	0.77	28.2	3.2	18	n.m	0	n.m.	19	m	56	n.m	14

Table 2. Coating thickness and porosity (mean, standard deviation and minimum), and main damage characteristics after thermal shock tests. Severe transverse cracking and chipping was observed for ECN-X, and TC-27 for all tests, for ECN-VI and TC-25 only after 100 shots. Moderate transverse cracking was observed for LTC-6 and LTC-7 at E=5.9 and 2.2 MJ/m2. Discolouration was observed for all coatings, in some cases starting at the lowest energy densities applied.

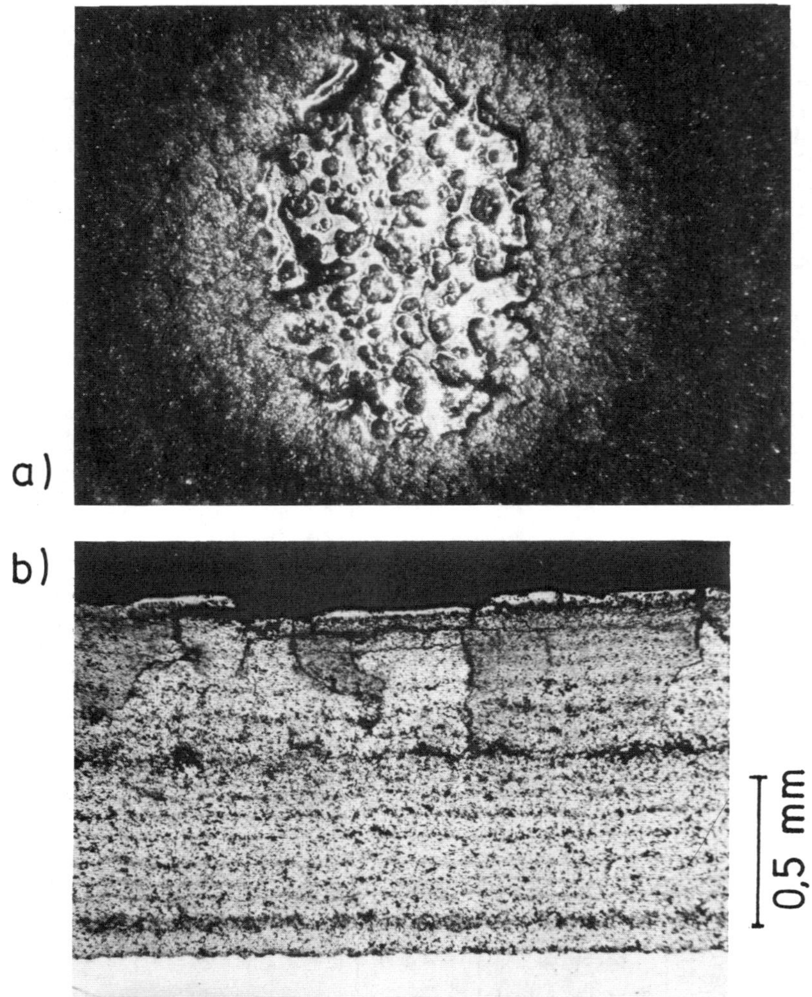

Figure 1. Optical micrograph of a) the coating surface and b) a cross sectional view of ECN-P after a single shot laser pulse of 5.9 MJ/m^2 incident energy. Surface melting is evident as well as spalling and a tendency to transverse cracking or chipping.

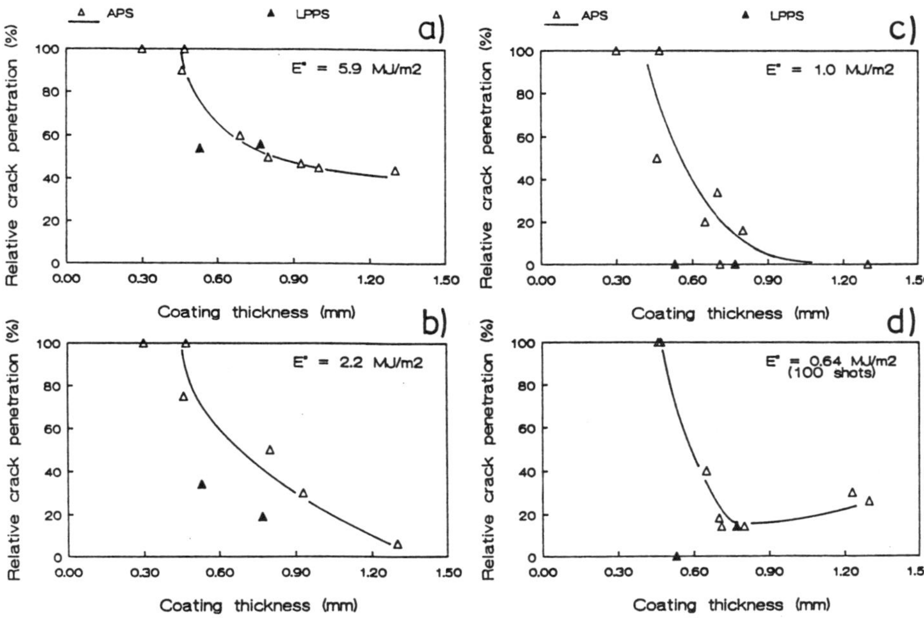

Figure 2. Plot of the relative crack penetration into the coating as a function of the thickness, for 10.0 ms laserpulses with a maximum incident energy density of a) 5.9 MJ/m², b) 2.2 MJ/m², c) 1.0 MJ/m² and d) 0.64 MJ/m² (100 shots, repetition rate 0.5 Hz). All figures indicate a minimum coating thickness of about 0.5 mm to prevent 100 % penetration.

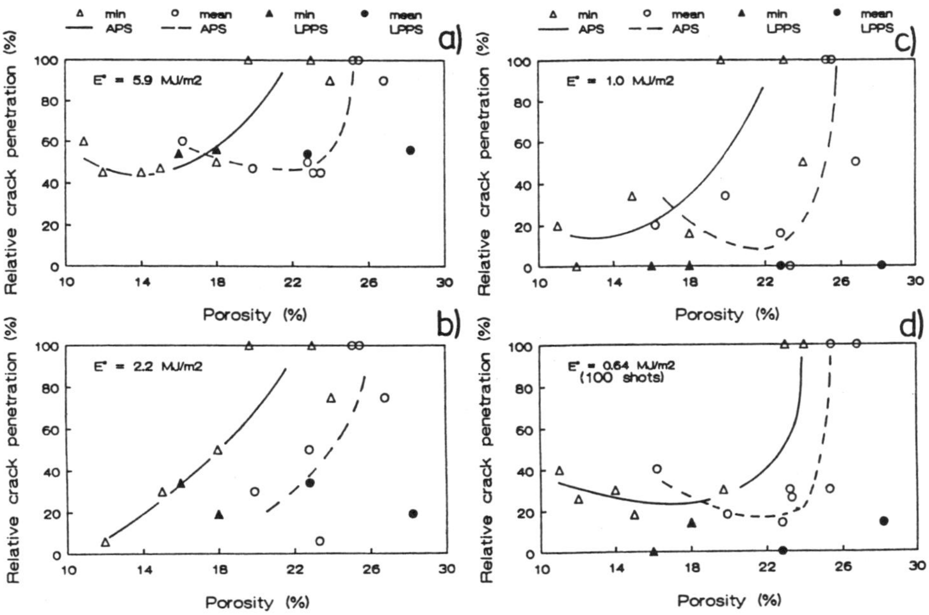

Figure 3. Plot of relative crack penetration versus the minimum and mean porosity, for 10.0 ms laserpulses with a maximum incident energy density of a) 5.9 MJ/m², b) 2.2 MJ/m², c) 1.0 MJ/m² and d) 0.64 MJ/m² (100 shots, repetition rate 0.5 Hz).

THE MECHANICAL AND CORROSION PROPERTIES OF THIN ALUMINA FILMS DEPOSITED BY MOCVD

R.W.J. Morssinkhof, T. Fransen, M.M.D. Heusinkveld, and P.J. Gellings,
Laboratory of Inorganic Chemistry, Materials Science and Catalysis,
University of Twente, P.O. Box 217, 7500 AE Enschede, The Netherlands.

ABSTRACT

Coatings of Al_2O_3 were deposited on Incoloy 800H and AISI 304 by means of Metal Organic Chemical Vapour Deposition (MOCVD) from aluminium-tri-isopropoxide (ATI) at reduced pressures. It is possible to grow Al_2O_3 with a reasonable growth rate, the quality of the coating depending on the reactant concentration and the deposition temperature. At high deposition temperatures the gas phase reaction becomes very important and determines the homogeneity and quality of the coating. Reducing the temperature to 250 °C results in good coatings. Coating with Al_2O_3 under the circumstances used does not increase the oxidation resistance of AISI 304, because thermomechanical and internal stresses cause degradation of the coating. These internal stresses seem to decrease with increasing deposition temperature, which can be explained by an increasing mobility of adsorbed species. For Incoloy 800H the oxidation resistance is much better because the coating does not crack. The weight gain is very small, and a significant attack only occurs at the edges of the substrate. Small traces of chromium oxide are observed at the grain boundaries of the substrate; at these places the coating is somewhat disrupted, and probably the diffusion through the coating is much faster at these places. The sulphidation resistance is the same as that of coatings deposited by atmospheric experiments. Treatment of the coated samples in air at 850 °C results in a 50 to 100 times higher sulphidation resistance, which is due to chromium oxide growing in the cracks and imperfect parts of the coating at the grain boundaries of the substrate.

INTRODUCTION

Stainless steels with a reasonable resistance to oxidizing environments are well known, but steels with an acceptable resistance to corrosion in sulphidizing environments at high temperatures are scarcely available. There is a large demand for materials which can be used in these atmospheres because of the increasing tendency to use fossil fuels containing sulphur, especially coal.

There are various ways to find a solution for this problem. Some ceramic materials, for instance, exhibit a good resistance to oxidation and sulphidation, but cannot be used due to fabrication requirements and/or their mechanical properties.

A combination of good corrosion properties of ceramics and the mechanical strength of metals might, however, lead to a solution.

Two methods to achieve such a combination are :
1. Chemical modification of the "natural" oxide of the alloy to be protected;
2. The application of a "foreign" type of oxide on the clean or oxidized metal.

Modification of the "natural" oxide may be realized by ion implantation of yttrium and/or cerium [1,2] or by superficially applying of these species by the sol-gel method [3] and results in a reasonably good protection against sulphidation. The direct application of an oxide for protective purposes was carried out by Bennett [4], who applied the Chemical Vapour Deposition technique (CVD) for the coating of several stainless steels with SiO_2. After treatment in argon this coating provides a good protection to sulphidation up to 900 °C. Above this temperature it cracks because of recrystallization of the SiO_2 layer.

Recently, two processes have been developed to produce thin Al_2O_3 films directly, and both are used in the electronic component industries. In the first process, $AlCl_3$ and water or CO_2/H_2 are used to form Al_2O_3 at 1000 to 1200 °C and at a pressure of 0.5 to 5 torr [5,6]. The second process has been described by Aboaf [7], who used Aluminium-Tri-Isopropoxide (ATI), to form a dense Al_2O_3 film at 420 °C at atmospheric pressure.

The process by Aboaf was used to form thin layers on stainless steel, but not for the protection against corrosion at high temperatures. Aluminium oxide forming alloys are nevertheless well known to provide a good protection against many types of corrosion. Morssinkhof et al. [8] used this process to apply thin alumina layers on stainless steel for protection against high temperature corrosion. The results were promising, but it was very difficult to obtain homogeneous coatings, because a good deposition regime was difficult to reach. In order to avoid these problems the system pressure was reduced from 1 bar to 3 torr in order to avoid gas diffusion problems.
The results are presented in this paper.

THEORETICAL CONSIDERATIONS

For a good understanding of the influence of the process parameters on the final quality of a coating, it is necessary to develop a model. Very complicated models for CVD systems have been proposed [9], but the practical usefulness of these models is limited because they require a detailed information of the process kinetics and this is rarely available.

A simple model that can be used for a basic understanding of a CVD process was set up by Bird [10], and is known as a 'film model'. This model results in two extreme situations for the growth rate determining step:

$k_r/k_g >> 1$: In this situation, the growth rate is determined by the gas phase mass transfer coefficient, k_g, and this situation is called diffusion limited growth.

$k_r/k_g << 1$: This situation is the opposite and refers to reaction rate limited growth. (k_r = reaction rate constant)

The ratio k_r/k_g is called the Sherwood number (Sh) (Van der Brekel [11] refers to it as CVD-number) and is an important factor because it influences the quality of the coating. If a scratch is present on the surface to be coated, the coating starts to grow on the whole surface, but after a certain time the entrance of the scratch becomes smaller if Sh >> 1. This is because the reaction is very fast: the reactive compound is deposited at the entrance, and will finally close the scratch, without filling the pore. This means that an inferior, porous coating is produced on damaged places on the surface.

The Sherwood number may also influence the homogeneity of the coating for Sh >> 1, because this leads to a concentration gradient of the reactive compound along the substrate.

Thus, in order to obtain good corrosion properties, the deposition should be controlled by the reaction rate. However, at 1 bar, it is difficult to deposit under the circumstances Morssinkhof [8] used. Because k_g is proportional to the square root of the reciprocal pressure, reduction of the pressure to 3 torr will lead to an increase of the mass transfer coefficient by a factor 15. No other process parameter is available for such a large shift in the value of k_g.

EXPERIMENTAL

The deposition of Al_2O_3

The Al_2O_3 films were produced by decomposing ATI (Merck art. 801079, purity > 98%, melting point 134-137 °C). This was melted in a bubbler heated by a silicon oil bath and saturated a dry nitrogen gas flow. The gas flow was diluted by nitrogen in order to obtain the desired gas phase concentration. The resulting mixture was led into a 3-zone horizontal furnace. In this furnace, 9 substrate specimens were attached to a 30 cm long glass rod and three thermocouples where placed inside the reactor in order to regulate the temperature. The flows were controlled by electronic mass flow controllers, and the pressure was controlled by capacitive pressure sensors.

The standard conditions were:

Substrate temperature	350 °C
Saturation temperature	134 °C
Pressure	3.5 torr
Carrier gas flow	10 ml/min
Diluent gas flow	990 ml/min
Position in furnace	20 cm from entrance

Fig 1 shows a scheme of the equipment used.

The coatings were investigated by means of optical microscopy and scanning electron microscopy and their thickness was determined by weighing.

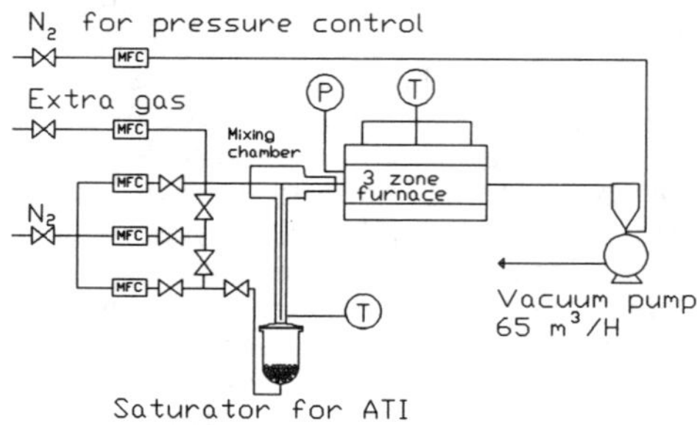

FIGURE 1 Experimental set up

Materials

AISI 304 and Incoloy 800H were used as substrates. Incoloy 800H was annealed for 1 h at 1323 K, water quenched, annealed for 1 h at 1223 K and water quenched again. This treatment prevents sensitization by the formation of titanium carbide.

Pieces (1 mm thick, 12 mm diameter) were cut from a rod and the surface finish was performed by grinding with 220, 320, 500, 800, 1000 and 4000 grit carborundum paper resp., and by finally polishing with 0.05 μm Al_2O_3 powder. The AISI 304 specimens were cut from an electropolished metal sheet. Both types of specimens were ultrasonically cleaned with hexane and ethanol prior to coating.

Table 1
Composition of materials

	Fe	Ni	Cr	C
AISI 304	Bal.	9.0	19.2	<0.08
Incoloy 800H	46.1	31.9	20.6	<0.04

Oxidation and sulphidation experiments

Some oxidation tests were carried out in an open-to-air furnace at 850 °C. The furnace was heated to 850 °C at a rate of 2 °C/min, kept at this temperature for 24 h and cooled with 0.5 °C/min to prevent spalling. The specimens were finally weighed. Continuous oxidation tests were carried out in a Setaram electrical thermobalance in air for 96 h.

Sulphidation experiments were carried out in a closed system. This was first evacuated and flushed with argon, followed by flushing with 1% H_2S, 19 % H_2 and 80 % Ar. The system was then closed and heated to 600 °C. The resulting P_{O2} was 10^{-32} bar and P_{S2} was 10^{-9} bar.

RESULTS AND DISCUSSION

Deposition experiments

The first experiments, starting with the conditions of the atmospheric experiments, did not result in good coatings. Changing the reactor configuration to reduce the reactor volume before the deposition zone, and introducing a mixing chamber for the diluent and carrier gas, led to good results. The circumstances required for these results are in good agreement with the circumstances used by Saraie et.al [12], although they used a cold wall reactor. It appeared that the position in the furnace is very important because the growth rate decreases along the reactor, due to a gas phase reaction. The latter results in a lower effective concentration at the surface of the substrates, and thus in a decreasing growth rate. The interference patterns on the substrates show that the deposition rate of Al_2O_3 on the first specimens was determined by diffusion limited mass transfer because it clearly indicated effects of the direction of the gas flow along the substrate. The last substrates showed one good centred interference ring, a result of reaction limited mass transfer.

This change of reaction regime along the furnace can be explained by a decreasing reaction rate at the surface due to an increasing concentration of waste products and a decreasing reactant concentration, as can be explained by mechanisms describing combined adsorption of reactant and waste products.

In fig 3 the results of a changing substrate temperature are shown, at a pressure of 3 torr. The gas phase reaction becomes less important with lower temperatures, resulting in a position independent growth rate at 250 °C. At these low temperatures no effect of diffusion limitation is observed, which is also found by Saraie [12]. A significant problem of the deposition of Al_2O_3 is the layer thickness. Coatings thicker than 1 micron show complete degradation due to cracks, and spalling of the complete coating, in agreement with Saraies observations [12]. Our oxidation experiments result in some more information regarding the degradation of the coating.

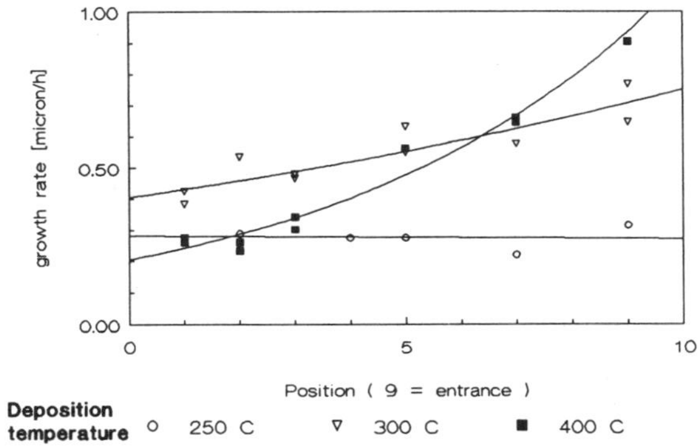

FIGURE 2 Growth rate as a function of the position in the furnace for various deposition temperatures.

CORROSION PROPERTIES

Substrate samples were coated with Al_2O_3 films of different thickness by changing the position in the support. Standard circumstances were used, only the deposition temperature was changed.

Both Incoloy 800H and AISI 304 specimens were tested by oxidation at 850 °C. For sulphidation only Incoloy samples were used.

Oxidation

Examination of the oxidized AISI 304 samples by optical microscopy and scanning electron microscopy (SEM) revealed that oxidation causes a degradation of the coating. This is caused by (thermo)mechanical stresses. Fig 3 shows a delaminated coating with curved free laying film particles. This is only possible when large internal stresses are present in the coating. These stresses seem to become larger at lower deposition temperatures. This can be explained by as follows:

-a decreasing deposition temperature results in an increasing temperature difference between the oxidation and the deposition temperature, and thus in larger stresses under the chosen oxidation circumstances;

-a decreasing deposition temperature results in a decreasing mobility of the adsorbed specimens on the surface and, as a result, these particles cannot move to the optimum position on the surface.

Because of this degradation, it is difficult to draw conclusions from the observed weight changes of the specimens, but the weight gain of the uncoated samples was very small. In fact the weight change during the oxidation is mainly due to spalling of the coating. In fig 4 these weight changes are shown as a function of the deposition temperature and the layer thickness. From this figure it can be concluded that the deposition temperature has a significant influence on the mechanical behaviour of the coating but this observation can be explained by both proposed mechanisms: a smaller temperature difference between the deposition and the oxidation temperature causes less thermomechanical stress, and a higher deposition temperature can result in a higher mobility of the adsorbed specimens. From an equation developed by Evans [13], relating the maximum layer thickness as a function of the properties of the coating and the substrate materials and the temperature difference, it is possible to

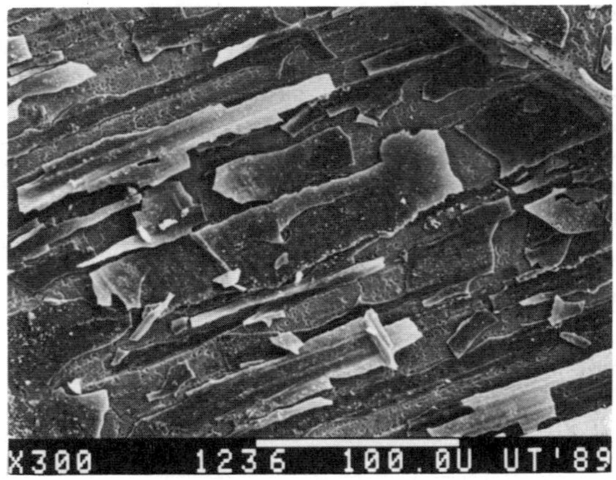

FIGURE 3 Coated sample after oxidation in air at 850 °C, showing a delaminated coating.

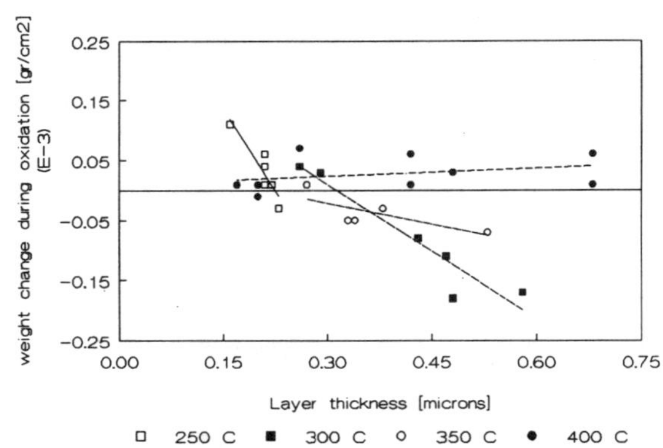

FIGURE 4 Weight change of coated specimen by oxidation at 850 °C, for specimen with different deposition temperatures.

estimate the importance of the thermomechanical stresses. According to this equation there is a maximum thickness, above which a coating cracks at irregularities. It is difficult to apply this equation to the coatings studied here because no data are available for the amorphous alumina produced here [8] and also the fracture toughness of the interface is unknown. It is allowed to estimate the elastic properties to be 60 % of that of crystalline material [14]. From the properties of polycrystalline alumina the maximum layer thickness as a function of the temperature is shown in fig 6. From this it follows that a coating with a thickness of less than 10 micron is not expected to crack at irregularities due to thermal stresses. As the thickness of the coatings produced in this investigation is below 1 micron this means either that the data used for the calculation deviate widely from the real ones or that there are other sources of stresses. Combined with the fact that rolled up sheets are formed by the cracking of the layer, we conclude that internal stresses must play an important role in the degradation of the coating.

Oxidation of Incoloy 800-Al_2O_3 combinations does not show such a serious degradation, although there are some similarities. With this material, increasing stress with decreasing deposition temperature can also be observed. However, the effect is not so dramatic; only at 250 °C some cracks can be observed. At higher temperatures only at the edges and at irregularities on the substrate cracks are found.

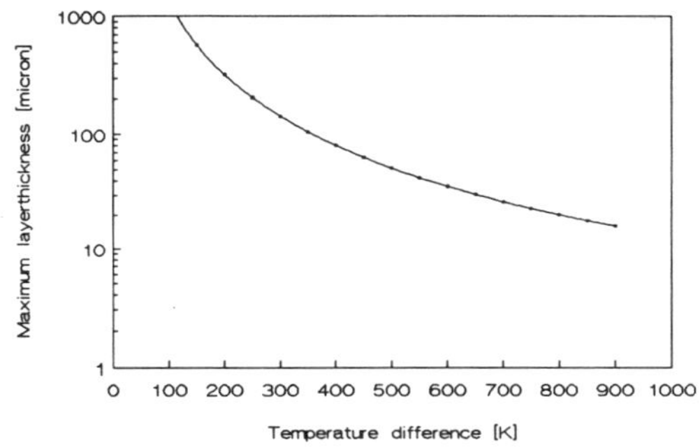

FIGURE 5 Maximum layer thickness as a function of temperature difference. (Fracture toughness : 3 10^6 $MN/M^{1.5}$, Elastic modulus = 250 GN/M^2, difference in expansion coefficient = 8.2 10^{-6} K^{-1}) [14]

A phenomenon, caused by oxidation, is the oxidation of the substrate at the grain boundaries of the substrate, resulting in black lines, but the specimens with only this phenomenon showed only very small weight gains, and by scanning electron microscopy only a little extra roughness could be observed at these places. An EDX scan over such a line does not show a significant difference between the Fe and Ni content of the dark and the light area, whereas only a very small decrease of Al and increase of Cr content can be observed. This may be indicative for some oxidation through the coating, probably because at these grain boundaries the morphology of the coating is different compared to that of the inner part of the crystallites. The oxidation resistance of these 'weak' places depends on the thickness of the layer; with decreasing thickness of the coating the colour at these places changes from 'no difference with the bulk' via lighter coloured, and grey lines to the already mentioned black lines, indicating an increasing amount of oxide under the coating.

Sulphidation

Prior to sulphidation all specimens were oxidized in air for 16 h at 850 °C. Without this treatment the previously mentioned cracks in the coating cause a relatively large weight gain, due to heavy localized attack, even though the overall sulphidation resistance is still improved by a factor 5 to 10 with respect to uncoated samples.

Since the oxidation experiments indicate that the cracks are filled with Cr_2O_3 during the oxidation the above mentioned pretreatment was applied, leading to better results. It follows from table 2 that this treatment increases the sulphidation resistance significantly.

An EDX scan over a crack of a specimen treated this way and sulphidized for 200 h shows a very low sulphur content near a crack and no sulphur at all on the main parts of the coating. The resulting weight gain is in fact mainly caused by inhomogeneities at the edges and the support hole.

CONCLUSIONS

It is possible to grow thin, uniform Al_2O_3 films on stainless steel samples by MOCVD at low pressures. The deposition takes place in the reaction limited regime at low temperatures. It seems that adsorption/desorption of the reactant and the waste gases play an important role. The reaction mechanism seems to be very important and is an object for investigations in the near future.

An Al_2O_3 coating on AISI 304 degrades completely during oxidation due to mechanical stress during oxidation. Incoloy 800H does not show this extreme behaviour. The oxidation and sulphidation behaviour are improved, and the sulphidation resistance increases significantly by a prior treatment in air at 850 °C.

Table 2
Weight gains, due to 24 h sulphidation in 1% H2S/ 19% H2/ 80% Ar at 600 °C of 0.4 μ Al2O3 on Incoloy 800H.

16 h 850°C[a]	*				
MOCVD	*	*	*		
LP MOCVD					*
16 h 850°C[b]		*		*	*
Results	+	+	++	---	++

*= Treatment applied
a= Treatment 16 h in air, before MOCVD
b= Treatment 16 h in air, after MOCVD

Weight gain :
-- = >3.00 mg/cm²   + = <0.1 mg/cm²
- = < 0.5 mg/cm²   ++ =< 0.025 mg/cm²

ACKNOWLEDGEMENTS

This research was partly supported by the Innovative Research Program on Technical Ceramics (IOP-TK) with financial aid of the Dutch Ministry of Economic Affairs.

REFERENCES

[1] Polman, E.A., Fransen, T., and Gellings, P.J., Mat. Sci. Eng., 1987, **88** 157

[2] Bennett, M.J., Dearnaly, G., Houlton, M.R., Hawes, R.W.M., Goode, P.D., and Wilkins, M.A., Corros. Sci., 1980, **20**, 73

[3] Fransen, ,T., Gellings, P.J., Fuggle, J.C., Laan, G. van der, Esteva, J.-M., Karnatak, R.C., Appl. Surf. Sci., 1985, **20**, 257

[4] Bennett, M.J., J.Vac.Sci.Technol. B, 1984, **2**, 800

[5] Wong, P., Robbinson, M., J.Am.Cer.Soc., 1970, **53**, 617

[6] Messier, D.R., Wong, P., J.Electrochem.Soc., 1971, **118**, 772.

[7] Aboaf, J.A., J.Electrochem.Soc., 1967, **114**, 948

[8] Morssinkhof, R.W.J., Fransen, T., Heusinkveld, M.M.D., Gellings, P,J, to be published in Mat. Sci. Eng.

[9] Jensen, K.F., Graves, D.B., J.Electrochem.Soc., 1983, **130**, 1950

[10] Bird, R.B., Steward, W.E., Lightfoot, E.N., Transport Phenomena, J.Wiley and Sons, New York, 1960 p. 658.

[11] Brekel, C.H.J. van der, J.Cryst.Growth., 1978, **43**, 488

[12] Saraie, J., Kwon, J., Yodagawa, Y., J. Electrochem. Soc, 1985, **132**, 890

[13] Evans, A.G., Crumley, G.B., Demaray, R.E., Oxid. Metals, 1983, **20**, 196

[14] Hardwick, D.A., Thin Solid Films, 1987, **154**, 109

INFLUENCE OF HEAT TREATMENTS UNDER OXIDIZING ATMOSPHERES ON THE MECHANICAL PROPERTIES OF RBSN MATERIALS

P. BELAIR, J. DESMAISON
Laboratoire de Céramiques Nouvelles, CNRS U.A. 320
Université de Limoges - 87060 LIMOGES Cédex - FRANCE

Y. BIGAY
Céramiques Techniques Desmarquest - 781890 TRAPPES - FRANCE

ABSTRACT

Heat treatments under oxidizing atmospheres of a slip-cast RBSN were investigated. A preoxidation at 900°C results in an increase of 45% of the room temperature strength and in the desappearance of the decrease of σ_R traditionally observed around 800°C.

INTRODUCTION

Reaction-bonded silicon nitride (RBSN) offers an almost near-net shape fabrication capability interesting for mass production at low cost. However, because of the residual porosity the strength of this material is limited and severe oxidation occurs, particularly at intermediate temperatures (1-3). The present paper summarizes results obtained on the effect of oxidation on the flexural strength of a slip-cast RBSN.

MATERIALS AND METHODS

The RBSN material was processed by slip-casting of a silicon powder whose mean particle size was 40 µm and the main impurities in Wt% were Al (0.54), Ti (0.09) Fe (0.08) and Ca (0.07). Its main characteristics are given in Table 1. The nitriding process was conducted during 70 h, between 1120 and 1490°C, under a nitrogen pressure of 50 mbars.

The oxidation kinetics were determined under pure flowing oxygen (5/l/h) using cubes (4x4x4 mm^3) and a symmetrical continuous recording thermobalance (4,5). All faces of flexural

TABLE 1
Properties of the RBSN specimens

Crystal structure	ß-phase
Density (g cm^{-3})	2.6
Total porosity (vol. %)	17
Open porosity (vol. %)	16.2
Average pore radius (µm)	0.25
Specific area (m^2/g^{-1})	0.47
Flexural strength (RT) ($MN.m^{-2}$)	145 ± 10
Fracture toughness ($MN.m^{-3/2}$)	2.28 ± 0.15

test specimens (4x4x25 mm^3) were polished down to 1200 grit SiC paper. The edges of faces under tension were chamfered (lengthwise) to prevent notch effects. Specimens were tested in 3-point bending with a span of 19 mm, using a Wolpert-TZZ machine at a crosshead of 0.2 mm/min. The high temperature bend tests were conducted in air with alumina knife edges.

RESULTS

The oxidation kinetics of Figure 1 show the classical behaviour for porous materials. The oxidation rate indeed, appears to decrease with raising temperatures above 1150°C.

The influence of oxidation on room-temperature strength and the variation in flexural strength as a function of temperature are illustrated in Figure 2. The two corresponding curves respectively show a symmetric increase and decrease in strength between 800-1100°C. In order to obtain a better understanding of the observed room-temperature strengthening, the influence of oxidizing heat treatments conducted at 900°C was studied. The flexural strength is almost independent on the duration (5-150h) of the treatment. After such a treatment, specimens were oxidized during 24 h respectively at 1300, 1400 and 1500°C. At 1500°C, a 40% increase in strength is observed (Fig.3) by comparison to untreated specimens. Concerning the decrease of flexure strength at elevated temperatures (800-1100°C), we have tested different preoxidation heat treatments (Table 2).

Independently of the treatment, the flexural stress-rupture results observed at 950°C are very similar. The value of is approximatively 65% higher than the corresponding one for untreated specimens. By the way the results concerning the treatments C and D at 900°C indicate that no degra-dation of the high temperature flexure strength is observed.

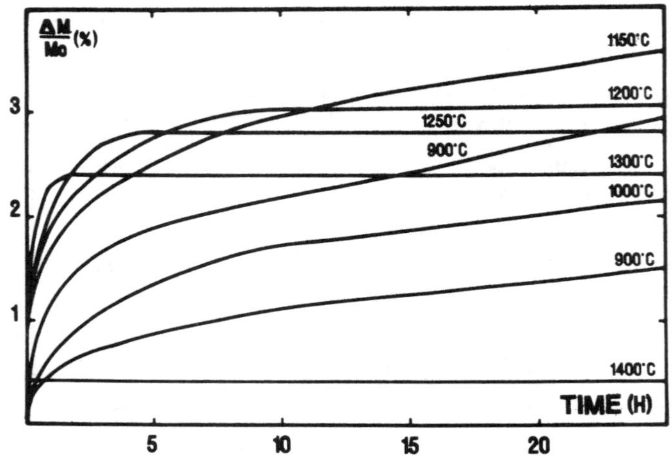

Figure 1. Oxidation kinetics.

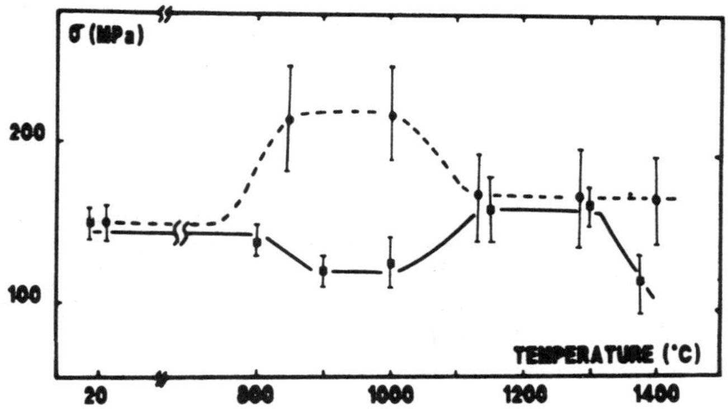

Figure 2. Comparison of the variation of the room temperature (---) strength as a fonction of oxidation temperature and of the high temperature (——) flexural strength.

TABLE 2
Evolution of the flexural strength as a function of the duration and temperature of the preoxidation

	Samples / Temperature of rupture	NON TREATED	A T=1300°C t=60 min	B T=1500°C t=60 min	C T=900°C t=48 h	D T=900°C t=5 h
σ_R (MPa)	Ambient	145 ± 10	175 ± 20	180 ± 25	210 ± 20	210 ± 20
	950°C	120 ± 9	227 ± 15	199 ± 10	200 ± 10	190 ± 15

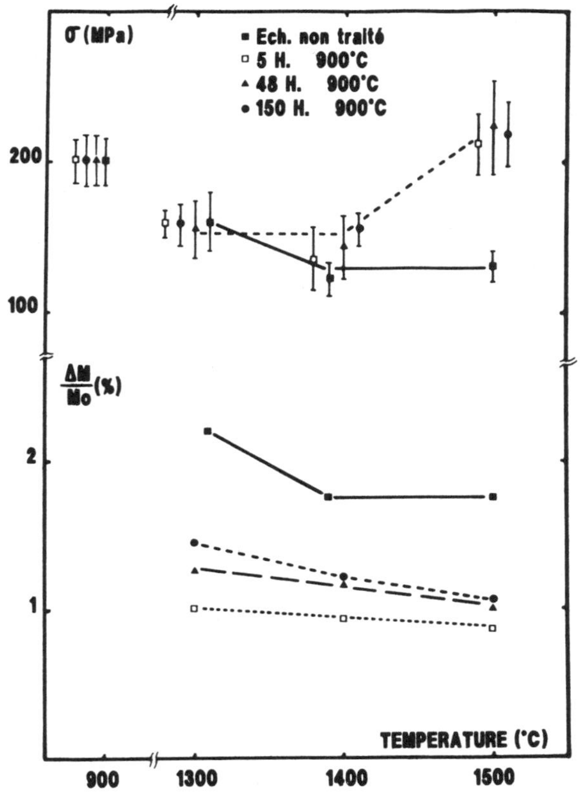

Figure 3. Variation of the room temperature flexural strength as a function of the oxidation temperature.

DISCUSSION

The room temperature three-point bend strength found here (145 MPa), which is lower than the usual values reported for products having similar densities, suggest the presence of large pores (1,4). Indeed, using the value of σ_R and K_{1C} of Table 1 a value of the critical defect $a_c \sim 145$ μm can be calculated.

The influence of oxidation on room temperature strength, which is characterized by an increase in strength between 800 and 1000°C (Fig. 2), may be explained by the rounding off of internal flaws or pores and crack-healing effects (1,4). Such an effect is preserved at higher temperature as a preoxidation treatment at 900°C leads to significative strength improvement at 1400°C and particularly at 1500°C (Fig. 3).

The drop in the high temperature strength around 900°C (Fig. 2), already reported by other authors, has not yet been fully clarified (1,4,5). The results of Table 2 suggest that the phenomenon is not directly linked to the internal oxidation. Indeed, a preoxidation at 900°C, during 48 h, where the internal oxidation predominates, leads to the same strengthening at 950°C (~45%) than a treatment at 1300 and 1500°C, where the oxidation is essentially external. One of the possible explanation (5) is to invoke a coalescence of pores facilitated by the presence of impurities at the grain boundaries. By the way the mechanical properties at higher temperature (1300°C) are not affected by such a preoxidation treatment. Therefore, the observed behaviour is not function of the quantity of oxide incorporated within the RBSN body.

CONCLUSIONS

The present results show that it is possible to increase significantly (45%) the room temperature flexural strength of a slip-cast RBSN material by a preoxidation treatment at 900°C. In addition, such a treatment prevents the decrease of the high temperature strength generally observed around 800°C and leads to a substantial strengthening above 1400°C, in particular at 1500°C (65%).

REFERENCES

1. ZIEGLER, G., HEINRICH, J. and WÖTTING, G., Relationships between processing, microstructure and properties of dense and reaction-bonded silicon nitride, J. Mater. Sci., 1987, 22, 3041-3086.
2. DESMAISON, J., ROELS, N. and BELAIR, P., High temperature oxidation-protection CVD coatings for structural ceramics : oxidation behaviour of CVD-coated reaction-bonded silicon nitride, Mater. Sci. Eng., 1989 (in press).
3. PORZ, F. and THÜMMLER, F., Oxidation mechanism of porous silicon nitride, J. Mater. Sci., 1984, 19, 1283-1295.
4. DAVIDGE, R.W., EVANS, A.G., GILLING, D. and WILYMAN, P.R., Oxidation of reaction-sintered silicon nitride and effects on strength, Special Ceramics, 1972, 5, 329-343.
5. ORANGE, G., EPICIER, T. and FANTOZZI, G., Comportement mécanique à haute température du nitrure de silicium fritté réaction ; influence de l'oxydation, L'industrie Céramique, 1982, 756, 829-835.

CHROMIUMCARBIDE: AN OXIDATION AND WEAR RESISTANT CVD COATING

G.J. van der Kooi; Philips-PMF, Eindhoven, The Netherlands,
L.R. Wolff, W.P.M. de Wilt; Centre for Technical Ceramics,
Eindhoven University of Technology, The Netherlands.

ABSTRACT

Hard-wear resistent coatings prepared by CVD are sometimes limited in their applications because of poor corrosion and oxidation resistance. CVD applied chromium carbide is shown to have good oxidation resistance as compared to TiC and TiN CVD coatings. The oxidation rate of chromium carbide was found to be at least a factor 10 lower than the oxidation rate of TiN under the applied test conditions.

INTRODUCTION

Wear resistance can be improved by application of hard carbide and nitride coatings. Coating hardnesses range from HV1400 - 2100 depending on the type of substrate, and are comparable with the hardness of cemented carbide. Hard wear resistant coatings prepared by Chemical Vapour Deposition (CVD) are sometimes limited in their applications because of poor oxidation resistance.

OXIDATION TESTS

The oxidation resistance of various CVD coatings on a number of substrates was tested at temperatures ranging from 600 - 1000°C for periods ranging from 1 - 160 hours. The oxidation tests were carried out in a furnace with a gentle flow of compressed air in order to prevent rate - controlling effects due to a limited O_2 supply at the surface. It is well known that the oxidation process of TiC in air starts at approximately 500°C (4). The TiN coatings are more oxidation resistant than TiC. Oxidation of TiN_x begins at about 650°C (5). In some applications in the electronic industry protective TiN coatings were found to last for months at about 600 - 700°C. In the oxidation tests of the TiN layers we found that oxidation starts at ± 750°C, even when subjected to short term oxidation experiments (1 hour). Chromium carbide layers gave a superiour oxidation behaviour as compared to the CVD coatings mentioned above.

Two examples :

- The oxidation rate of tool steel 1.2379 + TiN was found to be a factor 10 higher than that of the same substrate when coated with Cr_xC_y, while the oxidation rate of TiN on cemented carbide K15 is even a factor 1000 higher as compared to K15 + Cr_xC_y.

In Fig. 2 the experimental results are presented graphically.

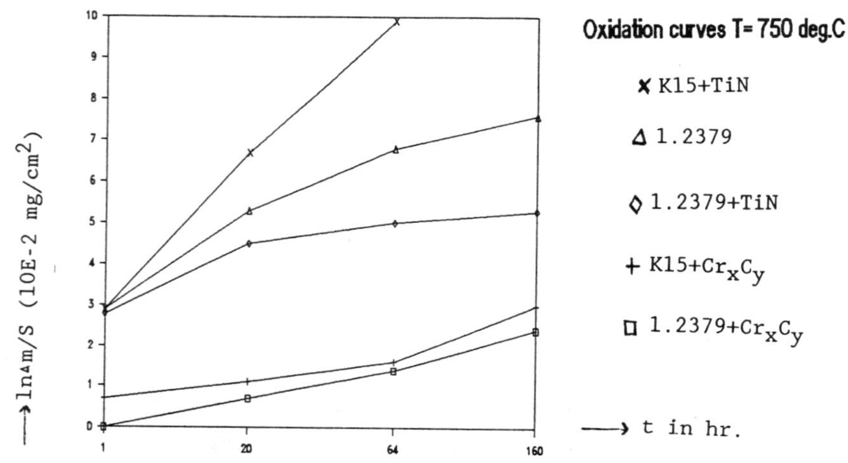

Figure 2. Oxidation of various substrate/coating combinations.

Especially for applications at high temperatures (> 600°C) the low oxidation resistance of these coatings can present a problem. This paper describes our current research in the field of oxidation resistance of various CVD coatings as well as a CVD process used for chromium carbide deposition.

CHROMIUM CARBIDE DEPOSITION

The industrial process known as chromizing has been well established for some time (1). Carbides formed during chromizing have been regarded as undesirable products because of their limited degree of plastic deformability. However, for applications e.g. in marine environments or at higher temperatures the high wear, corrosion and oxidation resistance of chromium carbide is recognised more and more (2). Although chromium carbide CVD found its origin in chromizing, it has been developed into a technique in its own right. It is normally carried out in a temperature range of 750 - 1000°C. The chromium source is gaseous $CrCl_2$. The in-situ production of $CrCl_2$ was accepted to be the most suitable method of controlling the chromium carbide deposition process (3). This is achieved by leading a mixture of gases (CH_4, Cl_2, H_2) over chromium powder. The following reactions are expected to occur at 900°C;

$$Cr\ (s) + Cl_2\ (g) \xrightarrow{T.H2} CrCl_2\ (g)$$
$$CrCl_2\ (g) + CH_4\ (g) \xrightarrow{T.H2} Cr_xC_y\ (s) + HCl\ (g)$$
$$CrCl_2\ (g) + [C]_{substrate} \xrightarrow{T.H2} Cr_xC_y\ (s) + HCl\ (g)$$

Figure 1 gives a sectional view of the equipment used for the chromium carbide deposition process. Because of the poor transport of the chromium chloride to the substrates it was found to be necessary to hang the objects to be coated in the reactor.

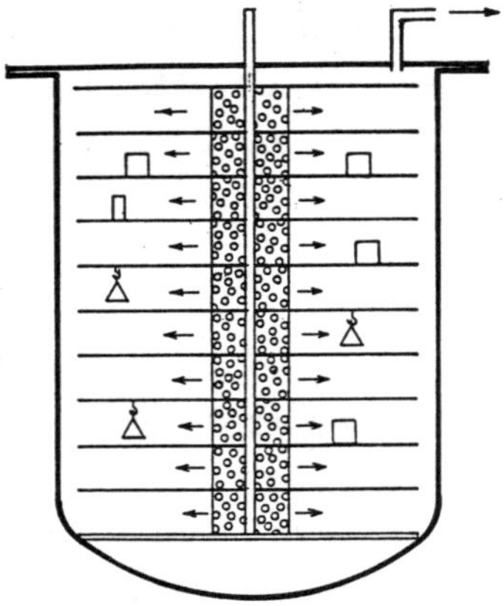

Figure 1
Schematic presentation of the chromium carbide CVD facility.

Chromium carbide can be deposited on carbon containing substrates as well as on carbon-poor or even carbon-free materials. The following table shows various substrates which were coated with chromium carbide.

TABLE 1
Various substrates coated with Cr_xC_y

Substrate	Thickness μm	Hardness $HK_{0,1}$	Composition
Toolsteel 1.2379	5.8	1700	Cr_7C_3
Toolsteel 1.3343	4.5	1400	Cr_7C_3
Cemented carbide K15	5.0	1700	$Cr_{23}C_6$
Nickel	3.0	-	$Cr_{23}C_6$
Cast iron	6.4	-	Cr_7C_3

The substrates containing large amounts of carbon, toolsteel and cast iron show the thickest layers. By X-Ray Diffraction (XRD) analysis they were shown to contain the carbon rich Cr_7C_3 phase. In the same way we found the chromium rich $Cr_{23}C_6$ phase on carbon-poor or carbon-free substrates such as cemented carbide and nickel. This suggests, that although carbon diffusing from the substrate is the main carbon source, the methane gas also plays an important role in the chromium carbide formation.

These results show that the chromium carbide layer can be a valuable CVD coating in applications where high temperature oxidation resistance is required in addition to wear resistance.

CONCLUSIONS

Chromium carbide can be deposited on a variety of substrates, e.g. tool steels, cemented carbides and various metals.
The supply of methane gas and the carbon amount in the substrates are both important in the chromium carbide CVD process.
The oxidation rate of chromium carbide was found to be at least a factor 10 lower than the oxidation rate of TiN under identical test conditions.

REFERENCES

1) Perry, A.J. and Horvath, E., J. Mater. Sci. **13** (1978) 1303-1310
2) Horvath, E. and Perry, A.J., Wear, **48** (1978) 217-224
3) Hänni, W., Hintermann, H.E., Thin solid films, **40** (1977) 107-114
4) Lavrenko, V.A., Glebov, L.A., Pomitkin, A.P., Chuprina, V.G., Protsenko, T.G., Oxidation of metals, **9**, no. 2, (1975)
5) Desmaison, J., LeFort, P., Billy, M., Oxidation of metals, **13**, no. 13, (1979)

COILCOAT ENAMELLING : PRODUCTION PROCESS AND NEW APPLICATIONS

L. GYPEN
Alliance Enamelsteel Corp. , B 3600 Genk, Belgium

First European Ceramic Society Conference, 1989, Maastricht, Netherlands
Keywords : Coilcoat, Enamel, Architectural, Whiteboards, Chalkboards, Radiation

1. INTRODUCTION

Coilcoat enamelling is a relatively new technique for the coating of thin steel band with porcelain (vitreous) enamel. The only coilcoat enamelling industry in Europe, i.e. Alliance Enamelsteel Corp., is situated in Genk, Belgium. This paper describes : (i) the production process used, (ii) the material produced i.e. "enamelsteel", (iii) some new test methods for characterizing the product and finally, (iv) industrial applications of enamelsteel.

2. COILCOAT ENAMELLING

Coilcoat enamelsteel is a thin and flexible composite material consisting of a thin steel core(0.3-0.4 mm), coated on each side with one or two thin layers of porcelain enamel.

The enamelling process itself (fig. 1) is a continuous process using and endless steel band . The ground coats are being applied by means of roller- coaters and the top coat by wet spraying. Rollercoater application of enamel slurry is unique in the enamelling industrie. Raw materials and coilcoat operation parameters are selected in such a way that compression stresses emerge in the hard vitreous enamel coatings and tensile stresses in the ductile steel, allowing the thin cladding material to be rolled up at the end of the production line on coils of min. 30 cm diameter, without any crack formation. It is in this semi-factured form that the majority of the coilcoat production is delivered. The resulting product, i.e. Alliance Enamelsteel, is a thin and flexible composite material combining the ductibility of steel with the hardness and durability of glass (vitreous enamel).

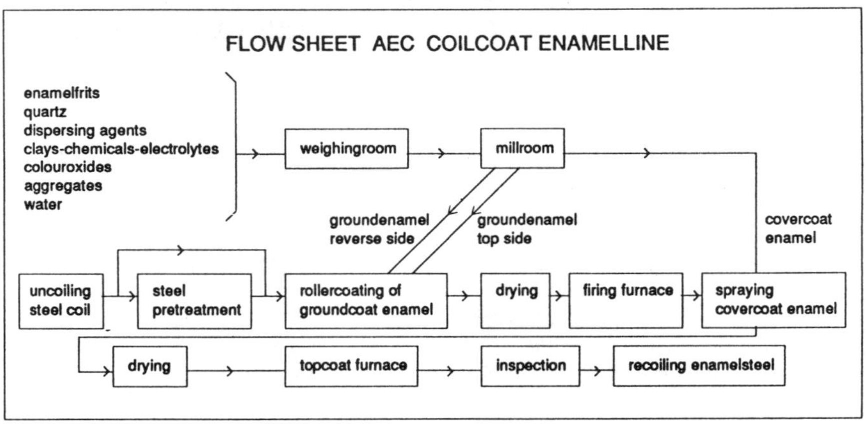

Fig. 1: Flow sheet AEC Coilcoat Enamelline.

At the end of the continuous enamelling line, or off line, possibly at the customer himself, the enamelsteel is cut to size and laminated as cladding material to appropriate substrates, such as cement fibreboard, wood cementplate, gypsum, massive fibreboard, light corrugated cardboard, honeycomb aluminium (underground trains), galvanized steel, polyurethane, polystyrene and all kinds of combinations as for insulating sandwich panels.

Coilcoat enamelsteel combines an exceptional amount of properties and advantages as summarized in table 1.

TABLE 1 : ADVANTAGES OF ENAMELSTEEL

- high scratch resistance	- colourfast	- non-toxic, not even in cases of fire
- high wear resistance	- frost resistant	- odour-free
- easy to clean	- stable to UV-light	- available in different colours
- graffiti resistant	- high weatherproofness	- magnetic
- hygienic	- non-flammable	- Alliance Enamelsteel : flexible, coilable

These outstanding properties make the material suitable for applications such as :
(i) architectural panels for indoor and outdoor applications (Ref 1) ,(ii) whiteboards (Ref 2) , (iii) chalkboards ,(iv) radiation heating elements.

3. ARCHITECTURAL APPLICATIONS (Fig. 2)

Fig. 2: Railway station Antwerpen using flat and curved architectural enamelsteel panels.

The major reasons for the ever-increasing use of coilcoat enamelsteel for architectural applications are its excellent weather, graffiti and scratch resistance. The weather resistance of Alliance coilcoat enamelsteel is discussed and illustrated in detail in ref. 1.

Comparative test data concerning the scratch resistance of several commercial architectural construction and cladding materials are given in table 2.

TABLE 2 : SCRATCH RESISTANCE TEST RESULTS OF DIFFERENT INDUSTRIAL ARCHITECTURAL CONSTRUCTION MATERIALS

	MOHS DIN-EN 101	AEC 41303/02 or DRAFT NEN 2713	ERICHSEN 318
Alliance Enamelsteel 6001 SM	5	10N	20N
Mineral coated fibrecement	4	3N	11N
Polyurethane coated fibrecement	1	3N	2N
Melamine coated panel of thermo-setting resins and cellulose fibres	4	5N	20N
Idem + acrylate transparent cover coat	2	1N	2N
Stove lacquered aluminium AA5050	2	1N	5N
Stove lacquered Al Mg 1 on polyethylene	1	1N	2N
PVF2 coilcoated galvanized steel	1	1N	3N
PVC coilcoated galvanized steel	2	2N	5N
Anodized aluminium on a fenol resin panel	2	1N	2N
Multiplex wood covered with a synthetic resin and a polyester top coat	2	3N	4N
Impregnated chip board with acry-late top coat	1		3N

Three different test methods were used i.e. :(i) the Mohs' method (DIN-EN 101), (ii) the Alliance method AEC 41303/02 (Ref 3) , (iii) the scratch resistance determination with the Erichsen 318 instrument.

AEC scratch resistance specification 41303/02 (Ref 3) is a test method recently developed to determine, on a quantitative basis, the scratch resistance of enamelsteel to sharp objects and high point loads (damage by ball- points, knives, car keys, etc...). On the contrary, Mohs' method rather determines the intrinsic hardness of the enamel (blunt objects, low point loads), without taking into account the enamel gas bubble structure is being penetrated when submitted to high point loads. The method makes use of a diamond with a 90 microns radius of curvature and a 90° cone angle and testloads of 1 to 10 Newton. The concentric scratches are coloured in with drymarkers. Details of the method are given in Ref 2. The method has recently been discussed in the Dutch normalisation committee for enamel and worked out in detail into draft NEN 2713 (May 1989).

The test data in table 2 reveal the outstanding scratch resistance of Alliance coilcoat enamel-steel in comparison to alternative construction materials. Recent applications of enamelsteel in public and private buildings, in railway and metro stations or vehicles are based on the very high scratch and graffiti resistance of this flexible and incombustable cladding material.

4. WHITEBOARDS (Fig. 3)

Enamelsteel, fired at 800°C, is covered with a thin and closed glaze layer which makes the material easily cleaned; In agreement with experimental test data showing a better erasability of enamelsteel for drymarkers, watermarkers and permanent markers in comparison with a variety of organic coated whiteboards (ref 2).

In addition, the very high scratch and wear resistance of enamelsteel, makes the material more durable (less functional degradation) as illustrated by the experimental test results in table 3, using durability test procedure AEC 41809 (Ref 2 and 4). The latter procedure simulates the wear effect due to prolonged use of whiteboards. Both the relative gloss change RG and the residual surface incoloration ΔE are negligable after this durability test ,in contrast to the test results on organic coated whiteboards of different types (table 3).

The excellent erasability and durability of enamelsteel (table 3) explains the increasing use of enamelsteel whiteboards all over the world.

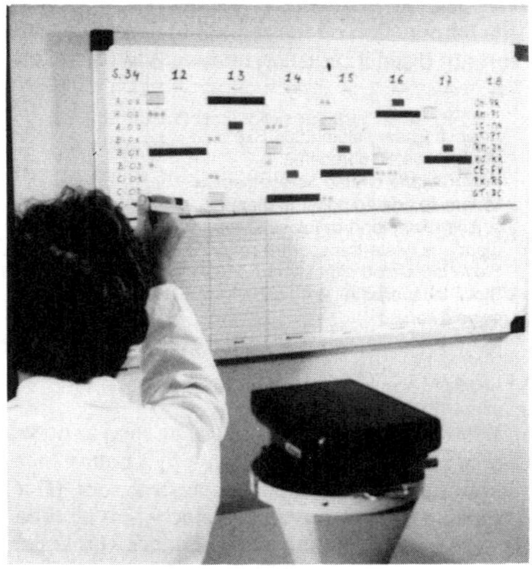

Fig. 3: Enamelsteel whiteboard (planning board).
Note : 1. Multicolor dry erasable writings with drymarkers,
2. Non-erasable enamel silkscreen line and letters,
3. Coloured magnetic strips,
4. Permanent magnets for fixing data-sheets on the whiteboard.

TABLE 3 : DURABILITY TEST RESULTS ACCORDING TO SPECIFICATION AEC 41809 FOR DIFFERENT WHITEBOARD MATERIALS

	Relative Gloss Change RG %	Residual surface Contamination ΔE
Alliance Enamelsteel 6001 WB	- 5 %	0.2
Polyester lacquered steel	- 35 %	8.9
Electron beam cured polyester lacquered steel	- 38 %	4.9
Dimethylsiloxane coating on galvanized steel	- 12 %	1.0
Melamine coated chip board	- 34 %	1.0
Melamine coated galvanized steel	- 36 %	3.4

5. CHALKBOARDS

Most coilcoat enamelsteel chalkboards in green and dark colours are becoming common now in schools and classrooms; despite the fact that users do not often know that their board is cladded with a thin sheet of wear resistant coilcoat enamelsteel.

6. RADIATION PANELS

The development of an electrically insulating ceramic backside coating resulted this year in the introduction on the market of coilcoat enamelsteel radiation heating elements as thin as 0,8 mm for : (i) distinct radiation heaters and (ii) radiation walls and ceilings.

Fig. 4: Coilcoat Enamelsteel radiation heating element (backside).

Fig. 4 shows an electrical circuit screen-printed on the backside of an enamelsteel radiation element. Connecting the element to the means leads to resistance heating of the element to +- 200°C for distinct radiation heaters or to +- 40°C for wall radiation. In the latter application the enamelsteel walls can be touched by hand, whilest in the first application a safety protection grill is built around the radiation element in order to prevent direct contact.

Advantages of this type of heating to conventional convection heating are : (i) a better temperature distribution from floor to roof, (ii) a lower required ambient temperature due to the direct radiation effect,(iii) a very limited warm-up time and (iv) a lower electricity and heat consumption as a consequence of the three effects just mentioned.

Applications : sport halls, public areas and buildings, dustfree areas, offices, private houses, stock-breeding, industrial applications.

7. CONCLUSION

Coilcoat enamelsteel is a unique material which combines the durability of steel with the hardness, cleanability, scratch resistance and corrosion resistance of glass. The use of this material is increasing all over the world in each of the following areas : (i) architectural pannels for both interior and exterior applications, (ii) whiteboards,(iii) chalkboards and (iv) very recently : radiation elements for electrical radiation heaters, walls and ceilings.

REFERENCES

1. L. GYPEN, "Coilcoat Emailstaal voor architectuurtoepassingen" (Coilcoat Enamelsteel for architectural applications), Klei/Glas/Keramiek, 1989, Nr 2, p.37-39.

2. L. GYPEN, "Coilcoat Emaillierungen für Weisstafel Anwendungen" (Coilcoat enamelling for whiteboard applications), lecture given at the VDEFA 1989 Conf., Bad Windsheim (FRG), to be published in : Mitteilungen VDEFA & DEZ.

3. AEC Specification 41303/02 : " Scratch resistance of Enamelsteel ", Alliance Enamelsteel Corp., Genk, Belgium, 1987.

4. AEC Specification 41809 : "Durability test whiteboards", Alliance Enamelsteel Corp., Genk, Belgium, 1986.

ELABORATION AND CHARACTERIZATION OF ZIRCONIA BASED THERMAL BARRIERS

A. MOUGHIL, G. FANTOZZI, A. VINCENT
Groupe d'Etudes de Métallurgie Physique et Physique des Matériaux
INSA - Bat. 502 - 69621 VILLEURBANNE(FRANCE)
Q. SAIF, D. TREHEUX
Laboratoire Matériaux-Mécanique Physique
URA CNRS 447 - Ecole Centrale de Lyon(FRANCE)

ABSTRACT

Zirconia based thermal barrier coatings are optimized with regard to their thermal fatigue behaviour, which is followed by ultrasonic imaging of the ceramic-metal interface. Two parameters are investigated : the nature of the bond coat layer and the plasma spraying procedure. The best thermal fatigue lifetime is obtained with bond layers produced by Al-20% Y slurry-coating and by using a low speed spraying procedure which leads to optimal microcracks and porosity in the coating.

INTRODUCTION

The thermal fatigue bahaviour of plasma-sprayed zirconia based coatings is of fundamental importance with a view to their development as thermal barriers to protect metallic pieces of heat engines. This behaviour is strongly influenced by various parameters such as the plasma spraying conditions, the stabilizing oxide content, and the nature of the bond coat which is placed between metal and ceramic to protect the substrate against oxidation and corrosion and to improve the ceramic-metal bonding.

The aim of this paper is to characterize the adhesion of the coating to the substrate with regard on one hand to the plasma spraying conditions and on the other hand to the nature of the bond coat which is placed between metal and ceramic.

EXPERIMENTAL CONDITIONS

Materials

The experiments were carried out on steel (0.38%C) samples, disc shaped, 25mm in diameter and 4mm in thickness. The bond coat layer was produced either by a thermochemical treatment (slurry coating [1]) aluminium based or, as reference, by a METCO 450 NS plasma sprayed coating (Ni-4.5%Al).

The ceramic coating was a METCO 201 NS (ZrO2-5%CaO) sprayed with a SNMI 4PG plasma gun. Two spraying procedures were investigated to produce coatings O.3 mm in thickness : in the procedure hereafter labelled **a**, the sample remained immobile and the coating was applied in one pass at a scanning speed of about 0.3 m/s. In the procedure **b**, the sample was placed on a rotating disc. This results in a higher scanning speed (7 m/s) and a number of passes of order of 2000 to reach the required thickness (0.3mm). Some characteristics of the coatings **a** and **b** were found to differ significantly : specially, micrographic examination revealed microcracks and a higher porosity in the zirconia sprayed by procedure **a**. This observation was corroborated by the microhardness measurements which showed that the procedure **a** leads to a lower hardness (700 Hv 0.2) than the procedure **b** (850 Hv 0.2). On the contrary, X-ray diffraction patterns were observed to be identical in both types of coatings.

Testing methods

The characterization of the adhesion of the various ceramic bond pairs to the substrate was ensured both by classical tensile tests and by thermal shock fatigue tests. In this latter case the bonding to the metallic substrate was followed by ultrasonic testing.
The tensile bond strengh tests are based on the glue method. All these tests were carred out on the as sprayed coatings.
The thermal fatigue shocks were produced between room temperature and 650C by exposing the coating side of the sample alternatively to the heat of a plane furnace and to a R.T. compressed air-flux. The heating and coating times were respectively 18mn and 4mn.
The experimental arrangement that was used to image the bonding damage has been described in details elsewhere [2]. The method is based on the C-scan pulse echo technique. The ceramic bond interface was examined from the substrate side by a wide band ultrasonic impulse (central frequency 10 MHz) focussed at the interface. In order to protect the coating against the water ingress during the examination, the coating side of the sample was maintained in an air-pocket.

EFFECT OF THE BOND LAYER

The effect of the bond layer on the thermal fatigue behaviour of the coating was investigated for the spraying procedure **b**. Three powders were used to produce the bond coat layer by thermochemical slurry-coating : pure Al, Al-10%Y, and Al-20%Y.
The results of the ultrasonic imaging after 126 thermal cycles are given in Fig. 1 for these three bond layers, in comparison with that of a plasma sprayed one (Ni-4.5%Al). It can be seen that the bonding damage, which appears as hills (high amplitude echoes) in the 3D representation, occurred very rapidly in the case of this Ni-Al bond coat. On the contrary, an improved behaviour was observed in the case of the thermochemical bond coat, specially when 20% of Yttrium was added to the Aluminium powder since no damage was detected in this case.
Furthermore, metallographic cross sections of the samples show that the origin of the damage is quite different with a plasma sprayed bond coat and a thermochemical slurry coating one : this is best illustrated in Fig. 2, where it can be seen that a debonding occurred at the bond substrate interface in the former case (Fig. 2a), whereas a crack was developed along the ceramic-bond coat interface in

the latter case (Fig. 2b). The former debonding (Fig. 2a) was presumably caused by an interfacial oxidation, which could be responsible for this poor behaviour.
Finally the tensile strengh and the thermal shock damage, which is expressed in terms of the percentage of damaged interface appearing in ultrasonic images, are reported in Fig. 3. The values given in this diagram are averaged over 4 samples for the tensile tests and 2 samples for the thermal shock damage. The comparison between these characteristics shows that the initial tensile strengh is not a good indicator for the ability of the coating to endure thermal cycling. This can be easily understood from the previous observations : the good initial tensile strength of Ni-Al bonding was destroyed by the interfacial oxidation.

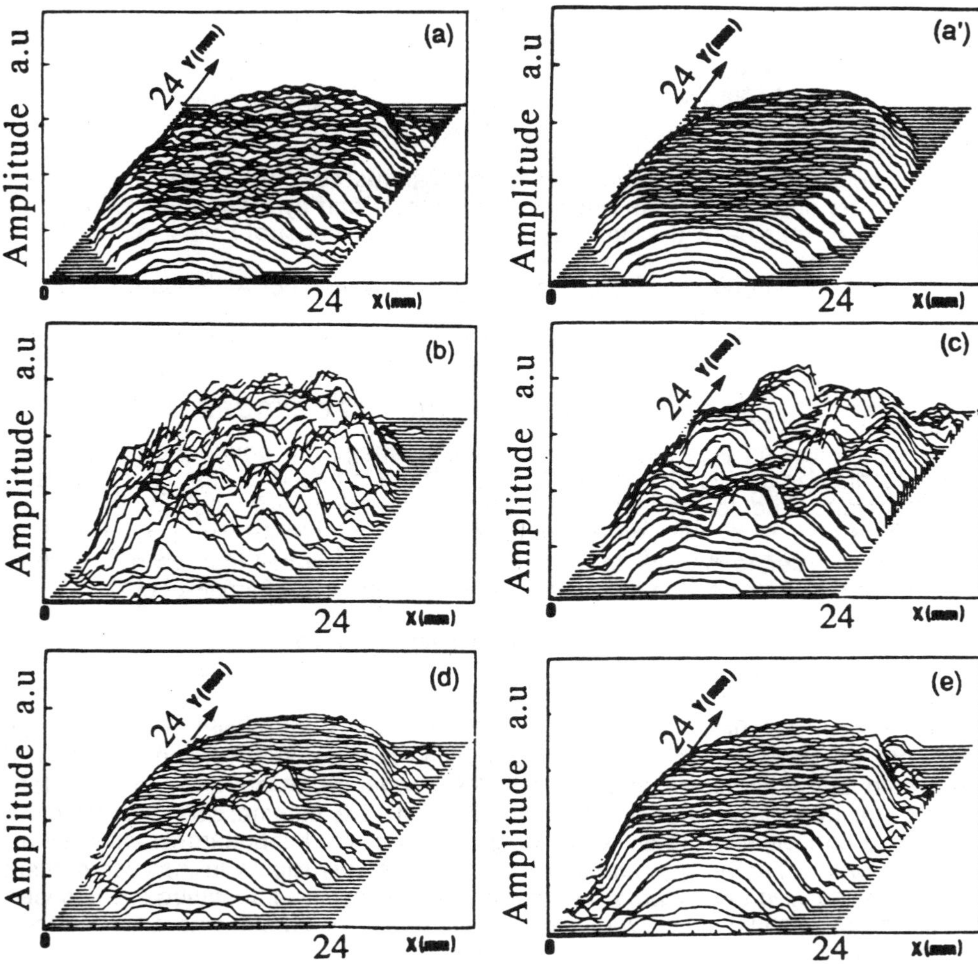

Figure 1. C-scan maps of the interface ceramic-metal: As sprayed (a) Ni-4.5%Al bond coat , (a') Al based slurry coating bond coat. After 126 thermal cycles: (b) Ni-4.5%Al, (c) Al, (d) Al-10%Y, (e) Al-20%Y bond coats.

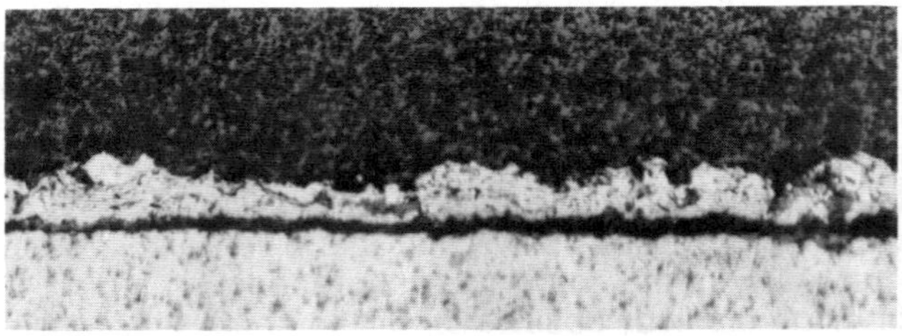

Figure 2 a. Metallographic cross section of coated samples after 126 thermal cycles (Ni-4.5%Al bond layer).

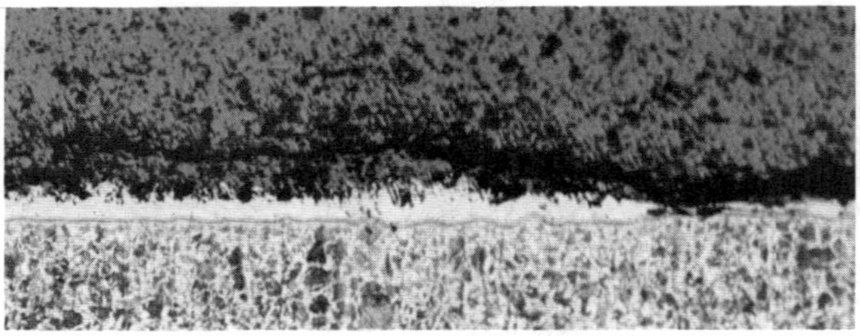

Figure 2 b. Metallographic cross section of coated samples after 126 thermal cycles (Al-10%Y bond layer).

EFFECT OF THE SPRAYING PROCEDURE

The effect of the spraying procedure on the thermal fatigue life was investigated on samples produced with an Al-10% Y bond coat layer, which presented a rather good behaviour when they were plasma sprayed with procedure **b**, i.e. 15% of the interface appeared damaged after 126 cycles. In order to compare the behaviour of samples of kind **a**, the thermal fatigue tests of these samples were carried on until an interface damage of an equal amount, i.e. 15%, was reached. This condition was fullfilled after 383 cycles, thus revealing an improved service life which results only from the spraying procedure : an example of C- scan image then obtained is given in Fig. 4.
Once again, the tensile tests did not show any marked correlation between the as sprayed tensile strength of the bond and its thermal fatigue life time : indeed, as shown in Fig. 3, the tensile strength values are lower for samples of kind **a** (than for those of kind **b**), whereas their thermal fatigue life time is extended. Therefore, the improved behaviour could be explained only in terms of internal stresses which are caused by the difference in coefficient of thermal expansion between ceramic and steel and by a strong thermal gradient in the ceramic during plasma spraying. These internal stresses could be significantly relaxed by the microcracks observed in the coating of kind b. Let it be mentioned, that such a beneficial effect of microcracks and porosity has been already reported by [3] for instance.

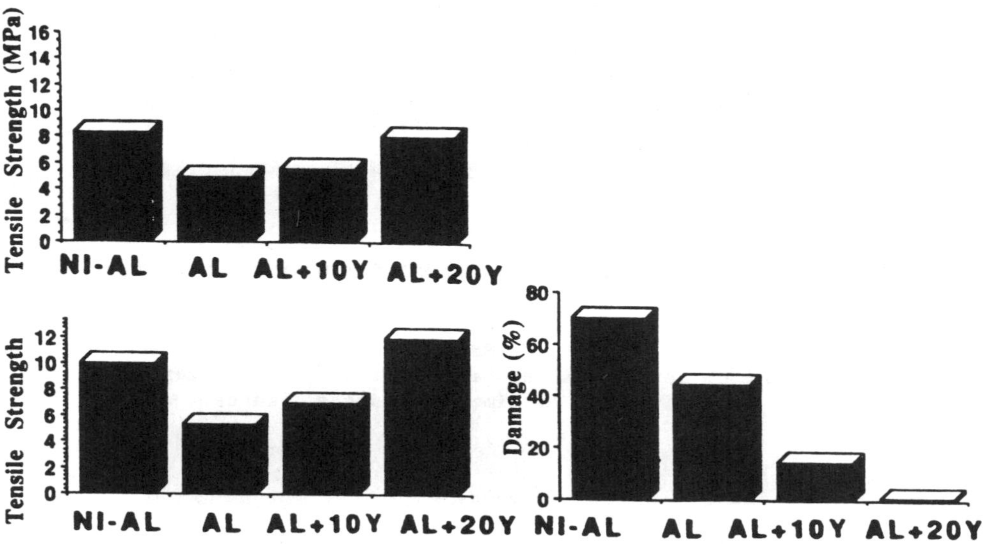

Figure 3. Tensile strength of as sprayed samples produced by procedure (a) and (b), and percentage of damaged interface after 126 thermal cycles for various bond coats.

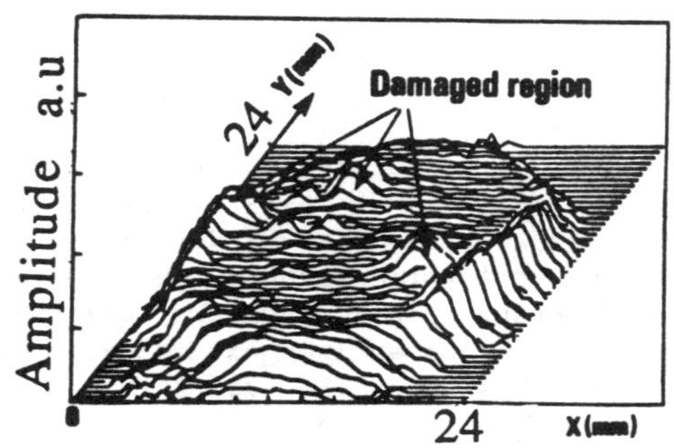

Figure 4. C-scan map of the interface ceramic-metal for a sample of " kind a ; bond layer Al + 10%Y" after 383 thermal cycles.

REFERENCES

1] TREHEUX, D., Traitements par slurry coating. Ecole d'été "Traitements de surface et protection contre la corrosion", to be published in Journal de Physique.

[2] VINCENT, A., and MOUGHIL, A., Ultrasonic characterization of zirconia based thermal barriers, 7th Colloquium "Progress in metals and new materials investigation methods" in Bulletin of the Cercle d'Etude des Métaux (1988).

[3] SUMNER,I.E., and RUCKLE, D.L., Development of improved-durability plasma sprayed ceramic coatings for gas turbine engines, 16th joint prop. conf., CT, AIAA paper 1-13 (1980).

OXIDATION OF HOT PRESSED SILICON NITRIDE: MODELLING

J.B. VEYRET and M.BILLY*
C.E.C.- Joint research Centre, Petten, The Netherlands
* University of Limoges, Limoges, France.

ABSTRACT

A model for the oxidation behaviour of a Hot Pressed Silicon Nitride (HPSN) material with 9 wt% yttria is described in the temperature range 800-1400°C.

INTRODUCTION

High-strength Silicon Nitride ceramics have gained great attention since the early 1970s because of their potential use as structural materials for high performance engineering applications. The use of yttria as a densification aid for Si_3N_4 sintering results in the formation of highly refractory secondary phases improving the high temperature behaviour compared to Si_3N_4 containing MgO. However, some of these materials are susceptible to structural degradation at low temperature (≈800°C) because of the instability of some of the inherent grain boundary crystalline phases towards oxygen. The volume change accompanying this oxidation process create surface stresses leading to cracking of the substrate.

In our study, we present an oxidation model for a silicon nitride hot-pressed with Y_2O_3, containing a unique crystalline grain boundary phase with apatite structure $Y_{10}(SiO_4)_6N_2$.

MATERIALS AND EXPERIMENTAL

The material under study (SN1 grade) was supplied by Feldmühle AG, West Germany. This material was hot-pressed with 9 wt% yttria at 1750°C under 40 MPa pressure. Typical impurities were reported to be in weight % : MgO:0.01, Fe_2O_3:1.7, ZrO_2:0.01, Al_2O_3:0.12, CaO:0.05. The X-ray diffraction pattern shows the presence of β-Si_3N_4, $Y_{10}(SiO_4)_6N_2$ and $FeSi_2$. Microstructural investigation with transmission electron microscopy (T.E.M.) showed a unique crystalline grain boundary phase, $Y_{10}(SiO_4)_6N_2$, with no evidence of vitreous phase.

The oxidation behaviour of SN1 has been investigated with continuous thermogravimetry using an automatic electrobalance (Stanton Redcroft,UK) between 800 and 1400°C in air (P = 1 atm) for 5 hours. Polished cubic samples (edge 7 mm) were tested by gradual increase of temperature and under isothermal conditions. The phases present on the surface after oxidation were identified by X-ray diffraction. The concentration of some elements across the oxide scale was determined using an electron microprobe. The morphology of the oxide scale was examined with a scanning electron microscope (S.E.M.).

RESULTS

The kinetic curves (Fig. 1) illustrate a pseudo-linear initial stage where the oxidation rate is temperature dependant. This step is then followed by a rate decrease which begins earlier as the temperature increases. The kinetics show parabolic behaviour in the temperature range 800-1000°C and an asymptotic behaviour above 1200°C. We observe that the oxidation resistance, as illustrated by mass changes, is lower at low temperatures (800-1000°C), with a maximum at 1200°C.

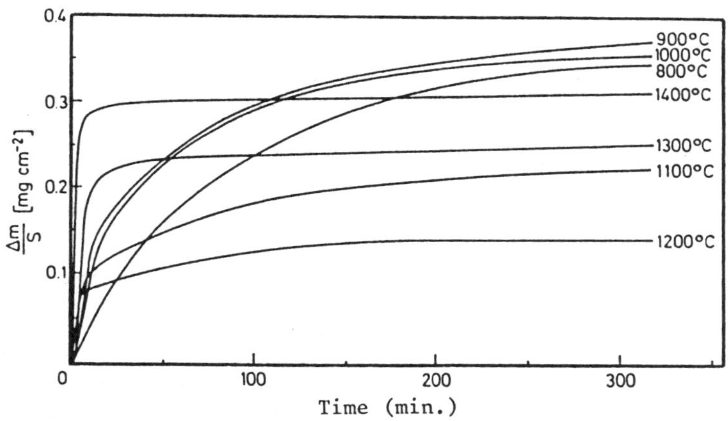

Fig. 1: Oxidation kinetics of SN1.

At low temperatures (800-900°C), the X-ray diffraction analysis of the oxide scale revealed SiO_2, $Y_{4.67}(SiO_4)_3O$ and very small amout of $Y_2Si_2O_7$. At high temperatures (1100-1400°C), only $Y_2Si_2O_7$ and SiO_2 were identified. The examination of the oxidized surfaces are shown in Figure 2. At 800°C (Fig. 2a) the surface is covered with small white humps which, according to X-ray analysis are $Y_{4.67}(SiO_4)_3O$. At 1400°C the surface was covered with plate-like $Y_2Si_2O_7$ inbedded in a silica rich layer.(fig. 2b).

Electron microprobe analysis of a polished cross section through a sample that had been oxidized for 100 hours at 1400°C showed the concentration profiles of Si, Y and Fe (the only elements found on this section) as in Figure 3. The thickness of the oxide surface layer, measured by optical microscopy, was about 12 µm. There is a 3 µm yttrium accumulation at the top of this oxide scale. At the internal interface there is only silica. The yttrium profile is very informative since it shows that there is no yttrium diffusion from the bulk to the oxide scale. In the substrate, which is not oxidized, iron and yttrium are not uniformly distributed.

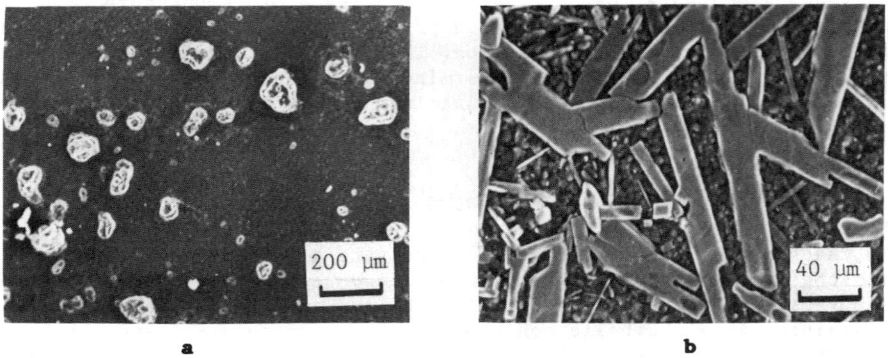

Fig. 2: SEM of the surface of SN1 oxidized for 5 hours at:
a) 800°C, b) 1400°C.

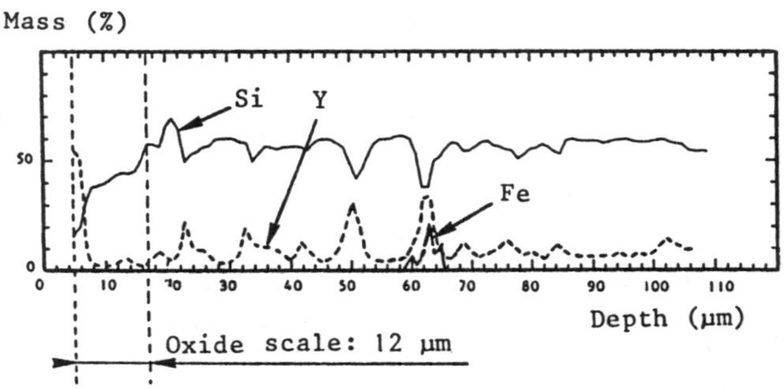

Fig. 3: EPMA scans of Si, Y and Fe through SN1 oxidized at 1400°C for 100 hours.

INTERPRETATION AND MODELLING

These results clearly show the differential oxidation between the intergranular phases and the silicon nitride grains. This is well illustrated in Figure 4, which shows the thermogravimetric curve obtained under rapid increasing temperature (50°C/min) with the morphology of the oxide scale at each step of the oxidation process.

Oxidation starts with the intergranular phase (nitrogen-apatite). At high temperature, silicon nitride grains oxidise to form a protective oxide scale which acts as an oxygen diffusion barrier.

There are two concurrent processes which compete for the overall reaction. They are:

- an "internal" oxidation of the cristalline grain boundary phase (N-apatite),
- an "external" oxidation of silicon nitride grains.

These processes are independent and occur in parallel, so that the faster of the two is the oxidation dominant process with:

$$v = v_i + v_e \qquad v_i : \text{internal oxidation rate}, \quad v_e : \text{external oxidation rate}.$$

or $$\Delta m = \Delta m_i + \Delta m_e.$$

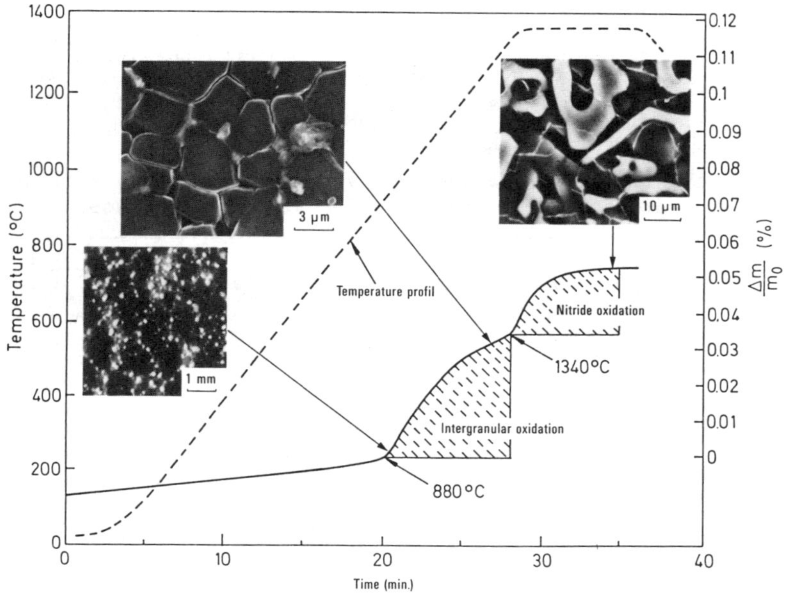

Fig. 4: SN1, mass gain in air under rapid increasing temperature (50°C/min).

At low temperatures (800-900°C): $\Delta m \approx \Delta m_i$.
There is only the oxidation of the N-apatite (Fig. 5.I). The oxidation product, $(Y_{4.67}(SiO_4)_3O$, is not protective, so that the reaction front progresses towards the bulk. But oxygen-uptake through gaseous diffusion is the slower process and therefore the rate limiting step. This is the reason why parabolic kinetics are observed.

At high temperatures (>900°C):
The reaction between oxygen and Si_3N_4 starts and produces:

a) a SiO_2 layer on Si_3N_4 grains. This reaction continues by oxygen diffusion through the silica layer according to:

$$\Delta m_e^2 = k_e S_e t \quad \text{with: } S = S_i + S_e, \quad S_e >> S_i,$$

S_e: external Si_3N_4 surface area,
S_i: secondary phases surface area.

b) SiO_2 formation at channel necks where the oxygen partial pressure is high. The oygen-apatite will be extruded (Fig. 5.II). The oxygen-apatite is unstable in contact with silica, so that $Y_2Si_2O_7$ is produced by reaction with the oxide scale (Fig. 5.III).
SiO_2 formation interferes with and minimises internal oxidation. The closing rate of grain boundaries is correlated to their number, similar to the pore closing mechanism according to Evans [1]:

$$\frac{dv_i}{dt} = -kv_i, \qquad \text{also} \qquad \frac{dS_i}{dt} = -kS_i.$$

Assuming that the intergranular attack is directly related to the number of accessible grain boundaries, then

$$\frac{dm_i}{dt} = k_i S_i = k_i S_{i0} e^{-kt}$$, which after integration gives:

$$\Delta m_i = \frac{k_i S_{i0}}{k} (1 - e^{-kt})$$

Finally, taking the parabolic silica growth on the external surface into consideration , we obtain the expression for the global mass gain:

$$\boxed{\Delta m = \Delta m_i + \Delta m_e = \frac{k_i S_{i0}}{k} (1 - e^{-kt}) + \sqrt{k_e S_e t}.}$$

This model which describes the experimental results well, explains the overall mechanism of oxidation:

- at low temperatures, where the oxidation rate of silicon nitride is slow (k_e and k small), the oxidation of the N-apatite progresses slowly by oxygen diffusion through the larger grain boundaries.

- at higher temperatures, SiO_2 layer formation is dominant, the grain boundaries are closed and the internal oxidation stops (changing slope on the kinetic curves). Silica growth is only possible on the external surface of the sample, explaining an apparent blocking of the reaction.

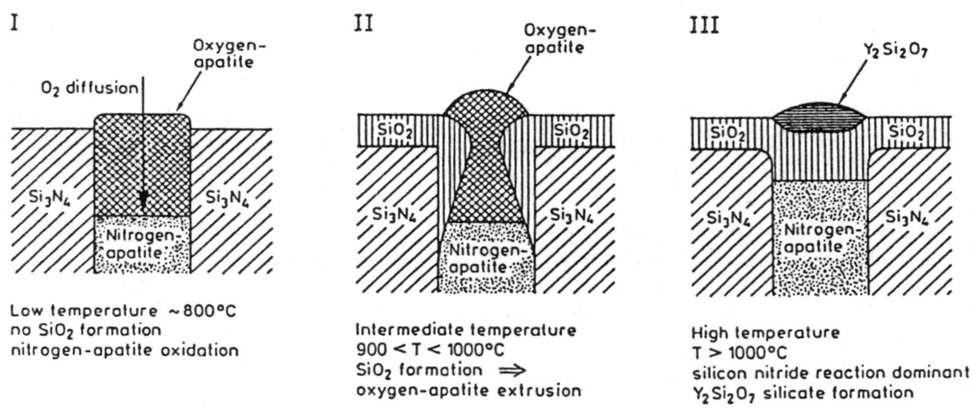

Fig. 5: SN1 oxidation model.

REFERENCE

1. EVANS U.R. - "The Corrosion and Oxidation of Metals", Edward Arnold, London, 1960, 834.

One of the authors (JBV) wishes to thank the Commission of the European Communities for the award of a doctoral grant.

CORROSION OF SILICON NITRIDE IN $H_2S/H_2O/H_2$ GAS MIXTURES AT 1200-1300°C

F. COSTA OLIVEIRA
C.E.C. - Joint Research Centre, Petten Establishment
Institute of Advanced Materials
P.O. Box 2, 1755 ZG Petten, The Netherlands

ABSTRACT

Little has been reported about the corrosion behaviour of silicon nitride in sulphur-containing gas mixtures of low oxygen potential. Four silicon nitrides were sintered with the aid of Y_2O_3 and Al_2O_3 in various ratios and exposed to $H_2S/H_2O/H_2$ gas mixtures. A new "volatility map" shows when the surface of silicon nitride should corrode as volatile SiO or SiS. Gas composition and temperature are critical : corrosion rates varied from 0.03 to 30 mm/year in these tests. Corrosion is fastest in "dry" gas at 1300°C where pSiS is high. This disastrous corrosion can be prevented either by (a) reducing the temperature to 1200°C, in which case a glassy SiO_2-rich layer becomes stable and suppresses SiS formation, or (b) by slightly humidifying the gas, which reduces the pSiS. In this case there is only a slow loss of SiO from the surface of the glassy layer. The rate is independent of Si_3N_4 composition, since it is limited by transport in the gas phase. However, Si_3N_4 composition is important at 1300°C in dry gas, where components of the intergranular phase enter the complex surface layer and slow the otherwise severe corrosion.

INTRODUCTION

In a number of industrial applications, e.g. coal gasification technology, chemical process industry and petrochemical industry, ceramic materials must operate at temperatures as high as 1400°C in sulphur-containing environments (e.g. gaseous environments produced by the reaction of coal with steam and oxygen in gasification processes consist of CO and H_2 with minor amounts of CO_2, H_2O, H_2S, HCl and NH_3). Under these circumstances, both oxidation and sulphidation can occur depending on the gas composition. Very little has been reported about the corrosion behaviour of silicon

nitride in low pO_2 gas mixtures : almost all work has been done under oxidizing conditions.
This paper describes the corrosion behaviour of four silicon nitrides, sintered with the aid of Y_2O_3 and Al_2O_3 in various ratios, exposed to gas mixtures containing H_2S, H_2O and H_2 at 1200 and 1300°C. It shows how volatility and phase stability diagrams can be used to predict corrosion rates.

MATERIALS AND METHODS

Materials and Environments: All four silicon nitrides were sintered at 1850°C for 2 h under 1 MPa N_2 pressure. Table 1 shows the materials and environmental conditions used in this study.

TABLE 1
Materials and environments used in this study

MATERIALS

Composition mass % (balance Si_3N_4)	SNA	SNB	SNC	SND
Y_2O_3	8	7	6	2
Al_2O_3	4	3	4	8
% open porosity	3.2	4.2	2.2	3.2
Apparent solid density (gcm^{-3})	3.25	3.23	3.12	2.95

ENVIRONMENTS

Cold gas composition* vol.%	Time h	Temp. °C	pO_2 (Pa)	pS_2 (Pa)
0.4% H_2S - H_2	150	1200	$1.4x10^{-17}$	0.10
0.4% H_2S - H_2	70	1300	$1.8x10^{-16}$	0.26
0.4% H_2S-0.75%H_2O-H_2	100	1300	$1.3x10^{-10}$	0.26

* dry gas impurities : 5 ppm H_2O, 2 ppm O_2

Experimental: The gaseous corrosion studies were performed in an autoclave capable of 1500°C and 0.5 MPa pressure. After loading, the autoclave was filled with active gas and heated (5°C/min.) to the experimental temperature, held at temperature for a specified length of time and slowly cooled to room temperature in static active gas. Samples were then removed for mass change determinations and microstructural analyses (XRD, EPMA, SEM/EDX).

RESULTS

At 1300°C in the dry gas, a mass loss was measured right from the start of the experiment : in the other cases there was an initial parabolic mass gain, attributed to the thickening of a silica-rich layer, followed by a linear mass loss, attributed to SiO and SiS formation (e.g. Figure 1). The figures in Table 2 refer to this rate, which will determine the long-term resistance of the materials. Also shown in Table 2 are the corrosion products, as identified by XRD.

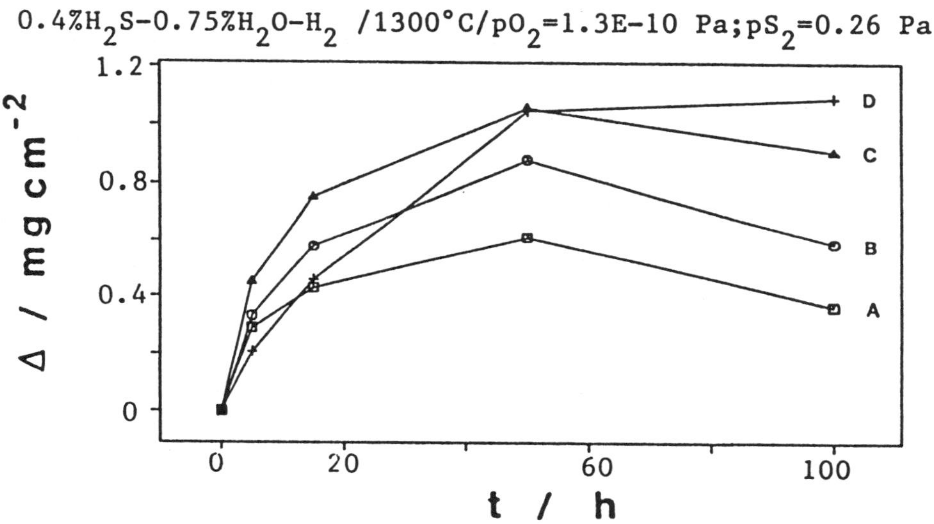

Figure 1. Mass change as a function of time of materials SNA, SNB, SNC and SND exposed to 0.4% H_2S/0.75% H_2O/H_2 at 1300°C for 100 h.

TABLE 2
XRD analysis of the corrosion layers and linear corrosion rates.

ENVIRONMENTAL CONDITIONS	CORROSION PRODUCTS	LINEAR CORROSION RATES ($\mu g cm^{-2} h^{-1}$) SNA	SNB	SNC	SND
0.4% H_2S-H_2/ 1200°C	α-SiO_2, $Y_2Si_2O_7$ (Si_2N_2O in SND)	-0.3	-0.5	-0.5	-1.1
0.4% H_2S-H_2/ 1300°C	Y_2O_2S, $Al_5Y_3O_{12}$	-250	-190	-25	-860
0.4% H_2S- 0.75%H_2O-H_2/ 1300°C	α-SiO_2, $Y_2SiO_2O_7$ (Si_2N_2O in SND)	-5.1	-8.1	-7.4	-5.3

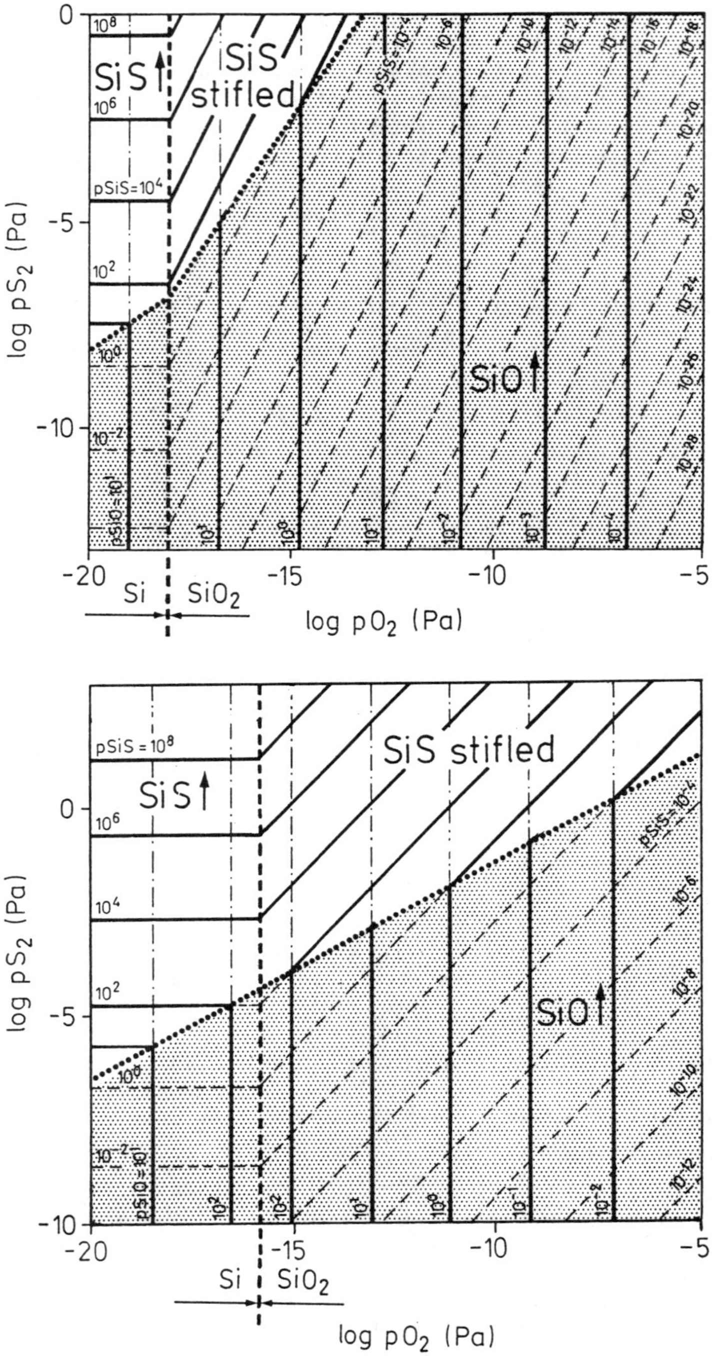

Figure 2. Volatility maps at 1200°C (top) and 1300°C (bottom).

DISCUSSION

In low oxygen potential atmospheres containing sulphur, thermodynamics predicts that volatile SiO and SiS should form at the surface of silicon nitride [1].
A volatility map has been constructed (Figure 2) to show partial pressure isobars of the volatile species (SiO and SiS) in equilibrium with Si or SiO_2 as a function of pS_2 and pO_2. This figure indicates that corrosion rates should be fastest in 0.4% H_2S-H_2, where there is a high pSiS. At 1300°C in this gas there was a rapid loss of material caused by SiS formation : the surface recession rate was up to 30mm/year. A thick (up to millimeters) porous layer of crystalline corrosion products was formed.
At 1200°C this disastrous corrosion is prevented by a thin (1-5µm) glassy layer which forms because SiO_2 is 'stable' (the heavy dotted line - towards left of map - divides the "silicon metal stable" from the "silica stable" region). When 0.75% H_2O was added to the gas mixture at 1300°C there was only a slow mass loss of SiO from the surface of the glassy layer. The rate is independent of Si_3N_4 composition, since it is limited by transport in the gas phase. However, Si_3N_4 composition plays an important role at 1300°C in 0.4% H_2S-H_2, where components of the intergranular phase affect the formation of the complex surface layer and can slow the otherwise severe corrosion.

CONCLUSIONS

- Material performance is highly dependent on the composition of the gas phase, the temperature, and the exposure time (average recession rates varying from 0.03 to 30 mm/year).
- Corrosion behaviour can be conveniently understood by the use of a volatility map showing equilibrium vapour pressures of volatile SiO and SiS as a function of the pO_2 and pS_2 partial pressures in the gas.
- The rate control of mass loss depends on the relative volatility of SiO and SiS. Where active oxidation predominates (pSiO > pSiS), rate control is by transport in the gas phase. Where active sulphidation was predominant (pSiS > pSiO) the rate was limited by diffusion in the surface layers.

REFERENCES

1. Van der Biest O., Barnes J., Corish J., Norton J.F.,
Corrosion of a silica-bearing ceramic in sulphur-oxygen atmospheres.
J. Am. Ceram. Soc., 1987, **70**, 456-59.

Acknowledgements

The author is most grateful to the Commission of the European Communities for the financial support, to Dr. R.A.H. Edwards for helpful discussions, and to P. Glaude (XRD) for his technical assistance.

CORROSION OF TECHNICAL CERAMICS BY MOLTEN ALUMINUM.

ULRICH SCHWABE, LODEWIJK R. WOLFF, FRANS J. J. VAN LOO,
GUENTER ZIEGLER
Centre for Technical Ceramics, P.O.Box 513
5600 MB EINDHOVEN, THE NETHERLANDS

ABSTRACT

Corrosion investigations on various types of nonoxide technical ceramic materials, two types of silicon nitride (HIPRBSN and RBSN) and two types of silicon carbide (HIPSIC and SiSiC), were carried out in aluminum (Al99.99) melts. HIPRBSN showed nearly no corrosion attack under the most severe conditions (1273 K for 500 hrs). The RBSN material with relatively high open porosity and a small content of free silicon was attacked already after 48 hrs. The HIPSiC was considerably more attacked than the HIPRBSN, however it is also fairly corrosion resistant. The SiSiC material showed the poorest corrosion behaviour of the materials investigated. The results are explained in terms of thermodynamics, diffusion through the metal/ceramic interface and wetting effects.

INTRODUCTION

For metallurgical applications of the new technical ceramic materials, as silicon nitride and silicon carbide, it is important to have knowledge about the corrosion behaviour of these materials in metal melts. In this investigation corrosion tests in aluminum melts were carried out using different testing methods. In addition, thermodynamic considerations were made on corrosion reactions. The experimental results were interpreted by means of theoretical considerations on thermodynamics of the corrosion reactions and on diffusion and wetting effects.

THERMODYNAMICS

Of particular importance for the planning of tests as well as for the interpretation of test results are the thermodynamics of corrosion reactions. With thermochemical data [1] and phase diagrams [2,3] known from literature thermodynamic considerations were made regarding the systems Al-Si-N and Al-Si-C. Simplified phase diagrams considering only the possible main products are shown in figure 1:

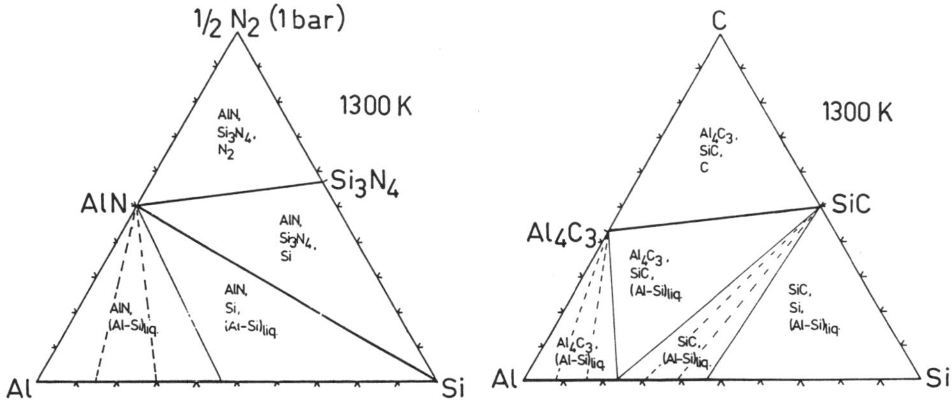

Figure 1. Ternary phase diagrams for Al-Si-N and Al-Si-C.

Silicon nitride can react with liquid aluminum in two ways:

$$Si_3N_4 + X\ Al = 4\ AlN + \{Al\text{-}Si\} \qquad (1)$$

$$Si_3N_4 + X\ Al = 2\ N_2 + \{Al\text{-}Si\} \qquad (2)$$

The silicon formed dissolves in the aluminum melt up to a molar fraction of 0.643 at 1300 K [2]. At 1300 K reaction (1) can procced up to the formation of the pure silicon phase. For reaction (2) the nitrogen partial pressure is dependent on the silicon concentration of the melt and vice versa. At 1300 K gaseous nitrogen can only escape at 3-phase lines, where ceramic and melt are both in contact with the atmosphere. Otherwise, the nitrogen would react with the aluminum in the melt to form aluminum nitride. Thus, reaction (2) may only play a role with open porous ceramics and a (nearly) nitrogen-free atmosphere. Then the nitrogen once formed at 3-phase lines in the pore system can escape into the atmosphere.

Silicon carbide reacts with liquid aluminum in the following manner:

$$3\ SiC + X\ Al = Al_4C_3 + \{Al\text{-}Si\} \qquad (3)$$

At a temperature of 1300 K this reaction can only proceed from the left to the right if the silicon formed is dissolved in the aluminum melt with a molar fraction below 0.24. Under the given experimental conditions there is more than necessary aluminum for a complete reaction of silicon carbide.

METHODS AND MATERIALS

Corrosion Tests

Small nearly cubic ceramic samples (5x5x5 mm) were placed together with pure aluminum (Al99.99) in crucibles which were heated in tube furnaces in flowing helium. The test temperature was 1273 K.

Short term tests: Graphite crucibles (diameter: 10 mm, height: 20 mm) were used with 2.5 g aluminum metal. The test temperature was kept for 48 hrs.

Long term tests: Crucibles of inert material (stabilized zirconium oxide, diameter: 22 mm, height: 30 mm) covered with a graphite plate and placed in a graphite crucible holder were used with 10 g aluminum metal. The test temperature was kept over 500 hrs.

Materials

Two types of silicon nitride and two types of silicon carbide were investigated:

- Hotisostatically pressed reaction bonded silicon nitride (HIPRBSN) with 5 wt.-% yttria additive (density 100 % th. d., β-silicon nitride, crystalline Y-Si-O-N second phases, amorphous grain boundary phases).
- Reaction bonded silicon nitride (RBSN), 72 % th. d., high open porosity, micropore size 0.05 μm, phase composition of silicon nitride: $\alpha/(\alpha+\beta) = 0.92$, free silicon content < 3 %).
- Hotisostatically pressed silicon carbide (HIPSiC) with 0.2 wt.-% aluminum (density: 100 % th. d.).
- Infiltrated silicon carbide (SiSiC, silicon content 12 wt.-%).

Characterization Methods

The changes of the materials upon corrosion were investigated by scanning electron microscopy (SEM) and electron probe micro analysis (EPMA). Further, light microscopy and X-ray diffraction analysis were used.

RESULTS

Silicon Nitride

Dense silicon nitride (HIPRBSN): X-ray mapping of aluminum , silicon and nitrogen showed that during the long term test a dense reaction layer was formed at the interface with an average thickness of about 7 μm after the 500 hrs test.

Porous silicon nitride (RBSN): After the short term test SEM investigations showed a strongly changed microstructure of the ceramic material. The porosity had decreased considerably. X-ray diffraction analysis of the ceramic material proves the formation of a substantial amount of aluminum nitride. The silicon nitride content was decreased to a relati vely small amount and some aluminum metal was found. In the aluminum melt some percent of silicon were observed.

Silicon Carbide

Dense silicon carbide (HIPSIC): A reaction layer of aluminum carbide of roughly 100 μm thickness was found after the 500 hrs test. The layer varied strongly in thickness and density.

Si-infiltrated SiC (SiSiC): After the short term test SEM investigations showed a strong change in microstructure of the SiSiC material. An aluminum carbide corrosion layer of about 500 to 600 μm was found. Inside the ceramic material the grains of silicon carbide were partially corroded, as indicated by changes in grain shape. The silicon between the silicon carbide grains was partially replaced by aluminum metal. The silicon content of the aluminum melt was found to be some percent.

DISCUSSION

Silicon Nitride

Dense silicon nitride: At the interface of dense silicon nitride with molten aluminum for thermodynamical reasons only reaction (1) can take place, which is connected with the formation of an aluminum nitride layer. This layer is acting as an effective diffusion barrier [3], thus inhibiting further corrosion attack.

Porous silicon nitride: In the case of silicon nitride with an extensive open pore system the reaction interface between ceramic material and aluminum melt is much larger than that of the dense material, provided that the melt is wetting the ceramic material as it is here the case. For silicon nitride with an open pore system connecting opposite sides of the ceramic, reaction (2) may have a chance to proceed as discussed in the paragraph THERMODYNAMICS.

Silicon Carbide

Dense silicon carbide: At the interface between silicon carbide and the aluminum melt reaction (3) takes place. The reaction product aluminum carbide is forming a layer at the interface. However, this layer turned out to be not so corrosion protecting as the aluminum nitride layer on dense silicon nitride. Obviously the aluminum carbide forms a more porous layer than the aluminum nitride, through which aluminum melt can permeate and attack further the ceramic. This transport process is much faster than the bulk diffusion through dense solid layers of aluminum nitride or aluminum carbide.

Silicon infiltrated silicon carbide: In this case silicon carbide grains are bonded together by metallic silicon, which easily dissolves in liquid aluminum. Thus, the microstructure is destroyed very rapidly. The now isolated silicon carbide grains exhibit an extensive interface to the melt, and thus, are strongly attacked.

CONCLUSIONS

The HIPRBSN investigated was found to be the most corrosion resistant of the materials studied in this work. The HIPSiC material was attacked slightly under the most severe conditions applied. The open porous RBSN was readily attacked resulting in extensive changes of microstructure. SiSiC did not show much corrosion resistance at all.

The corrosion behaviour is strongly determined by the interface between ceramic and melt. The corrosion attack is minimized as the effective contact interface is small and a stable dense layer of reaction products is formed. This is the case with the HIPRBSN material. If there are open pores and the melt is wetting the ceramic (as in the case of the RBSN material), then the effective contact interface is strongly increased. With HIPSiC the aluminum carbide layer is porous, and thus, less corrosion protecting. Most detrimental is the presence of free silicon in the ceramic material. This is particularly the case with SiSiC.

The corrosion resistance of materials which do not form an effective corrosion protecting layer of reaction products can be improved by applying an "artificial" reaction layer with the desired properties by means of various coating techniques.

REFERENCES

1. Barin, I., Knacke, O., Kubaschewski, O., Thermochemical Properties of Inorganic Substances, 1973 and Supplement 1977, Springer Verlag, Berlin/Heidelberg and Verlag Stahleisen, Duesseldorf
2. Hultgren, Desai, Hawkins, Gleiser, Kelley, Selected Values of the Thermodynamic Properties of Binary Alloys, ASM, Metals Park, Ohio, 1973, pp. 210-2.
3. Schuster, J. C., Weitzer, E., Bauer, J., Nowotny, H., Joining of Silicon Nitride Ceramics to Metals: The Phase Diagram Base, Materials Science and Engineering A 105/106 (1988) 201-206

Acknowledgement: We gratefully acknowledge the sponsorship of the IOP program commision.

MICROSTRUCTURE OF THE OXIDE LAYERS PRODUCED DURING OXIDATION OF SILICON NITRIDE

J. Echeberría and F. Castro

Centro de Estudios e Investigaciones Técnicas de Guipúzcoa,
Barrio de Ibaeta s/n, Apdo. 1555,
20080 San Sebastián, Spain

ABSTRACT

Oxidation of silicon nitride with additions of ceria + alumina, yttria + magnesia and yttria + alumina has been carried out in air at atmospheric pressure for up to 72 hrs at 1100 to 1425°C. Parabolic oxidation kinetics were observed in all cases, although the microstructure of the oxide layers formed, as studied by x-ray difraction and electron microscopy, were dependent on the initial chemical composition of the specimens, the oxidation temperature and the cooling rate. However, for yttria-containing specimens, the influence of cooling rate is only important for those having alumina; since the formation of enstatite ($MgSiO_3$), in those with MgO additons, which inhibits in turn the crystallisation of an yttrium-disilicate, seems to be independent of cooling rate. The microstructural changes of the substrate, induced by the oxidation treatment, were also studied by XRD and scanning electron microscopy.

INTRODUCTION

It is now well established that the oxidation resistence of nitrogen ceramics, consolidated by a liquid phase route, is very dependent upon the nature and quantity of the sintering aids used (1-3). Investigations in this field, related to silicon nitride, mainly include the reaction bonded form and hot pressed materials with additions of MgO (4-6), Y_2O_3 (7-9) and to a lesser extent with CeO_2 (6,10-12). These ceramics show a parabolic oxidation behaviour, but their oxidation kinetics presents significant differences which depend on composition. During oxidation, which proceeds from the surface to the interior, a composition gradient is formed (3,4,7,13) because oxygen diffuses in, and gaseous products, as well as cations from the original intergranular phase, diffuse to the oxide scale.

The composition gradient is not, however, the only variation through the oxide scale since, as demonstrated for Si_3N_4 containing ceria and alumina (14), it exhibits important microstructural changes from the surface to the reaction interface.

In the present work, the oxidation kinetics of three silicon nitride based ceramics are compared; although most attention has been devoted to the microstructural characterisation of the oxide products, formed at different temperatures and after slow and rapid cooling.

EXPERIMENTAL PROCEDURE

The materials used are high purity powders of mean particle sizes of 1μm or less. The mixtures in wt%: Si_3N_4 + 6 Y_2O_3 + 4 Al_2O_3 (SYA), Si_3N_4 + 6 Y_2O_3 + 4 MgO (SYM) and Si_3N_4 + 6 CeO_2 + 4 Al_2O_3 (SCA), were homogenised by dry ball-milling using silicon nitride milling media. Polished cylinders of 13mm diameter and 5mm height, produced in fully dense form after sinter-hipping following methods exposed elsewhere (15,16), were used for oxidation in static air at temperatures between 1100°C and 1425°C. The experiments were performed, for up to 72 hrs, withdrawing the specimens from the furnace at fixed time intervals. Additionally, at the end of every experiment a specimen was left inside the furnace, so to be cooled down slowly.

The characterisation of the oxide products was carried out by x-ray diffractometry (XRD) and electron microscopy. XRD was carried out directly on the surface of the oxidised specimens, whereas, SEM was used to observe, both, the outer surface and the "fracture surface" of the oxide scales, as obtained after detaching parts of them from the substrate.

RESULTS AND DISCUSSION

From the few experiments at low temperatures ($\leq$ 1200ºC), it was noticed that measurable weight gains were only obtained after oxidation at 1250ºC or higher. Above this temperature, the observed oxidation kinetics is parabolic. This behaviour may be appreciated in figure 1 for two temperatures. As illustrated in figure 2, within the experimental scatter, the activation energy for SCA and SYM specimens is constant all over the range of temperatures, and their values (350 KJ/mol and 865 KJ/mol respectively) are in reasonably good agreement with previously reported data (6,17). On the other hand, for SYA, data points do suggest a change of behaviour at high temperatures. In this case, a nearly continuous layer of $Y_2Si_2O_7$, located within the oxide scale and near to the surface was identified. It could therefore be that increasing the oxidation temperature, which facilitates the diffusion of ytrrium cations, the equilibrium composition for the formation of $Y_2Si_2O_7$ is reached, constituting a layer which acts as an additional passivation element. Thus, at higher temperatures, although

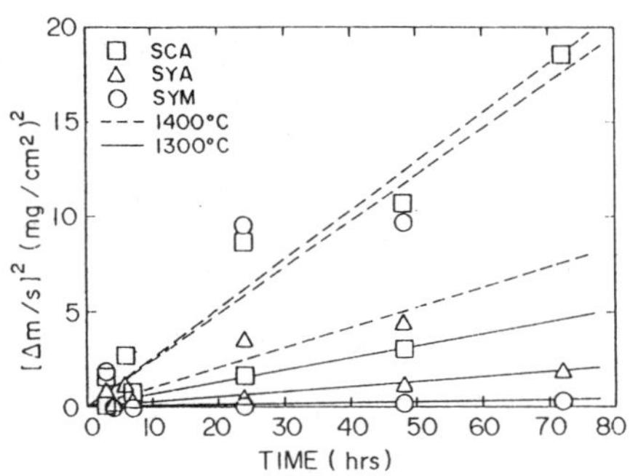

Figure 1 Parabolic plot through the origin after oxidation.

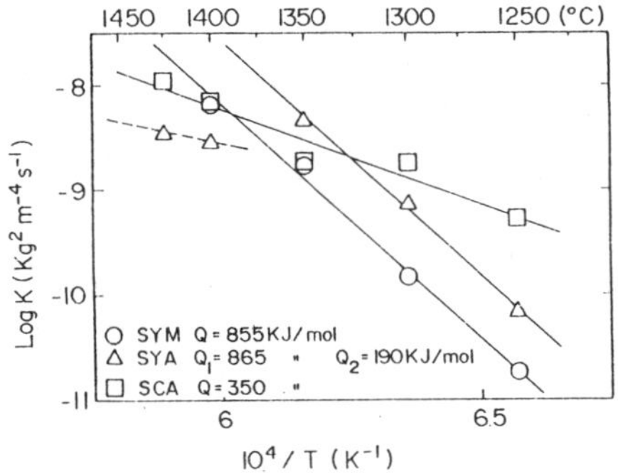

Figure 2 Oxidation rate constants as a function of temperature.

somehow unexpected, the oxidation rate may decrease, and as indicated in the figure, drawing two lines does not seem unreasonable.

Figure 3 shows the macroscopic changes induced in the bulk of the oxidised samples. The figure shows the appearance of an unoxidised specimen (a), the surface morphology after oxidation (b), the appearance of the oxidised specimen after light polishing (c), and a polished cross section of the same sample (d). As clearly appreciated in (d), appart from the oxide scale, the oxidation treatment causes the formation of a thin "black ring" at the interface between the oxide scale and the bulk sample, followed by a wider light grey area embracing a dark gray centre. Closer analysis revealed that the central core is a region unaffected by the oxidation treatment. The light gray sheath presented no apparent difference (except for its colour) to the central core. In contrast, as recently reported (14) the "black-ring" or subscale, is constituted by silicon nitride grains, silicon oxynitride (Si_2N_2O), and minor quantities of a Ce-rich (for SCA) or an Y-rich (for SYA and SYM) silicate glass. The formation of Si_2N_2O, most likely proceeds by the reaction $2Si_3N_4 + 3/2\ O_2 \rightarrow 3\ Si_2N_2O + N_2$, and in contrast to previous reports (18,19), it is not reoxidised to SiO_2 nor is formed only in small quantities, but gains stability as the oxide scale thickens so restricting the ingoing oxygen supply.

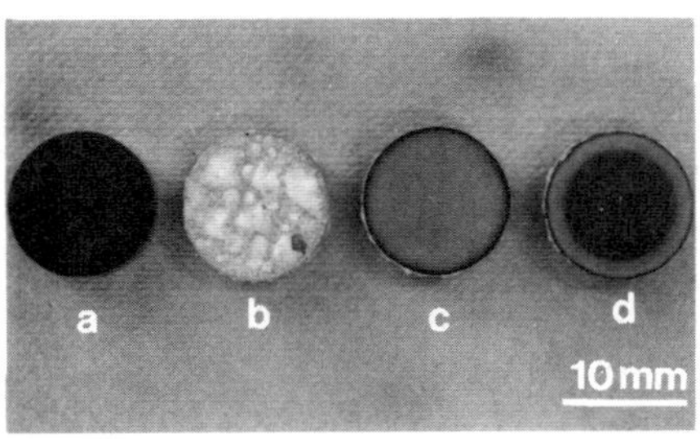

Figure 3 SCA specimens a) before and b), c), d) after oxidation.

The surface morphologies of the oxide scales vary with temperature, composition and cooling rate (9,10,14,17). Figure 4 substantiates this point,

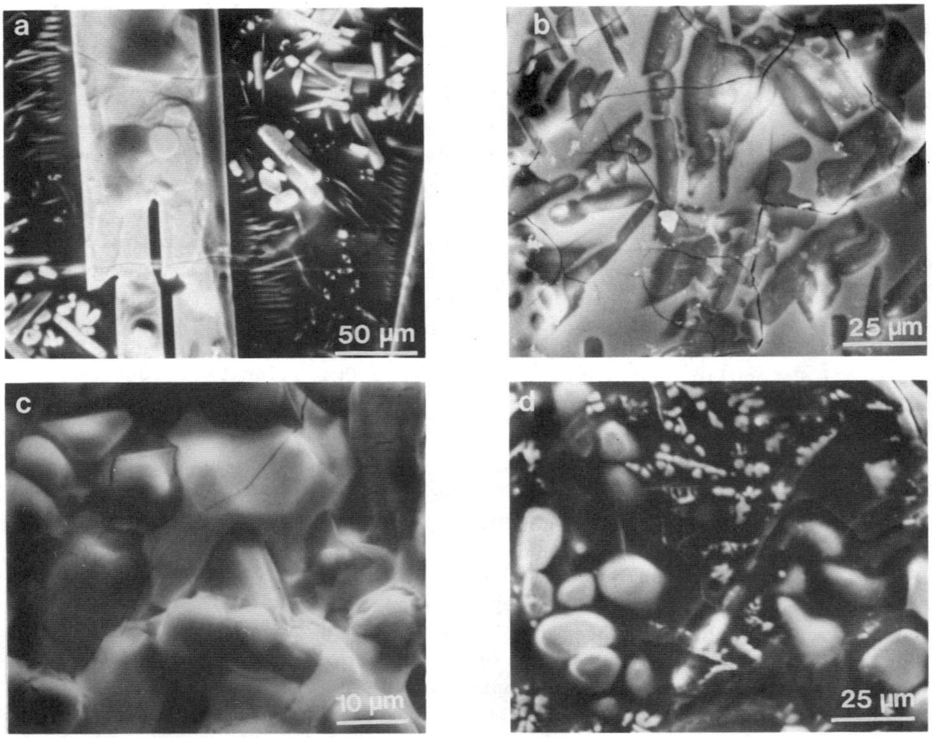

Figure 4 Oxide scale surface for a) SYA, b) SYA fast cooling, c) SYM and d) SCA.

for an oxidation temperature of 1350ºC as an example. Micrographs 4a and b, show that, after rapid cooling the main crystalline product is SiO_2 (cristobalite and tridymite) surrounded by an Y-rich silicate glass (in light contrast), but after slow cooling crystals of β-$Y_2Si_2O_7$ are precipitated out. Micrograph 4a shows in light contrast the Yttrium-disilicate plate-like crystals. These are of identical composition but differ in size, which suggests that the larger ones grow at the expense of the smaller ones, and as observed by XRD develop a crystallographic texture. Micrographs 4a and c show that the Yttrium-disilicate formed exhibits a different morphology between the cristobalite grains. For SCA (figure 4d) the microstructure consists of CeO_2 polygonal-like crystals, with small amounts in dendritic form, and SiO_2 surrounded by a Si-rich glass which contains some quantities of additives and impurities like Ce, Mg and Al.

Regarding the microstructure induced by the cooling rate, a difference is always observed for SYA (e.g figures 4a and b), however, for SYM this is only true above 1350°C since at lower temperatures the formation of $MgSiO_3$ inhibits the crystallisation of $Y_2Si_2O_7$. Besides, below 1350°C a lack of Yttrium on the surface (EDS analysis) was notorious, which apparently

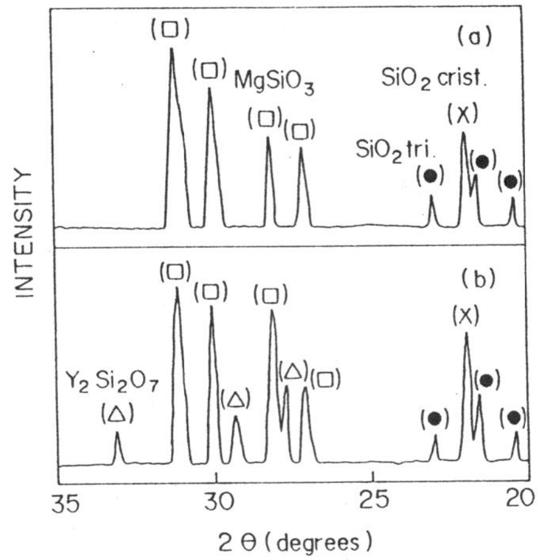

Figure 5 XRD traces of SYM (1400ºC) a) rapid and b) slow cooling.

indicated, as also reported before (5), that Mg had been selectively removed from the substrate and incorporated into the oxide scale as part of the oxidation process. This may be understood by considering that Mg is a fast moving cation (20) which diffuses to the surface aiding the formation of the equilibrium oxidation products (2,4,13), e.g SiO_2 and $MgSiO_3$. In this sense SYM behaves as if it were a MgO - dopped Si_3N_4, and forms a combination of phases on the surface of the oxide scale, as that shown in figure 5a irrespective of cooling rate; until at 1350°C or higher the diffusion of Y^{3+} is very much increased by thermal activation, thus forming an Y-rich silicate glass from which $Y_2Si_2O_7$ precipitates under slow cooling. At those tempera-

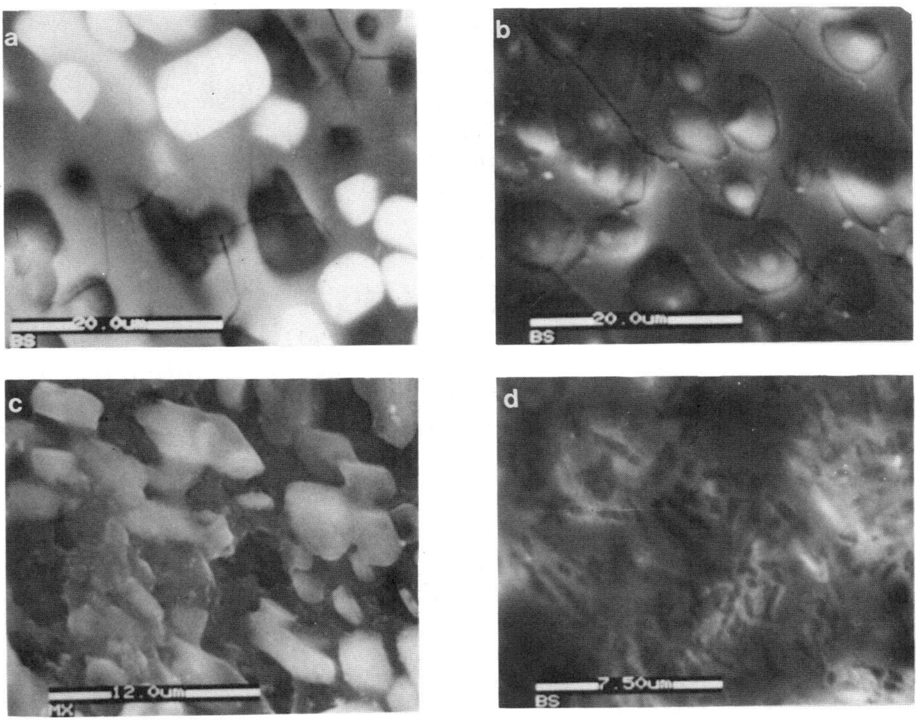

Figure 6 Oxide layers for SYA rapidly cooled (1350°C). a to d represent depth from just below the surface to the bottom of the oxide scale.

tures a typical phase content of the surface of the oxide scale in SYM, after slow cooling, is represented by figure 5b.

Oxide scales, in general, although analysed in cross sections to determine composition gradients (4,5,9), have been considered as monolitic units. Nevertheless, as substantiated by the micrographs in figure 6, they exhibit a layered structure with important microstructural variations from their surface to the reaction interface. This has been found for all compositions studied in the present work, independently of oxidation temperature and cooling rate, therefore indicating that the layers are not a product of cooling rate but are formed during the oxidation process. Also, the oxidation process causes the partial crystallisation of the intergranular phases in the substrate of SYA and SYM, forming δ and α-$Y_2Si_2O_7$ respectively, but not in SCA due to the low ceria/alumina ratio.

ACKNOWLEDGEMENTS

Departamento de Economía y Hacienda de la Diputación Foral de Guipúzcoa is acknowledged, for the economical support for the realisation of this work.

REFERENCES

1. K.H. Jack, J. Mater. Sci., 1976, **11**, 1135.
2. F.F. Lang, Int. Met. Rev., 1980, **1**, 1.
3. G. Ziegler, J. Heinrich and G. Wotting, J.Mater.Sci., 1987, **22**, 3041.
4. S.C. Singhal, J. Mater.Sci., 1976, **11**, 500.
5. D.Cubicciotti and K.H. Lau, J. Am. Cer. Soc., 1978, **61** (11-12), 512.
6. G.N.Babini and P.Vincenzini, p.427, in "Progress in Nitrogen Ceramics", ed. by F.L. Riley, M. Nijhoff Publ., The Netherlands, 1983.
7. S.C. Singhal, in "Nitrogen Ceramics", p. 607-626, ed. by F.L. Riley, Noordhoff International, Reading, Mass., 1977.
8. C.L.Quackenbush and J.T.Smith, Am.Cer.Soc.Bull., 1980, **59** (5), 533.
9. G.N.Babini, A.Bellosi and P.Vincenzini, J.Mater.Sci.,1984, **19**, 3487.
10. G.N.Babini, A.Bellosi and P.Vincenzini, J.Am.Cer.Soc.,1981, **64**, 578.
11. J.P. Guha, P. Goursat and M. Billy, J. Am. Cer. Soc., Discussion and Notes, 1980, **63** (1-2), 119.
12. D.M.Mieskowski and W.A.Sanders, J.Am.Cer.Soc., 1985, **68** (7), C-160.
13. D.R. Clarke, and F.F. Lange, J. Am. Cer. Soc., 1980, **63** (9-10), 586.
14. J.Echeberría and F.Castro, submitted to Mat. Sci. and Tech.
15. I. Iturriza, F. Castro and M. Fuentes, J. Mater. Sci., 1989, **24**,2047.
16. I. Iturriza, J. Echeberría, I. Gutierrez and F. Castro, submitted to J. Mater. Sci.
17. G.N.Babini, A.Bellosi and P.Vincenzini, J.Mater.Sci., 1983, **18**, 231.
18. T.N. Zabruskova and I.Ya. Guzman, Trans. D.I. Mendeleev. Inst. of Tech., 1971, vol.18, 127.
19. A.J. Kiehle, L.K. Heung, P.J. Gielisse and T.J. Rockett, J. Am. Cer. Soc., 1975, **58**, 17.
20. G.W. Brindley and R. Mayamin, Phil. Mag., 1965, **12**, 505.

OBSERVATIONS ON THE SLIDING WEAR BEHAVIOUR OF TRANSFORMATION TOUGHENED CERAMICS

W.M. RAINFORTH, R. STEVENS, J. NUTTING
SCHOOL OF MATERIALS, UNIVERSITY OF LEEDS, LEEDS LS2 9JT, UK.

ABSTRACT

Y-TZP (Tetragonal Zirconia Polycrystals) and Mg-PSZ (Partially Stabilised Zirconia) ceramics have been examined under sliding wear conditions, mated against both ceramic and metal counterfaces. The low thermal conductivity of the Zirconia was found to dominate the wear mechanism. When run against a soft metal counterface strong adhesive forces promoted transformation of tetragonal to monoclinic at the interface, resulting in increased wear. When run against a hard metal counterface, little transformation occurred because of reduced adhesive forces and because of temperature rises which reduced the driving force. A Y-TZP pin slid against a Zirconia Toughened Alumina (ZTA) disc showed evidence of very high flash temperatures at the interface promoting plastic flow in the Zirconia.

INTRODUCTION

Many researchers have highlighted the importance of fracture toughness in the wear resistance of ceramics. Zirconia engineering ceramics offer high toughness coupled with comparatively high hardness and good chemical inertness. Accordingly, Zirconias are increasingly being used as tribological components, such as extrusion dies and valve guides [1,2]. Although the microstructure-property relationships of Zirconia ceramics have received considerable attention, the role of the toughness of the Zirconia in its sliding wear resistance is not well characterised. This paper presents a selection of the results from a systematic investigation into the wear behaviour of a range of Mg-PSZ and Y-TZP ceramics, run against both metal and ceramic counterfaces. Detailed descriptions of the results will be published elsewhere [3].

METHODS AND MATERIALS

The Mg-PSZ materials were prepared from mixed oxides to give a nominal composition of 9 mol% MgO. Isopressed compacts were sintered and solution treated at 1775°C for 2 hrs followed by a rapid cool and age at 1420°C for 5 hrs, providing a toughness of 8.2 MPa $m^{\frac{1}{2}}$ (measured by indentation). 2 and 3 mol % Y-TZP materials were supplied by 'Dynamic Ceramic LTD' with fracture toughness values of 6.1 and 10.9 MPa $m^{\frac{1}{2}}$ respectively. Sliding wear tests were conducted on a tri-pin-on-disc machine, the details of which are reported elsewhere [4]. All surfaces were diamond lapped using a 1 μm diamond finish which produced a centre line average (R_a) of 0.008 μm. Tests were conducted at 0.24 m/s using various loads in the range 6-60 N under dry, ambient conditions. Ceramic pins were worn against a bearing steel disc and also against a ZTA disc. The wear of Mg-PSZ discs was also investigated run against stainless steel pins.

RESULTS AND DISCUSSION

METAL/CERAMIC WEAR

The wear of Zirconia, in common with other ceramics, is dependent on the crystallographic orientation of each grain as illustrated in Fig. 1. The mechanism for the production of this grain relief is not clear, but is associated with the variation in hardness with crystallographic orientation. This feature was observed on the worn surfaces of both the Mg-PSZ and Y-TZP materials.

Many of the grains of the Mg-PSZ in Fig. 1 contain parallel grooves, and occasionally isolated pits, which do not cross grain boundaries, and are perpendicular or within 30° to perpendicular to the sliding direction. The extent of this grooving increased with load, and was dominant on the Mg-PSZ disc worn against the stainless steel, but comparatively rare on the Mg-PSZ pins worn against the bearing steel disc. Transfer of metal to the ceramic followed the same trend as the grooving, being more widespread in the stainless steel case. Etching the surface in Hydrofluoric Acid to reveal the precipitate orientation demonstrated that the groove direction coincided with that of the precipitates. The grooving is similar in appearance to that reported by Hannink et al. [5] and coincides with an increase in monoclinic content of the surface. The most probable explanation for their formation is that transformation of the tetragonal precipitates to the monoclinic phase is occurring cooperatively in bands. The volume dilation and microcracking, coupled with the adhesive forces between the wearing surfaces, has resulted in surface eruption and enhanced wear. Transfer of the metal appeared to promote strong adhesive forces and therefore more surface eruption. Thus, wear of the ceramic was more severe against a soft metal compared to a hard metal counterface.

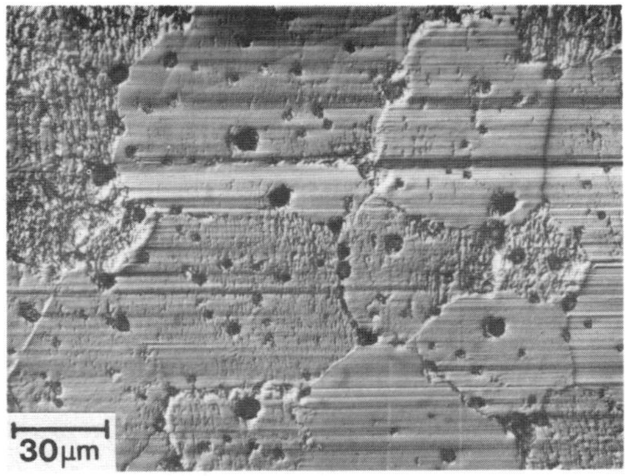

Figure 1. Optical micrograph (Nomarski) of an Mg-PSZ worn against a stainless steel pin. Metal transfer has been removed with HCl.

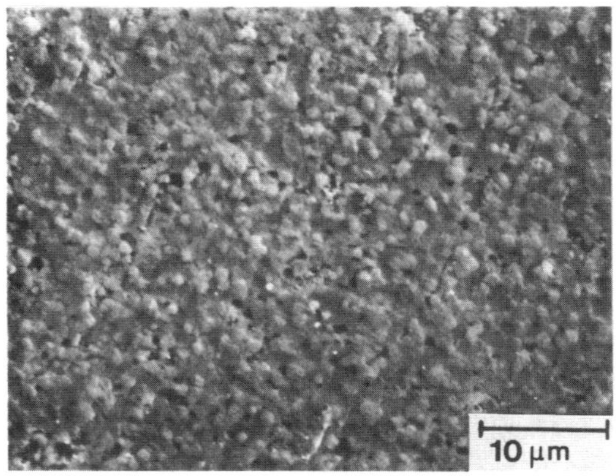

Figure 2. A 3Y-TZP worn against a bearing steel disc. Surface transformation has resulted in a 'pop-out' mechanism. SEM micrograph.

Figure 3. Back scattered electron image of a 3Y-TZP pin run against a ZTA disc. Extensive plasticity is evident combined with intimate mixing of the two materials.

With the Y-TZP materials surface 'porosity' was present in a few localised areas, Fig. 2. Since the residual porosity in these materials is low, grain removal from the surface must have occurred. It is improbable that such grain removal would originate by an intergranular fracture mechanism since the intensity of this 'pop-out' tended to reduce with load rather than increase. A more probable explanation is that suggested by Birkby et al [6], who considered that the grain loss was initiated by transformation of the tetragonal to monoclinic phase, and, in the absence of a matrix constraint, the volume dilation and microcracking resulted in the grain 'pop-out'. Since such a mechanism is not found in abrasive wear, but transformation clearly takes place, the adhesive forces present in sliding wear must be crucial to this mechanism. Thus, as with the Mg-PSZ materials, surface transformation was shown to be detrimental, although the extent of the transformation was minimal.

The majority of the surface for both the Mg-PSZ and Y-TZP pins run against bearing steel discs did not show any evidence of transformation. Indeed, no increase in monoclinic levels could be detected by X-ray diffraction. Given the high stresses generated at the interface, which would be expected to give extensive transformation, this observation suggests that temperature rises at the interface were sufficient to substantially reduce, if not eliminate, the driving force for transformation. This explains why the ceramic wear rate was found to be independent of toughness, with similar wear factors (8-33 x 10^{-7} mm^3/Nm) being found as a function of load for each of the TZP and PSZ materials.

CERAMIC/CERAMIC WEAR

A 3Y-TZP run against a ZTA disc exhibited very high wear rates as a result of extensive surface deformation, Fig. 3. Mixing of the counterface materials had occurred with no evidence of grain relief or transformation. The wear debris was frequently amorphous, containing variable mixtures of Zirconia and Alumina. A proportion of the debris was microcrystalline, with a grain size of the order of 50-100 nm. The tetragonal Zirconia structure contained up to 20 weight % Al^{4+} in solid solution, Fig. 4. When viewed in the dark, small sparks could be seen emerging from the interface. Clearly, recrystallisation must have occurred to produce such a refined grain size which, combined with the mixing of the two materials on an atomic scale, indicates that temperature rises were exceedingly high at the interface. These temperatures had permitted extensive plastic deformation in the near surface region, as demonstrated by cross sectional TEM [3].

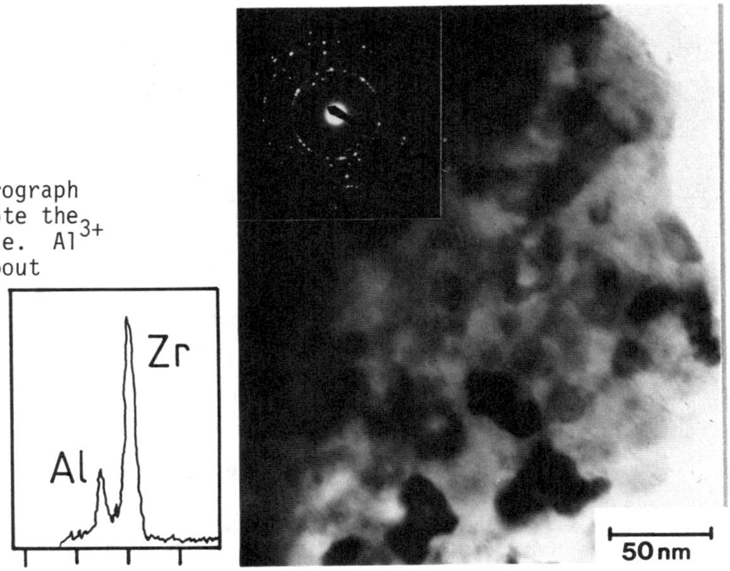

Figure 4. TEM micrograph of wear debris. Note the very fine grain size. Al^{3+} is present up to about 20 wt%.

CONCLUSIONS

Transformation at the worn surface, coupled with adhesive forces, increases the wear rate. Transformation is often suppressed by temperature rises, which are common in sliding wear as a result of the low thermal conductivity of Zirconia. When the Zirconia is mated with a material of low thermal conductivity, such as ZTA, very high temperature rises may occur which lead to gross plastic flow in the Zirconia, intimate mixing of the counterfaces and high wear rates.

REFERENCES

1. Fingerle, D. Ceramics for Engines, Proc. 2nd Int. Conf. on Mat. for Engines. Lubeck-Travemunde, 1986, p.1191.
2. Gulati, S.T., Hansson, J.N. and Hefinstine, J.D., Metal Progress, Feb. 1984, p.21.
3. Rainforth, W.M., Stevens, R. and Nutting, J., to be published.
4. Wallbridge, N., Dowson, D. and Roberts, E.W. Wear of Materials 1983, Ed. Ludema, K.C., Reston Va, ASME, 1983, pp. 202-211.
5. Hannink, R.H.J., Murray, M.J. and Marmach, M., ibid pp. 181-186.
6. Birkby, I., Harrison, P. and Stevens, R. Ceram. Eng. Sci. Proc., 1988, **9**, 1431-1442.

INFLUENCE OF MACHINING ON THE STRENGTH OF HOT-PRESSED SILICON NITRIDE

A.GALLEE; M. NAKAMURA; E. NAGY, D. McGARRY and S. PETEVES,
Hoogovens Groep, 1970 CA IJmuiden, The Netherlands; GIRI Nagoya, Nagoya 462, Japan; Inst. of Adv. Materials, CEC, 1755 ZG Petten, The Netherlands.

ABSTRACT

An extensive study has been conducted to determine the effects of cost-effective machining on the strength of hot-pressed Si_3N_4. The creep-feed cutting method was adopted and compared to the conventional surface grinding. Several machining parameters were evaluated on the basis of statistical flexure strength data, machining efficiency and fractography. Based on the results the optimal grinding/cutting conditions have been assessed.

INTRODUCTION

Advanced structural ceramic components require shaping to their design geometry, dimensional tolerances and surface quality. Despite the continuing efforts for near net-shape processes, machining will remain an expensive factor in the fabrication of structural ceramic components. Several studies have shown the influence of the machining parameters on the strength of the structural ceramics, silicon nitride [1-5], silicon carbide [4,6] and sialon [7], as well as on the efficiency of the process [8-10]. These investigations, mostly conducted under conventional grinding conditions, indicate that strength decreases with increasing material removal rates, with diamond grit size, and when the grinding direction is transverse to the stress axis of the tested piece. Consequently existing standards, for example, for machining 3 or 4-point bending ceramic bars [11,12] recommend that grinding is conducted with very low downfeeds and high table speeds, resulting in long machine times and thus high machine costs. In contrast creep-feed grinding offers significant productivity advantages for equivalent final workpiece quality [13] provided that suitable grinding conditions and machine are selected.

This investigation has been undertaken to evaluate creep-feed cutting in the production route of 4-point bending bars of hot-pressed silicon nitride, and to determine the optimal machining parameters for maximum material strength.

EXPERIMENTAL

The material used in this study was a hot-pressed silicon nitride (Ceradyne Co.) with 8 wt% Y_2O_3 and 1.35 wt% Al_2O_3 as sintering aids. The grinding was carried out on a Jung surface grinder (type JF415). During grinding the wheel and workpiece were cooled with a 1.5 wt% commercial emulsion in water. A resin bonded diamond wheel, grit size D181 and with diamond concentration of 100 was used. Dressing was carried out after each 45 mm cutting length. The surface grinder was equiped with a three-component dynamometer which enabled the measurement of the grinding forces, F_n, F_t and F_a (see Fig. 1) during the machining process. For each set of machining parameters at least 16 bending bars (1.5x2x25 mm^3) were sliced from the ceramic billet (150x150x15 mm^3), so that the short dimension of the tensile face was parallel to the hot-pressing direction. The room temperature fracture strength was measured under 4-point bending (20 mm outer and 10 mm inner span) with a constant downfeed of .5 mm/min. The strength-data were analyzed via Weibull statistics; the Weibull modulus m, characteristic strength σ_o, and the statistical significance (10% level) in the difference in strength between selected sets of data were estimated. Fracture surfaces of the test bars were viewed macroscopically and some of them were fractographically studied using SEM.

Three grinding parameters were investigated with respect to their effect on the strength of the silicon nitride. These were downfeed (h), table speed (v_w) and wheel speed (v_s). These parameters were related to the grinding forces, recorded after cutting 45 mm of the workpiece, and to the dimensional accuracy of the machined samples.

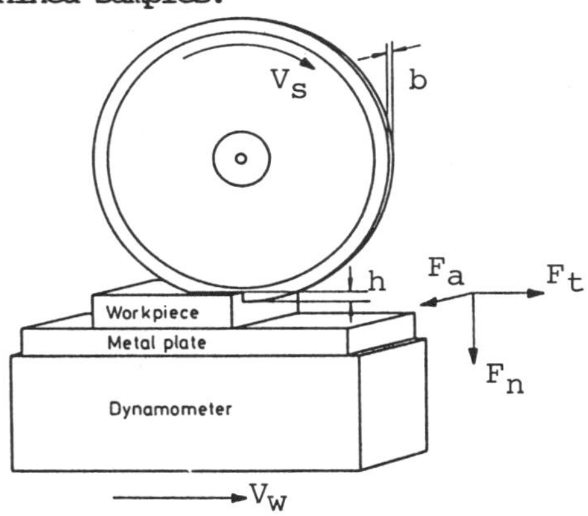

Fig.1: Schematic view of the experimental setup.

RESULTS

Surface grinding versus creep-feed cutting

The surface grinding and creep-feed cutting parameters used are given in Table 1. These creep-feed cutting parameters formed the data base for the later experiments. The flexure strength data of the optimally surface-ground and creep-feed cut bending bars are presented in the Weibull plot of Fig.2. The mean fracture strength, the Weibull analysis parameters and the statistical analysis results are summarized in Table 2.

Creep-feed cutting parameters

Four different downfeed rates were tested namely, 2,3,4 and 5 mm. The wheel speed and table speed were 30 m/s and 100 mm/min, respectively. Although the mean and characteristic strength values are about the same (see Table

TABLE 1: Creep-feed cutting(C.F.C) and surface grinding parameters(S.G)

		C.F.C.	S.G.
Table speed	V_w	100 mm/min	8 m/min
Downfeed	h	2 mm	4 μm
Final 10 μm		-	.5 μm
Crossfeed		-	7 mm/pass
Wheel speed	V_s	30 m/s	30 m/s
MRR (tensile face)		300 mm^3/min	64 mm^3/min
Wheel: Indimant 14A1 KS220		1.5x3 D181 C100	10x3 D46 C75

TABLE 2: Significance (10% level) statistical analysis

Optimally ground	creep-feed cut	creep-feed cut with chamfered edges	
σ = 1053 MPa	1000 MPa	987 MPa	
σ_o = 1090 MPa	1034 MPa	1033 MPa	
m = 15.93	14.67	12.94	
Sign. diff. σ_o	Yes, lower	Yes, lower	
Sign. diff. m	No	No	
V_w = 100 mm/min	V_w = 75 mm/min	V_w = 50 mm/min	
σ = 945 MPa	970 MPa	860 MPa	
σ_o = 994 MPa	1016 Mpa	924 MPa	
m = 9.38	10.00	6.67	
Sign. diff. σ_o	No	Yes, lower	
Sign. diff. m	No	Yes, lower	
Downfeed h = 2 mm	h = 3 mm	h = 4 mm	h = 5 mm
σ = 1000 MPa	1008 MPa	945 MPa	938 MPa
σ_o = 1034 MPa	1064 MPa	994 MPa	994 MPa
m = 14.67	8.61	9.38	8.11
Sign. diff. σ_o	No	Yes, lower	Yes, lower
Sign. diff. m	Yes, lower	Yes, lower	Yes, lower
V_s 30 m/s	V_s = 32 m/s	V_s = 28m/s	V_s = 26m/s
σ = 945 MPa	896 MPa	954 MPa	926 MPa
σ_o = 994 MPa	937 MPa	1004 MPa	970 MPa
m = 9.38	11.59	10.29	10.42
Sign. diff. σ_o	No	No	No
Sign. diff. m	No	No	No

2), there is a significant decrease of the Weibull modulus with increasing downfeed. The increased scatter in the strength data reflects the negative influence of the higher downfeed rates on the final dimensions of the samples, as shown in Fig. 3.

Tests were carried out at three different table speeds, 50, 75 and 100 mm/min, with a wheelspeed of 30 m/s and a downfeed of 4 mm. A low table speed of 50 mm/min results in a drastic decrease of the Weibull modulus (Table 2). On the other hand, table speeds of 75 and 100 mm/min hardly effect the strength data and result in comparable grinding stiffness, F_n/h, (Fig. 4) and dimensional tolerance results.

Four wheel speed values, 32, 30, 28 and 26 m/s were investigated while keeping a table speed of 100 mm/min and a downfeed of 4 mm, but the

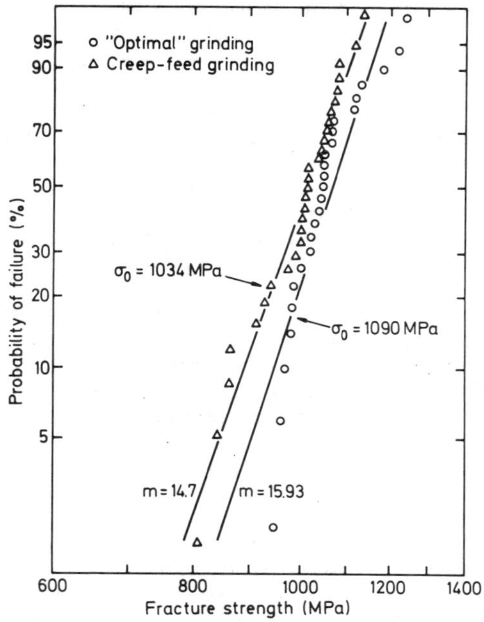

Fig.2: Weibull plot of machined HPSN samples.

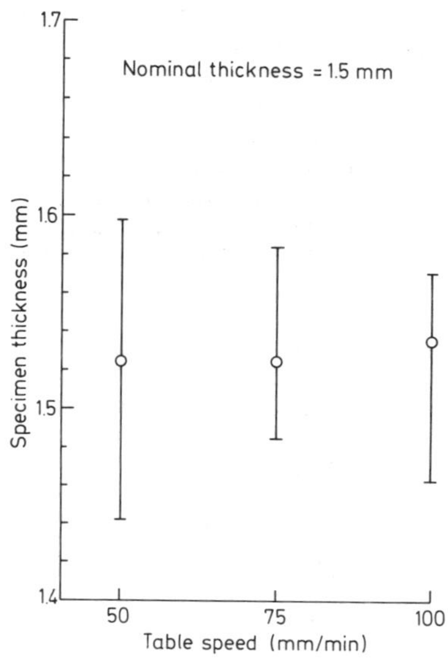

Fig.3: Actual specimen thickness versus table speed.

resulting differences in material strength were negligible (Table 2). The highest wheel speed gives the least machining accuracy while within the narrow range of speeds investigated the grinding stiffness slightly increases with increasing wheel speed.

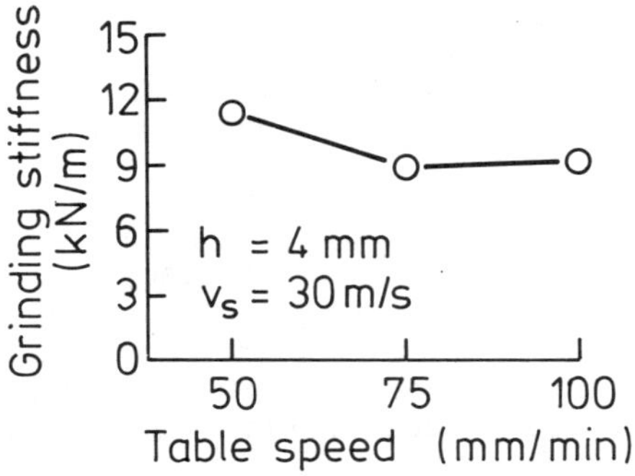

Fig.4: Effect of table speed on grinding stiffness (F_n/h).

DISCUSSION & CONCLUSIONS

This comparison of optimally ground and creep-feed cut bend bars, as shown in Fig. 2 and Table 2, indicates that creep-feed cutting is a very adequate time saving machining route for preparing ceramic test pieces. The statistical significance analysis (Table 2) showed that the scatter in the strength data is essentially the same in each case. However, the optimally ground samples showed a higher characteristic strength. Fractography examinations did not reveal any difference in the failure originating flaws between the two sets of samples.

Increased downfeed rates did not effect the fracture strength of the creep-feed cut bars, but drastically reduce the Weibull modulus by almost 50% for downfeeds larger than 2 mm, owing to the effect of downfeed rates on the final dimensional tolerance of the bending bars and thus on the parallelity of their top and bottom faces. The large normal grinding force associated with the higher downfeed rates deteriorates the machining accuracy. However, the retention of material strength suggests that the induced machining flaw population on the ceramic surface was not significantly changed by varying downfeed and table speed rates. During creep-feed cutting the axial grinding force F_a is the most important concerning surface damage. Although the measured axial forces were the highest for the deepest cut and the lowest table speed, still their magnitude was less than 10 N/mm and their increase with increasing downfeed and decreasing table speed was negligible. In metal grinding usually in order to improve productivity the wheel speed is increased. In the case of ceramics machining typically wheel speeds in the order of 30 m/s are used, with higher wheel speeds usually being avoided. The results of this study point out that, within the limited range of wheel speeds investigated, the wheel speed hardly affects any the resulting silicon nitride strength after machining (Table 2). Hence it would be interesting to evaluate if further improvements in machining efficiency could be obtained with increased wheel speeds.

Creep-feed cutting was shown to be a viable method in preparing bending bars of silicon nitride. The problem of utmost importance is the increased machining error due to the high grinding forces resulting from the large downfeeds. Consequently, in order to further improve the method higher rigid wheels and grinding machines are required.

REFERENCES

[1] C.Cm. Wu and K.R. McKinney, in The Science of Ceramic Machining and Surface Finishing II. Eds. R.W. Rice and B.J. Hockey., NBS, Special Pub.562, 1979, 477-81.

[2] C.A. Anderson and R.J. Bratton, ibid, 463-76.

[3] R.L. Allor, R.K. Govila and T.I. Whalen, in Proc.of the 10th Automotive Mat.Conf.. The Am. Ceram. Soc., Columbus, OH, 1982,392-404.

[4] R.L. Allor and R.R. Baker, Am. Soc. of Mech. Eng. 83-GT-203, 1983.

[5] M.B. Thomas, R.D. West and W.E. West Jr., in Proceedings of Intersociety Symposium on Machining of Advanced Ceramic Materials and Components. Eds. R.E. Barks, K. Subramanian and K.E. Ball. The Am. Ceram. Soc., Westerville, OH, 1987,218-34.

[6] W. König and J. Wemhöner, Am. Ceram. Soc. Bull., 1989,68,546-48.

[8] M.Hawman,P.Cohen,J.Conway and R.Pangborn,J.Mater.Sci.,1985,20,482-90.

[9] R.W.McEachron and S.C.Lorence, Am.Ceram.Soc.Bull., 1988,67,1031-36.

[10] T. Nakagawa and K.Suzuki, Annals of the CIRP, 1986,35,205-10.

[11] I. Inasaki and K. Nakayama, Annals of the CIRP, 1986,35,211-14.

[12] Jap. Ind. Stand., JIS R 1601, (1981).

[13] Mil. Stand., MIL - STD - 1942 (MR), (1983).

[14] K. Subramanian, Am. Ceram. Soc. Bull., 1988,67,1026-29.

CONTROL OF SURFACE DAMAGE IN ABRASIVE MACHINING OF ENGINEERING CERAMICS

E. LIJBRINK
Netherlands Energy Research Foundation ECN
P.O. Box 1, 1755 ZG, Petten, NL

C.A. van LUTTERVELT, J.J. SAURWALT
Delft University of Technology
Landbergstraat 3, 2628 CE, NL

ABSTRACT

This paper addresses the exploration of current basic knowledge and material engineering practices to find a serviceable way for a systematic approach of surface quality control in machining of engineering ceramics by grinding.

INTRODUCTION

In the field of development, production and application of new materials or of specially improved qualities of a sort, the reliability and unambiguity of specific property data and experimental test results is an essential prerequisite. Since the usefulness of ceramic materials in general is limited by their characteristic sensitivity for brittle fracture, the results of typical load tests are of considerable importance to a critical assessment of product quality.

The mechanical strength of a ceramic component depends to a variable extent on the internal defect structure of the base material. Those defects being located by random accident at the surface of the object play a decisive role in the onset of fracture. The eventual surface effect can be dealt with mathematically by appropriately standardizing the test method on the basis of statistical considerations. The actual test specimens have to be finish-machined accurately according to strictly imposed requirements, which can be met almost excludingly by grinding with diamond tools. As a consequence of abrasive machining, however, an additional category of surface defects is introduced which is alien to the inherent defect structure of the bulk material, and thus interferes with the generation of unambiguous test data. To neutralize also this effect, it is necessary to standardize the test specimen manufacturing routine as well.

Because of the relatively large stiffness and the small capacity for plastic deformation of ceramics, the bend test is a most practicable way of producing quantitative information on the strength and load-carrying properties of singular material samples. In view of the appreciably large numbers of test specimens required by statistical approaches, there is a large need for having effective control of those processing conditions which will lead consistently to a well defined test specimen quality. In this connection an investigation was started which is aimed at finding a practicable solution for the problem of surface damage by machining, on the basis of currently established knowledge and state of the art grinding techniques.

METHOD OF INVESTIGATION

Drawing on a continuing study of relevant literature, an outline was made of the current state of fundamental knowledge, theoretical modelling and working know-how in the field of grinding technology. The historic development of understanding the elements of grinding was based on empirical approaches by conducting grinding experiments of many sorts. In the first instance these were aimed at getting a knowledgeable grip on those processing conditions leading to outstanding achievements in the way of shaping, dimensional accuracy and surface finish of products made of iron and steel. The primary quantities which govern the kinetics of grinding are:

- v_c , the cutting speed, which is practically equal to the peripheral speed of the grinding wheel.
- a_e , the working engagement, which determines the thickness of the layer which is removed by a single continuous stroke of the machine.
- v_{ft}, the tangential table feed speed, or the relative velocity of the work surface towards the engaging area of the wheel periphery.

The principal feature of these basic process parameters is that they are independently adjustable variables. Investigators are constantly attempting to relate systematically observed effects to a specific influence of a single basic variable or of a particular compound parameter. Several models of the latter have been the subject of extensive experimental endeavour. Four of those have come forward as appreciably strong process variables, i.c.:

$$Q_w' = v_{ft} \cdot a_e \qquad (1)$$

$$v_{ft} / v_c \qquad (2)$$

$$h_{eq} = (v_{ft}/v_c) \cdot a_e \qquad (3)$$

$$l_g = \sqrt{a_e . d_s} \qquad (d_s = \text{wheel diameter}) \qquad (4)$$

Generally the investigations are directed at the assessment of the effect of specific parameters on the economics of grinding in terms of production rate and toolwear, next to surface finish quality in terms of relevant roughness numbers. Through the measurement of grinding forces it has been attempted to determine the relative power of single parameters from the quantitative evolution of F_t or F_n with incremental readjustments of the parameter in question. By relating significant characteristics of the variation of the grinding force to particular grinding results, it is expected to get a hold on the predictability of the practical consequences of an effective parameter setting.

Currently the perspectives of producing structural ceramics with wittingly tailored properties seem to be growing. These in turn provoke the development of new products of an advanced nature for applications of special importance. In those instances where high demands are exacted with respect to the accuracy of shape and final dimensions, there is practically no escape from the necessity of using grinding techniques in the finish machining process. At the introduction of a new category of structural materials it is natural, when setting out on proving the applicability of grinding methods, to revert to formerly established notions and relevant practices. Although basically the kinetics remain unaltered, the results of grinding structural ceramics are markedly related to the particular quality of single material samples. Because of the friable nature of ceramics the material is generally removed piecemeal in small fragments which are knocked out of the surface layer by brittle fracture, under the action of local forces being exerted by the cutting edges of individual diamond grains. During grinding some forms of sub-surface damage are introduced including particularly unfavorable microcracks. The latter can grow into potential sources of brittle fracture in case the component is loaded under critical conditions. For this reason an eventual enhancement of the sensitiveness for brittle fracture should be considered as an issue of conclusive interest, when purposefully staking out a practicable setting of the basic grinding parameters.

The extent of damage is determined by the intensity of forces being exerted by individual abrasive grains, so generally speaking the measurement of grinding forces has become part and parcel of grinding parameter and modelling studies. In a remarkable treatise by H. Möhlen [1] on the internal and external cylindrical grinding of a number of dense structural ceramics, the respective results of such measurements of F_n were discussed. Relative to discriminate parameters considered, the value of F_n appeared to take different courses during grinding in these two geometrically opposed configurations. Although in both cases the basic parameter settings were identical, internal grinding consistently yielded larger values of F_n than external grinding. Möhlen reasoned that thee apparent normal force must reflect the sum of the forces exerted by each of the simultaneously engaging abrasive grains. The number of grains in simultaneous engagement is proportional to the geometrically determined contact length l_g, which is the length of the arc of permanent contact between wheel circumference and work. The geometry of internal grinding apparently leads up to a longer arc of contact. So, under basically similar working conditions per grain, the number of effectually engaged grains will be larger in that case, which explains the consistently higher level of the resultant F_n connected with internal grinding.

Next Möhlen related the work done by a specific force per grain, F_n'/l_g, to the mean contribution of each working grain to the buildup of the equivalent continuous chip thickness h_{eq}, for the expression of which the latter also must be divided by l_g. When the experimental results were put up in this particular relationship, the results of both grinding configurations appeared to fall on a single curve. It was shown by the facts that by bringing in the compound parameter h_{eq}/l_g a relationship emerges which covers both lay-outs of the grinding process. From the given definitions of h_{eq} and l_g it can be concluded that:

$$h_{eq} / l_g = (1/\sqrt{d_s}) \cdot (v_{ft}/v_c) \cdot \sqrt{a_e} \qquad (5)$$

By the authors it is argued that, in terms of system geometry, surface grinding is nothing else but an intermediate form of grinding to be classed somewhere in-between internal and external cylindrical grinding. Relevant to the objectives of this investigation it was concluded therefore that any particular effect of surface grinding should get in with those of the other two grinding modes into the same generalized relationship with the parameter h_{eq}/l_g. Pursuing this notion it was inferred that an eventual derogation of the fracture strength of a fabricated component like a bend test beam specimen should be standing in some straightforward relation with h_{eq}/l_g as well, since the surface damage causing the problem is directly related to the working forces transmitted by the actively working individual grains.

To get an illustrative picture of such a relationship, from a number of different sources [2,3,4] the results of flexure strength tests were selected to be put up against the matching values of h_{eq}/l_g that could be assessed from the available information regarding the fabrication details of the bend test specimens involved. The result of this data processing operation is shown in the annexed graphical representation, in which own results are included under the designation NKA. From this strikingly straightforward looking picture it appears that the flexure strength σ_0 is related to the grinding parameter h_{eq}/l_g according to a generalized linear expression:

$$\sigma_0 = A + B.[P] \qquad \text{in which } P = h_{eq}/l_g \qquad (6)$$

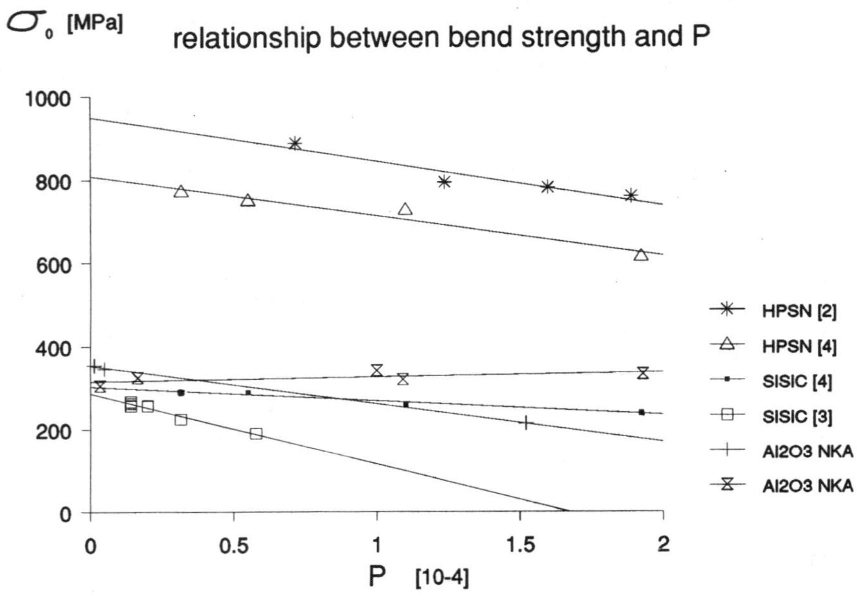

CONCLUSION

To meet current demands for reliable information on the fracture strength of structural ceramics, large numbers of beam-type bend test specimens have to be fabricated from ceramic material samples involving the use of grinding techniques. Under unfavorable grinding conditions microcracks and other defects may be introduced in the surface layer of the product. Because of the friable nature of structural ceramics, surface defects lower the fracture strength of any product and thus tend to spoil the unambiguity of bend test results. An examination of the literature regarding the current state of fundamental knowledge, theoretical modelling and working know-how in the field of grinding technology revealed a straightforward relationship between bend test results and the applied specific grinding conditions. It was shown that the flexure strength is related to the basic grinding parameters according to a generalized linear expression from which a practicable setting of the process parameters can be derived.

REFERENCES

1. Möhlen, H., Vergleichende Untersuchungen beim Innen- und Außenrundschleifen keramischer Werkstoffe, Vortrag anläßlich des Seminars 'Feinbearbeitung nichtmetallischer Werkstoffe' im Haus der Technik, Essen, 28-11-1985.

2. Thomas, M.B., West, R.D., West, W.E., Wyckoff, K., Effect of Machining Parameters On The Surface Finish And Strength Of Hot Pressed Silicon Nitride, THERM Incorporated Ithaca, New York.

3. König, W., Wemhöner, J., Optimizing Grinding of SiSiC, Ceramic Bulletin, 1989, **68**, No. 3, pp. 545-548.

4. Spur, G., Tio, T.H., Schleifschäden an der oberflächenrandzone keramischer Werkstoffe, IDR, 1987, **4**, pp. 234-242.

DETERMINATION OF RESIDUAL STRESSES CAUSED BY GRINDING OF SILICON NITRIDE CERAMICS

T. PRADELL, P.GLAUDE & S.D. PETEVES
Institute of Advanced Materials, CEC,
1755 ZG Petten, The Netherlands.
&
A.W.J.J. GALLEE
Hoogovens Groep,
1970 CA Ijmuiden, The Netherlands.

ABSTRACT

The residual surface stresses introduced in silicon nitride ceramics by abrasive machining have been studied. An X-ray stress analysis technique has been used for the characterization of the stresses on the Si_3N_4 surface prepared by several machining routes [1]. The appropriate x-ray elastic constants of the (323)-Si_3N_4 plane were measured and the residual stresses estimated.

INTRODUCTION

The properties of ceramics are more sensitive to surface defects than any other class of engineering materials. On the other hand most post-processing and assembly procedures of ceramic components create surface residual stresses which are detrimental to the surface integrity and strength of these materials. Abrasive machining and finishing for example, a routine manufacturing step for ceramic components, induces a sub-surface damage which can be the major strength reducing factor [2]. Consequently, the residual stresses need to be determined in order to assess the effect of surface conditioning on the properties of structural ceramic components and to evaluate further surface treatements designed to improve the useful strength of these materials.

X-ray stress analysis has been widely applied to the measurement of residual stresses in metals and, more recently, in ceramics [3-5]. The technique which is in principle non-destructive is ideally suited for quite shallow (tens of microns) depths and hence, for measuring near-surface residual stresses. Authoritative reviews exist on the principles and background of this technique [6], which is based on the property that a residual stress will alter the lattice spacing and therefore, the Bragg diffraction angle for a specific (hkl) plane. By evaluating this change of angle it is then possible to measure the strain and convert it to an equivalent stress via the isotropic theory of elasticity, provided that the elastic constants specific to the (hkl) plane are known [6].

The objectives of the present study were to develop a procedure for measuring the residual stresses in silicon nitride ceramics using the $\sin^2\Phi$ method of X-ray stress analysis, and to make a preliminary investigation of the effect of machining conditions on the residual deformation of the machined ceramic surface, whose strength has also been evaluated [1].

EXPERIMENTAL PROCEDURES

The material investigated was a hot-pressed silicon nitride with 8wt% Y_2O_3 and 1.35wt% Al_2O_3 as additives (Ceradyne Co.). A computer-automated Ω-type diffractometer (Phillips PW-1040), equipped with a proportional detector was used. The (323)-Si_3N_4 diffraction peak was selected as most suitable for the incident CuKα radiation (2θ = 141.56°), with penetration depths of 30μm (67% of the diffracted x-ray signal). The spot was 2x12.5 mm^2, and a step scan of 0.02° for a 2θ range of 140° to 143.5° was used; different fixed counting times for the samples depending on their size and on the effective irradiated area were used (12s for the samples used in the calibration and 4s and 24s, respectively for the machined samples analyzed in the parallel and in the perpendicular direction to the machining one). Each measurement was made using 13 tilt angles (-40° to +40°). The peak position after linear background substraction and LPA correction, was determined by the apex of an 11 to 15 point parabolic fit to the top portion of the diffracted profile [6].

Determination of X-ray elastic constants

For the determination of the (323) plane elastic constants bar specimens of 4x2x33mm^3 with three different surface treatments were used. All samples were first surface ground (D46 grit diamond wheel, 30 m/s wheel speed 8m/min table speed, 0.5μm depth of cut); subsequently one was polished to a final stage with 3μm diamond paste (20μm of surface material removed) and another was annealed (1200°C, 6h, N_2 gas pressure of 1MPa).

The experimental procedure involved first the determination of the bulk elastic modulus for each sample under 4-point bending, using strain gauges. The strain gauged sample was placed in an in-situ 4-point bend self-aligning loading jig (20 mm outer and 10 mm inner span) and mounted on the diffractometer (Fig.1). The X-ray elastic constants were obtained then by correlating the measured lattice strains (determined from the x-ray peak shifts) under known applied stresses (evaluated from the calibrated strain gauge) [6].

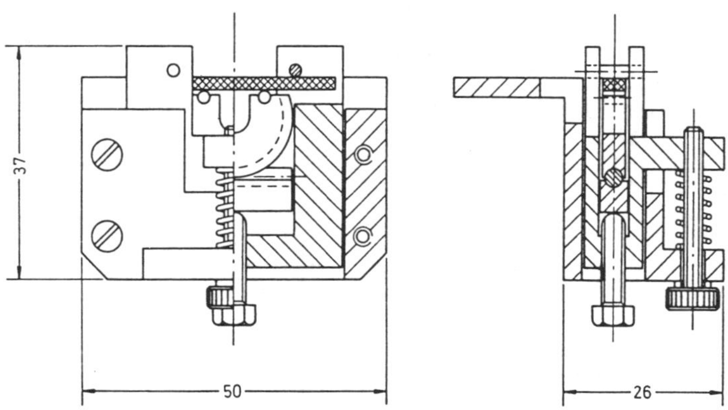

Fig. 1 Four-point bending jig for measuring X-ray Elastic Constants.

Evaluation of residual stresses caused by machining

The residual stresses induced by three machining routes [1], as given in Table 1, were measured on samples of 2x1.5x25 mm^3, in the direction of parallel and perpendicular to the machining direction. Furthermore, the residual stresses were also measured in another set of samples machined under fixed creep-feed grinding conditions (D126 grit, 30 m/s wheel speed, 100 mm/min table speed) while varying the depth of cut (5-50μm). The calculated statistical precision [7] in the stress determination was 7.2 MPa for the perpendicular direction and 8.9 MPa for the parallel direction. Surface stress measurements were made on two samples for each machining condition.

TABLE 1. Machining Conditions

Parameters	1	2	3
Table speed (m/min)	8	0.1	0.1
Wheel speed (m/s)	30	30	30
Depth of cut (μm)	0.5	$2x10^3$	$2x10^3$
Grit size	D46	D181	D181
Chamfered edges	No	No	Yes

RESULTS

X-ray elastic constants

Fig.2 shows the lattice spacing/$\sin^2\Phi$ relation for (323) diffraction of the polished sample under several applied stresses as indicated. The X-ray elastic constants $1/2s_2=(1+v)/E$ and $s_1=-v/E$, are obtained from the slopes and the cutting points ($d_{\Phi=0}$) of d_Φ vs. $\sin^2\Phi$ lines as a function of applied stress, respectively (Fig.3a,3b) [6]. The determined elastic constants and measured bulk modulus for all of the samples are summarized in Table 2.

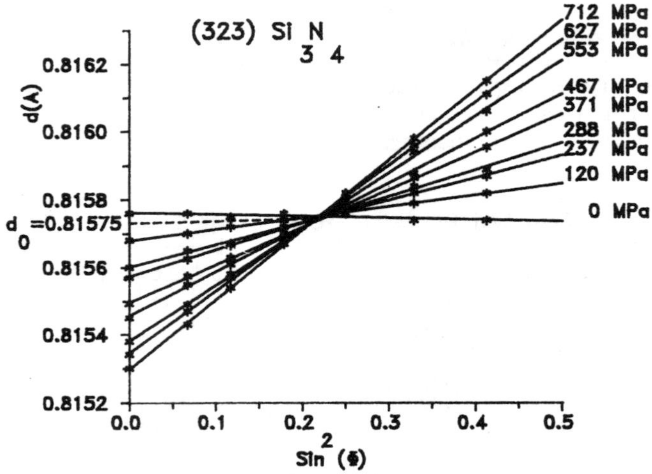

Fig.2 Lattice Spacing vs. $\sin^2\Phi$ as a function of applied stress.

TABLE 2. X-ray Elastic Constants

Sample	d_0 (Å)	$1/2s_2$	s_1	v (*)	v (+)	E XRD (GPa)	E (GPa)
As machined	0.81576(2)	3.58(6)	−0.78(2)	0.29(2)	0.277(7)	357(8)	340
Polished	0.81575(2)	3.66(6)	−0.80(2)	0.28(2)	0.282(7)	351(8)	349
Annealed	0.81570(2)	3.69(5)	−0.82(2)	0.29(2)	0.284(6)	348(6)	346

(*) Calculated from the crossing point of $d(\sigma)$ vs. $\sin^2\Phi$.[3]
(+) Calculated from the values of $1/2s_2$ and s_1.

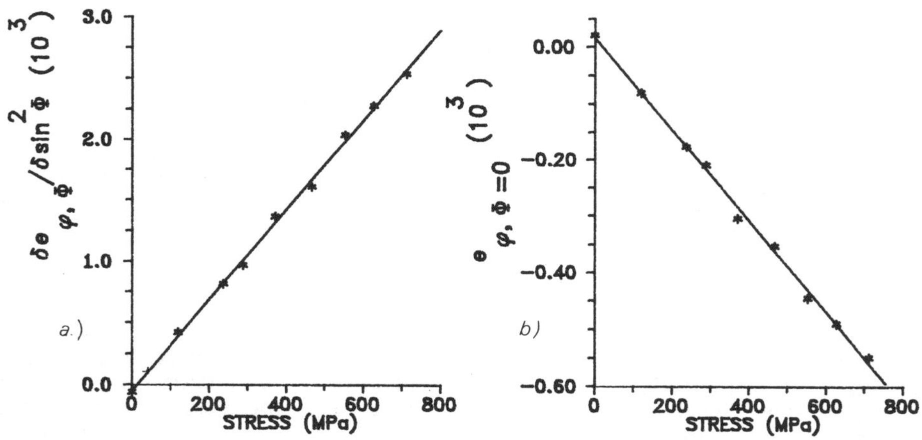

Fig.3 a) Lattice strain as a function of $\sin^2\Phi$ vs. applied stress.
b) Lattice strain as function of $\sin^2\Phi$ (at Φ=0) vs. applied stress.

Residual stress measurements

Table 3 lists the residual stress results for the machined samples, calculated using the experimentally determined elastic constants. The average fracture strengths (4-pt bending) of the machined samples [1] are also listed in Table 3.

TABLE 3. Residual Stresses of Machined Samples

Machining conditions (see Table 1)	Strength σ_f (MPa)	Residual Stresses $\sigma\|\|$* (MPa)	$\sigma\perp$*
1	1053	-12(6)	-25(4)
2	1000	-2(5)	-17(5)
3	987	-2(4)	32(5)

(*) || Parallel to the grinding direction.
⊥ Perpendicular to the grinding direction.

The effects of varying the downfeed during creep-feed grinding and of surface finishing for Si_3N_4 are shown in **fig.4**.

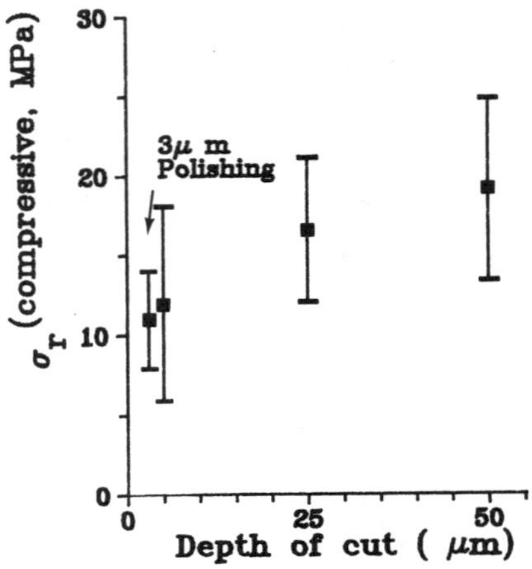

Fig. 4 Variation of residual stresses in creep-feed ground surfaces with depth of cut. The residual stresses of a sample polished with 3μm diamond paste are also shown.

DISCUSSION & CONCLUSIONS

Based on the present results the determined x-ray elastic constants are in very good agreement with the corresponding bulk values. Most important this method allows for a correct determination of the stress free lattice spacing (d_0) and of the elastic constants regardless of any treatment or finishing of the surface.

Surface grinding of Si_3N_4 has been shown to produce significant compressive residual stresses (up to 70-100MPa [3-5]) that extend to a depth as much as 30μm [4]. However, the measured low stress values of the machined samples (Table 3) most likely result from the adopted machining route in combination with the deep penetrating Cu-radiation. It is evident that the majority of the residual stresses in our case are within a surface layer < 30μm deep. Most of the measured values are within or near the indicated accuracy of our technique, which suggests that a less penetrating radiation (e.g. Cr) would be more beneficial in studying the machining damage.

Nevertheless, the measurements imply that creep-feed cutting (see Table 1, conditions 2 & 3), a far more productive machining route than surface grinding [1], does not induce increased residual stresses. These results concur with earlier findings that flexural strength was not significantly different for the three machining conditions (see Table 3). The residual stresses in the direction transverse to the grinding direction are higher than these along the grinding direction, which is consistent with earlier observations [4,5]. However, tensile transverse stresses were measured in the samples with chamfered edges, which is not understood, but it should be noted that these samples also showed the lowest strength and Weibull modulus among the variably machined samples [1]. Additional machining of the samples along their edges probably alters and further complicates the stress tensor due to grinding.

The observed increase in residual stresses with depth of cut during creep-feed grinding reaffirms the importance of the grinding force (normal to the ceramic surface) [8] on the machining damage. It seems that ceramic machining can be conducted at relatively large depths of cut only if the grinding forces are kept low by optimizing the grinding parameters, as in the case of creep-feed cutting [1].

REFERENCES

1. A. Gallee, M. Nakamura, D. McGarry, E. Nagy and S.D. Peteves, Influence of Machining on the Strength of Hot-Pressed Silicon Nitride, in this Proceedings.
2. R.L. Allor and R.R. Baker, Amer. Soc. of Mech. Eng. 83-GT-203, 1983.
3. Prümmer, R. & Pfeiffer-Vollmar, H.W. Determination of surface stresses of high temperature ceramic materials. Reunion franco allemande sur l'analyse des constraintes par Diffraction X. Freiburg 1983, 89-98.
4. K. Tanaka, T. Kurimura, E. Matsui and Y. Akiniwa, J. Soc. Mater. Sci. Japan, 36[407]1987, 33-38.
5. D. Johnson-Walls, A.G. Evans, D.B. Marshall and M.R. James, J. Amer. Ceram. Soc., 69[1]1986, 44-47.
6. a) M.R. James and J.B. Cohen, in Treatise on Materials Science and Technology, H. Hermon ed., Academic, NY, vol. 19 (1980), 1-62.
   b) V.M. Hauk and E. Macherauch, Adv. X-ray Anal., 27(1984), 81-99.
7. M.R. James and J.B. Cohen, Adv. X-ray Anal., 20(1977), 291-308.
8. K. Subramanian, Amer. Ceram. Soc. Bull., 67[6](1988), 1026-30.

X–RAY STRESS DETERMINATION IN ENGINEERING CERAMICS AND CERAMIC/METAL COMPOUNDS

B. EIGENMANN, B. SCHOLTES AND E. MACHERAUCH
Institut für Werkstoffkunde I, Universität Karlsruhe (TH),
Kaiserstrasse 12, D–7500 Karlsruhe 1, FRG

INTRODUCTION

In ceramic parts and ceramic/metal compounds, residual stresses are introduced by any processing step during manufacturing, e.g. by sintering, heat treating, machining, and joining. They may affect the mechanical behaviour of the parts either in a beneficial or a detrimental way. X–ray stress determination has proved to be a reliable method to determine residual and loading stresses in ceramic materials in a nondestructive way [1]. For the assessment of X–ray residual stress measurements, one has to distinguish between single-phase materials, multiphase materials and compounds of different materials. In this paper, some examples of typical residual stress distributions in ceramics and ceramic/metal compounds are presented, and their influence on the behaviour of materials and components is discussed.

X–RAY RESIDUAL STRESS DETERMINATION

Residual stresses are self-equilibrating stresses which exist in a material without external loading. With respect to the microstructure of the material investigated, a distinction is made between I., II., and III. kind residual stresses [2]. I. kind residual stresses are constant over large areas of the component, whereas II. kind residual stresses are constant over one grain, only. III. kind residual stresses are inhomogeneous over few atomic distances. The residual stresses at each point of a material can be described as the sum of residual stresses of the I., II, and III. kind. Only I. and II. kind residual stresses will be discussed in this paper.

The X–ray diffraction method is based on the fact that X–rays are diffracted by surface-near crystallites of polycrystalline materials. The angular positions θ of the maxima of the diffracted intensity are given by Bragg's law

$$\lambda = 2D \sin\theta \tag{1}$$

where λ is the wavelength of the monochromatic X–rays used, and D is the spacing of the crystallographic planes $\{hkl\}$ investigated. The total differentiation of eq. 1 directly yields the relation

$$\epsilon = \frac{D - D_0}{D_0} = -\cot\theta_0\,(\theta - \theta_0) \tag{2}$$

between the lattice strains ϵ and the angular shift of the diffracted intensity $(\theta - \theta_0)$ which can easily be measured by X–ray diffractometry. The values indexed with "0" relate to the stress-free state of the lattice. Referring to the sample-fixed coordinate system shown in fig. 1, the strain component $\epsilon_{\varphi\psi}$, measured according to eq. 2 in any direction given by the azimuth angle φ and the distance angle ψ, can be written for a biaxial surface stress state as

$$\epsilon_{\varphi\psi} = \frac{\nu^{X-ray}+1}{E^{X-ray}}\,\sigma_\varphi\,\sin^2\psi - \frac{\nu^{X-ray}}{E^{X-ray}}\,(\sigma_1+\sigma_2) \quad (3)$$

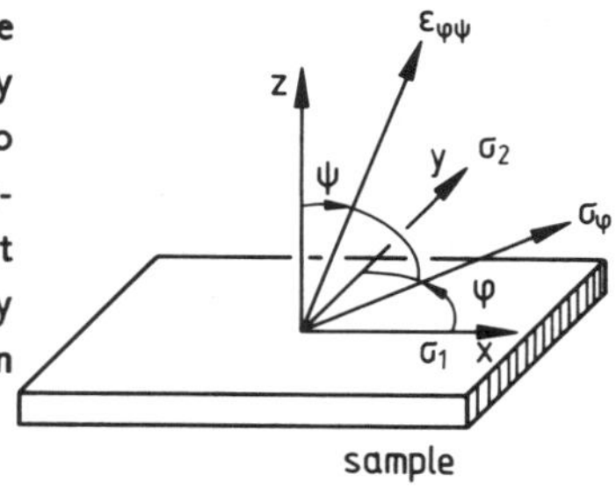

Figure 1: Coordinate system and angles used.

E^{X-ray} and ν^{X-ray} are Young's modulus and Poisson's ratio, respectively. They represent special X-ray elastic constants (XEC) which account for the elastic anisotropy and the coupling conditions of the crystallites in polycrystalline materials. Eq. 3 shows that, if lattice strains $\epsilon_{\varphi\psi}$ are measured in one azimuth $\varphi = const.$ and plotted versus $\sin^2\psi$, in case of a homogeneous biaxial stress state parallel to the surface, a straight line results. From the slope $\frac{\nu^{X-ray}+1}{E^{X-ray}}\,\sigma_\varphi$ of this line, the normal stress component σ_φ parallel to the surface of the sample in direction φ can readily be determined (s. fig. 1). This is the principle of the $\sin^2\psi$–method of X–ray stress analysis [3], which is commonly applied for X–ray stress determinations.

QUENCHING RESIDUAL STRESSES

Standard 4–point bending specimens of pure Al_2O_3 with ground surfaces were annealed or quenched as shown in fig. 2. Then the resulting surface residual stresses and bending strengths were determined. X–ray measurements were performed on the $\{416\}$–lattice planes using $Cu\ K\alpha$–radiation and the elastic constants $E^{X-ray} = 386\ GPa$ and $\nu^{X-ray} = 0.27$. The results are presented in fig. 2.

If the compressive grinding residual stresses in the surface are released by annealing for $2\ h$ at 1350^0C, a decrease of the bending strength results. Quenching the samples in oil or an oil–water emulsion leads to a mesh of thermoshock cracks in the surface layers of the sample, which is clearly visible due to the burnt–in traces of the silicon oil. Consequently, after quenching from 1450^0C, only a negligible small bending strenght is measured. Increasing compressive residual stresses in the surface layers and increasing bending strenghts of the

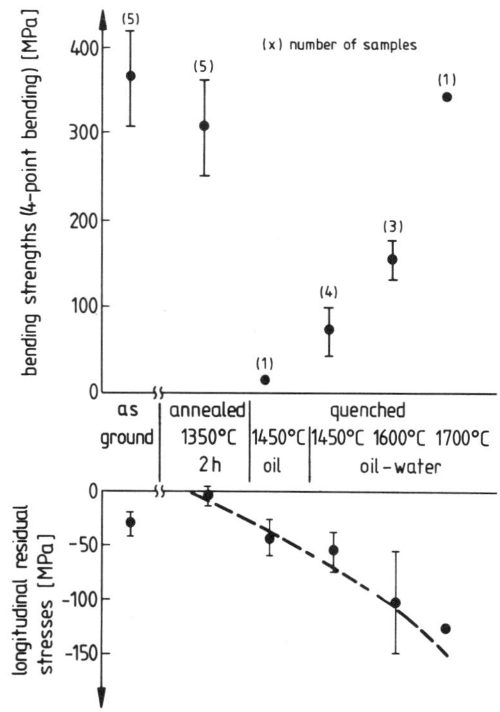

Figure 2: Longitudinal residual stresses and bending strengths of differently treated samples of alumina.

samples are found with increasing quenching temperature. In spite of the cracks, the sample quenched from 1700^0C reaches approximately the strength of the as ground samples. This may be attributed to the consequences of compressive residual stresses in presence of cracks. Cracks in a compressive residual stress field cannot open or spread until the compressive residual stresses are completely compensated by tensile loading stresses.

GRINDING RESIDUAL STRESSES

In most cases, grinding is necessary as final treatment of ceramic components. It is well known that machining of ceramics influences the strength of the parts by introducing cracks and residual stresses into a shallow surface layer. In order to assess the effect of grinding on the strength of components, it is of high interest to know the grinding residual stress state near the surface. As an example, fig. 3 gives a qualitative impression of the residual stresses in grinding direction in the surface of Al_2O_3/TiC $(5\ vol. - \%)$. The measured residual stresses are weighted averages over the penetration depth $\tau = \frac{\sin\theta \cos\psi}{2\mu(\lambda)}$ at $\sin^2\psi = 0.3$ of the X-rays, which is a more or less arbitrarily chosen mean value. τ represents the thickness of the surface layer from which 63% of the diffracted intensity stem, and $\mu(\lambda)$ is the linear absorption coefficient of the material for the X-rays used. A decrease of the penetration depth can be achieved by choosing diffraction profiles $\{hkl\}$ at low Bragg angles θ and by using X-rays with increasing wavelengths. It is found that the measured residual stresses increase tremendously if the penetration depth of the X-rays is decreased. Near the surface, very high compressive residual stresses are found. They might be even higher at the very surface, but the penetration depth cannot be decreased any further with standard measuring and evaluation techniques.

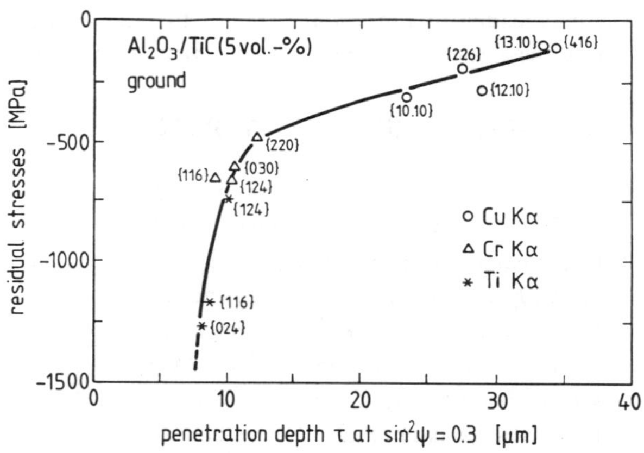

Figure 3: Grinding residual stresses in Al_2O_3 / TiC $(5\ vol. - \%)$.

RESIDUAL AND LOADING STRESSES IN MULTIPHASE MATERIALS

The selective diffraction of X-rays by crystallites with different crystal structures allows the determination of residual stresses in individual phases of multiphase materials. An example is given in fig. 4 for ZrO_2 (YTZP) / Al_2O_3 $(26.6\ vol. - \%)$. The measurements were performed with $Cu\ K\alpha$-radiation on the $\{416\}$-planes of the alumina phase and on the $\{440/404\}$-planes of the zirconia phase. In the as ground state, the sample showed compressive surface residual stresses which were higher in the ZrO_2-phase than in the Al_2O_3-phase. From this, the I. kind residual stresses in the surface can be calculated as

$$\overline{\sigma}^{RS} = \sigma^{RS}_{Al_2O_3}\, v_{Al_2O_3} + \sigma^{RS}_{ZrO_2}\, v_{ZrO_2} \tag{4}$$

where $v_{Al_2O_3}$ and v_{ZrO_2} are the volume fractions of the different phases, respectively.

Loading the sample with defined tensile stresses σ^{LS} leads to a linear increase of the stresses $\sigma_{Al_2O_3}$ and σ_{ZrO_2} in the individual phases. Due to the higher elastic modulus of Al_2O_3 compared to ZrO_2, the increase of stresses is more pronounced in the Al_2O_3–phase (s. fig. 4: $m_{Al_2O_3} = 1.4$, $m_{ZrO_2} = 0.9$). Calculating the I. kind stresses $\overline{\sigma}$ in analogy to eq. 4, it is found that residual stresses of the I. kind $\overline{\sigma}^{RS}$ and loading stresses σ^{LS} superimpose linearly, since $\overline{m} = 1$. The fact that $m_{Al_2O_3} \neq m_{ZrO_2}$ makes clear that also the average II. kind stresses $\sigma^{II}_{Al_2O_3} = \sigma_{Al_2O_3} - \overline{\sigma}$ and $\sigma^{II}_{ZrO_2} = \sigma_{ZrO_2} - \overline{\sigma}$ increase with increasing load σ^{LS}. This means that, in addition to the II. kind residual stresses (s. fig. 4 at $\sigma^{LS} = 0$), also II. kind loading stresses occur, which cause an increasing loading of the grain boundaries. Effects like this might contribute to the characteristic strength of distinct multiphase ceramics compared to single–phase materials.

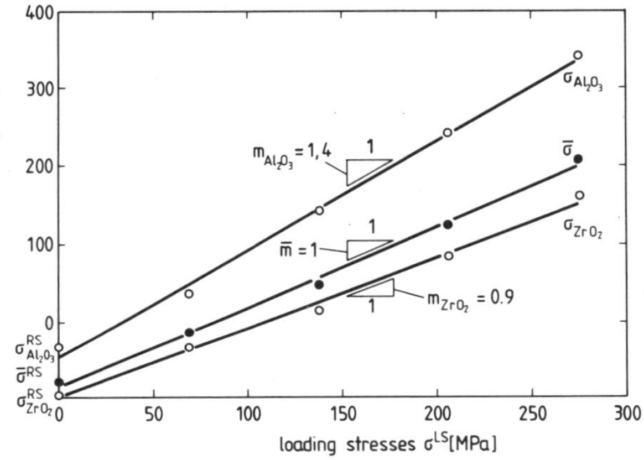

Figure 4: Residual and loading stresses in ZrO_2 / Al_2O_3 ($26.6\ vol. - \%$).

RESIDUAL STRESSES IN BRAZED COMPOUNDS OF Si_3N_4 AND STEEL

If ceramic and steel plates are joined by brazing at high temperatures (about 900^oC) in order to obtain a surface with high wear– and heat resistance, the compounds develop a complex residual stress state during cooling down to room temperature due to the thermal mismatch of the components used. As shown in the upper part of fig. 5 for Si_3N_4 and steel (german grade $Ck\ 45$), steel will shrink more than the ceramic plate which causes a bending of the entire compound. Consequently, tensile residual stresses result in the surface of the ceramic plate and compressive residual stresses at the steel surface. If no plastic deformation occurs, which is generally the case in the ceramic part, the residual stresses can be assumed to vary linearly over the height of the components. The lower part of fig. 5 shows the geometry influence on the magnitude of the resulting residual stresses. The tensile residual stresses in the ceramic surface increase with decreasing thickness of the steel plate.

Beside that, the deformation scheme in fig. 6 shows that on the side face of the compound near the solder layer local bending effects occur. They give rise to tensile residual stresses perpendicular to the solder layer in this area of the ceramic part. This is

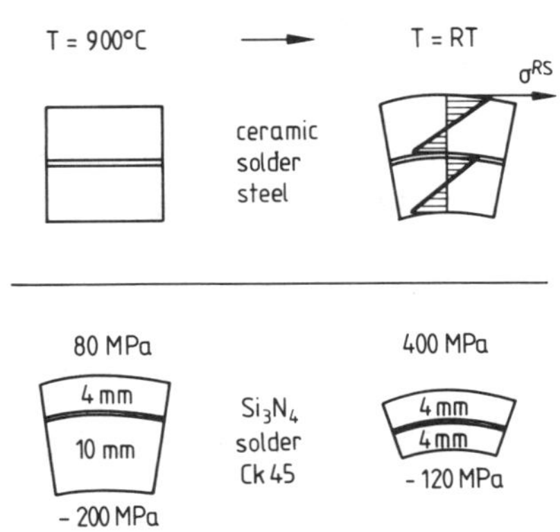

Figure 5: Residual stresses in brazed ceramic / metal compounds.

shown for a compound of Si_3N_4 (4 mm thick) and Ck 45 (4 mm thick) in fig. 7. Tensile residual stresses of about 200 MPa were measured on the side face of the ceramic plate at a distance of 0.3 mm to the solder gap.

Obviously, two failure critical regions with tensile residual stresses occur in brazed ceramic/steel compounds: The ceramic surface and the side face of the ceramic near the solder layer. In order to avoid failure, the tensile residual stresses must be decreased by optimizing the geometry of the compound and the brazing parameters [4]. The thermal mismatch of the components should be decreased by combining suitable materials.

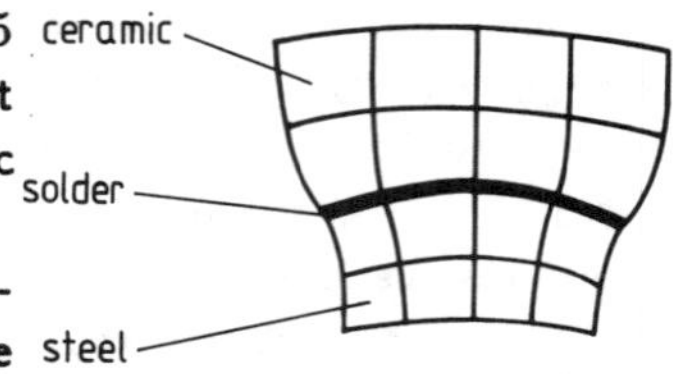

Figure 6: Elastic deformation of a brazed ceramic / metal compound.

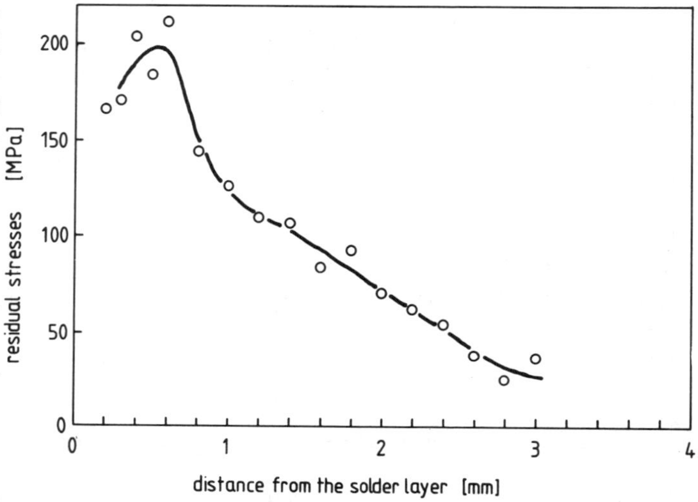

Figure 7: Residual stresses on the side face of the ceramic plate of a compound Si_3N_4 (4 mm thick) / steel (4 mm thick).

CONCLUSIONS

It has been shown by a few examples that X–ray stress measurements are a useful tool for the determination of residual and loading stresses in ceramics. The importance of an optimized residual stress state, especially in interaction with cracks has been shown with quenched samples of alumina. First steps were made in order to assess the influence of grinding on the strength of ceramic components. The determination of average II. kind residual stresses in multiphase materials might open a way to improve the strength of multiphase ceramics. Finally, the failure critical areas of ceramic/steel compounds have been pointed out.

This small number of selected examples shows that the knowledge of residual stresses in ceramics and ceramic/metal compounds is necessary for a better understanding of the materials behaviour during manufacturing and practical use.

REFERENCES

[1] B. Eigenmann, B. Scholtes and E. Macherauch, in Proceedings ICRS2, Nancy, 1988.

[2] E. Macherauch, H. Wohlfahrt and U. Wolfstieg, HTM, 1973, 28, pp. 201-211.

[3] E. Macherauch and H. Müller, Z. angew. Physik, 1961, 13, pp. 305-312.

[4] B. Eigenmann, B. Scholtes and E. Macherauch, in Joining Ceramics, Glass and Metal, W. Kraft, DGM Informationsgesellschaft mbH, Oberursel, 1989, pp. 249-256.

WEAR PROPERTIES OF CERAMIC WHITEWARE GLAZES

K.M. LINDE, S. KARLSSON and R. CARLSSON
Swedish Ceramic Institute,
Box 5403, S-402 29 Göteborg, Sweden

ABSTRACT

Wear studies of a number of ceramic whiteware glazes have been conducted by measurement of the frictional force of steel balls in contact with the glaze surface. Plates, cut out of ceramic whiteware, were exposed to steel balls sliding at low speeds under loads from 15 to 120 N. Friction coefficients for the sliding couples were determined and glaze damage arising during the test was studied. Characteristics of wear tracks on different glazes could be distinguished and related to the friction coefficients. The causes for the different wear properties are also discussed.

INTRODUCTION

The handling of ceramic tableware, at large restaurants etc., makes great demands upon its strength and wear resistance. Special attention has to be paid to the glaze which is continuously exposed to wear. Stacking and carrying cause damage, either by unglazed bottoms of plates scratching the surfaces of other plates (1) or by glazed surfaces scratching against each other. Sliding contact with cutlery results in scratches and transfer of metal to the glaze.

Friction and wear mechanisms for glass are well known. The friction is dependant upon the size of the real contact area and the strength of the interfacial adhesive bond (2). Environmental factors are of great importance. Even a monolayer of surface contaminants can influence the adhesion by reducing the bonding forces. If water is present, the friction and glass damage increases. Chemical reactions between glass and water make the glass less resistant to stresses. The frictional force of glass on glass in vacuum is one half the value obtained in saturated air.

Friction measurements and wear studies on glass are preferably conducted using a spherical body sliding on a flat surface. This geometry creates a system where the stresses can be theoretically calculated (3,4) and the wear situation can be related to real examples. This method has been used to study the wear behaviour of glass containers (5) and similar experiments have also been conducted on glazes (6). The loaded spherical indenter gives rise to a Hertzian stress field which is somewhat distorted because of the sliding movement. The tensile stress in the glass is highest at the trailing edge of the circular contact surface. At a critical stress level a partial Hertzian cone crack is formed. The critical stress depends on the coefficient of friction, the size and form of the fracture-causing defect and material properties such as hardness, fracture toughness and Young's modulus. The fracture origins are often surface discontinuities which can be divided into two groups, one consisting of defects originating from the manufacturing process and the other of scratches and cracks caused by mechanical contacts. Both defect types can influence the wear by increasing the friction and by crack initiation. Surface discontinuities (gas bubbles and other production defects) are common in glazes (7). Once the wear process is initiated, cracks and scratches will form and act as crack initiators and the wear damage will rapidly become more and more severe.

Elimination of defects and improvement of material properties has to be achieved by optimising the glaze compositions, the raw materials and the firing process. An increase in the wear resistance might also be achieved by development of present detergents and rinsing agents. However, a convenient way of evaluating the glaze quality and the influence of different surface treatments has to be found. Measurements of friction coefficients and studies of the initial wear behaviour at different loads have shown up as promising methods.

EXPERIMENTAL

The test equipment mainly consisted of a motor driven table, a horizontal arm (perpendicular to the direction of motion of the table and both vertically and horizontally pivoted) and a load cell from which the frictional force was recorded. The test piece was mounted on the table and the indenter at the underside of the arm. Driving the table, with the loaded indenter on the test piece caused a horizontal movement of the arm. This movement was taken up by the load cell as the frictional force.

The tests were carried out on four commercial table wares. Two were of different porcelains - feldspathic and alumina - for which the same glaze had been used. The two others were of bone china and earthenware. Specimens measuring 4x5 cm were machined out of the bottoms of plates. After cutting, the test pieces were cleaned in acetone. Prior to testing they were washed in detergent and water, thoroughly rinsed in hot water and dried at 100°C. Roller bearing steel balls with a diameter of 3.0 mm were used as indenters. These were ultrasonically cleaned in ethanol and kept dry and clean until testing.

Eight indenter loads were used, ranging from 15 to 120 N with a table speed of 0.83 mm/s. The specimens were in contact with the steel ball for a distance of four cm at each load. Each test was repeated 3-5 times. The steel ball did not rotate during the test. To keep a constant size of contact area the ball was changed for every third test piece.

The coefficients of friction were calculated and an average level was determined for each indenter load and each material. The specimens were etched in hydrofluoric acid (8%, 3 min) to make the wear damage clearly visible by optical microscopy. The wear tracks were studied and characterized for each glaze and the number of partial Hertzian cracks, formed during the tests, were counted. The hardness and the fracture toughness were measured by Vickers indentation (8).

RESULTS AND DISCUSSION

Two main types of wear damage could be distinguished while studying the wear tracks with the optical microscope (figure 1). Even at the lowest indenter load a track was formed by the ball and the wear debris. At higher loads partial Hertzian cracks had formed, perpendicular to this track. After etching the samples, both the wear tracks and the surface discontinuities were enlarged. Gas bubbles located just beneath the surface became visible as holes and dark spots at etching.

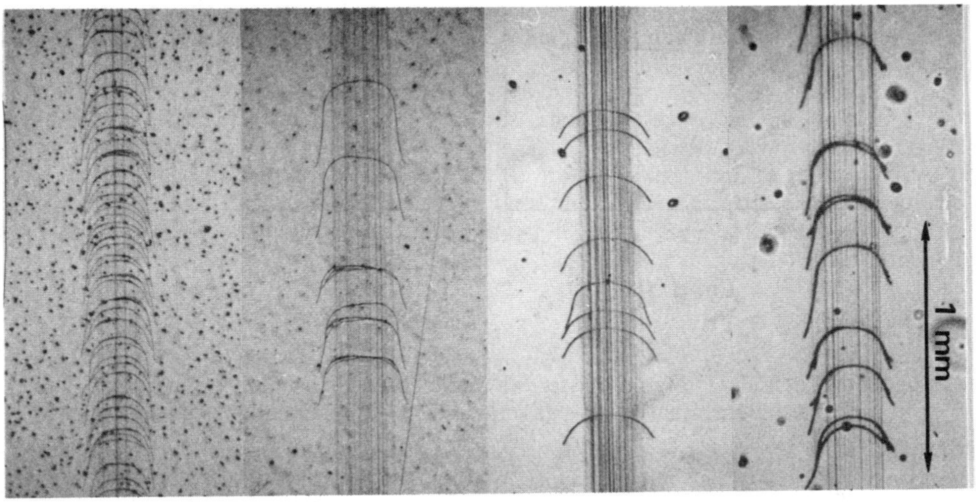

Feldspathic porcelain   Alumina porcelain   Bone china   Earthenware

Figure 1. Wear tracks in glazes formed during frictional measurements (glaze-steel ball) under a load of 60 N.

The average level of the frictional coefficient at each test was determined from the pen recorder curves. The mean value of these levels is marked in figure 2a, where the coefficient of friction is shown as a function of the load. Note that the coefficient of friction actually differed between the glazes and that these differences could be measured. However, the variation in the frictional force was unacceptable, both during one test and from one similar test to another. Probably the main reasons for the frictional variations were contamination and humidity on the surfaces and also the surface topography. To get less scattering and better reproducibility the test procedure has to be well standardized both with respect to the pretreatment of the specimen surface and the composition of the ambient atmosphere. Measurement of the surface topography together with the frictional force would probably explain most of the non-environmental dependant frictional variations.

For the bone china glaze the coefficient of friction seemed to be load independent while it increased more or less with the load for the other glazes. These variations can be related to differences in the crack resistance. At a certain load the contact stress is high enough to cause crack propagation. The crack formation itself and the resulting wear debris will increase the frictional force. Thus, the friction coefficient at low load gives information about the surface roughness and adhesion between the surfaces of the frictional couple. The rate of the frictional increase with load tells about the material properties which determine the stress required for crack propagation.

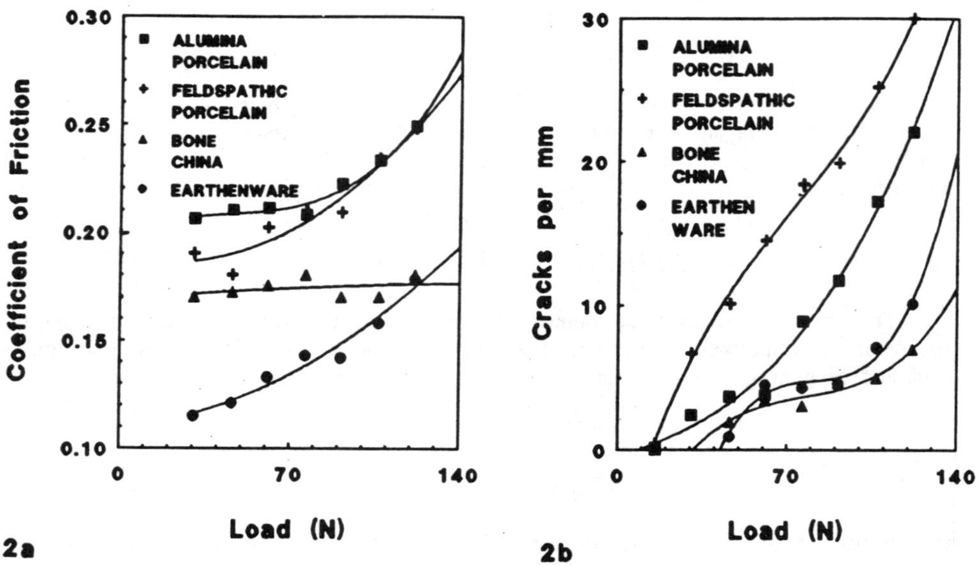

2a 2b

Figure 2. a. Coefficients of friction for whiteware glazes in sliding contact with steel.
b. Partial Hertzian cracks per mm formed during frictional measurements.

Figure 2b shows the number of cracks per mm of the wear track as a function of the load. For the feldspathic and alumina porcelain glazes, which had the highest coefficients of friction, cracks were observed even in tracks formed under the lowest load. The increase in crack density with load was higher for the feldspathic than for the alumina porcelain glaze, which corresponds to the difference in the load dependence of the friction curves (figure 2a). Figure 1 shows that the occurrence of gas bubbles was very high in the hard porcelain glazes, especially in the feldspathic porcelain glaze. Bubbles located near to the surface probably affect the surface smoothness and act as crack initiating flaws, which makes them the probable main reason for the high friction and crack density.

The coefficient of friction for the bone china glaze was also relatively high. In this glaze however, cracks first propagated at a load of 40 N and the crack density was relatively low at all loads. Thus, the crack resistance for the bone china glaze is inferior to that for the other glazes, which also is reflected in the independence of load of the friction curve. For the smooth earthenware glaze, figures 2a and b show that a specific load is required to make the friction high enough for crack initiation. Having exceeded this load, however, cracks are formed much more easily than in the bone china glaze.

The occurrence of gas bubbles was much lower in the earthenware and bone china glazes than in the porcelain glazes (figure 1) which corresponds to the results of friction and crack density. In the bone china glaze the crack radii were larger than in the other glazes which also indicates a higher crack resistance. The larger the crack radius, the higher the contact stress required to cause the crack. The bone china glaze has a high fracture toughness and a low hardness (table 1) which seems to be a favourable combination. The fracture toughness, which is of importance for the wear properties, is probably more influenced by the compressive stress in the glaze surface than by the microstructure.

TABLE 1
Fracture toughness and Vickers hardness of whiteware glazes

Glaze	K_{Ic} ($MPam^{1/2}$)	$H_V(0.5)$ (GPa)
Feldspathic porcelain	1.4	6.6
Alumina porcelain	1.7	6.4
Bone china	2.0	5.7
Earthen ware	1.2	5.6

The wear behaviour is determined by a combination of several materials parameters. Measurement of the frictional force, conducted under controlled conditions is a method of getting specific information about the wear behaviour of the glazes.

ACKNOWLEDGEMENTS

The authors thank Bengt Augustsson, PLM Hammar, for valuable advice and for providing of test equipment and Dr. Ian Brown for revision of the English text. This work was supported financially by the Swedish Board for Technical Development.

REFERENCES

1. Oel, H.J. and Kubicki-Gottlieb, G., On mechanical glaze damage (plate-bottom scratching). Ber. DKG, 1982, **59**, pp. 164-68.

2. Buckley, D.H., Friction and wear behavior of glasses and ceramics. Material and Science Research, 1974, **7**, pp. 101-26.

3. Hamilton, G.M. and Goodman, L.E., The stress field created by a circular sliding contact. J. Appl. Mech., 1966, **33**, pp. 371-76

4. Lawn, B.R., Wiederhorn, S.M. and Roberts, D.E., Effect of sliding friction forces on the strength of brittle materials. J. Mater. Sci., 1984, **19**, pp. 2561-69.

5. Augustsson, B.O., Changes in surface structure of glass from sliding contact. Glasteknisk Tidskrift, 1981, **2-3**, pp. 23-29.

6. Rose, M.E., A technique for measuring the scratch resistance of ceramic glazes. Trans. Brit. Ceram. Soc., 1975, **74**, pp. 171-75.

7. Willmann, G. and Varga, F., Production defects in glazed ceramics, Practical Metallography 1978, **15**, pp. 582-88.

8. Nihaara K., Morena R. and Hasselman P.H.D., Indentation fracture toughness of brittle materials for Palmqvist cracks. Fracture mechanics of Ceramics., 1984, **5**, pp. 97-105.

Characterisation of W-C:H low-friction layers.

W . van Duyn, B. van Lochem

Philips PMF
Centre for Material Technology and Innovation
P.O. box 218
NL 5600 MD Eindhoven
The Netherlands

Abstract.

Tungsten-carbon:hydrogen layers are made on steel by reactive DC magnetron sputtering. Chemical analysis shows that the layer consists of very small WC-particles, embedded in a polymer-like CHx-matrix. The hardness of the layer and the friction coefficients against steel, depend on the carbon content of the layer. The friction coefficients can be very low against metals.

1. Introduction.

Around 1970 "diamond-like" carbon films were reported in the literature (ref. 1.) These films could be of tribological interest because of their high degree of hardness and low friction against metals. However, there were, and still are, problems with high stresses in these layers and insufficient adhesion.

In 1983 the adhesion was improved significantly by Dimigen et al (ref. 2,3) by placing a metal interface between the substrate and the carbon coating. This paper presents some results of our investigations on W-C:H layers made in an industrial batch type sputtering machine (Balzers BAK 760) with a high capacity for coating tools or other small parts.

2. Process parameters

After degreasing the samples were mounted in the reaction chamber. The vacuum chamber must be pumped down to less than 10 E-4 Pa. The samples were then etched in an argon plasma. After this the tungsten layer was deposited. When this layer was about 0,2 micron thick,acetylene was slowly admitted into the system until the required partial pressure was reached. Because pre-heating of the samples was not necessary, the maximum temperature reached was not higher than 150 degrees centigrade.

3. Chemical structure.

3.1 Relative concentrations.

The carbon content was measured using a classical pyrolytic method: The layer was deposited on carbon-free ARMCO iron, then the sample was burned and the CO_2-emission was measured. The tungsten content was measured by XRF (X-ray fluorescence) using the absorbance of iron or chromium radiation by tungsten.
For measuring hydrogen we used ERD (elastic recoil detection), combined with RBS (Rutherford backscattering) (ref.5). From these measurements the relation between H-atoms and W-atoms was quantified. A disadvantage of this method is that the information is gained only from the top layer (100 nm) of the coating.

By combining these results the chemical composition of the layer can be plotted against the acetylene flow in the process. It is interesting to note that hydrogen appears in the layer only when the carbon content is higher than 50% (see fig.1)

4. Mechanical properties.

4.1. Layer thickness.

The thickness of the layer was measured with a Tayler-Hobson talystep. Table 1 shows that the deposition rate increases slightly when more acetylene is used in the proces.

4.2. Hardness.

The hardness was measured with a Knoop diamond. Two different loads were used, 50 grams and 100 grams. When the load of 50 grams was used, higher values for the hardness were obtained than in the case of 100 grams. This shows that the measured hardness is system dependent and the values can only be used in a qualitative way.
table 1 shows that the hardness decreases dramatically, if the carbon content of the layer is increased.

4.3 Scratch test.

Although there is still no reliable physical model for the scratch test, the test itself has been developed as a useful practical tool for studying thin hard coatings (ref. 11). table 1 shows that the load bearing capacity (measured with an acoustic signal) increases rapidly when the carbon content is increased. Study of the wear tracks using light and electron microscopy reveals that layers with a high carbon content are more ductile than layers with a high tungsten content.

4.4 Friction coefficients

The friction coefficients were measured with a pin-on-ring equipment. The normal load on the pin was 4,0 N. The pins were made of hardened tool steel (160CrMoV12) and coated, while the rings were uncoated and made also of the same steel or bronze (CuSn12).
The calculated initial Hertzian pressures were in the case of steel against steel 300 MPa and in the case of steel against bronze 280 MPa. The pins and rings were cleaned and degraesed carefully before testing. No lubricant was used. Uncoated pins and pins coated with TiN (PVD and CVD) and TiC (CVD) were tested as a reference.
The surface roughness of the contact areas was 0,1 micron Ra and the friction force was measured after 1500 revolutions (75 minutes). The relative velocity of the sliding surfaces was 3,77 m/min.

The results are evaluated in table 2. It can be seen that the friction decreases when the carbon content increases. The figure also shows that the friction of the W-C:H layers against steel is much lower than TiN and TiC layers under the conditions used. When sliding against bronze however, the friction coefficient of the TiC coating is also low.
This shows that the W-C:H coatings can be useful for tribological applications, especially when an oil-free state is required.

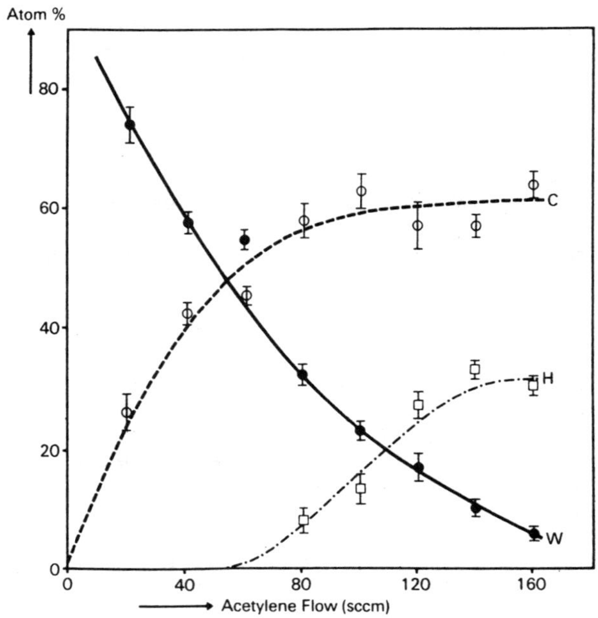

Figure 1. Atom percentages of W, C and H, measured by pyrolysis, XRF, ERD and RBS, plotted against the acetylene flow during deposition.

Table 1. Results of thickness measurements, Knoop hardness and scratch test. The substrates were made of hardened tool steel (160CrMoV12).

C_2H_2-flow (scc/min.)	d (μm)	$HK_{0.05}$ (kg/mm^2)	$HK_{0.1}$ (kg/mm^2)	L_c (N)	
				L = incr.	L = const.
40.4	4.2	4000	2600	7	6–8
80.8	4.6	3000	2100	17	16–18
121.2	5.7	2800	2100	24	20–22
161.6	5.7	1100	1100	42	34–38

Table 2. Results of the pin-on-ring friction tests.

COATING ON PIN	W-%	μ vs STEEL (a. 1500 rev.)	μ vs BRONZE (a. 1500 rev.)
W-C:H	58	0.93	0.59
,,	33	0.36	0.28
,,	16	0.17	0.32
,,	6	0.12	0.31
BLANC		1.00	0.82
TiN pvd		0.81	0.83
TiN cvd		0.95	0.75
TiC cvd		0.56	0.25

5. Conclusions.

The mechanical properties of the tungsten-carbon: hydrogen layers depend strongly on the chemical composition of the layer. However, the bonding state of the atoms is not clear yet. Further investigations are needed on this subject.

Acknowledgments.

For carrying out the analysis and for taking the pictures, we wish to thank M. Hendriks, L. IJzendoorn, H. van Wijk and R. van der Dennen. For the interesting and valuable discussions we thank Dr. Hoekstra, Dr. Dimigen and Dr. Heller.

References.

1. S. Aisenberg and R. Chabot: Journal Appl. Phys 42 (1971), 2953
2. H. Dimigen and H. Huebsch: Philips Techn. F v. 41 (1983/84), 186
3. H. Dimigen and H. Huebsch: US Patent No. 4 525 417 (1985)
4. R. Memming : Thin Solid Films 143 (1986), 279
5. C.J. Sofield et al.: Nucl. Instrum. Methods 203 (1-3)(1982), 509
6. Y. Mizokawa et al.: J. Vac Sci. Technol. A5 (5) (1987), 2809
7. K. Kasmiwagi et al.: J. Vac. Sci. Technol. A5 (4) (1987), 1828
8. I.T. Ritchie: Thin Solid Films 72 (1980), 65
9. G. Harding and B. Window: Solar En. Mat. 7 (1982), 101
10. E. Bergmann and J. Vogel: J. Vac. Sci. Technol.: A5 (1) (1987), 70
11. P. Burnett and D.S. Rickerby: Thin Solid Films 157 (1988), 233

A COMPARATIVE STUDY OF THE OXIDATION OF RBSN AND RBSN COATED WITH CVD-Si_3N_4.

A.P.M. ADRIAANSEN, H. GOOIJER

Centre for Technical Ceramics
c/o Eindhoven University of Technology
P.O. Box 513, 5600 MB Eindhoven
The Netherlands.

ABSTRACT

Reaction Bonded Silicon Nitride (RBSN) was coated with Si_3N_4 by Low Pressure Chemical Vapour Deposition (LPCVD). An amorphous coating was obtained, which, depending on the LPCVD growth parameters, could, or could not, be converted into crystalline Si_3N_4 by prolongued high temperature heat treatment.
The oxidation behaviour of coated and uncoated RBSN was compared at 1200°C in flowing air. After four hours the average increase in weight of uncoated RBSN was found to be four times as high as that of the coated RBSN!

1. INTRODUCTION

Reaction Bonded Silicon Nitride (RBSN) is a relatively inexpensive ceramic material in comparison with other kinds of silicon nitride e.g. Hot Isostatically Pressed Si_3N_4. Unfortunately the porosity is very high, in total mostly about 20%. This high porosity causes high oxidation rates of the RBSN when heated in air. However, if it is possible to reduce the open and closed porosity by coating the surface with Si_3N_4 by Chemical Vapour Deposition the oxidation resistance should increase. The authors attempted to achieve this result by LPCVD. The result of this coating process is a dense and uniform Si_3N_4 coating on the porous RBSN surface. It was found that the process conditions of the CVD process are extremely important for the effect on the oxidation resistance at high temperature in comparison with uncoated RBSN. In this paper the results of oxidation experiments of coated and uncoated RBSN at 1200°C will be evaluated.

2. THEORETICAL BACKGROUND.

2.1 The oxidation of sintered Silicon Nitride.

The oxidation of Silicon Nitride can proceed in two ways.
- Active oxidation at low partial pressure of oxygen.

$$2\ Si_3N_4(s) + 3\ O_2(g) \qquad 6\ SiO(g) + 4\ N_2(g)$$

- Passive oxidation at high partial pressure of oxygen.

$$Si_3N_4(s) + 3\ O_2 \qquad 3\ SiO_2(s) + 2\ N_2$$

Between 1000°C and 1600°C in air there is only passive oxidation (1). Because of the formation of the silica (SiO_2) the oxidation can be divided into two regimes. During the beginning of the oxidation the reaction rate is linear with time. After this initial phase the reaction rate changes to a parabolic time dependant behaviour. The reason for this change in behaviour is the formation of a dense silica layer. From then on the reaction depends on the diffusion of oxygen through the silica. In the initial state the oxidation of Si_3N_4 is kinetically controlled depending on the oxygen partial pressure (2).
The oxidation rate of Si_3N_4 will be expressed in a mass change per unit area.

2.2 The oxidation of CVD-Si_3N_4.

The oxidation behaviour of CVD Si_3N_4 is similar to that of the sintered Si_3N_4 discussed above. The crystallinity was found to be important for the oxidation rate. Hirai (3) examined the oxidation of amorphous and crystalline Si_3N_4 at 1600°C. He found that the oxidation rate of amorphous Si_3N_4 was a factor 3 lower than of crystalline Si_3N_4. The reason for this is probably the absence of grain boundaries in amorphous Si_3N_4.

3. LOW PRESSURE CHEMICAL VAPOUR DEPOSITION OF Si_3N_4.

Two types of coatings were produced using two different flow conditions of SiCl2H2 and NH3 given in table 1. The substrates were cubes with a lenght of 1 cm..

coating nr.	f1 (ml/min)	f2 (ml/min)	f1/f2	T (C)	P (Pa)	G (μm/hr)
1	30	90	1/3	800	54	0.6
2	15	75	1/5	800	54	0.3

Table 1. Processconditions for the production of CVD-Si_3N_4.
f1 : SiH_2Cl_2 flow
f2 : NH_3 flow
G : Growth rate of Si_3N_4 coating

The results of the oxidation experiments with the produced coatings are compared now:

4. OXIDATION EXPERIMENTS.

4.1 Oxidation of RBSN and RBSN coated with CVD-Si_3N_4.

The oxidation experiments were carried out in a thermo balance on samples in the shape of cubes. The weight change was measured as a function of time. The heating rate for all experiments was 20°C/min. The condition at which the oxidation experiments were carried out was 1200°C for 4 hours. During the whole experiment there was a constant flow of air of 150 ml/min. The weight increase per unit surface area of the samples was used as a measure of oxidation. An example of the weight increase of coated and uncoated RBSN is given in figure 1.

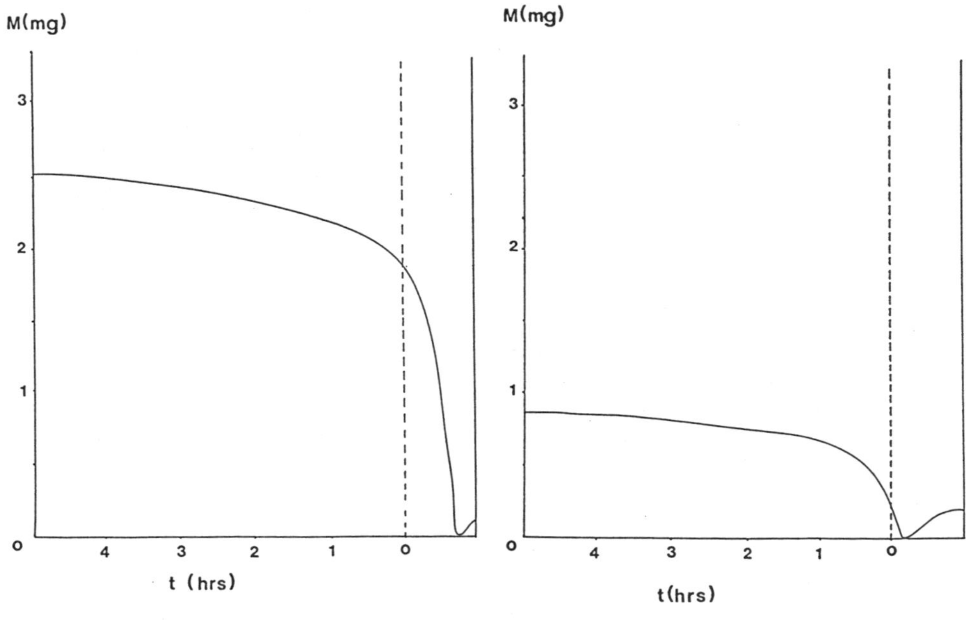

Figure 1. Weight increase of RBSN (left) and coated RBSN at 1200°C.

The average weight increase found for RBSN is 12.16 g/m^2 versus for coated RBSN (coating 2): 2.86 g/m^2. Thus the oxidation rate of RBSN is 4 to 5 times as high as that for the coated samples. The reason for this different behaviour is probably the reduction in inner pores at the coated samples. But a comparison of uncoated samples and samples coated with coating 1 showed no difference in oxidation behaviour probably due to the intrinsic porosity of the deposited coating. The ratio NH3/SiH2Cl2 = 3 is too low for a dense Si_3N_4 coating. The ratio NH3/SiH2Cl2 = 5 seems to be more favourable.
The variation in weight increase of coated samples is much smaller than in case of the uncoated samples.

In order to determine the time dependance of the oxidation a coated and uncoated sample were oxidized for 50 hours under the same conditions. No further increase in weight was found after four hours. The results are given in table 2.

	m/A (t=4 hrs) (g/m2)	m/A (t=50 hrs) (g/m2)
RBSN	10.68	10.72
RBSN with coating 2.	2.35	2.85

Table 2. Oxidation rate of RBSN and coated RBSN after 4 and 50 hours at 1200°C.

4.2 Determination of the parabolic rate constant for oxidation of RBSN and CVD-Si_3N_4 coated RBSN.

Some samples of RBSN and of CVD-Si_3N_4 on RBSN have been used for the determination of the parabolic rate constant kp for oxididation. The square of the slope of the second part of the oxidation is the parabolic rate constant of oxidation, since in this part the diffusion of oxygen through the silica surface layer is the rate controlling step in oxidation (see chapter 2). The parabolic rate constants of coated and uncoated RBSN are listed in table 3.

	parabolic rate constant kp (g2/m4s)
RBSN uncoated	$1.5\ 10^{-10}$
RBSN coated with CVD-Si_3N_4	$4.8\ 10^{-11}$

Table 3. Parabolic rate constant of coated and uncoated RBSN for the formation of silicon oxide at 1200°C.

The parabolic rate constant found for the oxidation of RBSN confirms the findings of other investigators (6). However the reduction in oxidation rate induced by coating the samples with CVD-Si_3N_4 is smaller than what Schlichting (7)and Singhal (1) had found. They

measured an oxidation rate for CVD-Si_3N_4 of 10^{-13} $g^2/m^4 s$

4.3 The oxidation of CVD-Si_3N_4 on Al_2O_3.

To systematically study the oxidation behaviour of the CVD-Si_3N_4 coatings, oxidation experiments were carried out on Al_2O_3 plates coated with Si_3N_4. Al_2O_3 is an inert material so if weight increase takes place it will be caused by the oxidation of the Si_3N_4 coating. The oxidation conditions were the same as for the (un)coated RBSN samples: 4 hours at 1200°C in flowing air.

One interesting point became apparent during these experiments. The Si_3N_4 coating 1 was found to be crystalline (α-Si_3N_4) after the oxidation experiment whereas coating 2 remained amorphous. Even when annealed for 20 hours at 1200°C coating 2 remained amorphous. It even stayed amorphous at 1400°C (time 2 hrs). These heat treatments were carried out in a nitrogen atmosphere. Crystallinity has been determined by X-ray diffraction.

5. CHARACTERISATION.

5.1 Pore distribution of RBSN.

By means of Hg-porosimetry and overall density measurements the pore distribution, density and open and closed porosity of RBSN was determined. With this technique the porosity can be differentiated into the percentage of open and closed porosity. This is important because only the open porosity is important in the internal oxidation. By coating the surface with CVD-Si_3N_4 the open porosity can be reduced.
From the Hg-porosimetry measurements it was found that more than 90 % of the pore volume consists of pores with a diameter between 0.01 and 0.1 µm.A About 5 % of the pore volume consists of pores with a diameter of more than 10 µm. Further results of the Hg-porosimetry measurements are presented in table 4. For the theoretical density of Si_3N_4 we adopted the value of 3.18 g/cm³.

D_{bulk} (g/cm³)	$D_{skeleton}$ (g/cm³)	P_{open} (%)	P_{closed} (%)	P_{total} (%)
2.53	2.87	11	10	21

Table 4. Results of Hg-porosimetry measurements of RBSN.

D = density.
P = porosity.

6. CONCLUSION.

The most important conclusion of this report is that the oxidation of RBSN can be reduced by coating the surface with Si_3N_4 by CVD. The oxidation rate of RBSN at 1200°C is reduced by a factor 4 to 5 times using a CVD-Si_3N_4 coating of 2 µm with a ratio of NH3/SiH2Cl2 = 5. Also the variation in oxidation rate is reduced substantially.
The oxidation time of the experiments was four hours at 1200°C. It was found that after four hours no further oxidation took place.
It is possible to make a CVD-Si_3N_4 coating which remains amorphous after heat treatment at 1400°C. When other processconditions are used the resulting CVD-Si_3N_4 coating becomes crystalline after one hour heat treatment at 1200°C.

7. LITERATURE.

1. S.C. Singhal. Oxidation of Silicon Nitride and related materials. F.L. Riley, (1977). 607-626.
2. G. Ziegler et al. J. Mat Sc. 22, (1987) 3041-3086.
3. T. Hirai et al. J. Amer. Cer. Soc. 63, (1980) 419-424.
4. Y. Imamura et al. Cer. Eng. Sc., 7, (1986) 828-838.
5. M. Peukert. P. Greil. J. Amer. Sc. 22, (1987) 3717-3720.
6. F. Porz. Characterisation, oxidation and mechanical behaviour of reaction bonded Silicon Nitride. F.L Riley (1983) 539-546.
7. J. Schlichting. Sprechsaal, 114 (2) (1981) 95-99.

MECHANICAL CHARACTERIZATION OF MACROPOROUS CERAMIC SUPPORT TUBES FOR MICRO/ULTRAFILTRATION

P.W. BACH, N.P.G. VAN DER BURG and R.A. TERPSTRA
Netherlands Energy Research Foundation, ECN
P.O. Box 1, 1755 ZG PETTEN, the Netherlands

At ECN microfiltration and ultrafiltration ceramic membrane systems are being developed. For these a macroporous support is needed, to give high mechanical strength to the membrane system with a very low hydraulic resistance. The support tubes are produced at ECN by extrusion. After controlled drying, the tubes are sintered at temperatures above 1500°C. Additionally commercially obtained support tubes have been used.
The tubes are characterized mechanically by bursting pressure tests and by C-ring tests. For the bursting pressure test a parameter study (length of the tubes, pressure application rate, clamping force) is carried out. The results of the mechanical tests are compared with microstructural data (pore size and -distribution) and permeability of the tubes.

INTRODUCTION

The two and three layer membrane systems that are developed at ECN contain a macroporous support tube as the first layer. As the actual membrane layers are very thin (3-30 µm), the function of the support tube is to give the system its mechanical strength. At the same time the support layer must have a very low hydraulic resistance, i.e. it should have a high porosity and relatively large pores. These properties (high strength, high flux) are conflicting and for each particular membrane application a compromise should be adopted.
In general, the actual process pressure for microfiltration is ≤ 5 bar, for ultrafiltration between 5 and 20 bar and for reverse osmosis > 20 bar.
The actual bursting pressure of the support tube should of course be substantially higher than the process pressure. The influence of the substrate resistance on the flux of the membrane system for different membranes can be easily calculated using a series resistance model (see for example [1]).
In this paper the mechanical strength is determined for three different potential support materials, two are obtained commercially and one is developed by ECN (National Ceramics Centre, NKA) for microfiltration application. In fact two tests (bursting pressure, C-ring) are compared and a parameter study is carried out.

MATERIALS AND METHODS

The substrate tubes which are developed in our laboratory are extruded using a ceramic paste which consists of α-Al_2O_3 powder, a binder, a lubricant and water. After drying for several hours (~ 20°C, ~ 50% RH) the tubes are sintered at 1550°C for 15 h. Some properties of this material and of the two commercial products (Schwendler Alox 180 and Haldenwanger F25) are given in table 1.
The pore properties are determined by Hg-porosimetry and the water flux is determined in a dead-end permeation rig using ultra-pure water.

TABLE 1

Tube	Porosity (%)	Mean Pore size (µm)	ø out (mm)	ø in (mm)	Permeability (l/h m² bar)
ECN/NKA 226	32	4	14	8	18.000
Schwendler Alox 180	35	3	20	14	1.200
Haldenwanger F25	32	5	20	14	9.000

Bursting pressure test
Support tubes were carefully sectioned by means of a grinding wheel into bursting pressure samples with a length of 50, 100 or 200 mm and into C-ring samples with a width of 10 mm. The position of the samples is systematically varied in order to cope with differences in properties over the tube length and between the tubes.
The tensile surfaces of the samples were unaffected and tested as produced. Ceramic support tubes for membrane systems are exposed to pressure gradients across the tube wall. A realistic type of test to characterize the strength of the tubes is by means of a bursting pressure test.
The effect of the bursting pressure test parameters on the determined strength is not clear. In order to investigate these effects a parameter study is carried out which includes a variation of the length of the tubes (50-200 mm), the pressure application rate (25-200 bar/min) and the clamping force (250-2000 N).

Due to the porous character of the support tubes they have to be sealed in a bursting pressure test. As sealing material a laboratory parafine foil (Parafilm M) is used.

C-ring test
A simple type of test to determine the strength of ceramic tubes is the C-ring test. To investigate the validity of the C-ring test in comparison with the bursting pressure test, C-ring samples from the same tubes are tested.

The C-ring samples were fractured at room temperature with an Instron 4501 Universal Testing Instrument operating at a cross head speed of 8,3 µm/sec.

RESULTS AND DISCUSSION

The strength of three types of porous support tubes are measured in the bursting pressure apparatus. Two types of tubes, Haldenwanger F25 and Schwendler 180, give a range of bursting pressure strenghts between 17 and 100 bar. With these tubes the parameter study is carried out. For each set of parameters 10 tubes are used. The average bursting pressure strength and the standard deviation are calculated. Typical values are 20 ± 1,5 bar for the Haldenwanger tube and 80 ± 6,5 for the Schwendler material. For the ECN/NKA material the average bursting pressure strength and the standard deviation are 25 ± 4,5 bar. This is near the value for the Haldenwanger material.

In Fig. 1 the average bursting pressure strength and the standard deviation are shown for the parameters length of the tube and clamping force.
These results show that there is no significant difference in the measured strength in the range of the parameter used. Also an increase of the pressure application rate from 5 to 200 bar/min gives no difference in the measured strength of the tubes. This means that the bursting pressure strength is not dependent on the test parameters in the intervals investigated.
For microfiltration applications all three support materials would be suitable with regards to their bursting pressure strength but if also the permeability is taken into account the ECN/NKA material is far the most suitable while the Schwendler material cannot be used as it would lower the permeability of the membrane system too much.
The maximum tangential stresses for the individual tubes with a length of 100 mm are calculated using formulae for thick shells of revolution assuming isotropic material [2]. The resulting data are fitted to a two-parameter Weibull equation and plotted in the Weibull graph shown in Fig. 2.

The maximum tangential stresses of the individual C-ring tests are determined using formulae for the bending of curved beams [3], [4] and are plotted in a Weibull graph (Fig. 3).
In order to compare the results of the C-ring tests and bursting pressure tests, the stress volume integrals are determined using numerical integration. The integrals are calculated on the basis of volume controlled failure in accordance with the observed microstructure.
Since the distribution of flaws and the direction of the tensile stresses are identical in the two specimen types, the measured and calculated strength quantities should be similar.
As shown in Figs. 2 and 3 the C-ring strength predicted from the bursting pressure test and the Weibull modulus are overestimated. On the other hand the bursting pressure strength is rather well predicted from the C-ring test in tension. The discrepancies between the predicted and measured values mean that there are other differences between the tests than the statistical volume effects based on the tensile stresses.
Although the shear and radial stresses in the C-ring test are small compared to the tangential stress, for the compressive stress this is not the case. Especially for porous ceramic material the tensile to compressive strength ratio is not as large as in dense ceramic material.
Also in the bursting pressure test the maximum compressive radial stress is about 35% of the maximum tangential stress.
For an extended comparison the effect of these stresses on the strength of the tubes have to be investigated.

REFERENCES

[1] Terpstra, R.A., Bonekamp, B.C. and Veringa, H.J, Preparation, characterisation and some properties of tubular alpha alumina ceramic membranes for microfiltration and as a support for ultrafiltration and gas separation membranes, Desalination, 70, 1988, pp. 395-404.

[2] Roark, R.J. and Young, W.C., Fomulas for stress and strain, McGraw-Hill Inc., Singapore, 1984, p. 504.

[3] Cernica, J.N., Strength of materials, Holt, Reinhart and Winston, New York, 1966, pp. 201-205.

[4] Ferber, M.K. et al, Fracture strength characterisation of tubular ceramic materials using a simple C-ring geometry, J. Mater. Sci., 21, 1986, pp. 2628-2632.

FIGURES

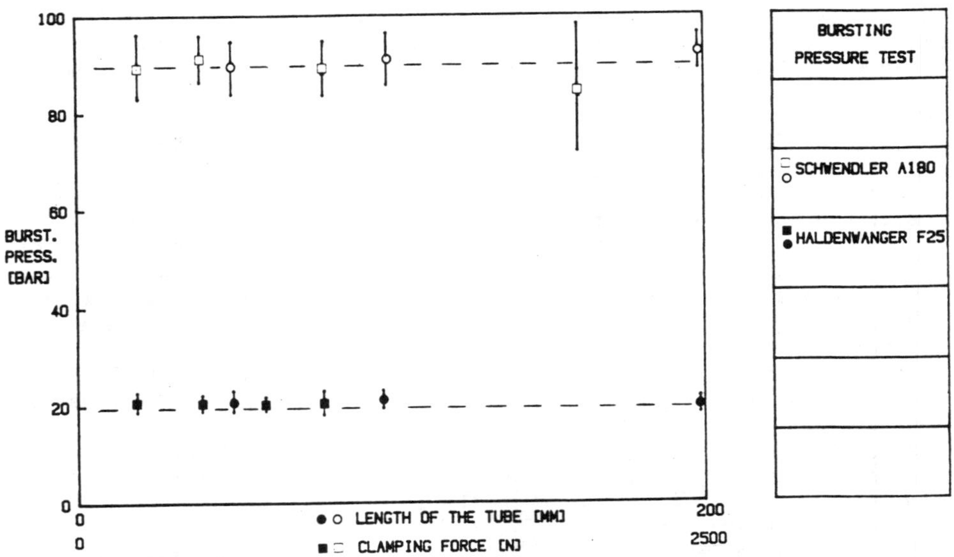

Figure 1. Bursting pressure data of the parameters length of the tube and clamping force.

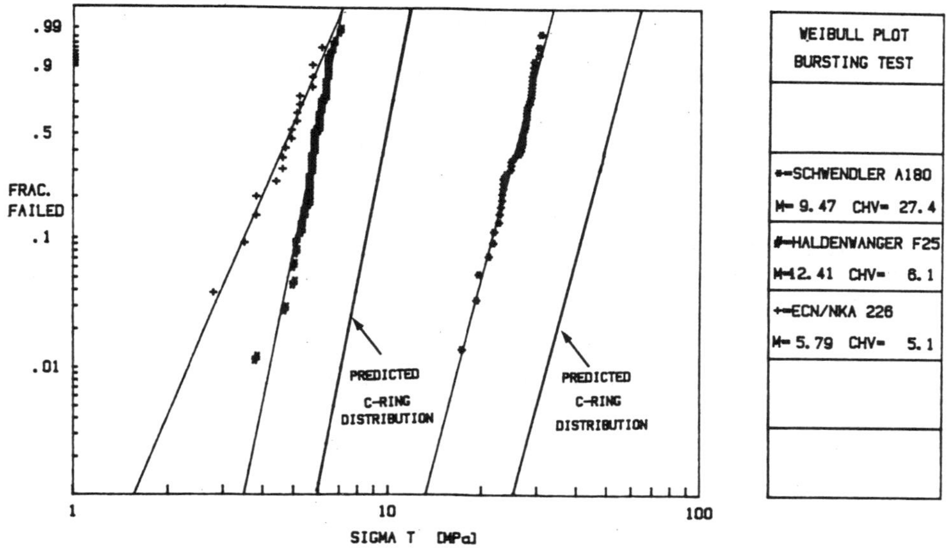

Figure 2. Weibull plot of the maximum tangential stress of the bursting pressure tests.

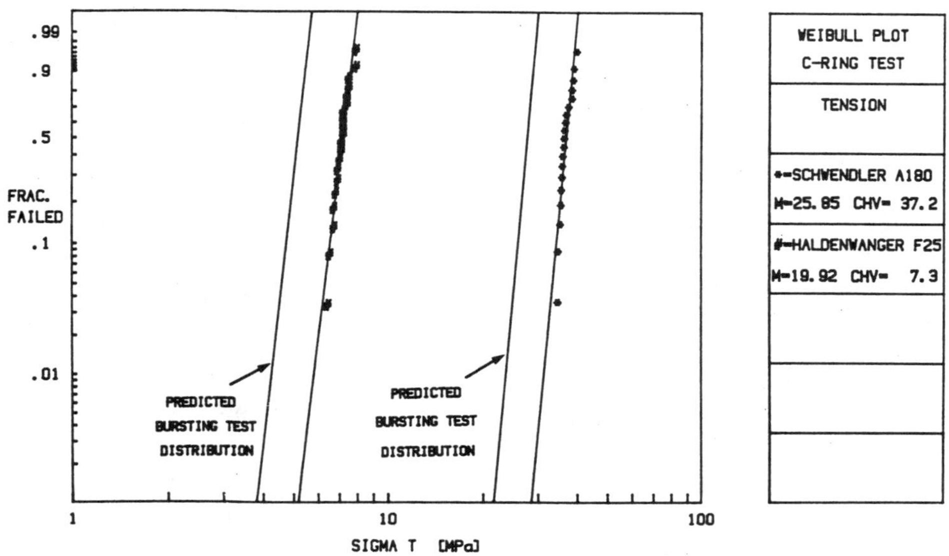

Figure 3. Weibull plot of the maximum tangential stress of the C-ring test.

MODIFIED SOL-GEL TECHNIQUES FOR THE PREPARATION OF MICROPOROUS CERAMIC MEMBRANES

M.H.B.J. Huis in 't Veld, R.J.R. Uhlhorn, K. Keizer, A.J. Burggraaf
University of Twente, Faculty of Chemical Engineering, Laboratory of Inorganic Chemistry, Material Science and Catalysis, P.O.Box 217, 7500 AE Enschede, The Netherlands

ABSTRACT

Two modification techniques to decrease the pore size and/or to influence the chemical nature of a γ-alumina membrane are discussed. In situ hydrolysis of magnesia, using the so-called reservoir method, can give MgO concentration in the pores to about 40 vol%. A problem is the formation of discrete crystalline particles upon calcining, leading to sudden shrinkage and pore opening. Modification with polymeric solutions of silica and titania gives a strong decrease of the effective pore size without crystallization into distinct crystalline particles. It results in microporous membranes (pore diameters smaller than 1 nm) with very promising results in gas separation properties.

INTRODUCTION

Ceramic membranes of e.g. alumina and titania can today be made through a sol-gel process, having small pores (2-6 nm diameter) and a sharp pore size distribution [1-3].Especially the good thermal and chemical stability of these membranes make them suitable for use in catalytic processes and gas separation applications. In order to make the membrane suitable for a specific purpose, one should be able to control the chemical and physical characteristics (especially pore size) of the membrane. This implies, that modification techniques of ceramic membranes must be developed.

This paper describes two modification methods of a γ-alumina membrane with a pore diameter of 2.5-3 nm and a sharp pore size distribution [1]. For catalytic purposes, it is important to influence the chemical nature of the surface [4]. For gas separation purposes it is important to decrease the pore size in order to obtain high selectivities [5]. Both aspects will be discussed.

The two methods are in situ hydrolysis of magnesia inside the pores, applying the so called reservoir method, and modification with a polymeric solution of silica and titania. Synthetical aspects will be shortly discussed. The influence of the modifications on the chemical characteristics and the pore size of the γ-alumina membrane are then presented.

EXPERIMENTAL

The preparation and characterization of supported and non-supported γ-alumina membranes is described elsewhere [1]. Non-supported and supported γ-alumina membranes were modified by the in situ hydrolysis. With this method, a solution of a magnesium salt and urea in water is brought into the pores of the γ-alumina and heated to 90 ^{0}C. The urea decomposes, thereby hydrolysing the metal salt. After the reaction is complete, the membrane is dried and calcined. The non-supported membranes were characterized by nitrogen adsorption-desorption, using a Micromeritics ASAP 400, and by atomic absorption spectroscopy. Supported modified γ-alumina membranes were characterized by helium gas permeability and SEM/EDS.

Polymeric solutions of silica and titania were prepared by acid catalysed hydrolysis and condensation reactions of water and the appropriate metal alkoxide, solved in an alcohol. The ratio of hydrolysis to condensation reaction, as well as the reaction rate is controlled mainly by the water and acid content.By carefully controlling the hydrolysis and the condensation rate, microporous materials can be obtained. Non-supported layers were dried, calcined and characterized by nitrogen adsorption-desorption. Supported γ-alumina membranes were modified, using the same polymeric solutions, and characterized by gas permeability.

RESULTS

When non-supported γ-alumina layers are modified with magnesia with in situ hydrolysis, no pore size decrease can be detected [7]. The loads vary between 1-3 wt% and are thus very low. When supported γ-alumina layers are modified however, loads are much higher, as indicated by SEM/EDS. This is due to the difference in pore size between the toplayer (pore radius 2.5-3 nm) and the support (pore diameter 200 nm). Therefore capillary force upon drying will be much higher in the toplayer. The support then acts as a reservoir, from where the modification solution in the toplayer is continuously refreshed. This method is therefore known as the 'reservoir method'.

Figure 1 presents the helium permeability of a supported γ-alumina membrane, before and after modification. After modification and subsequent heating to 100 ^{0}C, no permeability could be detected. The magnesium hydroxide is present in the pores as a plug, thus blocking gas flux (figure 2). After calcination at 400 ^{0}C, crystallization occurs and magnesia is formed. Since the density of magnesia is much lower, the pore opens again (figure 2). This is illustrated by the increase in permeability. The helium permeability after modification is still about two times smaller than before modification, indicating a decreased effective porosity. This was qualitatively supported by SEM/EDS measurements, where magnesia was solely found in the toplayer. Theoretically the load was about 40 vol%, based on the concentrations of precursor solutions. Quantitative experimental verification with XPS or Scanning Auger Microscopy has not yielded reliable results yet however.

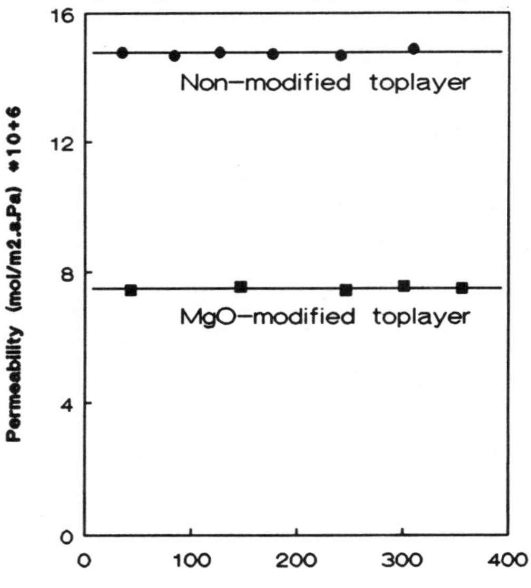

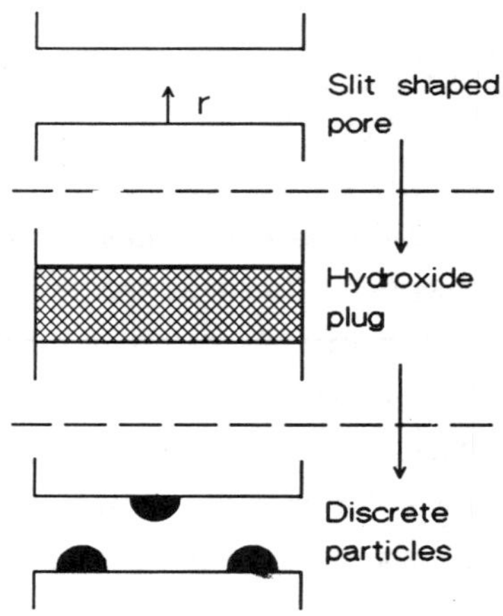

Figure 1: helium permeability of a non-modified and modified system

Figure 2: schematic view of an in situ modified system

The decrease in permeability does not necessarily indicate a pore size decrease. This is illustrated in figure 2. γ-alumina contains slit shaped pores [1]. The magnesia is present as plugs, increasing the resistance to gas flow, but not decreasing the effective pore radius r. From the schematic figure 2 it can be concluded, that high loads of 50 vol% or more are necessary to obtain an effective pore size decrease.

In order to prevent the deposited material to form discrete crystalline particles, modification with polymeric solutions of titania or silica were performed. Silica can be prepared in a microporous (pores < 1nm) [8] and thermally stable state till 900 ^{0}C, provided no water vapor at relatively high pressure is present [9]. Titania was chosen due to its better stability in the presence of water, although synthesis of microporous titania has not been reported so far.

Figure 3 gives nitrogen adsorption desorption isotherms of non-supported silica and titania layers. This type of isotherm is typically for microporous systems with pores < 1 nm. In this region, Kelvin's law is not anymore

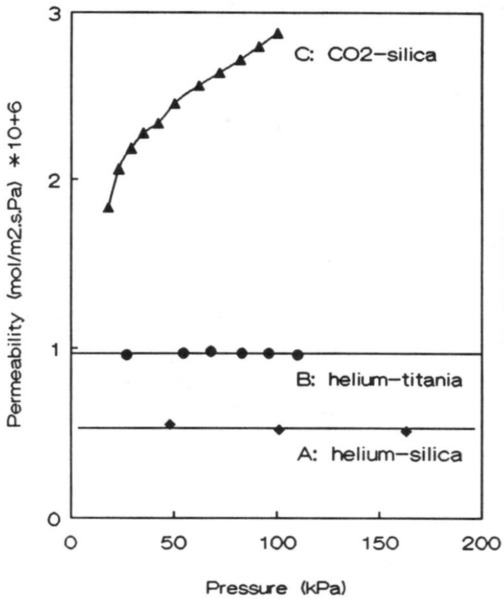

Figure 3: helium (A+B) and CO2 (C) permeability of silica (A+C) and titania (B)

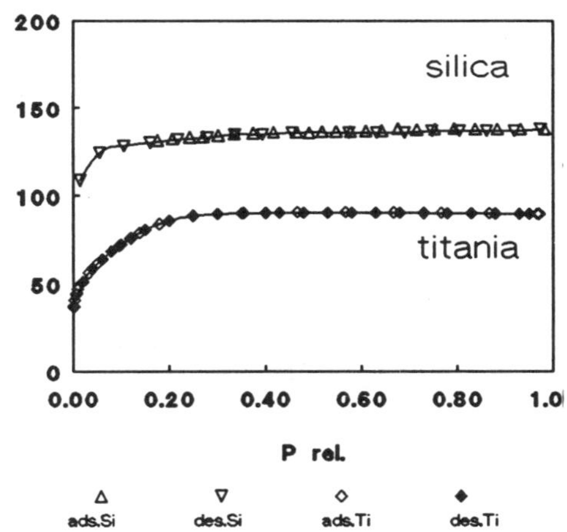

Figure 4: N2 adsorption-desorption isotherm of silica and titania

applicable and the hysteresis disappears. When titania is heated above 350 ^{0}C, the pores grow to about 4 nm diameter. This is due to crystallization to the anatase form, followed by particle growth. Silica is microporous till at least 600 ^{0}C, as indicated by nitrogen adsorption-desorption.

Supported γ-alumina membranes were modified with the same polymeric solutions as mentioned above, dried and calcined at 400 ^{0}C (silica) and 300 ^{0}C (titania). The helium permeability is given in figure 4. It can be seen, that the helium permeability has decreased strongly. This indicates a strongly decreased pore size and/or a decrease in porosity. The permeability of CO_2 however has been much less decreased (figure 4). This can only be understood, if a pore size decrease is assumed. It can be concluded, that a microporous system has been prepared, in which transport through activated diffusion takes place [10].It can be expected, that gas separation properties are largely enhanced by this pore size decreases. Further discussion on the structure of these systems and their gas transport and separation properties is given elsewhere [10].

REFERENCES

1. Leenaars, A.F.M., Keizer, K., Burggraaf, A.J., Structure, permeability and separation characteristics of porous alumina membranes. In ACS Symposium Series 281, Reverse Osmosis and Ultrafiltration, ed.S.Sourirajan, ACS, Washington, 1985, pp. 57-69
2. Larbot, A, Fabre, J.P., Guizard, G., Cot, L., Inorganic membranes obtained by sol-gel techniques, J.Membr.Science, 1988, **39**, 203-213
3. Gieselman, M.J., Anderson, M.A., Moosemiller, M.D., Hill, C.G., Physico-chemical properties of supported and unsupported γ-Al_2O_3 and TiO_2 ceramic membranes, Sep.Sc.Techn., 1988, **23**, 1695 - 1714
4. Zaspalis, V.T., Keizer, K., v.Praag, W., v. Ommen, J.G., Ross, J.R.H., Burggraaf, A.J., Porous ceramic membranes as catalytic active materials in catalytic processes, Proc. Brit. Ceramic Soc (1989) in press
5. Uhlhorn, R.J.R., Keizer, K., Burgraaf, A.J., Formation of and gas transport mechanisms in ceramic membranes. In Advances in Reverse Osmosis and Ultrafiltration, ed. T. Matsuura, ACS, Washington, 1989, pp. 239-259
6. Uhlhorn, R.J.R., Huis in 't Veld, M.H.B.J., Keizer, K., Burggraaf, A.J., New ceramic membrane materials for use in gas separation applications. In Science of Ceramics **14**, ed.D.Taylor, Buttler&Tanner ltd., London, 1988, pp. 551-556
7. Uhlhorn, R.J.R., Keizer, K., Burggraaf, A.J., Gas and surface diffusion in (modified) γ-alumina systems, J.Membr.Science 1989, in press
8. Brinker, C.J., Keefer, K.D., Schaeffer, D.W., Ashley, C.S., Sol-gel transition in simple silicates, J.Non.Cryst.Solids, 1982, **48**, 47-67
9. Iler, R.K., Chemistry of Silica: solubility, polymerization, colloid and surface properties and biochemistry, Wiley & Sons, New York, 1979
10. Uhlhorn, R.J.R., Keizer, K., Burggraaf, A.J., Theory and experiments on transport of condensable gases in microporous ceramic membrane systems, Proc. ICIM '89, 1989, to be published

THE CALCINATION AND THERMAL STABILITY OF CERAMIC Al_2O_3 MEMBRANES FOR GAS SEPARATION

H.M. VAN VEEN, J.P.B.M. TOL, R.A. TERPSTRA,
A.J.G. ENGEL and H.J. VERINGA
Netherlands Energy Research Foundation, ECN,
P.O. Box 1, 1755 ZG Petten, the Netherlands

ABSTRACT

The three layer tubular ceramic membrane system prepared by ECN, consists of an alpha-alumina substrate, an (alpha-alumina) intermediate or microfiltration layer and a gamma-alumina top layer. The microfiltration layer is applied by a film coating technique while the top or ultrafiltration layer is obtained by slip casting. The top layer has a narrow pore radius distribution in the nanometer region, a thickness of about 3 microns and it can be used for gas separation (and ultrafiltration).
With a recently developed carrier system it is possible to produce an almost defect-free gas separation membrane. In this paper various calcining procedures for the top layer will be compared and it will be shown that relatively fast calcining has no influence on the pore properties while a smooth layer without cracks is formed.
In order to study the thermal stability of the top layer, the membranes are first calcined at 600°C and then exposed to different temperatures for up to 600 hours. The membranes are then characterized by nitrogen adsorption/desorption and X-ray diffraction.

INTRODUCTION

In this paper the calcination and thermal stability of ceramic gamma-alumina membranes for gas separation (and ultrafiltration) are discussed.
The three layer tubular membrane system, see figure 1 (outer diameter = 20 mm, length = 5 - 70 cm) consists of a porous substrate (α-alumina sintered at 1550°C) with a microporous layer on the outside of the tube (α-alumina sintered at 1200°C). This layer has microfiltration properties but it can also be used as a support for a gas separation or ultrafiltration layer. The gamma-alumina top layer is calcined for 5 hours at 600°C. The preparation and properties of this membrane system have been reported elsewhere [1].
Up to now the gas separation layer in the membrane system has been calcined according to the recipe of Leenaars [2]. We have compared some different calcining procedures for the top layer [3, 4] with the former used procedure. We also used a relatively fast sintering procedure and have used SEM and BET to characterize the layers formed.
Although a major advantage of ceramic membranes is the use at high temperatures not much is known about the stability (crystallite size, porosity, pore size distribution and specific surface area) of the gamma-alumina top layer at high temperatures. For gamma-alumina it is known [2, 5] that calcining temperatures from 400°C up to 800°C, regardless of the temperature

hold time, no significant increase in crystallite size (thickness)is being observed. Furthermore, it is shown [2, 3, 6, 7] that at higher calcining temperatures or longer calcination time at constant temperature the BET surface area decreases and the pore size increases, whereas the porosity is nearly constant and exhibits no systematic change in the range of 400 to 800°C.

Figure 1. The three layer ceramic membrane system.

MATERIALS AND METHODS

For the top layer or gas separation layer a boehmite (gamma-AlOOH) sol is used, which is prepared according to the recipe of Leenaars [2].
The unsupported membrane layers are prepared by pouring the stable γ-AlOOH sol into some dishes. Supported membrane layers are prepared by "slip casting" the sol on the microporous support layer. After drying a thin γ-AlOOH gel layer is formed and this gel layer is fired for 5 hours at 600°C (standard procedure). The transition of γ-AlOOH to γ-Al_2O_3 takes place at about 390°C.

In order to get a faster sintering procedure for our gas separation layer we have compared some different procedures [2, 3, 4] and compared these with a fast (heating rate = 100°C/h) sintering procedure. We have used SEM (JEOL JXA-840 scanning microanalyzer) and N_2 adsorption/ desorption (Carlo Erba Sorptomatic 1800) to characterize the supported and unsupported membranes respectively.

To investigate the thermal stability of the gas separation layer an amount of unsupported top layers is calcined for 5 hours at 600°C. After this calcination, further heat treatments are carried out at 600, 550, 500, and 425°C for 5, 25, 125, and 600 hours respectively. Furthermore the unsupported membranes treated (upto 600 hours) at 600°C are exposed to 500°C for 600 hours. With X-ray diffraction and N_2 adsorption/desorption, the properties of the different layers are examined. The X-ray data are obtained with a Philips PW 1050 diffractometer.

RESULTS

Sintering procedures

No cracks due to sintering were observed after any of the sintering procedures applied.
In table 1 the results from the isotherms of N_2 gas adsorption on the membranes for the different sintering procedures are given.

TABLE 1
Results from N_2 gas adsorption.

ref. no. procedure	BET surface area (m^2/g)	mean pore size (nm)	porosity (%)
2*	240.9	4.5	55.3
2	269.3	4.4	42.9
2	245.4	4.3	59.7
3	253.1	4.4	53.6
4	260.3	4.3	56.1
8	258.6	4.0	55.6

* 34 hours constant at 600°C.

Thermal stability

X-ray diffraction: It is found by peak width measurement of the (440) reflection that the crystallite size is 30 ± 3 Å after sintering for 5 h at 600°C and that it increases to 38 ± 3 Å after sintering for 600 h at the same temperature.
N_2 adsorption/desorption: The results show that the porosity is independent of the calcination time at 600°C and it is not affected by any of the experiments done. The porosity varies from 54.5% to 60.5%.
In the figures 2 and 3 the specific surface area and pore sizes are given as a function of the temperature hold time. Also the results of the unsupported membranes calcined for several periods at 600°C and afterwards heat treated for 600 hours at 500°C are given in these figures.

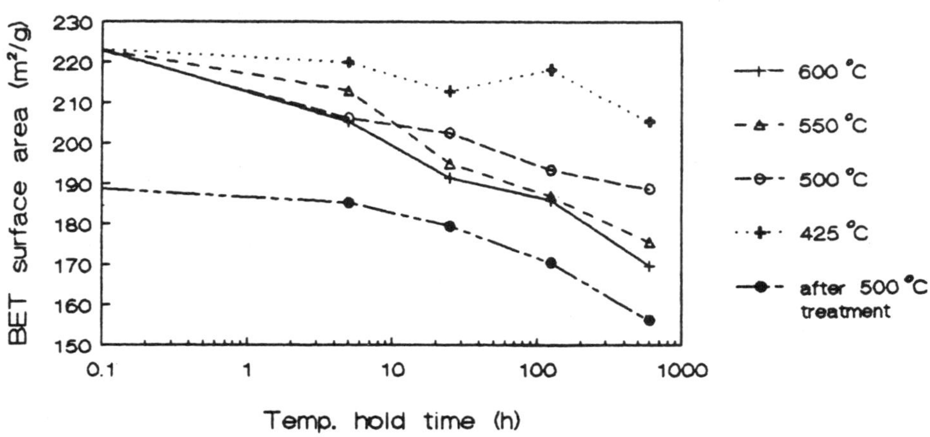

Figure 2. Temperature hold time vs. surface area.

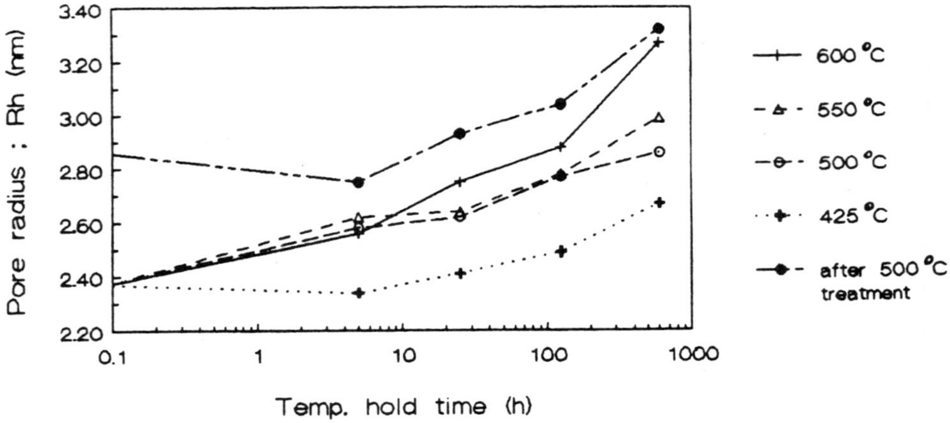

Figure 3. Temperature hold time vs. pore radius.

DISCUSSION

Comparison of the sintering procedures and results from table 1 show that there is no significant change in the porosity and specific surface area due to the different sintering procedures. The fastest (ECN) sintering procedure seems to give slightly smaller pores, and no cracks are observed.
A slight change in crystallite size and no (systematic) change in porosity has been found due to any of the heat treatments described.
Figure 2 shows that at lower (425°C) temperatures the decrease in surface area is small but the unsupported membranes regularly calcined for 5 hours at 600°C appear not to be stable after 600 hours at 425°C. The membranes treated for up to 600 hours at 600°C show a decrease in surface area after storing them for 600 hours at 500°C. The sample treated during 25 hours at 600°C shows a decrease in surface area, after storing them at 500°C for 600 hours, which is nearly the same as treating for 600 hours at 600°C and storing for 600 hours at 500°C. In figure 3 the increase in pore radius decreases with decreasing exposure temperature and seem to stabilize the pore growth at long exposure time.
Only a slight increase in mean pore radius occurs when the membranes stabilized for longer periods at 600°C are exposed to 500°C for 600 hours. Stabilization at 600°C for about 1000 hours will be enough for the membranes to be used at 500°C.
Keizer [9] reported the microstructure of the unsupported (about 200 µm thick) γ-alumina membranes is the same as for thin supported layers. In our experiments the unsupported membranes have a thickness of about 150-300 µm so we may assume the microstructures of the supported and unsupported membranes are the same.

CONCLUSIONS AND ONGOING INVESTIGATIONS

- A very fast sintering procedure can be used for the top layer without formation of cracks in it.
- Porosity and crystallite size of the γ-alumina top layers are not affected by any of the sintering procedures which were investigated.
- Membranes sintered for 5 hours at 600°C are not stable when exposed to temperatures above 425°C.

- After stabilization for 600 hours at 600°C, almost no pore growth is found when the membrane is heated for 600 h at 500°C (but the specific surface area still decreases).
- The decrease in surface area can be attributed to the disappearance of the smallest pores only, because the dominant sintering mechanism is surface diffusion: the surface area decreases and the pore size increases with increasing stabilization time, whereas the crystallite size and the porosity remain constant.

Investigations into the thermal stability of the membranes will be continued. Longer stabilization time at 600°C for the use of the ceramic membranes at 500°C and also stabilization at higher temperatures (e.g. 700°C) will be investigated. The gas permeation and segregative properties of supported γ-alumina membranes will also be part of this investigation.

ACKNOWLEDGEMENT

We thank P. van Vlaanderen for the X-ray diffraction measurements and R.G. Nyqvist and C. van Egmond for the N_2-adsorption/desorption measurements. The financial support by the Dutch Ministry of Economic Affairs (via the programme IOP-M) is gratefully appreciated.

REFERENCES

1. Terpstra, R.A., Bonekamp, B.C. and Veringa, H.J., Preparation, characterization and some properties of tubular alpha alumina ceramic membranes for microfiltration and as a support for ultrafiltration and gas separation membranes. Desalination, 1988, 70, 395-404.

2. Leenaars, A.F.M., Preparation, structure and separation characteristics of ceramic alumina membranes. Thesis, University of Twente, 1984.

3. Larbot, A., Alary, J.A., Guizard, C., Cot, L. and Gillot, J. New inorganic ultrafiltration membranes: preparation and characterization. Int.J.High Techn.Cer., 1987, 3, 143-151.

4. University of Twente, personal communication, 1987.

5. Dwivedi, R.K. and Gowda, G., Thermal stability of aluminium oxides prepared from gel. J.Mat.Sci.Lett., 1985, 4, 331-334.

6. Leenaars, A.F.M., Keizer, K. and Burggraaf, A.J., Porous alumina membranes. Chemtech, september 1986, 560-564.

7. Schaper, H., Doesburg, E.B.M. and van Reijen, L.L., The influence of lanthanum oxide on the thermal stability of gamma alumina catalyst supports. Appl.Catal., 1983, 7, 211-220.

8. ECN result, 1988.

9. Keizer, K., Uhlhorn, R.J.R., van Vuren, R.J. and Burggraaf, A.J., Gas separation mechanisms in microporous modified γ-Al_2O_3 membranes. J.Membrane Sci., 1988, 39, 285-300.

MODIFICATION OF CERAMIC MEMBRANES BY CVD AND EVD FOR GAS SEPARATION, CATALYSIS AND SOFC APPLICATION

Y.S. Lin, L.G.J. de Haart, K.J. de Vries, A.J. Burggraaf
Laboratory of Inorganic Chemistry, Materials Science and Catalysis, Department of Chemical Technology, University of Twente, 7500 AE Enschede, The Netherlands

ABSTRACT

In this contribution we report a unique approach for the modification of ceramic membranes by means of modified CVD, combined with EVD, for separation, catalysis and SOFC applications. In the modified CVD, pore size and internal pore surface chemistry are modified by depositing a solid oxide on the internal walls of the membrane. The deposit is the product of two vapor reactants introduced from both sides of the membrane. After the membrane pore is closed by the CVD deposit, a thin solid oxide electrolyte film can grow on one side of the membrane via EVD due to the mixed conductivity of the deposited oxide. Preliminary experimental results are presented to show the feasibility of this approach for membrane modification.

INTRODUCTION

Ceramic membranes are finding increasing applications in chemical processes for separation, purification and catalytic reaction, because of many novel properties of these inorganic membranes [1]. The synthesis of membranes with proper surface chemistry and desired pore size is essential to the membrane applications. On the other hand, due to the potential application and advantages of the fuel cell for power generation [2], considerable attention has been paid to the development of solid oxide fuel cells (SOFC). The efficiency of the SOFC, however, depends in large part on the ionic resistance of the solid oxide electrolyte. It is known that the efficiency can be increased by decreasing the electrolyte thickness [3]. There are several techniques [1] (e.g., sol-gel method [4]) reported for the synthesis of ceramic membranes, but the use of these developed techniques to synthesize membranes with pore sizes in subnanometer scale is rather difficult. In the present paper we report the modification of ceramic membranes to any desired pore size by modified chemical vapor deposition (CVD) and the growth of thin electrolyte films on membranes by the combined CVD and electrochemical vapor deposition (EVD). The general considerations on this unique CVD/EVD technique are discussed and some preliminary experimental results are presented to show the feasibility of the CVD/EVD technique for membrane modification.

PRINCIPLES

Different from the conventional CVD, the deposition of the solid oxide on the internal walls of the substrate pore by the modified CVD is due to the inter-diffusion and reaction of the vapor metal chloride and water (or oxygen) in the substrate pores. In the modified CVD process, the two vapor reactants, separated by the membrane substrate, inter-diffuse into the substrate pores from both sides of the substrate, as shown in Fig.1. The reaction takes place inside the membrane pores and the solid product is formed on the pore walls. If the CVD process is properly controlled, the modified membrane will have the following three forms (see Fig.2): (1) The pore walls of the original ceramic membrane is deposited with a thin ceramic oxide layer, thus modifying the internal pore surface chemistry (stage 1); (2) the pore size is narrowed to any desired size at one end of the substrate pore (stage 2); (3) the pore is closed with an oxide deposit (stage 3). The chemical reaction for such a CVD process can be generally expressed as:

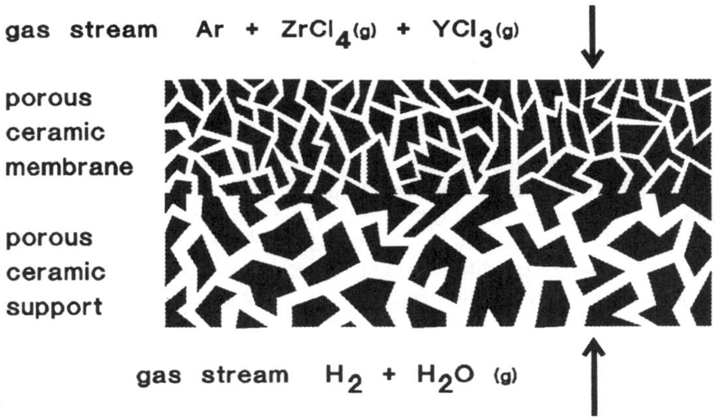

FIGURE 1. Schematic illustration of the CVD/EVD modification of supported ceramic membranes.

$$MCl_{2n}\ (g) + n\ H_2O\ (g) = MO_n\ (s) + 2n\ HCl\ (g) \tag{1}$$

If a mixture of two metal chloride vapors (e.g. $ZrCl_4$ and YCl_3) with proper composition is taken as one gas reactant, a solid oxygen-ion conducting oxide can be formed as the plug in stage 3 in the CVD process. Because of the slight electronic conductivity of this metal oxide plug, a metal oxide film can grow on the side of membrane disc exposed to the metal chloride vapor via the Wagner-scaling process [6] as shown in stage 4 in Fig. 2. If water is used as the oxygen source, the EVD electrochemical reaction can be written as:

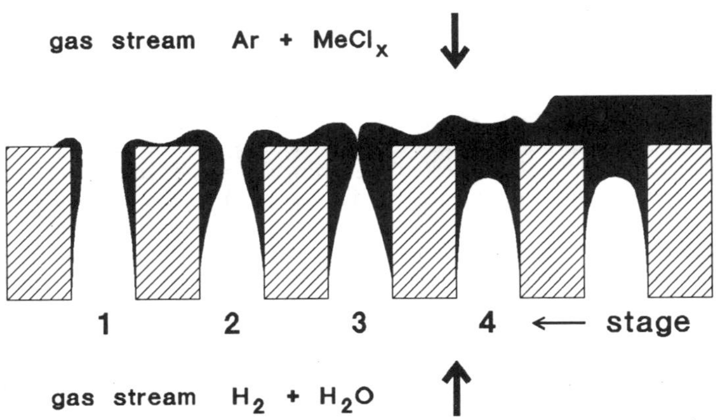

FIGURE 2. Detailed view of the membrane toplayer showing the different stages in the CVD/EVD membrane mofification.

At the metal chloride vapor and EVD film interface:

$$MCl_4 + 2\ O^{2-} = MO_2 + 2\ Cl_2 + 4e' \tag{2}$$

And at the water and EVD film interface:

$$2\ H_2O + 4e' = 2\ O^{2-} + 2\ H_2 \qquad (3)$$

With the general electrochemical reaction:

$$MCl_4\ (g) + 2\ H_2O\ (g) = MO_2\ (s) + 2\ H_2 + 2\ Cl_2 \qquad (4)$$

Thermodynamics

The above CVD reaction (1) is thermodynamically very favorable for the formation of the metal oxide. For example, the standard Gibbs free energy (ΔG) and equilibrium constant (K_e) for ZrO_2 (with n=2 in reaction (1)), estimated using the available data [5], range from -176.6 to -200.4 kJ/mol and $2.36x10^8$ to $0.12x10^8$, respectively, at T=1000-1478 K. Thus, this CVD process is primarily determined by the kinetics of diffusion and reaction in the substrate pores. However, for the EVD reactions with water as the oxygen source, the calculated result of the Gibbs free energy for reaction (4) indicates that for most metals this reaction is thermodynamically not favorable for the formation of the EVD layer (e.g. for ZrO_2, ΔG = 228.4 - 215.1 kJ/mol at T=1000-1478 K). Nevertheless, some experimental results [7-9] for the growth of yttria stabilized zirconia (YSZ) films by this EVD technique showed the formation of the metal oxide with water vapor as the oxygen source. Although the same results are confirmed by the present experiments, the explanation on the contradiction between the theory and experiment is still to be found. However, if oxygen instead of water or a mixture of metal chloride and hydrogen are used as the reactants, metal oxide formation is thermodynamically favorable in the EVD phase.

Kinetics

The kinetics of the CVD phase involves the following steps: (1) inter-diffusion of the two reactants into the substrate pore; (2) chemical reaction and deposition of the solid product on the substrate pore wall; (3) diffusion of the gas product (HCl) out of the substrate pore. The CVD process can be described by a mathematical model which takes into account diffusion, convection and chemical reaction in the pore [10]. The resulting mathematical model consists of a set of ordinary differential equations and its solution gives the deposit distribution across the membrane pore. The simulation results show that the deposit distribution is determined by the reaction kinetics and diffusion constant, and several experimental conditions such as substrate pore dimension, bulk phase concentrations of the two reactants, substrate temperature and total pressure drop over the membrane substrate. Thus, with the proper selection of the reaction system, substrate structure and experimental conditions, it is possible to modify the membrane to the forms as shown in stages 1, 2 and 3 in Fig.2.

If the oxygen gradient over the EVD film is considered as the driving force for the EVD process [7,9], the kinetics of the EVD film growth involves the chemical or electrochemical transfer of oxygen. In the case that the substrate pores get plugged close to the surface exposed to the metal chloride vapor, the film growth during the EVD process is determined by the following four steps in series: (1) water (or oxygen) diffusion in the substrate pore, (2) charge-transfer reaction at the interface between the EVD film and water vapor; (3) electrochemical transport in the EVD film and (4) charge-transfer reaction (formation of solid oxide) at the interface between the EVD film and metal chloride vapor. The theoretical analysis on the kinetics of the EVD film growth shows that the function of the EVD film thickness versus deposition time, H(t), is parabolic only when mass transfer step (3) as mentioned above is the rate-limiting step. If any one of the other three mass transfer steps (1, 2, 4) is the rate-limiting step, H (t) should be a linear function. Mathematical analysis also shows that under the conditions as reported previously [7-9] as well as in the present investigation the water or oxygen diffusion in the substrate pore is the rate-determining step. This suggests that the proper dimension of the substrate pore is critical to the growth rate of the EVD film.

EXPERIMENTAL AND RESULTS

Apparatus and Experimental Conditions

The CVD and EVD experiments for membrane modification were carried out in the self-made CVD/EVD apparatus. Fig.3 shows schematic representation of the apparatus which consists of three parts: reactor system, vacuum system and reactant delivery systems. The central part of the CVD/EVD apparatus, as schematically shown in Fig.4, is the reactor made of three dense alumina ceramic tubes, which are heated by a 6-zone furnace to give the desired temperature profile in the reactor. A porous alumina substrate disc, which separates the reactor into two chambers filled with MCl_x and water, respectively, was cemented into the end of the smallest dense alumina tube.

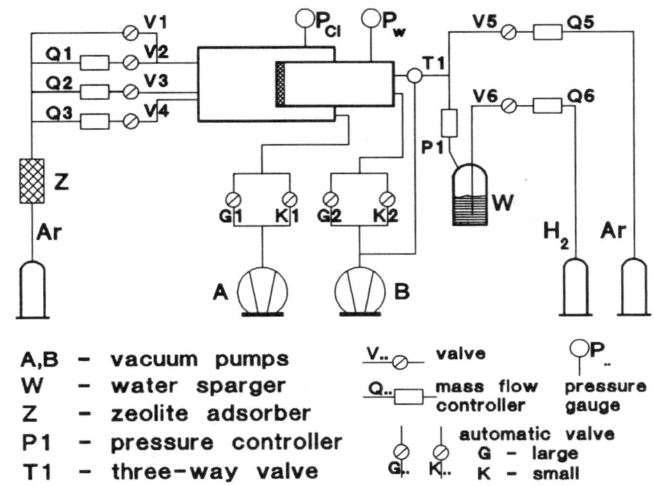

FIGURE 3. Schematic diagram of the CVD/EVD apparatus.

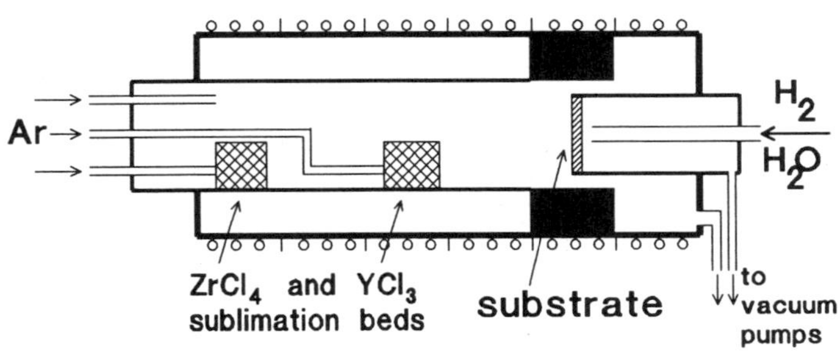

FIGURE 4. Detailed schematic view of the central part of the CVD/EVD reactor system.

In experiments, three argon streams of known flow rates controlled by the mass flow meters Q1, Q2, Q3 were introduced into the reactor. The mixture of $ZrCl_4$ and YCl_3 was generated by passing two of the argon streams through the heated sublimation beds of powdered $ZrCl_4$ and YCl_3 placed inside the reactor. The hydrogen/steam mixture was generated by bubbling hydrogen gas through a heated sparger (W) filled with distilled water to obtain a saturated mixture of water vapor and hydrogen. The hydrogen stream flow rate and total pressure of the water vapor and hydrogen in the sparger were controlled by the mass flow meter Q6 and pressure controller P1, respectively. All the experimental conditions such as the total pressures (P_{Cl} and P_w), the concentrations of metal chloride and water in the two chambers, and reaction zone temperature could be well controlled with this apparatus.

As a preliminary study, a coarse alpha-alumina porous membrane disc was used as the substrate. The characteristics of the substrate and reactants, and the experimental conditions for the CVD/EVD experiments are summarized in Table 1.

TABLE 1
Characterization of substrate and experimental conditions

Reactant sources:	$ZrCl_4$, YCl_3, H_2O
Carrier gas:	Ar (for chlorides), H_2/Ar (for water)
Substrate:	α-alumina porous disk
	diameter = 12 mm; thickness = 2 mm
	mean pore-size = 0.16 μm; porosity = 50%

Substrate temperature:	1000 °C
Reactor pressure:	1.5 mbar
$ZrCl_4$ sublimation bed temperature:	160 °C
YCl_3 sublimation bed temperature:	613 °C
Water sparger temperature:	40 °C
Chloride vapor concentration:	$2.0*10^{-9}$ mol/ml
$YCl_3/ZrCl_4$ ratio in vapor:	1/5
Water vapor concentration:	$3.5*10^{-9}$ mol/ml
H_2/H_2O ratio in vapor:	3/2

Characterization

The phase structure, morphology, composition and composition profile, and the EVD film thickness for the substrate after deposition were examined by XRD, SEM and EDS. The extent of the deposition and pore closing were determined by the permeation of Ar through the substrate during the deposition experiment (at reaction temperature). The permeation data were measured by monitoring the pressure rise in the water chamber, with a constant pressure of 200 mbar in the chloride chamber and an initial pressure of 100 mbar in the water chamber.

Deposition Results

Deposition was made on five alumina substrates with deposition time ranging from 8 hours to 15 hours. As the ratio of the pore size to the pore length of the substrate is very small, which results in a rather large Thiele modulus [9,10], the deposition of the metal oxide was found to take place mainly near the substrate surface exposed to the metal chloride vapor. The EDS data indicate that the deposit of the metal oxides is only present in the range of a few microns deep in the substrate pore from the surface. There is essentially no deposit in the pores deeper than a few microns. The amount of the deposited oxide in the substrate pore is found to increase towards the metal chloride side of the substrate. The Y_2O_3/ZrO_2 ratio of the deposit is roughly about 8%, apparently determined by the yttrium chloride to zirconium chloride ratio in the gas phase (see Table 1). The in-situ measured permeability for Ar through the substrate during deposition was found to decrease gradually as the deposition time increases, showing the pore narrowing during the deposition. The permeability data after 15-hour deposition (at 1000 °C), for example, were found to be about 30 times smaller than that before deposition (at 1000 °C), indicating the pore closure by the oxide deposit. For the substrates with longer deposition time, the SEM micrographs show that a thin layer of the metal oxide, with a thickness of a few microns, is also present on the surface of the substrate exposed to the metal chloride vapor, as shown in the SEM photograph in Fig.5. The XRD data show that this thin film is a cubic YSZ solid solution. The relative intensity of the XRD peaks among the YSZ and alpha-alumina also indicates the thickness of the YSZ layer thinner than 5-10 micron. A very critical step in the process is the 'ageing' of the metal chloride sources, probably due to slow oxidation.

CONCLUSIONS

A unique CVD and EVD technique was described for the modification of ceramic membranes. The preliminary experimental results on the deposition of YSZ on a coarse alumina substrate show the feasibility of this technique for the membrane modifications.

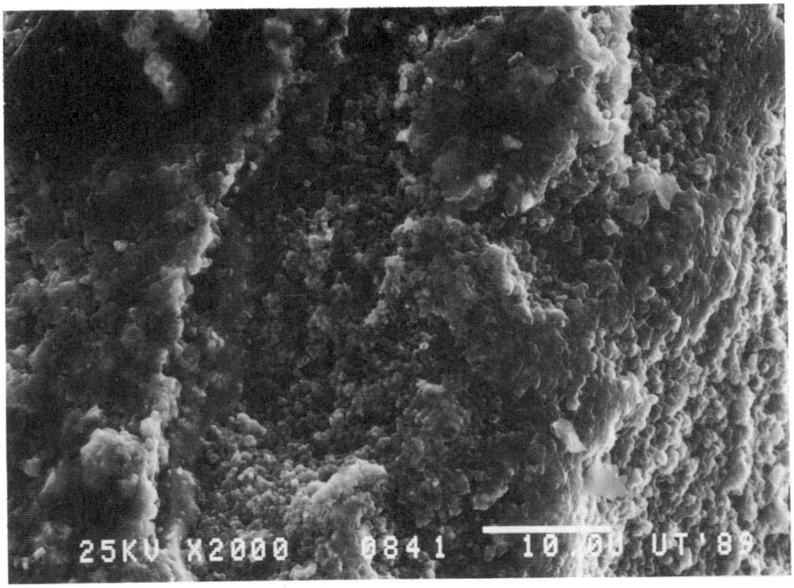

FIGURE 5. SEM photograph of a CVD/EVD deposit of YSZ on a coarse alumina substrate.

ACKNOWLEDGEMENT

This investigation was supported by the Dutch Ministry of Economical Affairs under grant: IOP Technical Ceramics No. 87 A045. Mr. P. Fransen and Mr. D. Wesseling are acknowledged for constructing the reactor and assistance in running the experiments.

REFERENCES

1. Hsieh, H.P., Inorganic membranes, AIChE Symp. Ser., 1988, **84**(261), 1-18
2. Mitchell, W., Fuel Cells, Academic Press, London, 1963.
3. Steele, B.C.H., Ceramic Electrochemical Reactors, Current Status and Application, Ceramionics, Surrey (UK), 1987.
4. Keizer, K. and Burggraaf, A.J., Porous ceramic materials in membrane applications, Science of Ceramics, 1988, **14**, 83-94.
5. Barin, I. and Knacke, O., Thermochemical Properties of Inorganic Substances, Springer-Verlag, Berlin, 1973.
6. Kofstad, P., High Temperature Oxidation of Metals, Wiley, New York, 1966, Ch. 5.
7. Isenburg, A.O., Growth of refractory oxide layers by electrochemical vapor deposition (EVD) at elevated temperature, ECS Symp. Electrode Materials, Processes for Energy Conversion and Storage, 1977, Vol. **77-6**, pp. 572-583.
8. Dietrich, G. and Schafer, W., Advances in the development of thin-film cells for high temperature electrolysis, Int. J. Hydrogen Energy, 1984, **9**, 747-752.
9. Carolan, M. and Micheals, J.N., Chemical vapor deposition of ytttria stabilized zirconia on porous supports, Solid State Ionics, 1987, **25**, 207-216.
10. Lin, Y.S., de Vries, K.J. and Burggraaf, CVD modification of ceramic membranes: simulation and preliminary results, accepted for the presentation at EURO-CVD 7, Perpignan, France, June 19-23, 1989.

CERAMIC MEMBRANES, APPLICATIONS AND PROPERTIES

F. Muilwijk / J.P.P. Tholen
Hoogovens Groep BV / Esmil Water Systems
Postbus 10.000 / Postbus 2033
1970 CA IJMUIDEN / 1110 PA DIEMEN

SUMMARY

Hoogovens Industrial Ceramics BV (HI Ceramics) has, in close cooperation with Netherlands Energy Research Foundation (ECN) and Esmil Water Systems (EWS), developed a new generation of tubular alumina membranes for cross-flow microfiltration. This development originates from earlier work done at the University of Twente (UT). The membranes developed by HI Ceramics differ from other alumina membranes in a very high permeability and a cost-effective way of manufacturing. At this moment extensive field tests of the membranes are being made and HI Ceramics is drawing plans for a so called production laboratory. In this plant membranes will be produced in a commercial way, but with all the care and attention of a ceramic membrane laboratory. As the next step in the separation area HI Ceramics is developing ceramic ultrafiltration and gas separation membranes both again in close cooperation with ECN and UT.

INTRODUCTION

Membrane separation is one of the many possible techniques in the field of separation. As a relatively new one it has to compete with established competitors like destillation, centrifugation, fractionation, sedimentation and chromatography. Membrane separation offers a number of advantages over these other techniques, being:

- separation can be achieved contiously;
- energy consumption is relatively low;
- separation can be achieved at ambient or process temperature;
- membrane units can easily be added to an existing process or to eachother.

Up till now the majority of the membranes are produced from organic compounds. This fact is due to the easiness and cost-effectiveness with which they can be produced. However, organic membranes suffer from two major setbacks: both their chemical and thermal stability are in many cases unsufficient. Ceramic membranes on the other hand are both chemically and thermally very stable but they are more expensive, rather brittle and limited in design.

In those separation areas where the fysical and chemical demands prevail ceramic membranes are expected to take their part of the market. Examples of these areas are the dairy industries, the fruit-juice, beer and wine processing, and chemical and biotechnical applications. Also the separation of oil and water, especially when contaminated with aggressive chemicals or abrasive metals is an area in which ceramic membranes are the best or only choice.

In fluid separations a total worldwide market of about 30,000 m^2 is foreseen in 1995. High temperature gas separation and membrane reactors will provide an even bigger market for ceramic membranes. However, for both applications there are still major technical difficulties which have to be solved before a succesful introduction of the membranes. HI Ceramics, supported by the combined knowledge of UT, ECN and Hoogovens Groep BV (a major steel and aluminium producer) will succeed in finding these solutions.

PRODUCTION ROUTE OF CERAMIC MICROFILTRATION MEMBRANES

As shown in scheme 1 the production of the HI Ceramics' membranes takes place in only a few steps. The real membrane layer is sintered directly upon the support, with no intermediate layer in between, and in case of tubular membranes also ceramic flanges are sintered onto the membrane tubes. This results in a rugged all ceramic inner part of the membrane module, with no differences in chemical and fysical properties between the membranes and the flanges.

SCHEME 1

Production route of the ceramic membranes

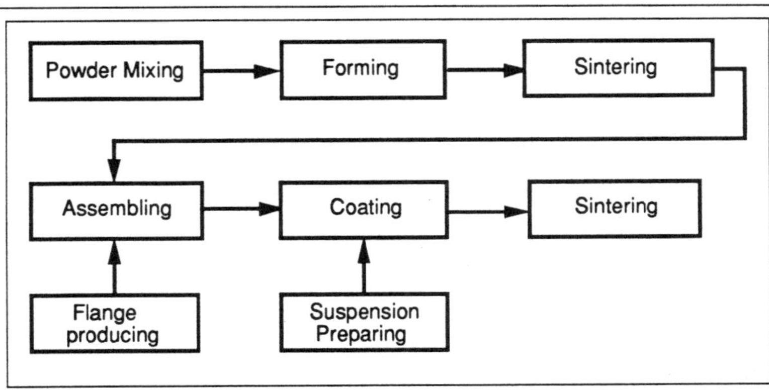

ELECTRON MICROSCOPE PHOTOGRAPH OF THE HI CERAMICS' MEMBRANE

Courtesy of ECN

PROPERTIES OF THE HI CERAMICS' MEMBRANES

The properties are given in table 1, both as they are realized now and as they are expected to be when produced on an industrial scale.

TABLE 1

Properties of the Hoogovens Industrial Ceramics membranes as realized in 1989 and expected in 1991

propertie/year			1989	1991
dimensions	mm	lenght	700	1500
		inner diam.	8 - 14	4 - 15
		wall thickness	3	1 - 3
burst pressure	bar		30	100
chemical stability	pH		1 - 13	1 - 13
thermal stability (membranes+flanges)	°C		1000	1000
mean pore radius	micrometer		0.13	1.0 - 0.1
backflush pressure	bar		>10	>20
water flux	l/m2.hr.bar	pore radius 0.13	1500	1500
		pore radius 0.25		5000

FIRST TEST RESULTS OF MEMBRANE SEPARATION

The test results are summarized in table 2. More extensive tests are being planned and will be carried out in the near future.

TABLE 2

First test results of the Hoogovens Industrial Ceramics membranes using single stage cross-flow microfiltration

	dimension	TEST 1*	TEST 2
poresize	micrometer	0.13	0.13
inner diameter	mm	14	8
feed composition		water with yeast cells	water with oil, lye and iron (hydroxides and particles)
feedflow	m/sec	24	37
pressure	bar	2	3
temperature	°C	16	55
permeate flux	l/m2.hr	360	480
permeate composition		no yeast cells 1500	iron reduced to 5% of feed, oil reduced to 25% of feed

*ECN-HI Ceramics results

CONCLUSIONS

The ceramic membranes developed by HI Ceramics in cooperation with ECN possess a number of advantages over both organic and other ceramic membranes. Future research, done at University of Twente, Netherlands Energy Research Foundation, Hoogovens Industrial Ceramics BV, the research laboratories of Hoogovens Groep and Esmil Water Systems will guarantee an even better microfiltration membrane and also very good ultrafiltration and gas separation membranes.

REFERENCES

B.C. Bonekamp, R.A. Terpstra, A.J.G. Engel and R. de Rooy, "Forming of a two layer tubular ceramic alumina membrane for microfiltration", in preparation.

R.A. Terpstra, B.C. Bonekamp, H.M. van Veen, A.J.G. Engel, R. de Rooy and H.J. Veringa, "Preparation and properties of tubular ceramic Al_2O_3 membranes for gas separation", Science of Ceramics, 1987, 14, pp. 5.5.7-5.6.2.

European patent application no. 88202577.8 "Composite ceramic micropermeable membrane process and apparatus for producing such a membrane".

A NEW APPLICATION OF MILLIPOROUS CERAMIC SHAPES

A.P. PHILIPSE, F.P. MOET and P.J. VAN TILBORG
Netherlands Energy Research Foundation, ECN,
P.O. Box 1, 1755 ZG PETTEN, the Netherlands
D. BOOTSMA
N.V. Nederlandse Gasunie
P.O. Box 19, 9700 MA GRONINGEN, The Netherlands

ABSTRACT

First results are presented of a feasibility study on the shaping of ceramic plates with a tortuous pore structure and on their application as burner material for low NO_x, modulating combustion of natural gas. The study shows that this application offers good possibilities and, further, points to the importance of an accurate pore structure control with respect to proper functioning of the porous plates in combustion equipment.

INTRODUCTION

At ECN shaping techniques are being investigated for ceramic shapes with irregular, open pore structures with pore sizes in the millimeter region ("milliporous ceramics"). A major objective is to gain accurate control of pore shapes and sizes. The importance of such a control became apparent in a feasibility study, performed in cooperation with the Nederlandse Gasunie, of a new application for the milliporous ceramics, namely its use as burner material for low NO_x modulating combustion of natural gas.
This combustion technique, investigated by the Nederlandse Gasunie, combines a low NO_x emission due to premixing of air and gas in stoichiometric amounts with a variable (modulating) power output. The modulation is important for household applications, for example to minimize the on-off switching frequency. At present, however, there is no (low cost) burner material available for the mentioned combustion technique. Existing (low cost) metal burners cannot withstand the high temperature involved (~ 1000°C). Existing ceramic burner plates, containing straight, parallel pore channels cause problems, since they only burn stable and noiseless in a narrow range of power output.
The main conclusion of the burner tests performed by Gasunie in the mentioned study is that milliporous plates can be fabricated which offer good possibilities, allowing among other things a wide range of power output. However, the functioning of the plates was found to be very sensitive to details of the pore structure, which points to the importance of the control referred to above.
This communication is a first, preliminary report on the study.

MILLIPOROUS CERAMICS

One way to fabricate porous ceramic shapes is to include organic material in a green product, which leads to a certain porous structure after a burn-out procedure. However, to obtain an open, irregular pore structure with pore sizes in the range 0.1 - 1 mm a more appropriate method is a replica technique. The technique comprises the coating of an organic matrix with a ceramic suspension, followed by the burning of the matrix and sintering of its ceramic replica. Using an open-cell foam as a matrix leads to a ceramic foam [1, 2], but other matrices may be replicated as well (for example, fiber mats).
Fig. 1 shows various magnifications of an alumina foam prepared from open-cell polyurethane foam and a suspension of alumina powders (PN-202 and DX-206, supplied by Martinswerke). The alumina filaments forming the polyhedral pore structure (Fig. 1A) are hollow (Fig. 2), as was also reported by Green et al. [1]. Apparently the burning-out of polyurethane leads to channels which do not close during sintering. Fig. 3 depicts flat porous shapes made from alumina-silica (50 w/w %), which were used in preliminary burner tests. One of the shapes is a replica of an organic air filter. The other shapes are replica's of polyurethane foams. Though the appearence of the porous plates is similar, they show marked differences in their functioning as burner material.

BURNER TESTS

Burner tests went briefly as follows. A fully premixed gas-air mixture was supplied to the burner material, which was fixed horizontally in water cooled aluminum fire place, 80 mm above a heat exchanger of aluminum tubes. The flames were directed downwards such that condenstation water could easily been drawn off. Burner tests comprised the measurement of NO_x and CO-emission, the pressure and temperature drop across the burner material and assessment of the homogeneity and stability of the flame front as a function of the power output (kW/m^2) and the excess of air (with respect to stoichiometric combustion) in the gas-air mixture.

RESULTS AND DISCUSSION

From the four porous plates in Fig. 3 plate 20A yielded the most promising burner test results which will be discussed below.
Fig. 4A maps the region of power output and excess of air (as measured by the oxygen content in combustion gases) where stable burning takes place. Outside this region the flame is blown off or extinguished.
The stability region is much larger than for other tested materials, such as the other plates in Fig. 3, where flash back of the flame front was observed at relative high power outputs. Presumably this is due to somewhat larger pore sizes in these materials than in plate 20A.
An illustrative example is given in Fig. 5 for a commercial cordierite foam (Selee Company). This burner material, incidently, has also a region where the flame front shows pronounced vibrations, which was not observed during testing of 20A. It is clear that, for eample, in household heating equipment modulation should be possible without vibration or flash back of the flame. In this respect the tested cordierite is unsuitable for practical applications, whereas plate 20A offers good perspectives.

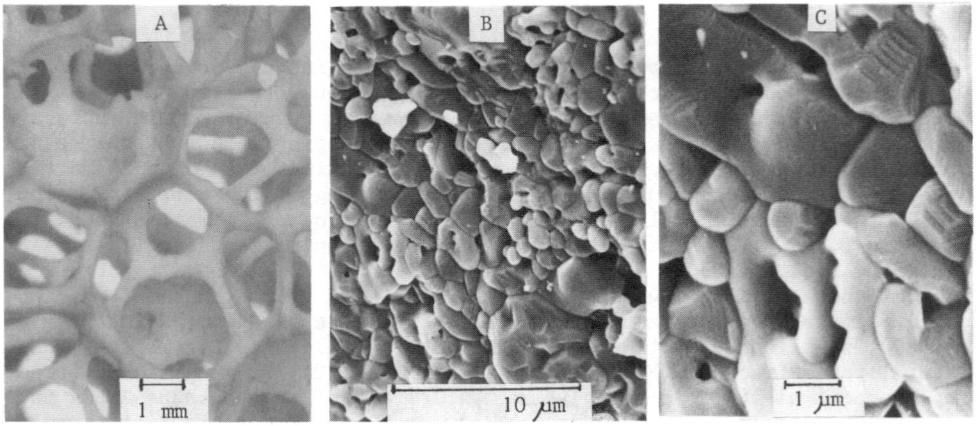

Fig. 1. Alumina foam structure (A) with various magnifications of an alumina filament (B, C).

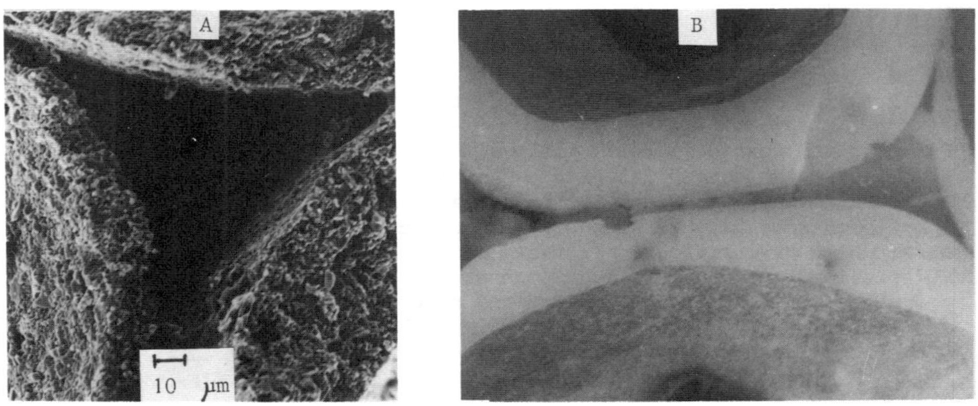

Fig. 2. Cross section of an alumina filament (A) showing the triangular pore channel left behind by burned out polyurethane. B shows a pore channel which connects two other pore channels.

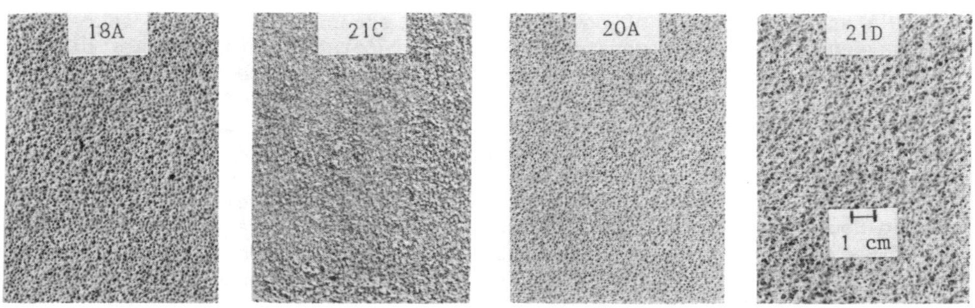

Fig. 3. Burner plates 18A, 21C and 20A, which are replica's of organic foams. Plate 21D is a replica of a fiber mat.

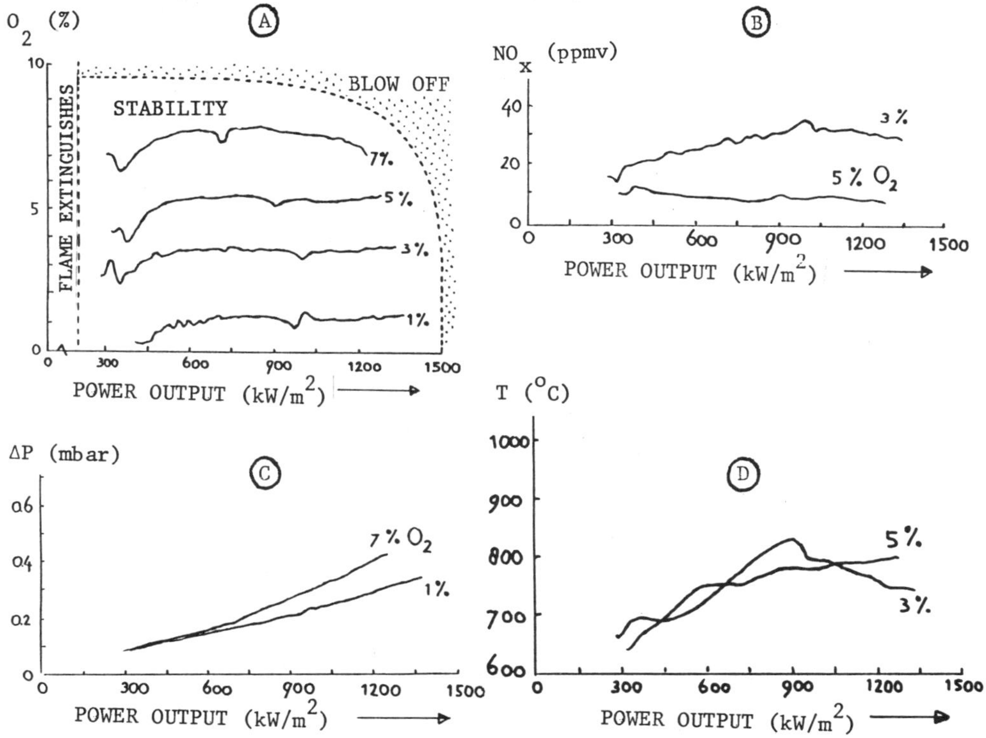

Fig. 4. Test results for plate 20A, showing the stability region of the flame front (A), the NO_x emission (B), the pressure drop across the plate (C) and the surface temperature (D), versus the power output (kW/m^2).

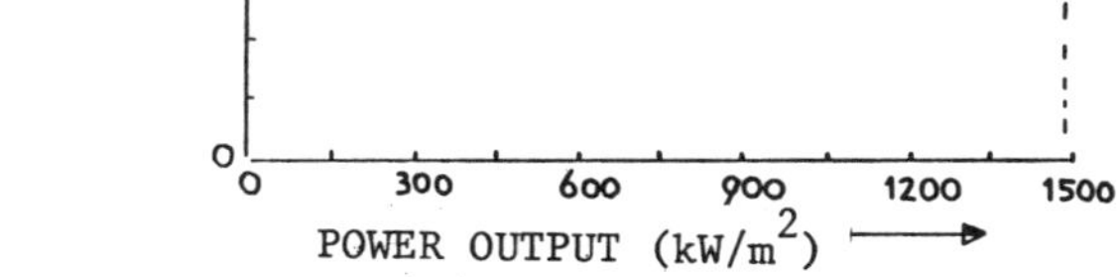

Fig. 5. Flame stability for a commercial cordierite foam as an example of a material with a too narrow stability region.

The NO_x-emission in the stability region (Fig. 4B) is virtually independent of the power output and varies between 10 and 30 ppm in the practical range of 3-5% O_2. Low emissions of this magnitude is indeed what one expects for fully premixed combustion.
The CO-emission (not shown here) in the stability region is smaller than 50 ppm in the range 3-5% O_2, which is acceptable, and showed little variation with power output.
The pressure drop across the burner material (Fig. 4C) increases from 0.1 to 0.4 mbar with increasing power input, i.e. with increasing flow rate of gases. A fan in a household heating equipment, however, would require a maximum pressure drop of 2 mbar.
Interestingly, a reproduction of plate 20A lead to a pressure drop of several mbar. So in principle it is possible to produce the pressure drop required for practical application of the burner material. The problem is, however, to fabricate porous plates with a narrow range in pressure drop. As the pressure drop is determined by the average pore size and the pore size distribution, the solution to the problem is a further increase in control and reproducibility of the pore structure.
The average surface temperature of burner plate 20A is in the range 600-800°C (Fig. 4D). At the "cold" side of the plate, where the air-gas mixture enters the ceramics, the temperature was always lower then 75°C. This is sufficiently low to avoid ignition of the fuel mixture.
For all the tested materials the combustion was inhomogeneous in the sense that the glowing surface of the ceramics showed "spots", i.e. local variations in surface temperature. These must be due to local variations in pore structure which give rise to variations in fuel flow velocity. This also points to the need of an increase in pore structure control.
With respect to materials properties of the milliporous shapes in Fig. 3 we only mention here that the shapes did not crack or fall apart during burner tests, or during machining to the desired dimensions. The shapes did, however, show some attrition. This "snowing" can also be observed for commercial ceramic foams, whenever they contain very thin ceramic filaments, as the shapes in Fig. 3.

CONCLUSIONS

Ceramic alumina-silica plates have been manufactured with a tortuous, open pore structure with pore sizes in the millimeter region. The plates offer good perspectives as burner materials for fully premixed low NO_x combustion of natural gas. They allow stable burning in a wide range of power input and excess of air, they are able to withstand a large vertical temperature gradient and they have a sufficient low thermal conductivity to avoid ignition of the gas-air mixture at the "cold" side of the plate. Local temperature variations at the burner side of the plates, as well as the difficulty of reproducing a certain pressure drop across the plates, indicate the need for a further increase in homogeneity and reproducibility of the porous ceramics.

PREPARATION, MODIFICATION AND MICROPOROUS STRUCTURE OF ALUMINA AND TITANIA CERAMIC MEMBRANE SYSTEMS.

W. van PRAAG, V.T. ZASPALIS, K. KEIZER, J.G. van OMMEN
J.R.H. ROSS AND A.J. BURGGRAAF.
University of Twente, Department of Chemical Technology,
Laboratory for Inorganic Chemistry, Materials Science and
Catalysis, P.O. Box 217, 7500AE Enschede, the Netherlands.

ABSTRACT

Crack-free ceramic membrane layers of aluminiumoxide, titaniumoxide and their binary combinations, supported on porous plate shaped α-alumina substrates are prepared by the sol-gel technique with a thickness up to 4μm. These membranes are subsequently modified with silver or vanadiumoxide, by making use of new impregnation techniques, in order to enhance their catalytic properties. Silver particles are concentrated only in the toplayer up to 50% of the available pore volume. The synthesis as well as the structural properties of the above mentioned systems are discussed. After impregnation of the ceramic membrane systems the porediameter measured with nitrogen adsorption/desorption remains the same while the porosity and the permeability are decreased. This can be explained by the existence of constrictions in the membrane pores.

INTRODUCTION

Ceramic membranes (e.g. microporous thin films of ceramic metal oxides) are important membrane classification because of their thermally and chemically stable structure and because these membranes can be used in heavy duty separation processes [1] and as catalytic materials in high temperature membrane reactors [2]. Silver modified γ-alumina based membranes are prepared as catalytic membranes for the dehydrogenation of methanol [3]. Vanadiumoxide modified titaniumoxide based membranes are prepared to be tested as catalytic membranes for the denox reaction. In this paper the synthesis and characterization of non- modified and modified porous ceramic membranes are discussed.

SYNTHESIS

Primary membranes

Three different types of membranes are prepared via the sol-gel process in supported and non-supported form, particulary alumina, binary (alumina and titania) and titania membranes.

Non-supported membrane layers are prepared by a process in which a sol is successively gelled, dried and calcined and are used for characterization of the microstructure. The non-supported membrane layers have the same structure with the supported ones [4]. Supported membrane samples consist of plate shaped α-alumina supports (porediameter=120nm), on top of which a thin membrane layer is deposited by dipcoating techniques using a colloidal suspension which contains additives [4].

Modified membranes

The ceramic membranes are modified with silver via the "in situ Urea hydrolysis" method or modified with vanadiumoxide via the batch adsorption method [5].

Silver modification: A supported membrane system is impregnated with a liquid consisting of a $AgNO_3$/Urea water solution. This system is dried under controlled conditions. Because of the smaller pores in the toplayer, all the liquid is concentrated in the toplayer by capillary forces. In such a way the support is used as a reservoir which continously supplies impregnate solution to the membrane layer. Subsequently the temperature is increased to 90-100^oC and the urea decomposes, producing NH_3. Due to the decreased pH the silver precursor is hydrolysed to give a hydroxide precipitate. The hydroxide is decomposed under carefully controlled heating till 400^oC. To get a better dispersion of silver in the membrane the system is calcined under hydrogen atmosphere [6]. In this way a load of 67 wt% Ag could be deposited equivalent to 50% of the pore volume while without the reservoir method only 15 wt% Ag could be incorporated.

Vanadia modification: The γ-alumina and titania membrane systems are modified with vanadiumoxide via the batch adsorption method. A solution of vanadiumacetylacetonate ($VO(AcAc)_2$) in toluene is added to the membrane system and is heated under stirring at 90^oC for 4h. The $VO(AcAc)_n$ complexes react with the surface hydroxyl groups (1).

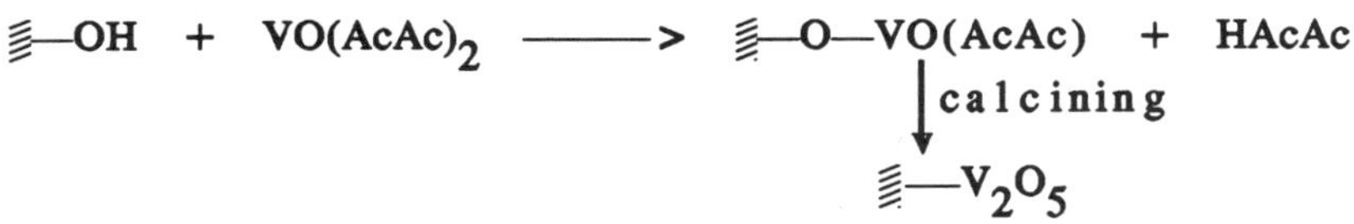 (1)

After the impregnation the membrane system is dried and calcined to $450^{o}C$. Since the toplayer (γ-alumina or titania) has much more OH-groups than the support (α-alumina) it is expected that there will be much more vanadium-oxide in the toplayer than in the support. This was in agreement with the observed experimental results.

RESULTS

Non modified membrane systems

Some structural data of alumina and titania membranes are described elsewhere [1]. The BET-surface, pore size and porosity values for binary membrane with 30wt% TiO_2 calcined at $450^{o}C$ are 260sqm/g, 3.8nm (diameter) and 48% respectivily. These values amount for a binary membrane with 65wt% TiO_2 calcined at $450^{o}C$ are 220sqm/g, 3.8nm (diameter) and 38% respectivily. These values are all close to that of the pure alumina membranes and indicates that a well dispersed system is present whose microstructure is determined by the phase which is present in excess.

Helium and water-permeability: The three supported ceramic membrane systems γ-alumina, titania and binary ones exhibit Knudsen diffusion characteristics (Fig1). That means that the membrane layers are all crack-free. The tortuosity factor k_t for titania calculated from Helium permeability measurements by the the Poiseuille equation was 2.4. This is in good agreement with the tortuosity factor k_t calculated for water permeability measurements by the Kozeny-Carman equation which was 2.1.

Modified membrane systems

γ-alumina modified with silver: The BET-surface, pore size and porosity for a silver modified alumina membrane loaded with 13.2wt% (5.1vol%) Ag is 159sqm/g, 3.2nm (diameter) and 47% respectivily. The same structural properties are for a non-modified alumina membrane are 202sqm/g, 3.2nm (diameter) and 50% respectivily.

TABLE 1
He-permeability of modified and non-modified supported alumina membranes.

silver (wt%)	silver (vol%)	perm. before impregn. (ml/bar.min.sqcm)	perm. after impregn. (ml/bar.min.sqcm)
7.5	1.4	176	163
10.0	1.9	165	136
15.0	3.0	187	143
67.0	26.3	206	108
67.0	26.3	241	124

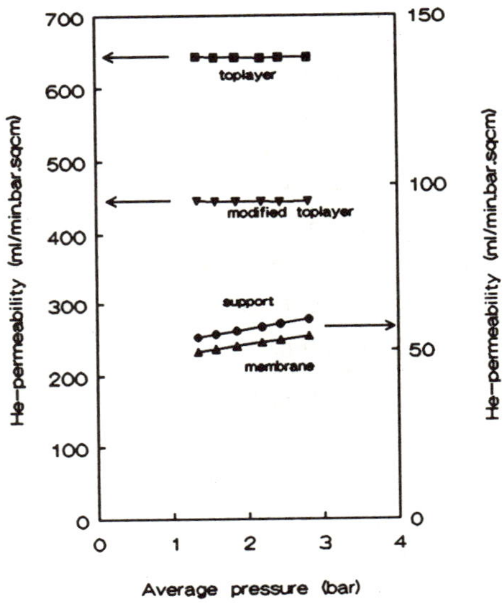

Figure 1. Example of He-permeability plots for a vanadia modified supported titania membrane system.

By using the support as a reservoir it is possible to increase the silver content in the toplayer up to 67 wt% (50% of the pore volume). Silver is only detected in the toplayer (SEM/EDS) in agreement with the previously mentioned mechanism. He-permeabilities are given in table 1 and indicate a decreased porosity and probably constrictions in the pores.

γ-alumina and titania modified with vanadia: The He-permeability of the vanadia modified alumina and titania membranes is decreased (fig 1). Table 2 shows a decrease of the BET-surface proportional with increasing wt% V and decreasing porosity.

TABLE 2
Structural properties of non-modified and modified with vanadia γ-alumina and titania non-supported membranes.

membrane system	wt% V	BET-surface sqm/g	pore size diameter nm	porosity %
γ-alumina	0	202	3.2[1]	50
γ-alumina	2.2	193	3.2[1]	45
γ-alumina	4.8	177	3.2[1]	46
γ-alumina	6.3	167	3.2[1]	42
titania	0	79	6.5[2]	37
titania	2[3]	39	6.5[2]	30

1 = slit shaped pore model
2 = cylindrical shaped pore model
3 = not exactly measured yet

ACKNOWLEDGEMENT

The financial assistance of the Dutch Innovative Research Program on membrane technology (I.O.P.-membranes) is greatfully appreciated.

REFERENCES

1. Uhlhorn, R.J.R., Huis in 't Veld, M.H.B.J., Keizer, K. and Burggraaf, A.J., New ceramic membrane materials for use in gas separation applications. Science of Ceramics, vol.**14**, 551-556, 1987.

2. Zaspalis, V.T., Praag, W. van, Keizer, K., Ommen, J.G. van, Ross, J.R.H. and Burggraaf, A.J., Modified alumina membranes as active materials in catalytic processes. To be published in ICIM-89 proceedings.

3. Zaspalis, V.T., Keizer, K., Ommen, J.G. van, Praag, W. van, Ross, J.R.H. and Burggraaf, A.J., Porous ceramic membranes as catalytic active materials, presented at the AICHE summer meeting (Denver 1988).

4. Leenaars, A.F.M. and Burggraaf, A.J., The formation of supported membranes. J. Coll. Interf. Sci., vol.**105**, 27-40, 1985.

5. Ommen, J.G. van, Bosch, H., Gellings, P.J. and Ross, J.R.H., The preparation and characterisation of iron and vanadium oxide monolayer catalysts on TiO_2 and ZrO_2. Preparation of Catalysts **IV**, 151-164, 1987. Elsevier Science Publishers B.V.

6. Strubinger Leslie.M., Geoffroy Geregory.L. and Vannice Albert.M., Ultra dispersed supported silver catalysts: Effect of preparation and properties at high O_2 pressures. Journal of catalysis **96** 72-81 (1985).

FACILITATED TRANSPORT THROUGH MOLTEN SALTS IMMOBILIZED IN CERAMIC MEMBRANES

J.L. BAKIEWICZ, K. KEIZER, A.J. BURGGRAAF
University of Twente,
Faculty of Chemical Technology
Laboratory for Inorganic Chemistry,
Materials Science and Catalysis.
P.O. Box 217; 7500 AE Enschede;
The Netherlands

Abstract:

α- and τ-alumina membranes have been modified with low melting point salt ($LiNO_3$) and salt mixtures (KCl-CuCl). These salt (mixtures) are able to adsorb oxygen reversibly. Aim was creating a LIM (liquid immobilized membrane) in which a molten salt is captured in the pores and using this system for the separation of oxygen from an oxygen/nitrogen mixture.

In this paper the conditions for facilitated transport and the preparation of liquid immobilized membranes based on porous alumina ceramics are presented.

Introduction:

In the past few years a number of papers have been published concerning the preparation and characterization of microporous τ-alumina membranes (1-4). Membranes with a narrow pore size distribution and a membrane porosity of 50% have been obtained (1,2). The formation of membranes on a support with pores of 120 nm diameter has been described (1). Recently gas permeation characteristics of pure gases have been determined (5). Until now separation with these membranes has occurred with separations mechanisms like knudsendiffusion and surface diffusion. But these membranes have an unique property. They can stand high temperatures for long times. The work in this paper makes use of this unique property.

The problem with separation with porous membranes is the relatively low selectivity. The measured separation coefficients are mostly not large enough for practical applications. An exception are the separation coefficients gained by facilitated transport but there the permeability is too low. Recent results with facilitated transport through molten salts are very promising (6) because high selectivities are coupled with high permeabilities.

Disadvantage of the previously mentioned system was the thick (0.2 mm) membrane. Our supported systems are having a toplayer with a thickness less than 10μm, so the permeabilities with this system should be higher than in (6).

This paper deals with the synthesis of these membranes and using them in separating oxygen from an oxygen/nitrogen mixture. The salts have a low melting point and are known for their interaction with oxygen.

Literature:

Facilitated transport:
Separation in membrane processes is the result of differences in diffusivity. In case of facilitated transport the difference in diffusivity is caused by an interaction between the interacting species (in this case oxygen) and the non-interacting species (in this case nitrogen) with the melt, see figure 1.

Separating gases with facilitated transport through an aqueous or non-aqueous phase is well known in the literature (7). Fairly knew is the use of molten salts for this process (6). In the just mentioned patents a few examples are given in which the liquid phase is a molten salt. For an oxygen separation from an oxygen/nitrogen mixture $LiNO_3$ is used as a molten salt. The results of this process is given in figure 2. As can be seen separation coefficients up to 170 were reached.In this case the oxygen bearing species is the NO_3^- ion. (I) describes the reversible uptake of oxygen by the NO_2- ion.

$$NO_2^- + \tfrac{1}{2}\, O_2 <--> NO_3^- \qquad \text{(I)}$$

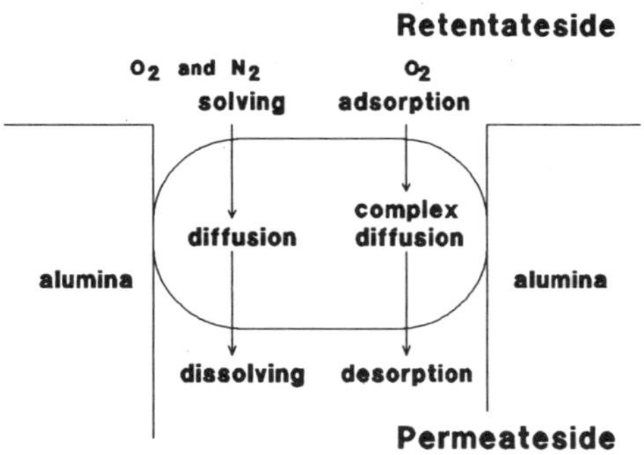

Figure 1: Modeldescription of facilitated transport

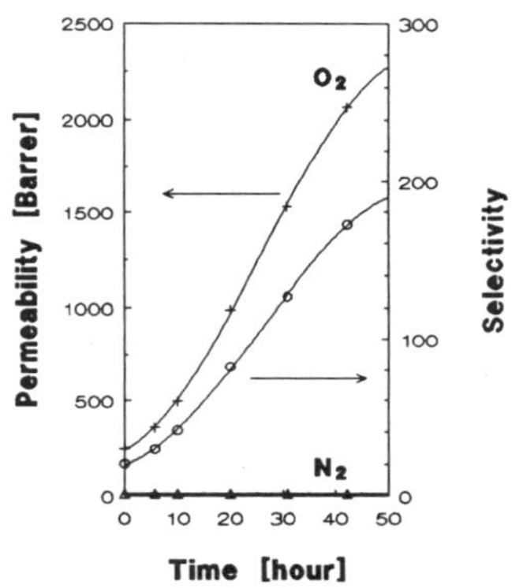

Figure 2: results of a facilitated transport using lithiumnitrate as liquid phase (6)

As shown in figure 2 the permeability of oxygen increases rapidly during the process. This is explained by the formation of superoxides in the melt.

Another molten salt known about the interaction with oxygen is the mixture of KCl-CuCl-$CuCl_2$ (8,9). This molten mixture is known as the Deacon catalyst. The adsorption of oxygen by this mixture is well investigated but the desorption of oxygen is hardly investigated. Only (8) mentions that desorption occurs mainly at a temperature between 450-500°C. (9) mentions that the oxygen adsorption is strongly enhanced by KCl and $LaCl_3$.

This is caused by the change of structure by adding the KCl. Molten copperchloride is likely to have a polymeric species $(CuCl_2)_n$. By adding the KCl this species is transformed in {I}:

```
Cl  Cl  Cl
 \  / \  /
  Cu   Cu
 /  \ /  \
Cl  Cl  Cl
```
{I}

The potassium is present as K^+. This complex has a valence state of 4^- This complex can much easier than the polymeric species be transformed in complex {II}, which has a valence state of 2^{-}(10).

```
Cl  O  Cl
 \ / \ /
 Cu   Cu
 / \ / \
Cl  O  Cl
```

{II}

The KCl-CuCl-$CuCl_2$ molten mixture is able to block pores smaller than 3 nm as is shown in (11). This patent also states that at 350°C the melt doesn't react with a silica carrier after 600 hours.

Model:

In figure 1 the basic model is given for this process. By applying this model, the major problem (facilitated transport) can be divided in subproblems. These subproblems are:

1. Prove a reversible oxygen uptake
2. Prove a sufficient wettability
3. Prove pore blockage
4. Prove facilitated transport

The reversible oxygen uptake is for both $LiNO_3$ and KCl-CuCl proved in (6) respectively (8). For $LiNO_3$ this is proved in the membrane process, but for the KCl-CuCl system by adsorption-desorption experiments as characterization for catalytic experiments. The result for the KCl-CuCl system was predominately adsorption at temperatures of 350-400°C and predominately desorption at temperatures between 450-500°C. There might be an optimal temperature for the facilitated transport than somewhere between 400-450°C.

A sufficient wettability is needed because of a necessary interaction between the molten salt and the ceramic carrier. If the wettability is not good enough the molten salt will not be sucked in the pores of the which causes a not well defined thickness of the salt layer. This must experimentally be determined.

Also the occurring of pore blockage and facilitated transport has to be determined experimentally.

Experiments:

synthesis of the liquid immobilized membrane:
The membranes can be modified with the molten salts on several ways, like a (non) aqueous impregnation, dipping in the melt or bringing up the solid form on the membrane and melting this into the membrane.

With a (non) aqueous impregnation the loadings are not high enough for blocking the pores. Recent literature claims that high loadings can be obtained by imprregnation with a dilute warm aqueous hydrochloric acid (12), but this will oxidize the Cu^{1+} to Cu^{2+} and therefore influence the composition of the melt. Dipping in the melt makes an uncontrollable loading. That is why the salt (mixture) is melted into the membrane after bringing it up in a solid form.

Adsorption-desorption experiments:
Adsorption-desorption experiments were carried out with the Cahn balance. Adsorption was investigated under an Oxygen atmosphere with a pressure of 55 kPa. Desorption was investigated under an Argon atmosphere with a pressure of 55 kPa.

Wettability:
The wettability of the molten salts is determined by view both on α and τ-alumina membranes. Molten salt are brought up in a solid form on a membrane that is kept at a temperature of about 250°C-300°C. The behavior of the molten salt is investigated.

Pore Blockage:
Pore blockage is investigated in an experimental set up that is given in (6), see figure 3.

As feed gas technic air was used. As sweepgas helium was used. Both permeate flow and retentate flow were analyzed with a massaspectrometer. If pore blockage occurs than the retentate flow is equal to the feed flow and the permeate flow is equal to the sweep flow.

Facilitated transport:
Facilitated transport will be investigated in the set up just mentioned. The permeate flow is analyzed with a massaspectrometer, type Spectramass DX 100.

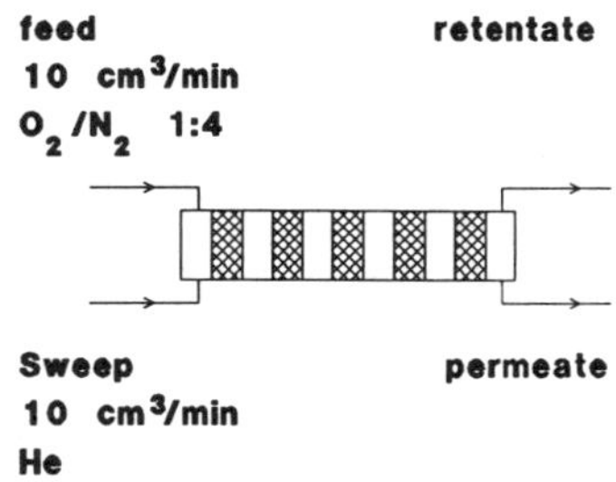

Figure 3: schematically set up

Results:

Cahn balance experiments:
These experiments were carried out with a mixture of KCl-CuCl at a temperature of 300°C. First oxygen adsorption was allowed at an oxygen pressure of 55 kPa. When equilibrium was reached oxygen desorption was allowed in an argon atmosphere at a pressure of 55 kPa. The experimental result is given in figure 4.

Figure 4 shows clearly that both adsorption and desorption occur at a temperature of 300°C. Both adsorption and desorption are slow.

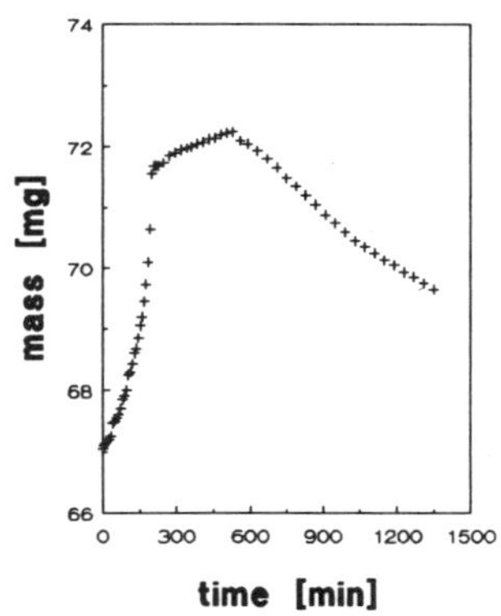

Figure 4: Adsorption/desorption of oxygen on KCl/CuCl. T = 300°C; t = 0 min; oxygen added; t = 550 min; argon added.

Wettability:
The lithiumnitrate seems to penetrate into the pores by capillary forces. Even after adding more lithiumnitrate than needed for filling the pores the molten salt doesn't penetrate through the pores. When the pores are filled with lithiumnitrate more lithiumnitrate leads to a complete film on top of the porous sytem. This film can easily be poured of the membrane.

For copperpotassiumchloride the situation is completely different. First the molten mixture doesn't spread over the membrane like the lithiumnitrate did. Secondly, the molten salt leaches through the pores with high loadings. But this molten salt is also thixotroop. Therefore the mixture has to be on a temperature far above the melting point for being fluid enough.

Pore Blockage:
Pore blockage does not occur on a membrane modified with lithiumnitrate if the lithiumnitrate film is poured of the membrane. If the lithiumnitrate film on the membrane is present, than pore blockage occurs.

Pore blockage is determined several times using copperpotassiumchloride as molten salt.

Facilitated transport:
Facilitated transport is not determined with both lithiumnitrate or copperpotassiumchloride as a molten salt at a temperature of 400°C with an experimental time of about 3 hours. The membrane thickness was 2 mm.

Discussion:

Facilitated transport is not determined because the experiments were carried out on α-alumina membranes (poresize 120 nm) with a thickness of 2 mm. This thickness is the cause for a slow process. However, the experimental time was limited to a few hours on the temperature used (400°C). because of the sealing of the reactor. Below these temperatures facilitated transport was not detected which is probably caused by a slow diffusion of the complex.

Experiments with thin supported layers with copperpotassiumchloride were difficult because preliminary results showed a reaction of the molten salt with the τ-alumina. Experiments with the supported layer modified with lithiumnitrate weren't successfull too because the lithiumnitrate film on top of the supported layer is necessary. So facilitated transport through thin supported layers could not be measured.

With lithiumnitrate pore blockage was only determined when a membrane with a film was used. However, for sealing liquid systems an other type of sealing is necessary. Development is going on in this direction.

Conclusions:

Liquid immobilized membranes are realized in thick α-alumina porous systems. Facilitated transport was not obseverd. That was caused by sealing problems.

The τ-alumina membrane reacts with the copperpotassiumchloride at temperatures higher than 425°C and is too sensitive for using as carrier when the copperpotassiumchloride is used as a liquid phase. But other materials can be used as carrier in a thin layer model (13). Further investigations will be made.

References:

1. A.F.M. Leenaars: Preparation, structure and separation characteristics of ceramic alumina membrane. PhD-thesis (1984)
2. K. Keizer, A.F.M. Leenaars, A.J. Burggraaf: Sci. Ceram. **12** (1983) 101
3. M. Asaeda, L.D. Du: J. Chem. Eng. Jpn. **19** (1986) 72
4. M. Asaeda, L.D. Du, M. Fuji: J. Chem. Eng. Jpn. **19** (1986) 84
5. R. van Vuren, B.C. Bonekamp, K. Keizer, R.J.R. Uhlhorn, H.J. Veringa, A.J. Burggraaf; in P. Vicenzini (Ed.) Materials Science Monographs (High Tech Ceramics) **38c** (1987) 2235
6. G.P. Pez, R.T. Carlin: US patent 4,617,029 Oct (1986) ; Eur. Pat. Appl. 194,483; 20 februari 1986
7 Liquid membranes; Theory and Application. ACS Symp. Ser. **347** (1987) Ed. R.D. Noble and J.D. Way
8. C.M. Fontana, E. Gorinn et al.: Ind. Eng. Chem. (1952) **44** 363, 369, 373
9. D.M. Ruthven, C.N. Kenney: Chem. Eng. Sci. (1967) **22** 1561
10. C.N. Kenney: Catal. Rev. **11** (1975) 197
11. Shell Internationale Research Maatschappij N.V.: British Patent 908,022. 10 okt 1962
12. V. Rao, R. Datta: J. Catal. **114** 377 (1988)
13. W. van Praag, V.T. Zaspalis, K. Keizer, J.G. van Ommen, J.R.H. Ross, A.J. Burggraaf: to be presented at the "First International Conference on Inorganic Membranes" july 36 1989 Montpellier France.

STRUCTURAL PROPERTIES OF CERAMIC ALUMINA MICROFILTRATION MEMBRANES AS A FUNCTION OF SINTERING TIME AND TEMPERATURE

R.A. TERPSTRA[1], H.H. VISSER[2], A.J.G. ENGEL[1] and H.J. VERINGA[1]
[1]Netherlands Energy Research Foundation, ECN
P.O. Box 1, 1755 ZG PETTEN, the Netherlands
[2] Hoogovens Groep B.V., P.O. Box 10.000,
1970 CA IJMUIDEN, the Netherlands

ABSTRACT

Ceramic membranes possess some superior mechanical, thermal and chemical properties over the more conventional polymeric membranes. They are therefore expected to penetrate the already existing membrane market, but also new applications, for instance at high temperature, are foreseen. The mechanical strength of our membrane system is provided by a macroporous support tube which is extruded using a water based paste. After careful drying and sintering, the tube is coated with an aqueous alumina suspension. This results after drying and sintering in a smooth thin microfiltration layer. The membrane fabrication route will be presented and the results will be discussed of a study on the influence of the sintering time and temperature on the pore properties of the system, the water permeability and the bursting pressure.
It is found that the bursting pressure of the substrate, and the water permeability of both the substrate and the microfiltration layer increase significantly with increasing temperature.

INTRODUCTION

At our institute (ECN) we are developing ceramic microfiltration (MF) membranes in close cooperation with Hoogovens Industrial Ceramics.
This membrane system is tubular and consists of two layers:
- the substrate which provides the mechanical strength to the system
- the microfiltration layer which is the actual membrane layer.

In most separation processes in which membranes are involved, still polymeric membranes are used, but these have in general the disadvantages of a low mechanical strength, and a low chemical and thermal stability. With ceramic membranes steam sterilization and high process and backflush pressures, for cake wash-off, can be applied.
Applications in chemically aggressive and/or high temperature environments are also possible. In this paper we investigate the change of some proper-

ties, like the mechanical strength and the water flux, as a function of sintering temperature and time. This was done with one of the substrate and microfiltration materials which we have developed so far.

MATERIALS AND METHODS (see also [1], [2] and [3])

Substrate

The substrate tube (~ 1 m length, inner diameter = 14 mm, outer diameter = 20 mm) is formed by extrusion of a ceramic paste. This paste consists of a coarse and a fine α-Al_2O_3 powder, a binder, a lubricant and water. After drying for several hours, the extruded tubes are cut into five pieces of approximately 15 cm length. The two "small" tubes obtained from the ends of each "large" tube are used as a reference for the remaining tubes in between. The reference tubes are all sintered under standard conditions (1550°C, 15 hours). The properties of the other tubes are compared to those of the reference tubes. The following sintering conditions (4 tubes per experiment) are used: 1550, 1620 and 1700°C respectively for 1, 2, 4, 8 and 15 hours respectively. After sintering, the tubes are characterized by measuring the following properties:

- linear shrinkage
- porosity, from the volume and the mass
- pore size, by mercury porosimetry (the diameter at 50% Hg-intrusion is used)
- permeability, for ultrapure water of 20°C
- bursting pressure (see also [4])
- microstructure, using Scanning Electron Microscopy (SEM).

Microfiltration layer

The microfiltration layer is prepared by film coating a macroporous alumina tube with a suspension of α-Al_2O_3. The viscosity is adjusted (using a polyelectrolyte) so that a layer thickness of 20-30 µm is obtained at a specific coating speed. The layer is then dried for a few hours under laboratory conditions. Then the following sintering procedures for the membranes are compared: 1200, 1300, 1400 and 1500°C respectively for 2 and 4 hours respectively. After sintering, the membranes are characterized by measuring their water flux and by SEM (microstructure, layer thickness).

RESULTS

Substrate

It is found that with increasing sintering temperature and time:

- the linear shrinkage increases, as can be expected
- the porosity decreases
- the pore size increases (Fig. 1)
- the permeability increases (Fig. 2)
- the bursting pressure increases (Fig. 3).

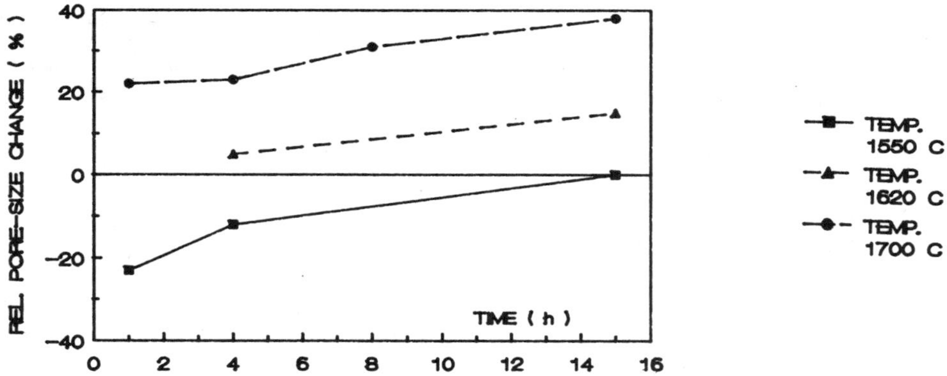

Figure 1. The mean relative change of pore size of a substrate tube sintered for a specific time and temperature as compared with a tube sintered at standard conditions.

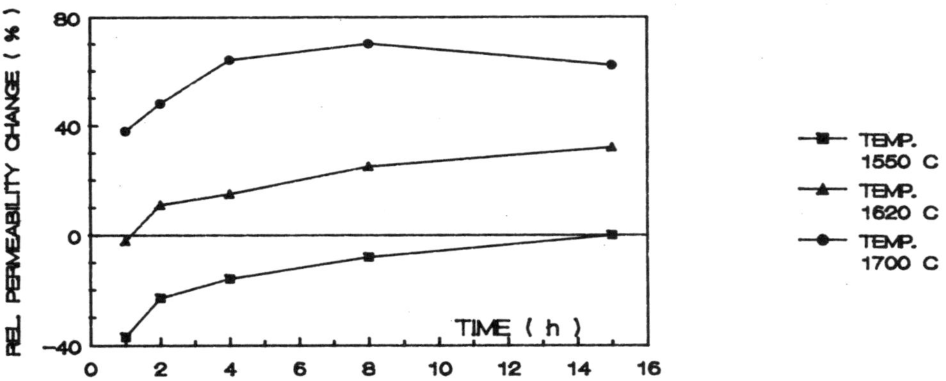

Figure 2. The mean relative change of permeability of a substrate tube sintered for a specific time and temperature as compared with a tube sintered at standard conditions.

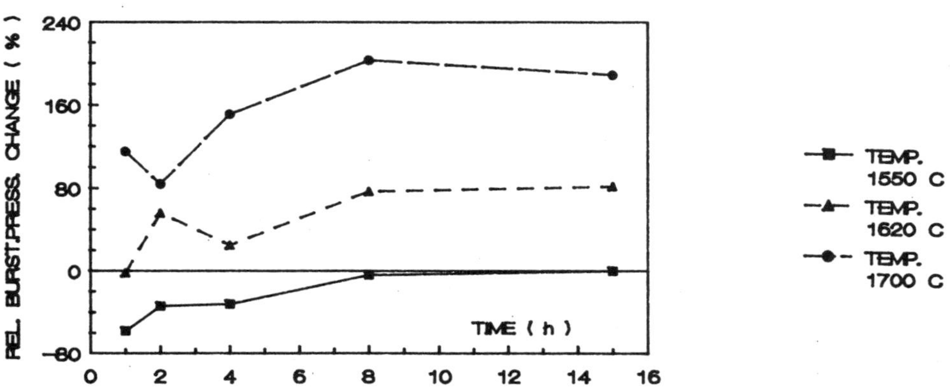

Figure 3. The mean relative change of the bursting pressure of a substrate tube sintered for a specific time and temperature as compared with a tube sintered at standard conditions.

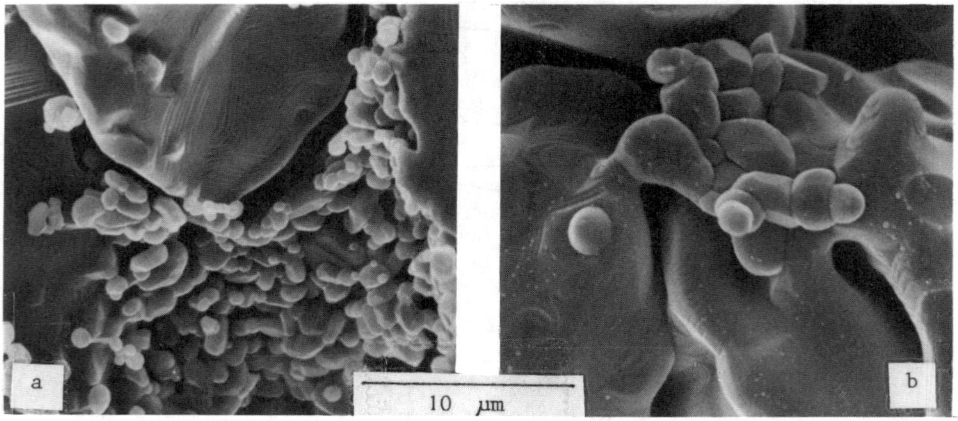

Figure 4. The microstructure of the substrate material after sintering for 15 h at (a): 1550°C and at (b): 1700°C.

Microfiltration layer

The water flux of the two layer system for different sintering temperatures and times is shown in figure 5.

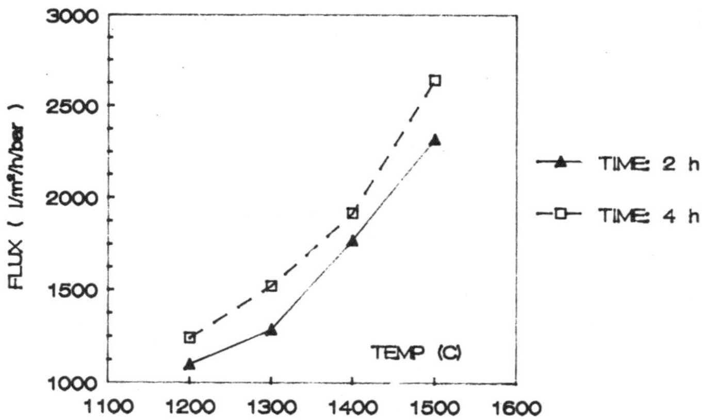

Figure 5. The water flux of the two layer system for different sintering temperatures and times.

The general trend for the water flux is that it increases for membranes sintered at increasing temperature and slightly increases with time (Fig. 5).

From the SEM-micrographs we find no significant decrease in the layer thickness. However, the pore size seems to increase with increasing sintering temperature.

After sintering the membrane at 1200°C for 2 hours, a small number of cracklike defects can be identified with the SEM. After sintering at 1500°C for 2 hours this number seems to have increased and the cracks are broader (1-2 μm compared to < 1 μm after sintering at 1200°C).

CONCLUSIONS AND DISCUSSION

Substrate

It appears that by increasing the sintering temperature and/or sintering time of the substrate tube, the bursting pressure as well as the water flux can be increased significantly.

The increase of burst pressure cannot be fully explained by the decrease of the porosity, using the formula for the strength of porous materials proposed by Ryshkewitch [5]. An important additional reason for the increase of the strength (i.e. the bursting pressure) is probably the forming of necks between the coarse particles due to material transport from the fine particles (Fig. 4). The increase of the water flux can mainly be explained by the increase of the pore size due to the disappearing of small pores and the growth of larger pores as was determined with mercury porosimetry. An additional factor is probably the smoothening of the pore channels which reduces the hydraulic resistance of the pores. It can easily be calculated that the increase of the pore size is of much greater influence on the water flux than the decrease of porosity.

Microfiltration layer

It is easily shown that the slight increase of the number and size of the defects cannot at all account for the observed increase of the water flux. This increase of the water flux with sintering temperature and time is probably mainly due to the increase of the pore size which we have observed qualitatively.

ACKNOWLEDGEMENTS

We thank mr. W. Tams for the SEM-work and mrs. T. Zomerdijk for typing the manuscript.

REFERENCES

[1] Terpstra, R.A., Bonekamp, B.C., Van Veen, H.M., Engel, A.J.G., De Rooy, R. and Veringa, H.J., Preparation and properties of tubular ceramic Al_2O_3 membranes for gas separation, in Science of Ceramics 14, ed. R. Taylor, 1987, p. 557-562.

[2] Terpstra, R.A., Bonekamp, B.C. and Veringa, H.J., Preparation, characterization and some properties of tubular alpha alumina ceramic membranes for microfiltration and as a support for ultrafiltration and gas separation membranes, Desalination, 1988, 70, 395-404.

[3] Van Veen, H.M., Tol, J.P.B.M., Terpstra, R.A., Engel, A.J.G. and Veringa, H.J., The calcination and thermal stability of ceramic Al_2O_3 membranes for gas separation, Proceedings ECerS '89, Maastricht, the Netherlands.

[4] Bach, P.W., Van der Burg, N.P.G. and Terpstra, R.A., Mechanical characterization of macroporous ceramic support tubes for micro/ultrafiltration, Proceedings ECerS '89, Maastricht, the Netherlands.

[5] Ryshkewitch, E., Compression strength of porous sintered alumina and zirconia, J. Am. Cer. Soc., 36, 65 (1953).

CERAMICS FOR CARBONATE FUEL CELLS

S.B. VAN DER MOLEN, R. DE ROOY, E.J. SIEWERS AND H. DEN UIL
Netherlands Energy Research Foundation, ECN
P.O. Box 1, 1755 ZG PETTEN, the Netherlands

ABSTRACT

The ECN molten carbonate fuel cell (MCFC) programme started in 1986. It includes component research which has been concentrated on the development and testing of porous ceramic components of different size.
Optimum electrical cell performance can be realized using highly porous electrodes, Ni-$LiCrO_2$ as anode and lithiated NiO as cathode material, with a bimodal pore size distribution: large pores (4-8 micrometer) for the gas transport and small pores (< 1.0 micrometer) for electrolyte retention. Ion conduction is obtained by sandwiching porous $Al_2O_3/LiAlO_2$ matrix material (pores < 1.0 micrometer) filled with a eutectic mixture of Li_2/K_2CO_3 between the electrodes.

INTRODUCTION

A short description of the molten carbonate fuel cell will be given, followed by the requirements for the active components in the fuel cell. These requirements are based on an optimum carbonate distribution in the electrodes and matrix.
The performance of these components is tested in three types of test cells, small scale lab cells (3 cm^2) for screening tests, bench scale cells (100 cm^2) for testing under operating conditions for energy production and tests for upscaled areas (1000 cm^2).
Pre- and post-test porosimetry form the key to analyse the influence of component morphology on measured cell performance.

THE CARBONATE FUEL CELL COMPONENTS

In a fuel cell the Gibbs free energy of a chemical reaction is available for transformation into electrical energy. The efficiency for this type of electricity generation can therefore be much higher than that of a Carnot process. The most promising fuel cell types with high efficiencies (~ 60%) are the molten carbonate fuel cell (MCFC) with an operating temperature of 650°C and the solid oxide fuel cell (SOFC) operating at 1000°C.

Electrodes

The principle of the molten carbonate fuel cell is illustrated in fig. 1.

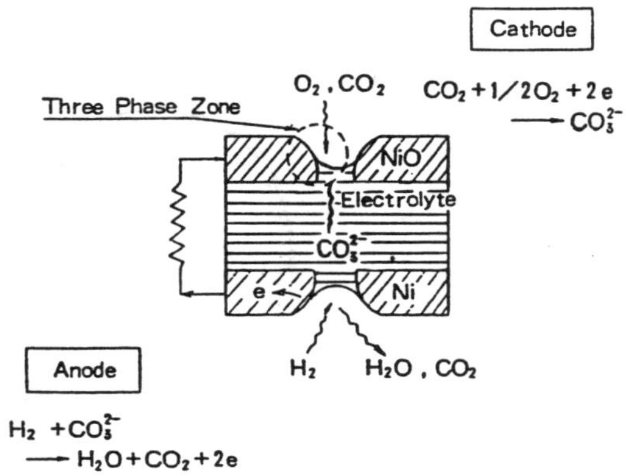

Figure 1. Principle of operation of carbonate fuel cell

The electrodes have to be porous to be accessible for the reactant gases and the molten carbonate. Therefore, they must have large pores for gas transport and small pores filled with carbonate, so the electrode materials must have a bimodal pore size distribution. Furthermore, the electrodes have to be catalytically active for the electrochemical reactions and have to be conductive for transport of the produced and consumed electrons respectively.

For the anode nickel is used as catalyst. Degradation of the porous nickel structure, due to sintering at the operating temperature of the cell, is prevented by the addition of Cr to the Ni. In the fuel cell the Cr is oxidized and in the presence of Li_2CO_3 converted into $LiCrO_2$.

The cathode is fabricated as a nickel structure and in-situ oxided. The cathode becomes conductive by lithiation of the NiO to $Ni_{1-x}Li_xO$ ($x \sim 3$ mol %).

The pre-test electrodes only contain large pores. Due to the oxidation and lithiation reactions the required bimodel pore size distribution is formed in the cell (figure 2).

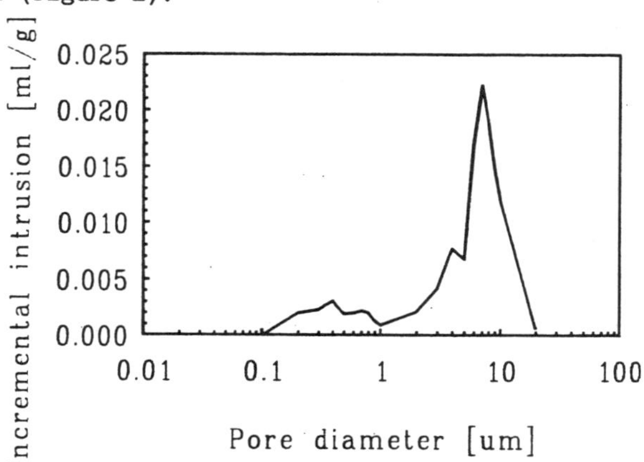

Figure 2. Bimodel pore size distribution of cathode material

Electrolyte matrix

Porous $LiAlO_2$ is used as matrix materials for electrolyte retention. Only γ-$LiAlO_2$ appears to be stable under operating conditions. The carbonate retention property of the porous structure is rather important for two reasons: a) combination of maximum ion conductivitiy with complete electronic insulation between the two electrodes and b) prevention of gas cross-over between anode and cathode compartment.

The ionic transport is directly related to the electrolyte content, and therefore, to the porosity of the $LiAlO_2$ matrix. The maximum allowable pressure difference between the two electrodes depends on the maximum pore size of the matrix material and the wetting properties (surface tension) of the electrolyte-$LiAlO_2$ combination.

The pore size distribution in the matrix is matched with that of the electrodes in such a way that the matrix material is completely filled while the electrodes are partly filled. This can be obtained by mixing high active with low active surface area $LiAlO_2$ powders or by mixing $LiAlO_2$ with Al_2O_3 fibre material. In this way, electrolyte matrix material with pores < 1.0 micrometer can be made.

Bubble barrier

To prevent cross-over of gases due to matrix cracking, a gas sealing component called bubble barrier which is made of Ni-γ-$LiAlO_2$ is used. The rather tough and porous material is placed between anode and matrix. The pores are smaller than 1.0 micrometer and like the matrix material completely filled with carbonate.

CERAMIC FABRICATION TECHNIQUES

The raw materials used are carbonyl Ni, Cr, γ-$LiAlO_2$ + Al_2O_3 and Li_2CO_3/K_2CO_3 mixture. The fabrication techniques [1, 2] to obtain green components include suspension preparation, tape casting, drying and roll compaction. Sintering of electrodes and bubble barrier is necessary to acquire the pretest pore size distribution as specified in Table 1. The characterization of the raw materials and the fabricated components is described in a poster presentation at this conference [3].

Components have been made for 3 cm^2 material screening tests, which are performed under ideal operating conditions. Upscaling of the fabrication techniques was needed to produce 100 cm^2 and 1000 cm^2 components for performance tests under more severe conditions.

Table I. Characteristics of porous components

	Anode	Cathode	Matrix	Bubble barrier
Material	Ni-10 wt.%Cr	Ni	γ-$LiAlO_2$	Ni-$LiAlO_2$
Porosity	50-60 %	≈ 75 %	65 %	≈ 50 %
MPS	6-8 µm	8-10 µm	100% < 1.0 µm	97% < 1.0 µm
Thickness	0.6 mm	0.8 mm	1.0 mm	0.2 mm

MATERIALS TESTS

The material screening tests in 3 cm^2 cells have been used to investigate several types of electrode and matrix materials. Furthermore, for the electrodes the influence of the pore structure and for the matrix the influence of the porosity on the cell performance has been investigated. Variation in the pore size distribution and/or porosity of the materials has been achieved by varying the operating and fabrication conditions. After screening, the materials are tested in 100 cm^2 bench scale cells and 1000 cm^2 cells. In these cells the operation conditions for electricity production are simulated. During operation, the cell voltage, the total internal resistance and electrode polarizations are measured at a mean current density of 150-160 mA/cm^2. To determine the fuel and oxidant utilization, the outlet gas compositions are measured for different inlet gas flows.
After cell testing the porosity and pore size distribution of the components are determined by Hg-porosimetry and related to cell performance.

RESULTS AND DISCUSSION

A standard cell shows an increase in cell performance with time. Post-test analysis of the components gives the change of porosity and pore size as a function of operating time. Comparing those results (figure 3) suggests that the cell performance is related to the percentage of small pores in the electrodes. The improved cell voltage corresponds to the increase in the amount of pores < 1.0 µm obtained by the oxidation and lithiation of Ni-Cr to Ni-$LiCrO_2$ for the anode and of Ni to lithiated NiO for the cathode material.

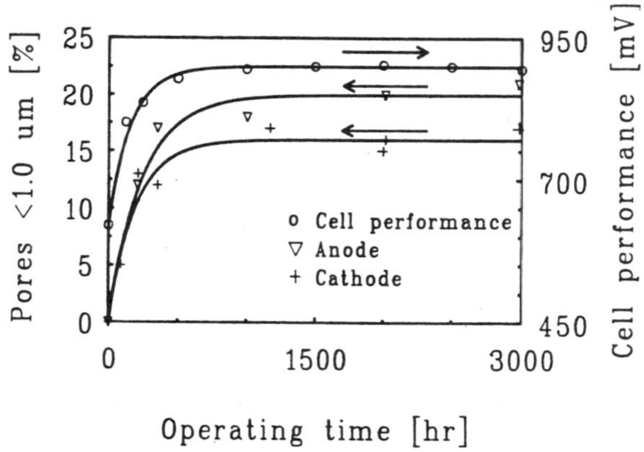

Figure 3. Electrode pore structure and cell performance versus operating time

Due to the increased number of small pores and consequently to the redistribution of the carbonate over the matrix and electrodes (see fig. 4), a reduction of electrode polarization and resistance was measured for both the cathode and anode independently. The final anode polarization and ohmic resistance is reached in a relatively short period and is only slightly influenced by its microstructural change. However, the influence of the cathode microstructure on polarization and cathode conductivity is evident.

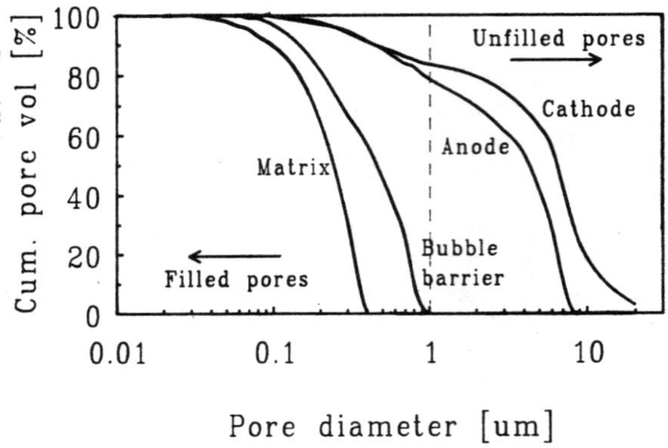

Figure 4. Carbonate distribution in the porous components

Fig. 5 illustrates that a cell voltage greater than 900 mV can be obtained when the percentage of cathode pores < 1.0 µm is 17-20% of the total porosity.

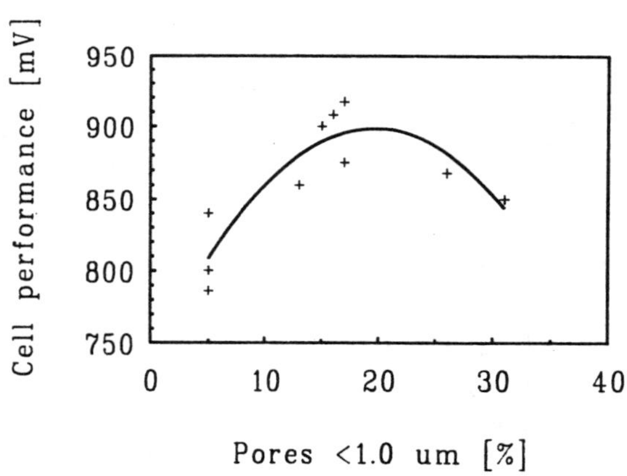

Figure 5. Cell performance versus cathode pore structure

The influence of the matrix porosity on cell performance is given in figure 6. The matrix porosity primarily affects the carbonate ion transport. The tests show two categories, one for the pure γ-$LiAlO_2$ and one for the reinforced γ-$LiAlO_2$-Al_2O_3 matrix material.

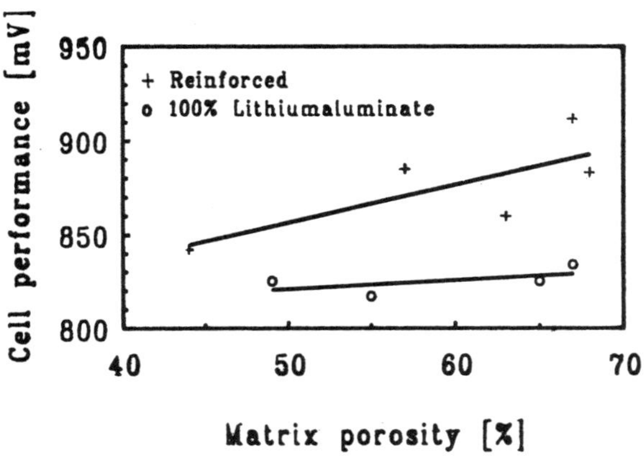

Figure 6. Cell performance versus matrix porosity

Comparison of 100 cm² and 1000 cm² cell tests with the 3 cm² screening tests shows comparable performance. The ohmic resistance in the lab cells and the 1000 cm² cell is 350 mΩ cm². Upscaling of the component fabrication methods, therefore, appeared to be suitable for series fabrication of 1000 cm² components for ECN fuel cell stacks (1 kW MCFC).

CONCLUSIONS

Comparison of the cell performance and pre- and post-test characteristics of the MCFC components shows the influence of the porosity of the matrix material and of the bimodal pore size distribution of the cathode.
The cathode pore size distribution strongly influences the cell resistance and cathode polarization. An optimum cell voltage of > 900 mV is obtained for cathodes with about 17-20% of the pores < 1.0 µm.
The anode microstructure slightly influences the cell performance. With the present γ-$LiAlO_2$-Al_2O_3 matrix material, a rather high porosity of 65-70% is needed to get cell voltages > 900 mV.
Cell tests with upscaled areas showed comparable results, so developed ceramic fabrication techniques are suitable for series fabrication.

ACKNOWLEDGEMENT

The project is financially supported by NOVEM on behalf of the Ministry of Economic Affairs.

REFERENCES

1. Van der Molen, S.B., Siewers, E.J., Den Uil, H. and Goris, M.J.A.A., Porous MCFC component development, Paper presented at seminar Fuel Cell Technology Applications, the Netherlands, 1987.

2. Boersma, R.J., Van der Molen, S.B., Den Uil, H, and De Vries, J.E, The development of porous components for molten carbonate fuel cells at the Netherlands Energy Research Foundation, ECN, Paper presented at Fuel Cell Seminar, Long Beach California, 1988.

3. Nammensma, P.A. and Van der Molen, S.B., Characterisation of porous ceramic fuel cell components, This conference.

MEMBRANE-BASED THIN LAYER SOFC COMPONENTS

J.P.P. HUIJSMANS, S.B. VAN DER MOLEN and E.J. SIEWERS
Netherlands Energy Research Foundation, ECN,
P.O. Box 1, 1755 ZG PETTEN, the Netherlands

ABSTRACT

A solid oxide fuel cell (SOFC) air-electrode of Sr-doped $LaMnO_3$ (SLM) is developed at ECN. Initially, it will be supported by porous alumina. It will act as an electronically conductive, oxide ceramic substrate for a thin ion conducting electrolyte structure of Y_2O_3-stabilized zirconia (YSZ). The electrolyte structure will be deposited by (E)CVD techniques to be developed by UT. SLM powder is made by a citrate synthesis route. The fabrication of Al_2O_3 support material and the application of a thin layer of SLM on this support is based on production techniques developed in the past by ECN for three-layer alumina membranes.

INTRODUCTION

The solid oxide fuel cell (SOFC) is considered as a third generation fuel cell. Like the second generation molten carbonate fuel cell (MCFC) it is characterized by a high operating temperature (1000°C, in comparison with 650°C for MCFC). The main difference between the two is that operation of the MCFC is dependent on a liquid electrolyte, while the SOFC operates as a completely solid, oxide ceramic device. State-of-the-art SOFC materials for the cathode, electrolyte and anode are strontium-doped $LaMnO_3$ (SLM), Y_2O_3-stabilized zirconia (YSZ) and nickel-dispersed YSZ. A schematic representation of a flat plate SOFC reactor with appropriate electrochemical reactions is given in Fig. 1.

An important problem of SOFC reactors is the high interface resistance observed between different components. This may be caused by chemical reaction and formation of insulators, as a result of high temperatures during fabrication and operation [1]. Reduction of the operating temperature (e.g. from 1000°C to 800°C) and, therefore, also of the fabrication temperature, decreases the interaction between electrode and electrolyte material. However, low temperatures also increase the specific (ionic) resistance of YSZ (Table 1). Thickness reduction of the electrolyte layer from commonly used values of 100-500 µm to values of about 20-50 µm would counterbalance this effect (Table 1).

TABLE 1
The influence of SOFC operating temperature and electrolyte thickness on the ohmic or iR losses.

T (°C) SOFC	specific resistance YSZ (Ohm.cm)	$d_{electrolyte}$ (µm)	ASR (Ohm.cm²)	iR losses (mV)
1000	10	500	0.5	100
1000	10	100	0.1	20
1000	10	20	0.02	4
800	50	100	0.5	100
800	50	20	0.1	20

ASR = area specific resistance; i = current density, which has been taken as 200 mA/cm². Values for specific resistance of YSZ from Steele [2].

To try and find a solution for this problem ECN has recently started a collaborative research project with the University of Twente (UT). The objective of this project is the development of fabrication techniques for flat plate SOFC components and composites, which consist of thin layers of conductive oxide ceramics.

The research includes the following activities: 1. development of a flat plate Al_2O_3-supported air-electrode (carried out by ECN); 2. modification of the microstructure of the air-electrode surface as a basis for thin electrolyte structures (carried out by ECN and UT); 3. application of a thin electrolyte structure by (electro-)chemical vapour deposition (E)CVD (carried out by UT); 4. characterization of microstructure and electrochemical properties of components and composites (carried out by ECN and UT); and 5. study of the interaction of air-electrode material with thin electrolyte strutures at SOFC fabrication and operation temperatures (carried out by ECN and UT). A schematic representation of the supported air-electrode/electrolyte structure is given in Fig. 2. This paper describes the first results of ECN with respect to fabrication of the supported air-electrode, which will be used in the (E)CVD reactor [3].

EXPERIMENTAL

The following activities have been carried out: 1. development of suspension technology for Al_2O_3 and fabrication of support structure; 2. fabrication of SLM powder with 15 mol % Sr (15SLM); 3. development of suspension technology for SLM and integration of air electrode with support material. Al_2O_3 support material was made by tape casting a suspension of mixtures of commercially available alumina powders. 15SLM powder was made by a modified citrate pyrolysis route after Pechini [4]. After pyrolysis the ash was calcined in air at 750°C (1 h) followed by a soak at 850°C (2 h). A suspension of 15 SLM powder was ball-milled for 22 h and used for tape caste experiments on teflon carrier material and on sintered support material. The Al_2O_3/air-electrode composite was sintered at 1100°C for 6 h.

RESULTS AND DISCUSSION

Al_2O_3 support material

The development of Al_2O_3 support material is based on ECN's production techniques of support tubes for three-layer alumina membranes for micro- and ultrafiltration and gas separation at low and high temperatures [5]. In order to grow a thin electrolyte structure on the supported air-electrode by (E)CVD, the support material has to be porous to allow (E)CVD reactant gases to diffuse to the reaction site at the air-electrode surface [3]. Specifications for the support material were determined at the beginning of the project, i.e. thickness of the layer 1 mm, porosity 50% and mean pore size of 10 µm. By comprehensive investigation of suspension preparation techniques, types and quantities of alumina powders and sintering programme, it was possible to obtain Al_2O_3 tapes with dimensions and microstructure very close to the specifications, i.e. thickness of the tape 1 mm, porosity 41.8 - 47.2% and mean pore size 8.0-11.0 µm. The resulting microstructure of the Al_2O_3 support material is shown in Fig. 3. below.

SLM air-electrode material

XRD analysis shows that the calcined ashes from the citrate synthesis route consist of SLM with a rhombohedral symmetry. The morphology of the particles strongly resembles the morphology of the precursory ash, i.e. thin (0.1 µm) sheets up to 100 µm in diameter. The sheets themselves are made of submicron SLM crystallites, which are slightly sintered together. Mean particle size of the calcined powder is 17.7 µm and the specific surface area is 9.6 m^2/g. Distribution of La, Mn and Sr turns out to be homogeneous (EDX).

Preliminary results of conductivity measurements (modified 4-probe ac impedance spectroscopy) on pressed pellets of 15SLM powder (porosity of pellets 34%) indicate that the electronic conductivity (76 S/cm at 900°C) is comparable to conductivity data usually cited [2].

Integration of air-electrode with support material

Target specifications for the microstructure of the air-electrode are: thickness of the layer 10-15 µm, porosity 50% and mean pore diameter 0.5-1.0 µm. In order to satisfy these specifications, the particle size of the SLM powder had to be reduced. SEM analysis showed that ball-milling of the suspension resulted in a particle size range of 0.2-1.0 µm with agglomerates up to 5 µm. Tape cast experiments with this 15SLM suspension were carried out to test: 1. the quality and stability of the suspension; 2. the minimum tape thickness that can be obtained for SLM material; 3. the sintering behaviour of the tapes; and 4. the resulting microstructure of the SLM layer. This resulted in tapes which, after sintering for 10 h at 1000°C were as thin as 40 µm with a porosity of 70% and a mean pore diameter of 0.4 µm. Although these tapes could be handled, SLM powder came off easily. Moreover, their microstructure will have to be adjusted to the specifications given above.

Finally, 10 and 35 µm layers of SLM were applied on a porous plate (10x10 cm) of Al_2O_3 support material by multi tape casting. Sintering of the composite at a higher temperature (1100°C) improved the coherence between the SLM particles and also resulted in good adherence of the SLM layer to the Al_2O_3 support material. The resulting ceramic composite with an SLM layer of 35 µm is shown in Fig. 3. Although the microstructure of the electrode layer could not be determined directly by Hg-porosimetry, because it is connected to the support, it is clear from SEM that 1 µm pores are present. It is expected that the pore characterisitics of the layer are similar to the ones given above for the SLM tape. Disks with a diameter of

12 mm, which will be used in (E)CVD-experiments, were cut from the resulting composite with a laser beam.

ACKNOWLEDGEMENTS

The project is financially supported by the CEC within the Non-nuclear Energy R and D Programme (contract no. ENE 3E-0173-NL).
We thank G.H. Lieftink for the production of SLM powder and for his contribution to the research results presented in this paper.

REFERENCES

1. McPheeters, C.C., Dees, D.W., Dorris, S.E. and Picciolo, J.J., Argonne monolithic solid oxide fuel cell fabrication. 1988 Fuel Cell Seminar, Long Beach, California, 1988, pp. 29-32.

2. Steele, B.C.H., Ceramic electrochemical reactors, Current status application, Ceramionics, Surrey, 1987, pp. 59.

3. Lin, Y.S., Haart, L. de, Vries, K. de and Burggraaf, A., Modification of ceramic membranes by CVD and EVC for gas separation, catalysis and applications. This conference.

4. Pechini, M., U.S. Patent No. 3,330,697, July 11, 1967.

5. Terpstra, R.A., Bonekamp, B.C., Veen, H.M. van, Engel, A.J.G, Rooy, R. de and Veringa, H.J. Bereiding en enkele eigenschappen van buisvormige keramische alumina membranen voor gasscheiding. Membraantechnologie, 1987, 2, 64-65.

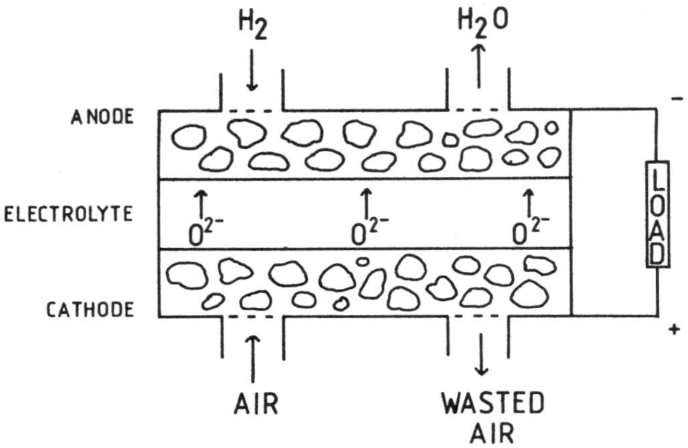

Figure 1. Principle of a flat plate SOFC reactor. Cathode reaction: $O_2 + 4e^- \rightarrow 2O^{2-}$. Anode reactions: $2H_2 + 2O^{2-} \rightarrow 2H_2O + 4e^-$. Reduction of oxygen and oxidation of hydrogen is considered to occur at the electrode/electrolyte interface.

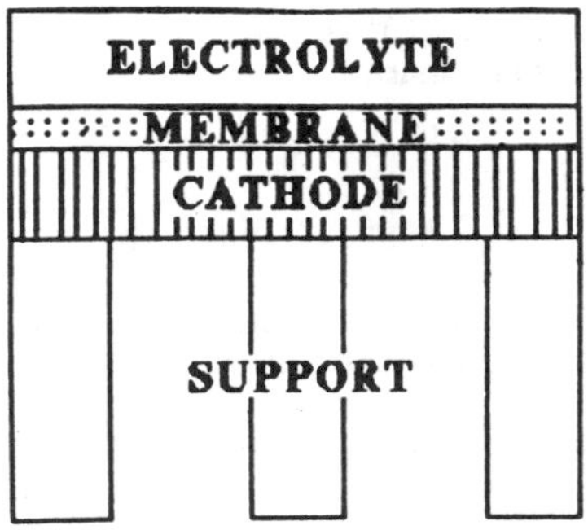

Figure 2. Supported air-electrode/electrolyte structure which will result from the collaborative research project between ECN and UT. Support = porous Al_2O_3; cathode = porous Sr-doped $LaMnO_3$; membrane and gastight electrolyte = Y_2O_3-stabilized zirconia.

Figure 3. Al_2O_3 supported air-electrode of 15SLM.

CONDUCTIVE LiFe(Mg)O_2 CERAMICS FOR MOLTEN CARBONATE FUEL CELLS

J.P.P. HUIJSMANS AND S.B. VAN DER MOLEN
Netherlands Energy Research Foundation, ECN,
P.O. Box 1, 1755 ZG PETTEN, the Netherlands

ABSTRACT

$LiFe_{0.97}Mg_{0.03}O_2$ ($LFMg_3$) is tested at ECN as an alternative cathode material for molten carbonate fuel cells (MCFC). To obtain the required electrode microstructure - i.e. microporous, catalytically active, small agglomerates (3-8 µm) and large open gas distribution pores (10 µm) - various amounts of pure carbon are mixed as a pore former with $LFMg_3$ powder. Cell tests indicate that the presence of molten carbonate positively influences the conductivity characteristics of $LFMg_3$. Polarization losses are high, due to the lack of small (< 1 µm) pores in the electrode microstructure.

INTRODUCTION

Lithiated NiO is state-of-the-art cathode material in molten carbonate fuel cells (MCFC). A schematic representation of a MCFC is given by Van der Molen et al. [1]. A major draw back of NiO is the solubility in molten carbonate under cathode conditions [2] according to the simplified reaction:

$$NiO + CO_2 \rightarrow Ni^{2+} + CO_3^{2-} \quad (1)$$

In a reducing environment, e.g. at the anode and in particular locations of the electrolyte, dissolved Ni^{2+} is precipitated as nickel metal. Due to this precipitation a concentration gradient is established, which promotes further dissolution of the cathode structure. Operation of MCFC at elevated pressures (i.e. higher P_{CO_2} at the cathode, which is attractive in terms of MCFC efficiency) increases this process.

Dissolution: 1. affects the microstructure of the electrode; 2. shortens the envisaged life-time of MCFC (40.000 h); and 3. eventually may cause short circuiting of the fuel cell, due to precipitation of Ni in the electrolyte.

Recent investigation [3, 4] have shown that $LiFeO_2$ meets most of the requirements for an alternative cathode material, i.e. 1. sufficient chemical stability; 2. low solubility; and 3. stability of dissolved material in molten carbonate under anode conditions. However, conductivity of $LiFeO_2$ is low and depends on cover gas conditions as was shown [2, 4, 5] on the basis of synthesis and conductivity experiments. Use of cathode gas (30%

CO_2 in air) increases the specific resistivity (ρ_o) of $LiFeO_2$ to values well above 20 Ohm.cm, which, on the basis of the electrode microstructure [3], is considered as a maximum value. Therefore, doping of $LiFeO_2$, e.g. with Mg, Mn, Co or Cu, is neccessary to improve conductivity characteristics.

For reduction of oxygen the cathode reaction-gas has to diffuse into the porous cathode structure and through the electrolyte-film which covers the cathode material. The reaction is considered to occur at the cathode/electrolyte interface. The reaction product (CO_3^{2-}) is transported through the electrolyte-matrix structure to the anode, where it is used in the anode reaction. For these processes to occur the cathode must have the following characteristics: 1. sufficient electronic conductivity to the reaction sites; 2. admittance of O_2 and CO_2 to the reaction sites; 3. adequate wetting characteristics for molten carbonate; and 4. good catalytic activity.

Fabrication of alternative cathode material should aim at the production of relatively small, microporous agglomerates with adequate catlytic surface and a typical diameter of approximately 3-8 µm [3]. These agglomerates can be flooded with molten electrolyte. Large, open gas pores between the agglomerates typically should have a diameter of approximately 10 µm. A porosity of 50-60% is desirable. A schematic representation of a porous cathode structure with bimodal pore distribution is given in Fig. 1.

$LiFeO_2$ is tested as an alternative ceramic cathode material in molten carbonate fuel cells at ECN. This paper presents the results of the development of an appropriate electrode microstructure for $LiFe_{0.97}Mg_{0.03}O_2$ (LFMg3) material by mixing and grinding various amounts of LFMg3 powder with carbon. It is expected that burn-out of the carbon will result in an increase of open porosity and in the formation of macropores or gas distribution pores (Fig. 1). First results of cell-testing of this material in small scale (3 cm^2) MCFC's are also presented.

EXPERIMENTAL

Samples of LFMg3 were prepared from appropriate mixtrues of Fe_2O_3, Li_2CO_3 and $Mg(CH_3COOH)_2{*}4H_2O$. Excess Li_2CO_3 was added (Li/Fe=1.03) to account for loss of lithium during calcination. Mixing of the reactants was carried out in an agate mortar under aceton. The reaction mixture was calcined in cathode gas for 17 h at 650°C. After calcination, the powder was pulverized under aceton in an agate mortar and ground with a binding medium and various amounts of high-surface (activated) carbon. Mean particle size of the pulverized LFMg3 powder and carbon particles was determined with a Malvern MasterSizer. Mean particle size of ground carbon was determined by dissolving LFMg3 from the mixture, in concentrated HCl. The powders were subsequently pressed in a 19 mm steel die. After carefull burn-out of binder and carbon the pellets were sintered in cathode gas for 8 h at 850°C. Electronic conductivity was measured using a modified 2 probe ac impedance technique.

RESULTS AND DISCUSSION

Development of bimodal pore distribution

XRD analysis shows that calcination of the reaction mixture results in the formation of α-LFMg3 with traces of γ-LFMg3. After sintering the pressed pellets only consist of α-LFMg3. Mean particle size of LFMg3 and carbon in the ground mixture are 7.8 and 33 μm respectively and particle size of the latter is independent of the wt. % carbon added to the powder mixture.

Table 1 shows the pore characteristics of the sinterd pellets as a function of carbon content in the green phase. For comparison, characteristics are also given for a state-of-the-art (soa) MCFC cathode. The latter is fabricated as a nickel structure, which only contains large pores (pre-test structure). The required bimodal pore size distribution is formed after in-situ oxidation and lithiation [1] (post-test structure).

TABLE 1
Pore characteristics of sintered LFMg3 pellets as a function of carbon content in the green phase.

Sample nr.	Carbon content (%)	Porosity (%)	Median pore diameter (μm)	80% pore range (μm)	Pore volume < 1 μm (%)
pre-test soa	-	75	9	5 - 18	-
post test soa	-	60	6.6	0.6 - 11.7	14
1	0	19	0.4	0.2 - 0.5	93
2	5	38	1.3	0.4 - 2.0	42
3	10	45	2.0	0.5 - 3.6	23
4	30	66	3.6	1.0 - 5.6	10
5	40	70	4.2	1.4 - 16.0	4
6	50	76	12.2	2.0 - 20.4	3
7	70	86	20.0	4.2 - 48.0	1

soa = state-of-the-art Ni and NiO. Data from Micrometics, type Autopore II 9220 (soa) and from Malvern particle size analyzer (other samples).

The data in Table 1 show that carbon is an effective open pore former, even if relatively small amounts of carbon are added (5-10 wt.%). Addition of carbon results in an increase of the open porosity and in a broadening of the total pore size population towards larger pore sizes. Meanwhile, with increasing carbon content the 10% pore range shifts from values of 0.2 to 4.2 (Table 1). An illustration of the microstructure which results from the addition of carbon is given in Fig. 2. The data in Table 1 also show that additon of 40-50 wt.% carbon is required to obtain the desired microstructure. However, a comparison of the experimentally obtained data with the microstructure characterstics of post-test NiO (Table 1) shows that the former lack small pores in the < 1 μm range.

Conductivity measurements

Conductivity measurements on pressed pellets of LFMg3 showed that the specific resistivity (ρ_0; recalculated to 100% density of the sample) at 650°C is in the order of 70 Ohm.cm. Obviously, a porous microstructure will negatively influence these conductivity characteristics.

Cell testing

Cell tests for LFMg3 in small, laboratory scale MCFC's were carried out for a period less than 1000 h. Microstructure for the cathodes was comparable to the samples 5 and 6 in Table 1. Surface area of the cathode was 3 cm^2 and thickness 0.7-0.8 mm. Prelimianry results indicate that the specific resistivity (ρ) of porous LFMg3 measured in these cell tests is

< 40 Ohm.cm. Recalculation of this value (ρ) to the case of a 100% dense sample (ρ_o) will even decrease the specific resistivity. The discrepancy between specific resistivity measured in conductivity experiments and observed in cell tests can not be explained yet, but may be related to the presence of excess molten carbonate [4, 5].

Polarization losses for LFMg3 are high (± 1700 mOhm) in comparison to NiO (125-200 mOhM), which is probably due to lack of pores smaller than 1 µm. The latter are thought to represent the small pores in the catalytically active agglomerates (Fig. 1).

CONCLUSIONS

LFMg3 is a potential candidate for use as an alternative cathode material in MCFC. Addition of carbon as a pore former is successful, as far as the formation of macropores is concerned. However, cell tests indicate that polarization losses are high. An increase of small pores (< 1 µm) in microporous agglomerates will probably improve cell performance.

Specific resistivity (ρ) of LFMg3 in MCFC cell tests is relatively low in comparison with values measured with impedance techniques. It is suspected that this may be explained by the presence of exces smolten carbonate in MCFC's.

ACKNOWLEDGEMENT

The project is financially supported by NOVEM on behalf of the Ministry of Economic Affairs. We thank E.F. Sitters for carrying out conductivity measurements on LFMg3.

REFERENCES

1. Molen, S.B. van der, Rooy, R. de, Siewers, E.J. and Uil, H. den, Ceramics for carbonate fuel cells. This conference.

2. Pierce, R.D. and Smith, J.L., Investigation of alternative MCFC cathode materials at Argonne National Laboratory. IAE Int. Symp. on fuel cell and avanced battery, Tokyo, 1986, 1-5.

3. Smith, J.L., Kucera, G.H. and Minh, N.Q., Progress on molten carbonate fuel cell alternative cathodes, Fuel Cell Seminar, Tucson, Arizona, 1986, 163-67.

4. Smith, J.L., Kucera, G.H., Minh, N.Q. and Moreschi, J.R., Electronic defects in $LiFeO_2$. Fuel Cell Seminar, Tucson, Arizona, 1986, 234-38.

5. Minh, N.Q., Kucera, G.H. and Smith, J.L., Influence of preparation conditions on electronic resistivity of $LiFeO_2$ synthesized in molten carbonates. In Proc. of the fifth Int. Symp. on molten salts, eds. M.L. Saboungi et al, The Electrochemical Soc., Vol. 86-1, Pennington, NJ, 1986, pp 597-603.

6. Yuh, C.Y. and Selman, J.R., Polarization of the molten carbonate fuel cell anode and cathode. In Molten carbonate fuel cell technology, eds. J.R. Selman and T.D. Claar, The Electrochemical Society, Vol. 84-13, Pennington, NJ, 1984, pp 465-87.

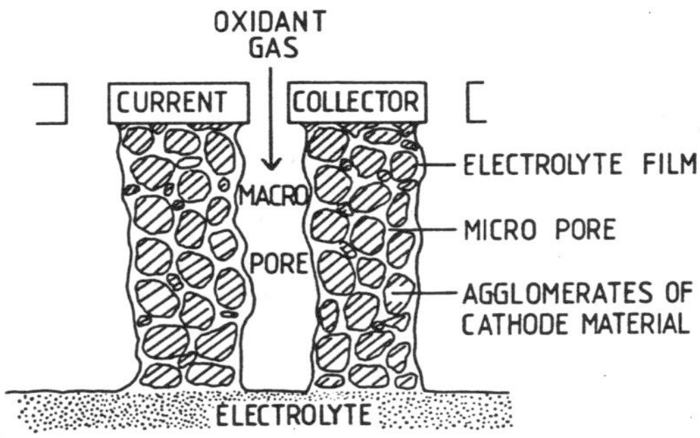

Figure 1. Schematic of a porous cathode structure with bimodal pore distribution. Modified after Yuh and Selman [6].

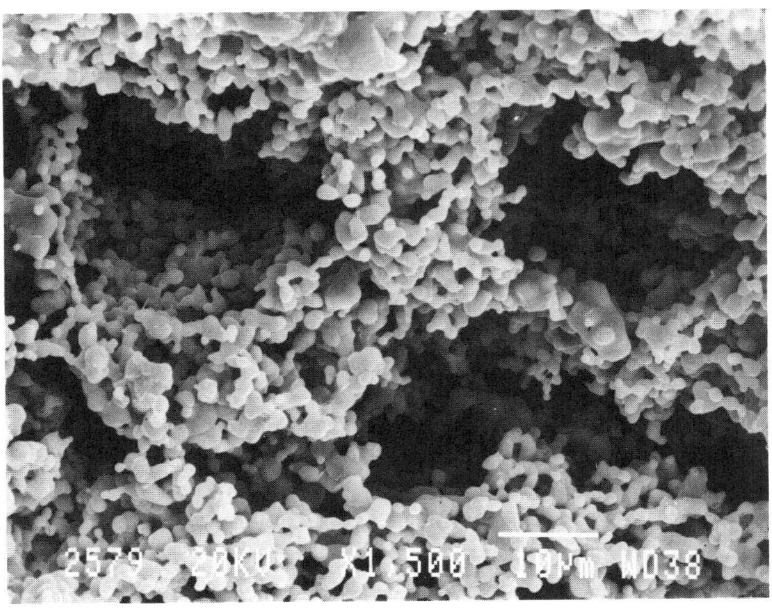

Figure 2. Microstructure of sintered LFMg3, which contained 50 wt.% pure carbon in the green phase as a pore former.

CERAMIC SENSOR FOR DETERMINING CO/CO_2 RATIO IN ALUMINIUM ELECTROLYTIC CELL

EDOARDO PROVERBIO and RANIERI CIGNA
Dept. ICMMPM University of Rome "La Sapienza"
Via Eudossiana 18, 00184 Roma, Italy

ABSTRACT

Continuous monitoring of electrolytic bath is one of the main problems in aluminium production. The CO/CO_2 ratio in anodic gas is linked to the current efficiency of the electrolytic cell. A bibliographic survey on the use of ceramic probes for determining CO/CO_2 ratio has been carried out. There are very few references in literature concerning the use of ceramic probes in aluminium industry: besides, since stabilized zirconia is the more used and tested materials in other industrial activities, it was selected for an experimental preliminar test. Probe was tested in laboratoty as well as in a production cell; the results show that the measured emf is correlated to CO concentration in the gases, thus to the current efficiency.

INTRODUCTION

The need for continuous monitoring of numerous industrial processes, and their computerized control, strongly influenced the development of electrical ceramics.
These materials, used as sensors, are particularly promising because of their sensitivity, low susceptibility to ageing and poisoning, high resistance to aggressive environment even at high temperature, and low cost [1].
In the aluminium industry one of the most important problems concerns the control of the current efficiency CE:

$$CE = 100 - \%\ CO/2 = 50 + \%\ CO_2/2$$

Hence, the usefulness of the determination of the above gases in the bath and/or in off-take gas, where CO concentration lies between 10 and 50%.
The development of ceramic sensors specific for CO

determination is actually limited to the field of internal combustion engines and of the combustion process in boilers. There are no references concerning the industrial use of such sensors in the aluminium industry, except one, in which generic suggestions are given [2].
The ceramic materials to which greater attention was paid for uses in CO/CO_2 determination are substantially three, each operating on a different physical principle: zirconia, titania and SnO_2.
The electronic conductivity of stabilized zirconia is practically nil, while the ionic conductivity, due to the mobility of oxygen ion in the fluorite-like lattice, differs and increases with temperature, becoming acceptable as soon as the material reaches temperatures higher than 400°C.
The most common stabilizers are CaO and Y_2O_3, the latter being preferred for lower activation energy and better behaviour with regard to ageing. Moreover, since yttria is very expensive, it is partially substituted by the cheaper magnesia, which does not significantly vary the electrical and physical properties of the solid solution.
A typical cell with solid oxygen-ions-conducting oxide electrolyte is shown in Fig. 1. The solid electrolyte is a disc at the centre of a tube, surrounded by heaters. Therefore there are two distinct compartments: one contains either a gas or a sealed metal/metal oxide (Ni-NiO; $Cu-Cu_2O$; Fe-FeO; Pd-PdO) in equilibrium to give a reference oxygen pressure, while the other compartment is the sample chamber. When air is used, the reference potential becomes unstable and depends on the gas flow-rate at low temperature as well as on its impurity. Besides, when a metal/metal oxide mixture is used, an intimate contact between the metal, its oxide and the electrolyte must be insured; moreover there is an upper operating temperature limit above which the metal is very unstable and transforms rapidly into oxide.
The disc is covered on either side by a porous and electronically conducting electrode, usually platinum, bearing the connections.
If in the sample chamber there is a gas containing oxygen at a partial pressure p', while in the reference chamber the oxygen partial pressure is p" at a temperature T, the emf, following Nernst equation, is:

$$V = (RT/4F)\ln p''/p' \qquad (1)$$

The emf also depends on the presence of oxidizable gases such as CO, H_2 and hydrocarbons. When CO is present, the emf is strongly influenced by its partecipation to the anodic electrochemical reaction:

$$CO' + O^{=} \longrightarrow CO_2' + 2e \qquad (2)$$

where CO' and CO_2' denote gases in the vicinity of the anode electrolyte surface.
In this case the electrochemical cell is the following:

$$Pt,\ P_{CO'}//\ \text{stabilized zirconia}//\ P_{O2(air)},\ Pt$$

whose open circuit voltage is given by [3]:

$$V= V°_{O} - V°_{CO} + (RT/2F)\ln(P^{\frac{1}{2}}_{O2}*P_{CO'}/P_{CO2}) \qquad (3)$$

When CO' is present together with oxygen, the local concentration at the anode may be depleted because of the reaction

$$CO' + \tfrac{1}{2}O_2 \text{ ---> } CO'_2 \qquad (4)$$

when the anodic reaction is

$$2O^{=} \text{ ----> } 4e + O'_2 \qquad (5)$$

Therefore the electrochemical cell is simply an oxygen cell:

$$P_{O2(anode)},\ Pt//\ \text{stabilized zirconia}//\ Pt,\ P_{O2(air)}$$

in which P_{O2} is the oxygen pressure when the reaction (5) is complete. In the electrode/electrolyte region where the metal electrode (e.g. Pt), the solid electrolyte, and the gas are simultaneously present (triple points), CO and O" compete for adsorption following reactions (2) and (5). The triple points fraction occupied by adsorbed CO_2 (f_{CO2}) may be calculated by means of the Langmuir adsorption isotherm. The cell emf may be found by application of Norton's theorem to the network shown in Fig 2:

$$V= f_{O2}\{V°_{O2} + (RT/4F)\ln[P_{O2(air)}/P_{O2(anode)}]\} + f_{CO}\{V°_{CO} +$$
$$+ (RT/2F)\ln[P^{\frac{1}{2}}_{O2(air)}*P_{CO(anode)}/P_{CO2(anode)}]\} \qquad (6)$$

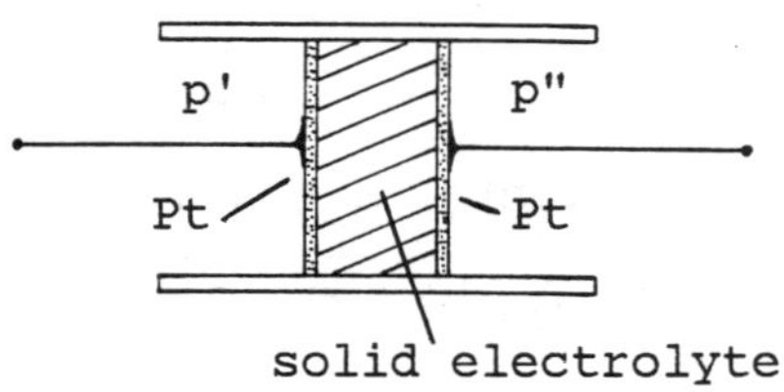

Fig.1 Structure of an oxygen-ion -conducting solid cell

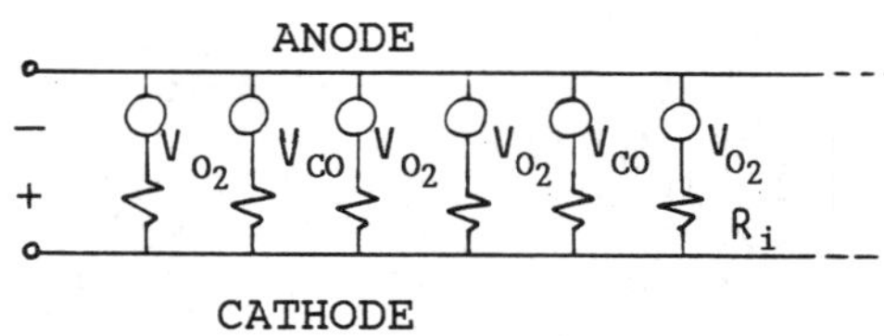

Fig.2 Equvalent electrical net work of a CO,O_2 cell

The chemical resistance of zirconia in the cryolitic bath of electrolysis cells for aluminium production is quite good as far as the attack by liquid aluminium is concerned [4]:

$$ZrO_2 + 4/3Al \text{ ---> } 2/3\ Al_2O_3 + Zr \qquad (7)$$

Moreover, the solubility of zirconia in these baths is low.
As far as titania is concerned, it must first be pointed out that when such oxide is pure and stoichiometric, it has a very high resistivity at room temperature. The loss of oxygen during

heating, mainly in reducing atmospheres, causes lattice defects such as oxygen vacancies, or titanium interstitials, which act as electron donors. As oxygen loss increases the resistivity falls further. In the range 300-1000°C,titania, when 99.5 pure, is an n-type semiconductor except at high oxygen pressure when conductivity rises with increasing P_{O2}, showing that the material is becoming p-type.
CO and CO_2 also cause a resistivity change: the molecules are adsorbed into the ceramic surface, creating pits or sources of electrons which interact with oxygen [5]:

$$O_{2gas} + \Sigma \longrightarrow O_{2ads}$$

$$O_{2ads} + \Sigma \longrightarrow 2O_{ads}$$

$$CO_{ads} + O_{ads} \longrightarrow CO_{2ads}$$

where Σ represents the lattice points in which adsorption is possible. Sensors utilizing titania have been developed mainly for vehicle engine combustion control, where it is extremely stable chemically.
The most common commercial devices actually made of tin dioxide are usually in the shape of porous pellets of oxide doped with a metal used as catalyst (Pt, Pd, Pb), which have a high degree of sensitivity together with simple construction and low cost. The major disadvantage lies in their poor selectivity (giving responses to many reducing gases) and the necessity to operate between 300 and 400°C. The addition of the other oxides to SnO_2 may substantially better its properties [6].
There are not yet industrial uses of tin dioxide sensors, or uses in particularly aggressive environments.
The bibliographic review showed that the ceramic sensors field is still open to new research themes, and subject to rapid changes as more specific materials are discovered. As far as the aluminium industry is concerned, the use of ceramics is almost ignored, probably because of the complexity and aggressivity of the environment.
Form among all the devices proposed for the control of CO and CO_2 concentration, only zirconia was selected for some preliminary tests,being the material utilized in an environment similar to that of aluminium production.

Materials and methods

The probe used for the laboratory and plant tests is a stabilized commercial zirconia, fabricated by FER, usually adopted in annealing furnaces, incinerators, and in any combustion process to allow the in situ measurements of oxygen concentration (Fig. 3). Its external surface must be in contact with the environment under control, while reference air is sent inside the tube. A Pt/Rh 6% - Pt/Rh 30% thermocouple is present beside the zirconia tube. The external protective tube is made of very pure sinterized and recrystallized alumina with suitable holes to allow contact between the cell and the environment.

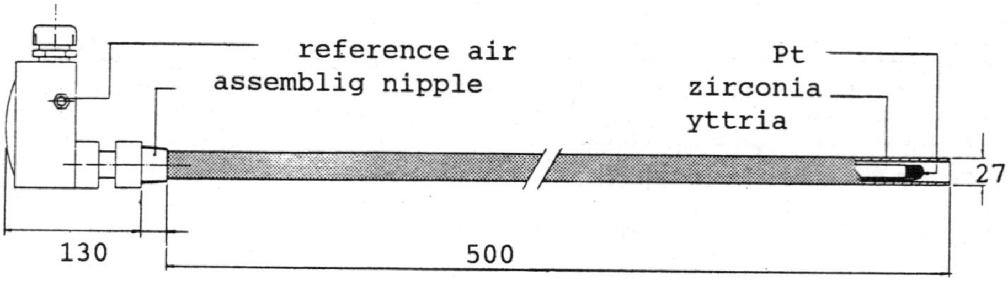

Fig.3 Zirconia sensor (courtesy of FER)

The laboratory test were carried out by placing the probe inside a quartz tube inserted into a horizontal furnace; in the quartz tube a mixture of CO and CO_2 at various concentrations flowed from two cylinders each having a flow meter at the outlet. Temperatures of 1250 and 950 °C were tested (Fig. 4).

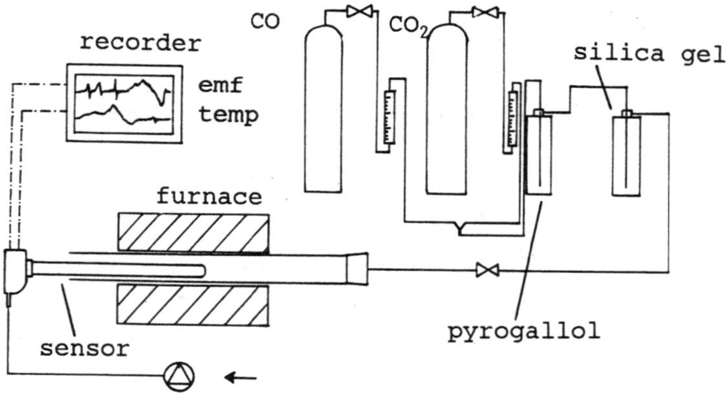

Fig.4 Circuitry for laboratory test

In order to eliminate the oxygen present in the gases, these were passed through a pyrogallol solution and then into a silica gel container to avoid any trace of humidity. The reference air was sent to the probe by means of a small alternative pump, at a flow rate of approximately 1 litre per hour.
The plant test was carried out with the same probe inserted, using a kind of steel bell, in an electrolysis cell: a hole was deliberately made in the cryolite crust between two anodes already consumed. The reference air was sent to the probe by a cylinder.

Results

The values of the emf as a function of CO/CO_2 molar ratio, plotted in Fig.5 show that there is a good agreement, at least in the slope, between the lines actually obtained and the theoretical lines calculated by the equation (3).

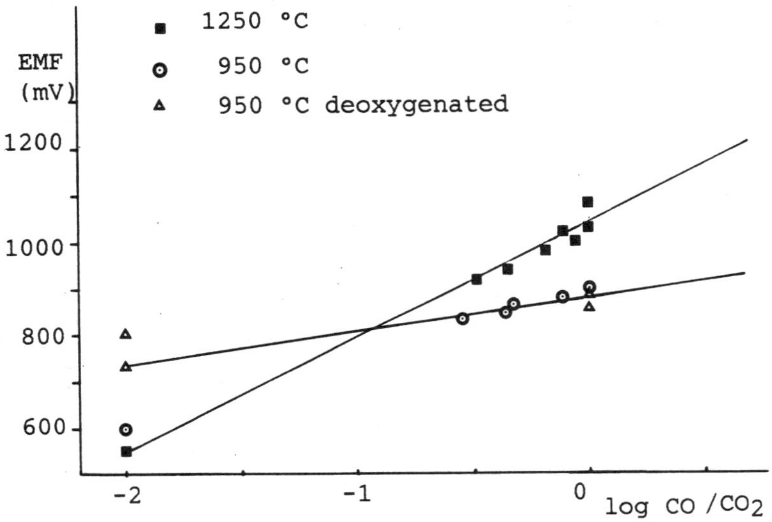

Fig.5 EMF generated by the cell vs. CO/CO_2 ratio

In addition, the results obtained in the plant tests showed that again there was a fairly good agreement between the variations of emf and those of the bath resistance during both the normal operation and an anodic effect period (Fig. 6).

Conclusions

In the aluminium industry, it would be very important to dispose of a probe to control the cell efficiency through the knowledge of the CO/CO_2 ratio. The bibliographic review showed that the stabilized zirconia may be considered promising for a very aggressive environment such as the one present in the aluminium electrolytic production plant.

The laboratory tests gave some good and reproducible results while interpretation of the plant tests results demonstrate the need for deeper experimentation. There, the development of other gases such as CF_4, C_2F_6, SiF_4, and HF can clearly interfere with CO in the absorption phenomenon, by reducing for example the free active sites fraction, and thus competing through reactions with lattice oxygen.

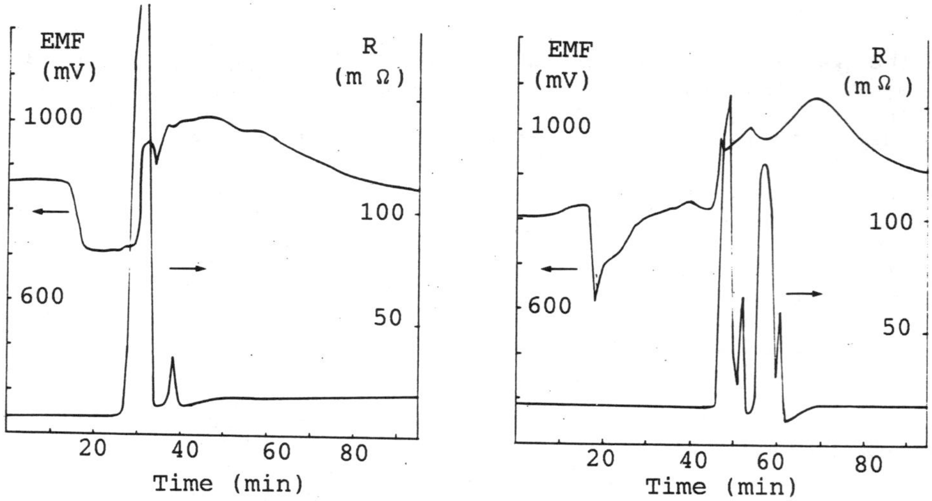

Fig.6 Results of plant test

This study was made within a collaboration contract between ALUMINIA Spa and ENEA.

REFERENCES

1. McGeehin, P. and Williams, D. E., Ceramics for sensor and monitors, Ceramics in advanced technologies, Proceedings of Europ. Coll., Joint Research Centre, Petten, 20-22 September 1982.

2. Fray, D. J., Possible uses of sensors in aluminium industry, Materials science and technology, 3, January, 1987.

3. Fleming, W. J., Physical principles of zirconia exhaust gas sensor, IEEE Transaction VT-23, 4, November, 1974.

4. McLeod, A. D., Lihrmann, J. M., Haggerty, J. S., Sardoway, D. R., Selection and testing of inert anode materials for Hall cells, Light metals, 357-365, 1987.

5. Brailsford, A. D., Logothetis, E. M., A steady-state diffusion model for solid-state gas sensors, Sensor and actuators, 7, 39-67, 1985.

6. Chemical sensors, Proceedings of the International meeting on chemical sensors, Fukuoka, September 19-22, 1983, Edited by Seiyama, Fueki, Shiokawa, Suzuki.

LIST OF CONTRIBUTORS

INDEX OF FORMULAE

SUBJECT INDEX